TEACHING HIGH SCHOOL SCIENCE:

A Sourcebook for the Biological Sciences

TEACHING HIGH SCHOOL SCIENCE:

A Sourcebook for the Biological Sciences

EVELYN MORHOLT
CHAIRMAN, DEPARTMENT OF BIOLOGICAL SCIENCES,
FORT HAMILTON HIGH SCHOOL, BROOKLYN
CURRICULUM CONSULTANT, NEW YORK CITY

PAUL F. BRANDWEIN
DIRECTOR, DIVISION OF EDUCATION, CONSERVATION
FOUNDATION;
GENERAL EDITOR AND CONSULTANT TO SCHOOLS,
HARCOURT, BRACE;
FORMERLY CHAIRMAN, DEPARTMENT OF SCIENCE,
FOREST HILLS HIGH SCHOOL

ALEXANDER JOSEPH
SCIENCE DEPARTMENT, BRONX HIGH SCHOOL OF SCIENCE;
LECTURER, SCIENCE EDUCATION, NEW YORK UNIVERSITY;
CONSULTANT, PHYSICAL SCIENCE STUDY COMMITTEE,
MASSACHUSETTS INSTITUTE OF TECHNOLOGY

HARCOURT, BRACE AND COMPANY   NEW YORK / BURLINGAME

Caution to the Reader

The teaching procedures—of all manner and description—offered in this book have been tested over more years than the authors care to remember in actual teaching of high school students, of different levels of ability, in general science, biology, health science, and field biology. The topics to which these procedures and techniques apply were selected on the basis of a study of fifty-eight courses in general science, biological science, and health given in typical communities (cities, towns, and county organizations) in the United States.

A good number of these procedures were also tested in a course titled "Laboratory Techniques in the Teaching of Biology" given as an in-service course in the New York City schools by Dr. Morris Rabinowitz, George I. Schwartz, and Paul Brandwein. A mimeographed text of the techniques developed in the course was also put together in 1940–42 under the title of the course.

Certainly there are in this book more techniques, procedures, demonstrations, projects, experiments, and suggestions than any teacher can use in any one year. These procedures are typical of the kinds of things that teachers do, or want to do, as they teach biological science—in the variety of forms this takes. Since the method of teaching is and must remain a personal invention, we leave to each teacher the selection of those techniques which are useful in a specific teaching situation.

We have included techniques and procedures not only for the "average" class, if there is such a thing, but for the variety of individual students who make up classes, no matter how they have been grouped. There are demonstrations involving visual effects, those requiring manipulation of various materials—from simple clay models to advanced histological techniques—those requiring reading, observing, thinking: all the many processes which make up science. There are suggestions for short- and long-range projects. It is our hope that there are here demonstrations and techniques for every student, no matter what his beginning interest or ability in science may be.

This volume is one of a series; following the Table of Contents are condensed outlines of the two companion volumes, *Teaching High School Science: A Book of Methods,* by P. F. Brandwein, F. G. Watson, and P. E. Blackwood, Harcourt, Brace, 1958; and *Teaching High School Science: A Sourcebook for the Physical Sciences,* by A. Joseph, P. F. Brandwein, and E. Morholt, Harcourt, Brace, 1959.

We take this opportunity to express our appreciation to the many teachers from whom we have drawn inspiration; we particularly offer thanks to Herbert Drapkin and Leon Rintel for their careful and encouraging critiques of the book in galley proof.

We should like nothing better than to correspond with teachers who find certain of these techniques difficult to perform, or difficult to apply, or wanting in any manner. Certainly if a better technique is available, or if one we have described has been improved, we should consider it a privilege to include the contribution in a revised edition with appropriate credit. The opportunity we seek is that of being of service to teachers.

EVELYN MORHOLT
PAUL F. BRANDWEIN
ALEXANDER JOSEPH

Contents

Section Four   **APPENDIX**

TEACHING HIGH SCHOOL SCIENCE: *A Book of Methods*
by Paul F. Brandwein, Fletcher G. Watson, and Paul E. Blackwood

CONTENTS

A Sourcebook for the Biological Sciences

Section One INTRODUCTION

Patterns in the use of laboratory techniques and procedures

Teaching is a personal invention. No one can reasonably hope to include in one book all the individual procedures and the patterns in which they are used, and their variations, which different teachers have found practicable. Each teacher will have his own ways of using the great variety of techniques and procedures included in this book; he will use them selectively. He will use some of them as the basis for individual laboratory work, for group work, for field trips, for projects, and for his own demonstrations, as well as many other approaches. The purpose of this chapter is to indicate how teachers in groups or as individuals have used the procedures included in this text to build their personal invention—their teaching technique.

An example of techniques and procedures within a unit

Clearly the technique, the procedure, the device—whatever it is—fits within a *pattern,* the *curricular pattern.* A teacher or group of teachers plans a unit of work. At the end of the unit the students are to have mastery of a large idea. In planning to help students achieve learning of this large concept or idea, the teacher uses all methods and techniques at his disposal, fitting them in to meet the total philosophy and practice, both administrative and pedagogical, of his school.

As an example, let us examine a unit in biology prepared by a committee of teachers. These teachers have selected techniques for specific purposes; of course, not all the available techniques are used. It is our purpose in this first section of the book to show that *techniques are never used in isolation but are part and parcel of the teaching development within a unit.*

TABLE 0-1   *How do living things obtain food?**

(Overview by the teacher and planning with pupils)

Content	Objectives	Learning Experiences
1. What living things obtain their food as independent organisms? a. Plants	1. To acquaint the student with the fact that green plants are the only independent living things 2. To learn how plants manufacture sugar during photosynthesis 3. To acquire an understanding of solutions and osmosis 4. To gain an appreciation of the importance of photosynthesis to all living things 5. To show where the raw materials for food-getting come from 6. To gain an appreciation of the structure of a plant	Work out the equation for photosynthesis [*p. 13*]** Experiment to show a covered leaf will not manufacture sugar [*p. 15*] Experiment to show that a chlorophyll-free leaf will not produce sugar [*p. 16*] Charts showing root hairs, stems, and leaves [*pp. 43, 45, 417*] Microscopic study of the stem, roots, and leaves [*pp. 292–99*] Germinate seeds on blotters to show root hairs [*pp. 44, 398*] Set up an osmosis experiment using egg, molasses, carrot, etc. [*pp. 34, 52–53*]
b. Animals	1. To learn why animals are classed as herbivorous, carnivorous, or omnivorous 2. To acquaint the student with various methods used by animals in getting food (grazing, gnawing, tracking, trapping) 3. To learn how to feed a dog, horse, cow	Student drawings [*Bibliography, pp. 411, 417*] Group discussions [*pp. 235, 417*] Pictures [*p. 418*] Specimens of animal skulls [*supply houses, pp. 410, 479*] Visit farm or zoo at feeding time [*pp. 10, 263–65*] Observe amoeba feeding [*p. 29*]
2. What living things are semidependent for food-getting? a. Plants	1. To show that some plants lack strong stems and must cling for support 2. To show that some plants lack nitrogen and, to supply this need, catch insects	Use pictures to show climbing roses, grapes, poison ivy, etc. [*pp. 293–95*] Collect or buy a variety of insectivorous plants and grow them in a terrarium [*pp. 233, 394, 397*]
b. Animals	1. To learn that few animals are semidependent (Drone bee is probable example) 2. To learn what bait to use when fishing	

* Unit II from *Course of Study in Science for Secondary Schools*, Bull. 400, Commonwealth of Pennsylvania, Dept. Public Instruction, Harrisburg, Pa.
** The italic page numbers in brackets refer to pages in *this* textbook in which a description of this technique is presented.

Content	Objectives	Learning Experiences
3. What living things are totally dependent on other living things for food-getting? a. Plants	1. To show that plants that lack chlorophyll cannot manufacture food materials for themselves 2. To learn the difference between parasites and saprophytes 3. To learn what plants are totally dependent	Make a collection of parasitic and saprophytic plants [*pp. 118, 185, 229, 231, 283, 390*] Grow some bread mold and observe its structure [*pp. 387, 390*]
b. Animals	1. To acquaint the student with types of animal parasites and scavengers 2. To learn how to get rid of rats, flies, lice, etc.	Pictures Specimens [*supply houses, p. 479; also 229–34*] Charts [*p. 417*] Student reports [*Bibliography, pp. 234, 453*]
4. What living things form partnerships with other living things and assist each other in food-getting? a. Plants	1. To learn what plants live together for their mutual benefit	Collect lichens for the laboratory terrarium [*pp. 232, 391*] Have a student bring in some clover to show the nodules containing nitrogen-fixing bacteria [*pp. 232, 235*]
b. Animals	1. To learn what animals live together for their mutual benefit	Group discussion [*Bibliography, pp. 234, 453*] Report on the protozoa in the digestive tract of the termite [*p. 311*] Motion picture of a social insect [*films, pp. 168, 467, 472*] Get tapeworms from a veterinarian [*or from supply houses, p. 479*]
5. Why is the maintenance of a food chain necessary for the welfare of all living things?	1. To show that no plant or animal is totally self-sufficient 2. To learn what jobs are concerned with producing and distributing food Other objectives suggested by pupils	Group discussion [*conservation, Chapters 14 and 15*]
6. Other problems suggested by pupils		Other activities suggested by pupils [*pp. 40, 242, 264, 266; Chapter 16*] Continuous use of references Evaluation Direct teaching as needed

Examples of techniques and procedures within a total curricular pattern

More and more teachers are realizing the need for examining the entire curricular range — from kindergarten through high school. One result of this examination is to avoid repetition of experiences in the same context. For instance, teachers in a given school system know what is going on in elementary school and build on the experiences made available earlier.

Note, for instance, the range of activities exemplified in the following curricular plan.[1] Clearly, if teachers follow this plan —or prepare their own plan—grade level for grade level, it will be well to know what went on in prior work, so that greater growth in learning can be achieved.

By studying this *one* area of the total curricular plan teachers recognize that through the grades broad concepts concerning living things, soil, and water are developed. In fact, many times the activity may seem similar (for example, field trips), but the perception of students increases as they have more meaningful experiences. Youngsters "see" more as they grow and know more.

Those children who have had some of these experiences in the primary grades bring a richer knowledge of the interrelations among plants and animals, soil and water, to their classwork in high school biology.

We have selected only a few of the activities suggested for each grade level. A similar development may be undertaken for any other unit or broad concept we teach at the high school level. In any event students come to high school with experiences gained in the elementary grades.

[1] *An Outline for Teaching Conservation in Elementary Schools*, PA-268, Soil Conservation Service, U.S. Dept. Agriculture, Washington, D. C., Aug. 1955.

FIRST GRADE
Getting acquainted with plants, animals, and the soil

Make field trips to nearby farms, gardens, orchards, woods, and parks to study leaf litter and different kinds of plants, trees, fruits, and wildlife. [*Chapters 14, 15*][2]

Plant flower seeds in a pot or box of good soil and the same kind of flower seeds in a pot or box of poor soil. Tend them for a month and report on difference in growth, and appearance of plants, and appearance of soil. [*pp. 44, 232, 235, 398*]

Note how water soaks readily into good soil but stays on top of poor soil. Note also that a hard crust forms on the top of the poor soil. [*pp. 235–42*]

Make a balanced aquarium. [*pp. 86, 356, 363*]

Plant seeds in two pans. Keep the soil in one pan well watered, but do not water the soil in the other one. This will show that seeds need water to grow. [*pp. 44, 108*]

SECOND GRADE
Man's use and care of plants, animals, and soil

Have a "plant-growing race" by using different kinds of soil in each of several flower pots or boxes—rich garden soil, forest soil, soil from rich farmland, soil from eroded farmland, soil from pasture or ranch land, subsoil, coarse sand, road dust. [*pp. 108, 111, 236*]

Make a trip to a well-sodded sloping area. Dig up a clump of sod and note how soil clings to the grass roots. A good sod holds soil in place. [*pp. 236, 238, 239*]

Soon after a rain, make a trip to a nearby farm, field, or vacant lot where the ground is bare and watch the water wash the topsoil away. Observe how soil washed from sloping fields is deposited on lower-level lands. Observe that soil did not wash off grass-covered areas. Observe how barriers that slow or break the force of running water cause silt to be deposited. [*pp. 238, 240, 241*]

Make a miniature farm in the classroom and show conservation practices. [*pp. 235, 263–65*]

[2] These italic page numbers in brackets refer to pages *in this text* where a description of the technique is presented.

THIRD GRADE
Natural resources of the
nation and community

Try "What is it?" tests— ask pupils to bring samples of different soils, plants, seeds, flowers, woods, and animal skins, and let other pupils identify them. [*Chapters 11, 14, 15, 18, 20; also see Bibliography for keys and fieldbooks; also lists of films and supply houses, pp. 463, 479*]

Make field trips to study soils and soil formations—study soil profiles at roadside cuts and note differences between topsoil and subsoil; note differences between soils in forests, grasslands, fields, and gardens. [*pp. 236, 237, Chapter 15*]

FOURTH GRADE
Depletion of
natural resources—soil erosion

Make field trips to study soil erosion. Visit neighboring field or farm soon after a heavy rain and observe muddy water, sheet erosion, silt collected at foot of slopes. Visit a field that has been abandoned because of severe erosion. What can be done about it? [*pp. 238, 240, 242*]

Make a trip to an industrial plant and note which natural resources it uses and how it uses them. Observe any waste. Does the factory dump waste products into a stream and pollute its waters? What effect does water pollution have on plant and animal life? Find out what the community does about pollution and report to the class. [*p. 234, Chapter 15*]

FIFTH GRADE
Conservation of natural resources

Make field trips to farms where conservation farming is being practiced. Observe the different conservation practices and ask the farmer to explain them. Note the ways in which trees and other plants are used to protect the soil. Note the wildlife homes in shrubs and grass along field borders, stream banks, and roadsides. [*pp. 7, 10, 215, 218, Chapters 14, 15*]

Make field trips to game preserves, fish hatcheries, wildlife refuges, and tree nurseries. [*Chapter 15*]

Plant trees or grass on eroding land in the schoolyard or at home. [*pp. 236, 238–40*]

SIXTH GRADE
Conservation and society

Start a school wood lot. Plan the work with other classes so that the activity can become a whole-school project. [*pp. 242, 244, 264–66*]

Plant shrubs and grass for wildlife food and cover. [*pp. 240, 264*]

Build bird feeders and houses for songbirds. [*pp. 243, 264*]

SEVENTH AND EIGHTH GRADES
The science of conservation

Obtain land-capability maps of some farms from nearby or local soil conservation districts. Study the maps and then take them to the farms where they were made and compare the way the farmer is using the land with the land capability as shown on the map.

Study some soil conservation practices on local farms and have the farmer explain their value and how they were installed. [*pp. 7, 10, Chapter 14*]

Borrow a farm level or make a simple farm level and practice running contour lines on the school ground or a neighboring field. [*p. 239; also activities, p. 242*]

Prepare a conservation exhibit for a local fair or for a school exhibit. [*pp. 8, 10, 228, 235, 239, 242, 264, 294, Chapters 18–20*]

While on a field trip, make a map of a farm or landscape, showing land suitable for growing crops; for forests, brush, or wildlife areas; for pastures. [*Chapters 14, 15*]

GENERAL SCIENCE—
NINTH GRADE [3]
General science and conservation

Field trips to study soil, water, forest, range, and wildlife conservation practices. [*Chapters 14, 15, 20*]

Discuss the interrelationship between the organic resources. [*Chapters 14, 15, 18–20*]

List and describe the scientific principles employed in the various conservation practices. [*Bibliography, p. 457; Chapters 14, 15, 20*]

TENTH GRADE
Biology and Conservation

Make a field trip to study the relation of natural vegetation and wildlife to their environment. [*pp. 7, 10, 215, 218, Chapters 14, 15*]

Make a cross-reference chart showing the different ways in which soil, water, plants and animals, and man depend on each other. [*pp. 18, 22, 29, 45, 56, 58, 86, 97, 212, 215, Chapters 14, 15, 18–20*]

---

[3] *An Outline for Teaching Conservation in High Schools*, PA-201, Soil Conservation Service, U.S. Dept. Agriculture, 1952.

Make a field trip to study soil erosion and water loss. [*Chapter 14, pp. 264, 266*]

Make a field trip to a farm where a complete conservation farming program is being followed. Have the farmer or a conservationist explain the different conservation practices. [*Chapter 14, pp. 10, 243*]

Examples of techniques and procedures within the lesson

Just as the use of techniques and procedures is expressed in teaching patterns known as "syllabuses" or "courses of study" or "curriculums," so the use of various laboratory and field techniques and procedures may be expressed in patterns in the classroom. Again this depends on the special situation in which the teacher finds himself, and his personal preferences. There is no one best way, and no one way. *Below are various ways, just for example.*

As a self-demonstration. Many teachers use procedures which give students directions to guide them in a learning activity. The following guide to activity is addressed to the student:

WHY MUST STARCH BE DIGESTED?[4] You may discover the answer to this question in the following way. Add 1 gm of cornstarch or arrowroot starch to 1 liter of water. Heat this gently to form a thin starch paste. Now test a sample of this paste for the presence of glucose by boiling a bit of it in Benedict's solution in a Pyrex test tube. If it turns green or reddish-orange, glucose is present. If no color change takes place, you may use the mixture.

Fill a test tube half full of starch paste. Get a goldbeater's membrane from your teacher, wet it, and fasten it tightly over the mouth of the test tube with a rubber band. Then invert the test tube in a beaker of water as in Fig. 0-1. The starch paste in the tube represents food in the intestine. Let the membrane over the mouth of the tube stand for the lining of the intestine.

The question is: Can starch pass through the membrane? Prepare two duplicates of Fig. 0-1 but substitute these materials for the starch paste: in one, dilute corn syrup, molasses, or glucose solution; in the other test tube, starch paste and some of your saliva. Cover each tube with a membrane as before; stand each in an individual beaker of water.

Within a half hour you may test the water in the first of the three beakers with iodine. Did starch go through the membrane? In a Pyrex test tube heat to boiling, with Benedict's solution, a sample of water from the second beaker. Did simple sugar go through the membrane in the second tube? Now test the water in the third beaker for glucose (simple sugar). From where did the glucose come when the tube originally contained only starch paste and saliva? In the light of these results, explain why starch must be digested.

As an exercise in planning an experiment. Sometimes a teacher may modify a technique described as a demonstration, and turn it to another purpose.

IS LIGHT NEEDED BY GREEN LEAVES TO MAKE STARCH? Could you plan an experiment to answer this question? Let us assume that you were given the materials in Fig. 0-2; write an explanation of your plan of action and show it to your teacher before you start work. Have you provided for a control? How could you find out whether leaves made starch? If leaves were covered, would they make starch? Com-

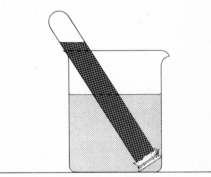

Fig. 0-1 Can starch pass through a membrane? Test tube of starch paste covered with a membrane inverted in a beaker of water.

---

[4] The techniques and procedures in this chapter are only examples of the many varied ones to be found (developed in the context of a curricular unit) throughout this book.

Fig. 0-2 Materials for demonstrating that green leaves need light to make starch: carbon paper or aluminum foil; pins; geranium; alcohol; dilute iodine; and beaker on electric hot plate *or* test tube in water bath over a burner.

pare your results with those of other students in class. In this way, you will be able to draw conclusions from many investigations, not just one. What is your conclusion?

As a specific exercise in planning controls. Students learn to use this method of scientists by "doing."

IS CARBON DIOXIDE USED BY GREEN PLANTS? Do water plants use carbon dioxide? Since carbon dioxide is a colorless gas, we shall need a harmless indicator, such as brom thymol blue, to keep track of the amount of carbon dioxide in water. Fill a large beaker with brom thymol blue solution and blow into it through a straw. What happens? The carbon dioxide in your breath caused this change in color from blue to yellow. What color should result if the carbon dioxide is removed from the solution?

Fill four test tubes with this brom thymol yellow (rich in carbon dioxide). Add sprigs of elodea plants to two of these tubes. Wrap one tube containing elodea in carbon paper; also wrap another tube without the plant in carbon paper. Set all the tubes in bright sunlight (or electric light). Within an hour examine the tubes for any change in color. In which tube (or tubes) has the brom thymol yellow changed to blue? Explain this change in color. Did the plant in the dark use carbon dioxide? Explain your answer. Compare your results with those of your classmates. Why should you make this comparison? In summary, do green plants use carbon dioxide in light? What two common tactics of scientists have you used here?

As a simple investigation. This kind of activity may be used as a teacher demonstration or a student project.[5]

---

[5] You will find many projects suggested throughout. See also Philip Goldstein, *How to Do an Experiment,* Harcourt, Brace, New York, 1957.

WHAT IS THE ACTION OF UREASE? One product of the breakdown of proteins in living cells is urea. Urea is changed to ammonia by the enzyme urease. With your teacher's permission, you may want to demonstrate the action of urease in class. (Both urea and urease are obtainable from a supply house.)

Dissolve a bit of urea in water and half fill two large test tubes with this solution. Add a small amount of the indicator phenolphthalein to each test tube. Then add a few crystals of urease to *one* test tube. What color change results? How fast did the action take place? (Phenolphthalein changes from colorless to red in the presence of an alkaline.) Is the resulting ammonia an acid or alkaline? What caused the change in color? Repeat the demonstration. Why was the other test tube used?

As a plan for a field trip. Throughout this book, specific procedures are suggested for undertaking many out-of-doors studies in biology.

HOW TO COLLECT PLANTS. If a group of students, or your class, should plan a field trip, you'll need this equipment: collecting nets, jars with covers, pen knives, pads of paper and pencils for taking notes, comfortable shoes, and a first-aid kit. Plan where you intend to go so that you will know what to look for. Take with you some books as guides to identification of plants. For example: *How to Know the Wildflowers* by Alfred Stefferud (Holt, 1950; also Mentor); *Plant Families* and *How to Know the Trees,* both by H. E. Jaques (Brown, Dubuque, 1948); Conrad's *How to Know the Mosses* (Brown, 1944); and Durand's *Fieldbook of Ferns* (Putnam, 1949). Your library probably has many other references you can use.

Water plants may be collected with a dip net; put the plants in jars of pond water.

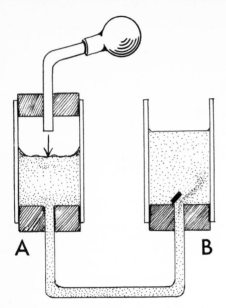

Fig. 0-3 Model of a valve. This will show how a valve works, but the bulb will not work continuously unless it has a valve of its own. (From E. Morholt & E. T. Smith, *Experiences in Biology*, Harcourt, Brace, 1954.)

Avoid packing too many specimens in one container, for they will die quickly. If you find mushrooms or other fungi, keep them in dry jars. You may wrap patches of mosses in newspaper. Transport ferns and small seed plants in folds of newspaper. As soon as you get back to school, transfer the water plants into large open jars. Put fungi, mosses, and ferns, along with any small seed plants you may have found in the same area, into terraria.

Twigs, leaves, seeds, and fruits of seed plants may be mounted on cardboard to show their life cycle. Be sure to label the plants clearly. If you have use of bulletin boards and hall cases, arrange to display the specimens you have collected. A committee of students might change the display regularly so that your classmates have the opportunity to learn a wide variety of plants. If you collect regularly throughout the year, you can display all the

stages of some seed plants—winter buds, flowering stages, and seeds.

As suggestions for preparing models. There are many models to use in class besides charts and commercial models. Many such are suggested throughout this text.

WHAT IS THE APPEARANCE OF PROTOPLASM? You can imitate the appearance of protoplasm in this way. Place the white of a hen's egg into a small dish. Then shake black pepper over the egg white and beat it with a fork. What is the main difference between this mixture and living protoplasm? What name is given to substances that have the physical make-up of protoplasm?

MODELING A VALVE.[6] You can demonstrate the action of valves in the veins or heart by making the apparatus shown in Fig. 0-3. Fill the glass tubes with water to which you have added red ink or some dye. When you squeeze the bulb, the increased air pressure forces the water through A into B. Why doesn't water flow back into A again? What prevents the backflow of blood in the veins of your legs?

As a project for a class. This may be done by groups outside of class time. You will find other group projects suggested throughout this book.

WORKING WITH OTHER MEMBERS OF YOUR CLASS. Find the height and weight of each member of your class. Make two tables, one showing the number of students of each height (disregard fractions of an inch) and one showing the number of students in weight groups (76–80 lb, 81–85 lb, and so on).

Then prepare a bar graph to show the variations in height in your class. Put the units of height on the *y* axis, or vertical line, and the number of students on the *x* axis, or horizontal line.

Now in your notebook prepare a graph similar to the one just described to show variations of weight in your class. Decide what units should be along the bottom line and what units along the side.

Examples of techniques and procedures in extending the lesson

Homework. Sometimes students raise questions, or the teacher finds it desirable to extend the lesson into the home. Several kinds of procedures have been

found useful. Usually the student does not have the apparatus at home to

[6] Paul Blackwood, *Experiences in Science*, Harcourt, Brace, New York, 1955.

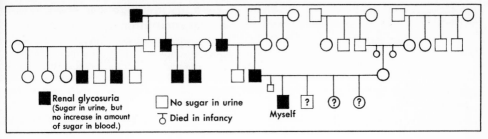

Fig. 0-4 Family pedigree of a student who suffered from renal glycosuria, excess sugar in the urine. (From E. Morholt & E. T. Smith *Experiences in Biology,* Harcourt, Brace, 1954.)

carry on actual experimentation or self-demonstration. Such procedures for which apparatus is readily available—e.g., collecting—will, of course, be used. However, there are paper and pencil procedures which stress various aspects of investigative procedures in science. You will find other types of procedures like these throughout the text.

STUDYING A TRAIT IN YOUR FAMILY. Try to trace the occurrence of some trait in your family as a biology student diagramed a pedigree of a trait inherited in his family (Fig. 0-4). In this family sugar in the urine (but not in the blood) was frequent. Look at the large number of relatives included in this pedigree (the males are represented by squares, the females by circles). How many generations are shown? Which sex seems to be affected in this family? From this one family history, could you draw reliable conclusions as to the way the trait is inherited? Why?

Select a definite trait such as tasting P.T.C. paper, freckles, hair color, attached or free ear lobes, eye defects, long eyelashes, and so on. Develop a key as in Fig. 0-4 to show squares (males) and circles (females); shaded symbols represent those who have the trait, unshaded symbols those lacking the trait. (You may use a half-shaded symbol for a trait which seems to exist to a lesser degree than usual.)

HAS THE LIFE SPAN BEEN EXTENDED? Figure 0-5 compares the average length of human life at different periods from ancient to modern times. What seems to have been the average life span in Rome some two thousand years ago? Only two hundred years ago in two New England states? At the turn of the century in the United States? Try to list at least ten factors that have contributed to the increase in the average life span in the United States (almost seventy years now).

Simple projects. Apparatus of sorts may be devised from materials at hand.

PRESERVING FOOD.[7] Soak some beans or peas overnight; then crush them into seven test tubes of water. What kinds of chemicals may be used to preserve these beans or peas? Into

[7] *Ibid.*

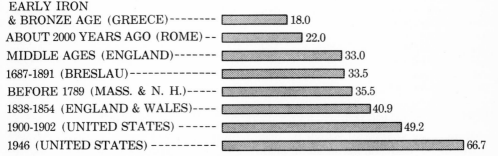

EARLY IRON
& BRONZE AGE (GREECE)-------- 18.0
ABOUT 2000 YEARS AGO (ROME)-- 22.0
MIDDLE AGES (ENGLAND)------- 33.0
1687-1891 (BRESLAU)------------- 33.5
BEFORE 1789 (MASS. & N. H.)----- 35.5
1838-1854 (ENGLAND & WALES)---- 40.9
1900-1902 (UNITED STATES) ------ 49.2
1946 (UNITED STATES) --------- 66.7

Fig. 0-5 Comparison of human life span from ancient Greece to modern times. (After L. I. Dublin, A. J. Lotka, & M. Spiegelman, *Length of Life,* Ronald, 1949.)

each test tube add the chemicals as shown in the chart. Over several days, keep a record of the color, odor, and any other observations you may make.

Tube and contents	Condition of preservation, observations			
	1	2	3	4
1. Water only				
2. 1 tsp vinegar				
3. 1 tsp salt				
4. 1 tsp sugar				
5. ¼ tsp boric acid				
6. ¼ tsp alum				
7. Pinch benzoate of soda				

DOES SALIVA CHANGE STARCH? If you have your parents' permission, try this at home. Mix a bit of starch (arrowroot or cornstarch) in a cup of cold water; add to boiling water and stir for a few minutes. While the starch paste is cooling, prepare the rest of the materials for your experiment. Add a drop of iodine from the medicine chest to half a glass of water. Now with a teaspoon, transfer an amount of starch paste about the size of a drop to a flat dish. Add a drop of the diluted iodine. What causes this light-blue color? Now add a large drop of your own saliva to the blue drop. Why does the blue color disappear?

Field trip investigations. (Other types are suggested throughout the text.)

EVIDENCES OF EROSION. On a trip around the school grounds or nearby look for evidences of bare slopes where soil has been washed away. Can you find a region cut through by erosion so that you see the roots of trees and vegetation? How do roots help to slow down erosion of soil? Perhaps you can see the top layer of dark soil rich in organic matter which supports vegetation.

Look for evidence of layers of soil. What are the characteristics of the layers under the topsoil layer? What constructive measures might be put into practice to correct the kinds of erosion you find?

SEEDLINGS ON THE LAWN. Examine a number of trees in fruit, such as maples and elms. Estimate the number of seeds a tree produces. After a month or so return to this region and look for seedlings. How many do you find growing on the lawns? Why are there so few seedlings when there was an abundance of seeds? What factors tend to check the possibility of growth of all the seeds? Explain what is meant by survival of the fittest.

Inventory-type projects. There are many projects which do not require apparatus.

MAKING A STUDY OF YOUR FAMILY.[8] In your notebook paste small pictures of your father, mother, and yourself. To what extent have you inherited your physical characteristics from your parents? To what extent can the things you do change these characteristics? Which characteristics is it impossible for you to change?

Examples of techniques and procedures for long-term projects

Clearly we have not exhausted even the most common patterns involving the use of laboratory techniques and procedures as employed by teachers. But we cannot ignore patterns which involve long-term investigations. The examples below are included here to show the nature of an investigation which takes two to three years and which is "original" in the high school meaning of the term. The reader will not fail to note that students began with a simple technique (which helped resolve a relatively simple problem), then evolved the problem into a full-scale investigation. Here are the summaries of two examples, and titles of several others (numbers 3–10).

1. *An Ultraviolet Photosensitization in Para-aminobenzoic Acid and Panthothenic Acid Fed to* TRIBOLIUM CONFUSUM[9]

   I have read that when mice were fed buckwheat and were placed in a strong

8 *Ibid.*
9 Report of Michael Fried, Senior, Forest Hills High School, N. Y.

light they died, while mice lacking either the light, the buckwheat, or both, thrived. Lacking mice, I tried to duplicate the results on insects. I worked with the Confused flour beetle, *Tribolium confusum*.

The effect in mice can be duplicated on the flour beetle. I am reasonably certain that:

1. The ultraviolet rays of the light, acting with an agent (or agents) in the buckwheat, seem to cause the reaction known as a photosensitization.

2. When panthothenic or para-aminobenzoic acids (in a concentration of 5 per cent or higher) are added to the diet of the flour beetle, the photosensitizing effect does not occur.

It may be that the photosensitizing reactions are caused by the conversion of either (or both) panthothenic acid or p-AB, both of which are needed by the cells to synthesize anti-metabolitic structural analogues. The cells seize upon these structural analogues but cannot utilize them; the cells thus suffer from a deficiency of these vitamins. Death may be the result.

2. *Hematology of the Chick Embryo*[10]

Research was started by reading from Krackes' *Diseases of the Blood* about normal blood and its origin. It was learned that hematologists believe blood cells mature and that young cells can be distinguished from older and mature cells on a stained slide. At the suggestion of Dr. Cora Downs of University of Kansas it was decided to study the blood development of the chick embryo, and to see if there is a definite increase and maturation of young cells.

The second step was to learn to use hematological equipment with reasonable accuracy. Using oxalated human blood, red- and white-cell counts were made over and over until they checked. Smears were made, stained, and differentials done until they too checked.

Blood was needed in larger quantities than could be obtained quickly, so the heart was chosen as the source. Next, a cut was made into the chest cavity of the chick embryo and an incision made into the heart, which is found directly posterior to the breast bone. This method made it possible to be certain that the blood was not diluted with cell fluid. It was discovered that blood of the chicken embryo coagulates very fast, making it difficult to obtain counts.

Total counts per cubic millimeter done on the chick embryo between 16 and 20 days of incubation showed no steady regular increase, but all were definitely below the average normals found for the adult chicken. If a method could be devised to obtain enough blood from younger embryos to do total counts, it may be possible to show a change in total counts.

It was found that there is a definite decrease in the number of blast cells and young cells about the 8th day. After this the differential counts were within the normal range of the adult chicken blood.

I have become very interested in the field of hematology, and I plan to do further work in this field. I wish to acknowledge the help and encouragement given me by Mrs. Ruth Deer.

3. "Cannibalism: As Developed by Nutritional Variations in *Blepharisma undulans* in Microvivaria" (Peter Roemer, Senior, Forest Hills High School)

4. "The Optimum Concentration of Terramycin, in Conjunction with Nutrients, on the Reproductive Rate of *Paramecium caudatum*" (Roberta Fishman, Senior, Forest Hills High School)

5. "The Erosional History of a Selected Area in the Osage Questas" (John C. Davis, Neodesha High School)

6. "Investigation and Procedure Necessary for Identification of Bacteria Found in Common Environments" (Mike McCluskey, Neodesha High School)

7. "Effects of Gibberellic Acid on Tomato Plant Roots" (Erik F. Eikenberry, Broad Ripple High School, Indianapolis, Ind.)

8. "Effects of Colchicine on Drosophila" (Susan K. Iknayan, Charleston Community Unit High School, Charleston, Ill.)

9. "The Otoliths of Recent and Fossil Fish" (John H. Campbell, University High School, Minneapolis, Minn.)

10. "The Firefly and the Chemical Nature of Its Bioluminescence" (Leland N. Edmunds, Jr., Newport News High School, Newport News, Va.)

---

[10] Summary of a paper by Billie Kneebone, Neodesha High School, Neodesha, Kansas. Reproduced with the permission of Miss Vaughn, science teacher, Neodesha High School.

A word in closing

What we have been trying to indicate is that while science does mean "doing one's damnedest with one's mind, no holds barred,"[11] the fruits of science are developed in the deed. Brain and muscle, mind and hand are in constant collaboration.

Science is not "chalk-talk"; it is *experi-ence in search of meaning.* In this chapter we have tried to indicate how certain techniques can be fitted into some patterns which are characteristic of the science teacher's approach to teaching science. As we have said, the entire text is given over to a description of activities which encompass a vast range of experience which serves this search for meaning.

[11] P. W. Bridgman, *Yale Review,* XXXIV, 444-61, 1945.

CHAPTER 1

Plants: food-makers

Much has been learned about photosynthesis since van Helmont set up his experiment and concluded that a willow tree was mainly transmuted water. The current story of photosynthesis is diagramed in our modification of the simplified schema devised by Rabinowitch[1] (Fig. 1-1).

In the classroom, you may want to demonstrate several aspects of photosynthesis. You may show the need for light as a source of energy by comparing the starch content of a covered and an exposed leaf. Students may determine for themselves that carbon dioxide is absorbed and oxygen evolved in the process, and that chlorophyll is required for food-making.[2] Students may do proj-

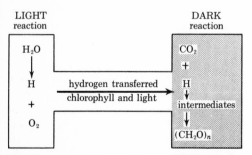

LIGHT reaction   DARK reaction

H_2O

H

+

O_2

hydrogen transferred
chlorophyll and light

CO_2
+
H
↓
intermediates
↓
$(CH_2O)_n$

Fig. 1-1 Schematic outline of photosynthesis, modified from Rabinowitch. Water is broken down in the LIGHT reaction; free oxygen is released and the hydrogen is picked up by an "acceptor." Carbon dioxide is "fixed," then reduced by the hydrogen given up by the "acceptor." Finally, enzyme transformations carry through many intermediates to carbohydrates.

[1] Eugene Rabinowitch, *Photosynthesis and Related Processes,* vol. 1, Interscience, New York, 1945. Also see reviews of photosynthesis in *Scientific American* (Aug. 1948 and Nov. 1953).

[2] Naturally, we expect a teacher will select those techniques which are applicable to his class situation. If you'd care to see how teachers over the country have organized activities in this area, look at the "Guide for Teachers in Junior High Schools," *Sci. Curriculum Bull.,* 20, Indianapolis Schools, Ind., 1955.

ects to develop the idea that photosynthetic activity is greatest in the orange-red area of the spectrum; for example, they may use sheets of colored cellophane as filters to discover this for themselves.

Sugar-making, conversion to starch, and allied processes

Green plants combine CO_2 and H_2O in the presence of light to form simple sugar. Most green plants, namely most dicotyledons, support further reaction in the leaves; they convert the sugar to starch. However, some green plants do not form starch in their leaves. The fleshy leaves of the onion, leaves of corn, sugar beets, and many other monocotyledonous plants (especially members of the Liliaceae), may be tested to show the presence of stored glucose rather than starch. In corn, the path of glucose from leaves may be traced to the seed, where it is stored. In sugar beets, glucose formed in the leaves is transported to the beet root to be stored as cane sugar. However, in the bean, and most dicotyledonous plants, the conversion of glucose to starch continues in the leaves.

Role of light and chlorophyll in photosynthesis

Starch-making by green leaves. Select healthy leaves from a geranium or Golden Beta Yellow coleus plant which has been placed in the sunlight for several days. First, boil the leaves for a few minutes in water in a small Pyrex beaker on an *electric* hot plate. This preliminary step softens the leaves by breaking down cell walls. Next, transfer the softened leaves to a beaker half full of ethyl or methyl alcohol and warm on the hot plate. Where a hot plate is not available, precautions must be taken to avoid igniting alcohol fumes. Alcohol may be heated in a water bath (Fig. 1-2) with the alcohol in a small beaker or long test tube standing in a larger Pyrex beaker of boiling water. (An electric immersion heater, such as is

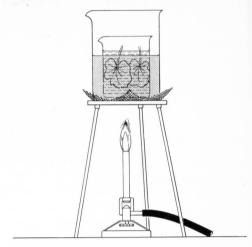

Fig. 1-2 If an electric hot plate is not available for heating a small beaker of alcohol, use a water bath as shown.

described in the companion volume,[3] makes a fireproof alcohol-heating device.)

Chlorophyll is soluble in alcohol, and the pigment should be extracted completely from the leaves in about 5 minutes. For thick leaves, decant the alcohol and replace with fresh alcohol. Then heat again until all chlorophyll is removed. Wash the blanched leaves; spread them flat in open Petri dishes and cover with a dilute aqueous iodine solution such as Lugol's solution (p. 409). After several (2 to 5) minutes, rinse off the excess iodine solution; hold the leaves up to the light to show the blackish areas which indicate the presence of starch. It may take as long as 15 minutes for all the iodine to react with the starch in the leaf.

You may want to show the reaction by

[3] A. Joseph, P. Brandwein, E. Morholt, *Teaching High School Science: A Sourcebook for the Physical Sciences,* Harcourt, Brace, New York, 1958.

first adding iodine solution to starch paste in a test tube. Students might show the absence of this reaction with other pure nutrients, such as sugar, fat, or proteins. However, the absence of starch is not a positive test that photosynthesis has not occurred (see above).

Sugar-making by green leaves. Sprouted onion bulbs grown in light show the presence of simple sugars in the shoots. Cut 1-inch lengths of the green shoots into a Pyrex test tube; add about 1 inch of either Benedict's or Fehling's solution (p. 405). Then bring the contents of the tube to a boil over a Bunsen burner or alcohol lamp. A change in color from blue to shades of green, to reddish-orange indicates the presence of simple sugars. This color reaction (as a test for simple sugars) may be checked by demonstrating the change in color when glucose solution or molasses is boiled with Benedict's solution.

Test for cane sugar in plants. Before you test for the presence of cane sugar in a plant, you may want to demonstrate the sugar test (using pure cane sugar). To a small quantity of cane sugar in a test tube add about 15 cc of distilled water. Next add 1 to 2 cc of a 5 per cent solution of cobalt nitrate, prepared by adding 5 gm of cobalt nitrate to 100 cc of distilled water. Then add a small quantity of strong sodium hydroxide solution, prepared by adding 50 gm of sodium hydroxide sticks to 100 cc of distilled water. A violet color reaction is a positive test for cane sugar.

Note: A weak solution of cane sugar (sucrose) may be changed to glucose by adding a few drops of concentrated hydrochloric acid, and boiling gently for a minute or so. [Saliva will also change cane sugar ($C_{12}H_{22}O_{11}$) to glucose ($C_6H_{12}O_6$) on standing.] Neutralize the hydrochloric acid with sodium carbonate until no further effervescence occurs. Then test with Benedict's or Fehling's solution for the presence of glucose.

Role of light in starch-making by green plants. Select geranium plants which have been in the dark for at least 24 hours. At the start of the experiment, some of the leaves should be tested for starch (since leaves originally free of starch will serve as one control). Have students cover several leaves of the plants with tin foil or carbon paper, or pin thin discs cut from cork, to the top and the bottom surfaces of several leaves (Fig. 1-3). Incidentally, to avoid denuding the plants of their leaves, only a portion of each leaf need be covered; the rest of each of the leaves (exposed) serves as a control. Then place the plants in sunlight, or artificial light from a 75-watt bulb 2 feet from the plant.

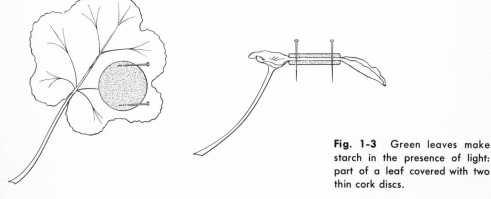

Fig. 1-3 Green leaves make starch in the presence of light: part of a leaf covered with two thin cork discs.

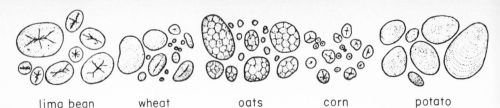

| lima bean | wheat | oats | corn | potato |

Fig. 1-4 Starch grains from some plants. (From L. J. Milne & M. J. Milne, *The Biotic World and Man*, Prentice-Hall, 1952.)

After 24 hours or so, remove two or more covered leaves and an equal number of leaves exposed to the sunlight (be sure to identify them); place them in boiling water, extract the chlorophyll from the leaves in heated alcohol, and finally add diluted iodine as already described—all this to test for starch. Only the exposed leaves or areas should show the dark blue-black indicative of starch formation.

Or you can get results in 15 minutes by using a 500-watt lamp, 3 feet away from the plant. Make certain that the plants are not overheated. Blue cellophane can arrest part of the heat.

Starch grains. You may want to have students examine the shape and size of starch grains, since these are characteristic of specific plant species. In fact, starch grains are used to identify many plants. For example, in the potato the starch grains are irregularly oval in outline, and seem to consist of alternating dark and light lines in the grains; compare these with starch grains of other plants (Fig. 1-4).

Prepare a mount of starch grains by scraping the cut surface of a raw white potato; mount this in water and flatten it with a coverslip. Then allow a drop of dilute iodine solution (p. 409) to run under the coverslip as filter paper is placed near the opposite edge of the coverslip to draw up some of the water. Compare these cell inclusions with those from cereal plants.

Role of chlorophyll in starch-making. Variegated coleus leaves showing white regions, or silver-leaf geranium leaves, may be used to show that chlorophyll is needed for starch-making. First, make a diagram of the leaves showing their pattern of green and white. Then students may test several leaves for starch, using the standard method which has been described, that is, transferring leaves through boiling water, into alcohol, then into iodine. The parts which previously contained chlorophyll show the presence of starch (these stain blue-black); the original white parts of the leaves, which lack starch, stain the brown of iodine.

Analysis of chlorophyll. Students have seen how chlorophyll is extracted from leaves heated in denatured ethyl alcohol (see technique, p. 14). As a demonstration (or part of a student project), this extracted chlorophyll might now be analyzed by paper chromatography, a useful technique for separating the organic compounds out of a mixture. In this case, chlorophyll A and B and xanthine (xanthophyll) may be separated out of the chlorophyll extract.

Probably the simplest technique in paper chromatography is a disc technique which uses 3-inch discs of filter paper. As in Fig. 1-5a, cut two parallel slits, ⅛ inch apart, from the edge of the disc to the center. Then bend this narrow section downward at right angles to the circle of filter paper. Place the filter-paper disc on top of a container of freshly extracted chlorophyll so that the ⅛-inch strip of filter paper hangs into the liquid and acts as a wick. (Students may grind about 10 gm of spinach leaves in 20 cc of acetone. Some laboratories use equal parts

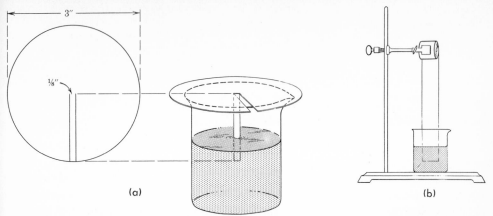

Fig. 1-5 Apparatus for paper chromatography: (a) disc technique; (b) technique using filter-paper roll.

of acetone and petroleum ether as the solvent; others use alcohol in "rough" demonstrations.) Within the class period, students can observe the rise of the chlorophyll components up the wick onto the center of the filter paper. These components diffuse out from the center at different rates forming distinct, concentric rings: outermost ring (fastest moving molecules) is carotene, then xanthophyll 1 and 2, followed by chlorophyll A and B.

Students may also use 2-inch wide, flat strips of filter paper suspended from a stand into a mixture of the organic substance and a suitable solvent, as in Fig. 1-5b. In this case a horizontal streak will form on the filter-paper strip for each of the compounds in the mixture. In fact, scientific supply houses have rolls of filter paper specially designed for chromatography. The color and width of the streaks are indices of the approximate composition of the compounds found in the organic mixture. (Students may want to analyze cell sap and plant sap. In subsequent chapters many organic substances are under study, such as blood plasma and digestive juices; students may want to use these paper chromatography techniques to find out something about their composition.)

On occasion, students may also want to use a technique based on the electrostatic attraction of compounds or molecules—electrophoresis. Here, too, the migration of complex biological compounds along a moist filter-paper strip can be traced. The advantage of electrophoresis over paper chromatography is to be found in the greater speed of molecular migration and the wider separation of compounds, but the technique is complex for high school biology students.

Chloroplasts in elodea plants. The chlorophyll in leaves is found in small bodies called chloroplasts, in the cytoplasm of green plant cells.

One of the best plants in which to examine chloroplasts is a healthy elodea plant, *Anacharis* (Fig. 1-6). Mount a leaf in a drop of aquarium water (p. 312, wet mounts) and examine under low and

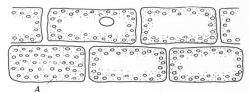

Fig. 1-6 A microscopic examination of cells of elodea, showing chloroplasts lining the cell walls. Cell A is a view near the top of the cell, showing the layer of chloroplasts just inside the top wall; the other cells are viewed through the center, showing the distribution of chloroplasts near the side walls.

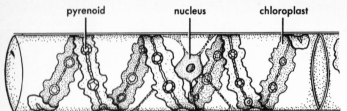

pyrenoid   nucleus   chloroplast

Fig. 1-7 *Spirogyra* cell (diagrammatic) showing pyrenoids. When stained with Lugol's solution, these appear black, showing that they contain starch. (From C. L. Wilson & W. E. Loomis, *Botany*, rev. ed., Dryden, 1957.)

high power. When the leaves from young, growing tips are examined, the chloroplasts may appear to be moving in the cytoplasm of the cells. In reality, it is the cytoplasm which is circulating, and the chloroplasts are being carried by the moving "stream" of cytoplasm (p. 312).

Chloroplasts in *Spirogyra*. In *Spirogyra* we find that the chloroplast is spiral (Fig. 1-7). Mount one or two threads in a drop of water. One species of *Spirogyra* has one spiral chloroplast; another fairly common species has a double spiral chloroplast. When Lugol's solution (p. 409) is added to a wet mount, the pyrenoids along the chloroplasts stain darkly, showing that they contain starch.

Absorption of carbon dioxide by green leaves

The fact that carbon dioxide is absorbed in the presence of light is indirect evidence of its use in the process of food-making. One of the simplest methods of demonstrating this uses the absorption of carbon dioxide from water by water plants, such as elodea.

Absorption of carbon dioxide by a water plant. The procedure to be described is a modification[4] of a titration method adapted originally by H. Munro Fox. In this method the absorption of carbon dioxide from water by green plants in light is revealed through the change in the color of an indicator.

Brom thymol blue[5] is the indicator used; it is blue in alkaline solution and yellow in acid medium. It has a fairly narrow range in pH from 6.0 (yellow) to 7.6 (blue), so that slight changes in hydrogen-ion concentration show up quickly. Thus a slight increase in acidity, as when carbon dioxide is added to the solution, will change the blue color (alkaline) to yellow. When carbon dioxide is absorbed, as in photosynthesizing plants, the yellow color (due to carbon dioxide in solution) is changed back to blue.

You may prepare a 0.1 per cent *stock* solution of brom thymol blue by dissolving 0.5 gm of brom thymol blue in 500 cc of water. To this add a trace of ammonium hydroxide (1 drop or so per liter) to turn the solution *deep blue*. In a beaker dilute the 0.1 per cent *stock* solution with aquarium water in which elodea has been growing. Be certain that the solution is a deep blue. If not, turn it blue by adding just enough of the dilute ammonia. Then breathe through a straw into the indicator solution until the color *just* turns yellow. Now students might pour the brom thymol yellow into large test tubes. Prepare these demonstrations, and cork the tubes: (a) one set with no plants, exposed to light; (b) another set, each tube with a sprig of a vigorously growing elodea plant, each having an end bud, also exposed to light; (c) a series like (b),

[4] Paul F. Brandwein, "A Method for Demonstrating the Use of Carbon Dioxide by a Plant," *Teaching Biologist*, 7:76, 1938.

[5] Although dictionaries usually list this indicator as "bromothymol blue," we shall follow common scientific usage, as here, throughout this book.

except that each test tube is covered with carbon paper or kept in the dark.

Those tubes containing plants, placed in sunlight, show a change from yellow to blue within 30 to 45 minutes (depending upon the intensity of sunlight). On cloudy days, the series of tubes might be placed near a 75-watt bulb. Results similar to those in sunlight will take about 45 minutes. Since the (a) and (c) tubes show no color change, the color change in the tubes in the (b) series may be taken as indirect evidence of the absorption of carbon dioxide by green plants in the presence of light.

Phenol red is another indicator with a narrow range of pH (6.8 acid, to 8.4 alkaline) which may be substituted for the brom thymol blue. As the carbon dioxide is absorbed, the color change is from yellow (acid) to red (alkaline).

Absorption of carbon dioxide by a land plant. Plants such as geranium or coleus may be used to show absorption of carbon dioxide through their leaves. The carbon dioxide content of the air reaching the plant may be modified, removed, or increased, to demonstrate a change in the rate of starch-making.

First, reduce the carbon dioxide content around the plant in the following manner. Place a healthy geranium plant on a tray or large sheet of glass together with an open, wide-mouthed jar or beaker of solid potassium or sodium hydroxide (pellets or sticks).[6] Cover with a bell jar; seal the bottom of the jar to the sheet of glass with Vaseline to make it airtight (Fig. 1-8). The hydroxide serves to remove the carbon dioxide from the enclosed jar. Then set up a similar demonstration, but in this one omit the hydroxide; place both preparations in

Fig. 1-8 Reducing the CO_2 content of the air surrounding a green plant. The beaker contains KOH or NaOH pellets.

moderate sunlight. After several days, the leaves may be tested for their starch content. The plant with the carbon dioxide absorbent will show little or no starch.

A more elaborate means[7] for reducing the carbon dioxide content in the air is shown in Fig. 1-9. Begin with a geranium plant which has been in the dark for at least 24 hours, and which gives a negative starch test. An aspirator draws air through bottles containing barium hydroxide or strong soda lime in solution or pellet form. In this way the air that enters the bell jar lacks carbon dioxide. Later, test the leaves for the presence of starch.

The effect of an increased carbon dioxide content of air on the rate of photosynthesis can also be shown (Fig. 1-10). Select a geranium plant which gives a negative starch test and enclose it in the bell jar. Connect a delivery tube from a carbon dioxide generator (or a flask containing dry ice) into the bell jar. (Leave the clamp open while carbon dioxide is

[6] Solid NaOH or KOH should be handled with forceps; for safety and first-aid procedures, see Chapter 22.

[7] Stuart Dunn, *Elementary Plant Physiology*, Addison-Wesley, Reading, Mass., 1949, p. 98.

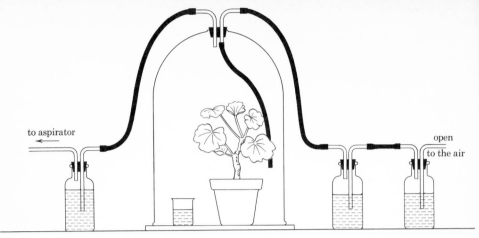

Fig. 1-9 A more elaborate way of reducing the carbon dioxide content of the air surrounding a green plant. The bottles and beaker contain $Ba(OH)_2$ or soda lime.

entering the bell jar; notice the safety tube on the generator.) Later, test these leaves for starch. There should be a significant increase in the amount of starch produced in the leaves of the plants grown in a carbon dioxide atmosphere. However, this is a relatively unsatisfactory demonstration to use because the relative difference in starch content is difficult to detect unless a comparison of

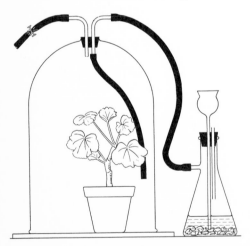

Fig. 1-10 Increasing the carbon dioxide content of the air surrounding a green plant: dilute acid and marble chips ($CaCO_3$) react to generate CO_2. Notice the safety tube in the flask.

the dry weight of the two sets of leaves is made.

Stomates, the air passages of leaves. To show that stomates serve as air passages in the leaves, students may press the petioles of leaves between the fingers while the blades of the leaves are immersed in hot water. The air in the leaves will expand in hot water and escape as air bubbles through the stomates.

Floating water plants will show the stomates on the upper surface only, while most leaves will show them on the lower side. In the sunflower, clover, daffodil, and grasses, bubbles of air can be seen to escape from both surfaces of the leaves, indicating that stomates are found on both surfaces.

The epidermal layers may be peeled off the leaves and mounted for microscopic examination to confirm these observations (see p. 21). The fleshy leaves of *Peperomia* and types of *Crassula* allow easy removal of the lower epidermis.

Entry of carbon dioxide into leaves through stomates. At another time, you may want to show that stomates are the regions through which carbon dioxide enters the leaves of land plants. Select thin-leaved plants, such as geranium or coleus, which have stomates on the lower surface of the leaves. (Other useful plants are listed in Table 1-1; the average number of stomates on the upper and lower epidermal layers is indicated.)

Select two plants, geraniums for example, which have been kept in the dark overnight, or until the leaves give a negative starch test. Coat both sides of several leaves with melted Vaseline to close the stomates. On other leaves, coat the upper surface only; on still others, the lower surface only.

After the plants have been in light for several hours, wipe off the Vaseline (or remove it with ether or carbon tetrachloride). Boil the leaves in water, heat in alcohol until the chlorophyll is removed, and finally test for starch. Where Vaseline has clogged the stomates and prevented the entrance of carbon dioxide, students should find that starch-making has been arrested. The success of this demonstration depends on very careful techniques, e.g., complete clogging of the stomates.

Examining stomates under the microscope. Such leaves as *Bryophyllum, Sedum, Echeveria, Sempervivum, Kalanchoë, Peperomia,* "hen and chicks," *Tradescantia, Zebrina,* lettuce leaves, or Boston fern may be used for this demonstration. Tear the leaf toward the main vein. Then with a forceps pull off strips of the thin membrane which is the lower epidermis and mount in water; examine under the microscope (Fig. 1-11).

TABLE 1-1
Number of stomates per sq mm*

Leaves with no stomates on upper surface

	lower surface
Balsam fir	228
Norway maple	400
Wood anemone	67
Begonia (red)	40
Barberry	229
Rubber plant	145
Black walnut	461
Lily	62
White mulberry	480
Golden current	145
Lilac	330
Nasturtium	130

Leaves with few stomates on upper surface

	upper surface	lower surface
Swamp milkweed	67	191
Pumpkin	28	269
Tomato	12	130
Bean	40	281
Poplar	55	270
Bittersweet	60	263

Leaves with stomates more nearly equal on both surfaces

	upper surface	lower surface
Oats	25	23
Sunflower	175	325
Pine	50	71
Garden pea	101	216
Corn	94	158
Cabbage	219	301

* From B. Duggar, *Plant Physiology*, Macmillan, New York, 1930.

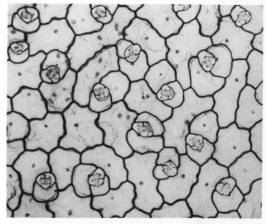

Fig. 1-11 Photomicrograph of epidermis from leaf of *Sedum*, showing stomates and guard cells. (Photo: General Biological Supply House, Inc., Chicago.)

Especially desirable for the purpose of examining stomates is the epidermis of certain species of *Tradescantia* whose cells (vacuoles) contain a pink pigment. The guard cells bounding each stomate contain chloroplasts.

Where the epidermis is difficult to pull off, blanch the leaves in boiling water for a few minutes. Then the epidermis may be loosened easily. In this condition, as well as in the fresh state, the cells may be stained with methylene blue or dilute iodine (pp. 309, 409).

Cross section of a leaf. Where a study of the other layers of cells in leaves is planned, it may be desirable to make free-hand cross sections of leaves. This procedure is described in Chapter 17.

Turgor in the guard cells surrounding stomates. How do guard cells serve to regulate the size of stomates? Students will want to strip off the lower epidermis of a plant (p. 20, above) which has been standing in bright sunlight. Mount a bit of this in a drop of water. Examine the guard cells under high power. Now place a drop of a 0.4 M calcium chloride or sodium chloride solution (see solutions, p. 403) near the edge of the coverslip and draw off the water from the opposite end of the coverslip with filter paper. Examine the guard cells and the size of the stomates again. Notice the reduced size of the stomates as the guard cells lose turgor, because of removal of water by the sodium or calcium chloride. (For an explanation of plasmolysis and diffusion, with additional examples, see pp. 33, 52, 308.)

Students may return the tissue to water and note the increase in turgor of guard cells and the opening of stomates.

Oxygen evolved in photosynthesis

No satisfactory classroom demonstration has yet been elaborated to show the

Fig. 1-12 Sprig of elodea gives off oxygen in light.

evolution of oxygen during photosynthesis. Those devices used by biochemists are too complex to be used in the classroom. (See *Practical Physiological Chemistry* by Hawk, Oser, and Summerson.) It would be a contribution if a suitable demonstration, simple enough to be used in the classroom, were devised. Until one *is* devised, the following demonstrations may be useful.

Counting bubbles of oxygen as evidence of photosynthesis. Bubbles of oxygen escape from the cut stems of elodea sprigs placed in bright sunlight.

To show this, invert a 3-inch tip of a vigorously growing elodea sprig into a test tube or beaker containing aquarium water to which about 2 cc of a 0.25 per cent solution of sodium bicarbonate has been added for every 100 cc of aquarium water (which has been boiled to drive off dissolved gases and then cooled). The bicarbonate will provide a source of carbon dioxide, since the small quantity of carbon dioxide ordinarily found in aquarium water acts as a limiting factor in photosynthesis. Tie the sprig to a glass rod immersed in the container so that it will be held down in place (Fig. 1-12).

The plant should be exposed to a bright light source. Shortly, the number of bubbles of oxygen escaping from the cut stem per minute may be counted. You may want students to compare the rate of production of oxygen in relation to light intensity by moving the test tube or beaker varying distances from the light source. Compare this with a control placed in relative shade or in darkness.

"Funnel" method for collecting oxygen. In this method the escaping gas is collected so that it can be tested and identified. Fill a large beaker or battery jar with aquarium water to which sodium bicarbonate solution (see technique above) has been added. Then cut the basal ends of five to ten sprigs of fresh elodea, and arrange them in a glass funnel so that their cut stems lie within or near the stem of the funnel. Force the wide mouth of the funnel to the bottom of the beaker (Fig. 1-13). Then cover the upper stem of the funnel with a test tube completely filled with water. Finally, set the preparation in bright light for a number of hours.

The water in the test tube should be displaced, more or less completely, by bubbles of gas rising from the cut stems of the elodea. Test the gas collected in the test tube for oxygen by inserting a glowing splint. Ganong[8] has criticized this method on the grounds that there is not enough oxygen produced to cause the splint to flare up. However, the probability of getting a positive test for oxygen is increased if the first ½-inch sample of gas, which usually has a good deal of air in it, is discarded. If the water has been

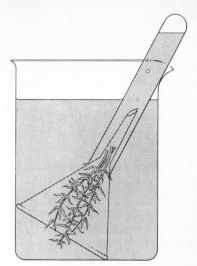

Fig. 1-13 Funnel method of collecting oxygen liberated by sprigs of elodea.

boiled and then cooled, most of the dissolved gases will have been removed.

Indigo carmine test for oxygen production by leaves. Palladin[9] describes a demonstration which shows that oxygen is liberated by water plants such as elodea in the presence of light. The reagent is that of Shutzenberger, a solution of indigo carmine decolorized by $NaHSO_3$. The solution is yellow when prepared but turns blue in the presence of oxygen. Place elodea plants in large test tubes containing a dilute solution of the reagent; then expose to light. Within a few minutes the reagent turns blue. However, this test is extremely difficult to do because the reagent turns blue in air. This is the case with most reagents which turn color in the presence of O_2; they turn color in air as well. We do not recommend this test for general use. But it might furnish the basis of a project: the use of indigo carmine as a test for oxygen.

U-tube method to show the volume of oxygen production. This method has

[8] W. F. Ganong, "The Erroneous Physiology of the Elementary Botanical Textbooks," *School Sci. and Math.,* 6:297, 1906.

[9] Vladimir Palladin, *Plant Physiology,* Blakiston (McGraw-Hill), New York, 1926.

frequently been used to show that oxygen is given off in photosynthesis. Aquatic plants such as green algae are put in a glass chamber of about 10 cc capacity, along with the water in which they have been growing. To this add a few cc of a 0.25 per cent bicarbonate solution. When photosynthesis occurs, the oxygen produced can be measured by the change in the volume of a U-tube as shown in Fig. 7-11.

Evolution of oxygen by land plants. Many variations of the following method have been described. The best-known technique is probably the one in which a plant, such as a geranium, is placed under a bell jar with a burning candle. The bell jar is then sealed with Vaseline to a glass plate. When the candle is finally extinguished, presumably by the exhaustion of oxygen, the experiment is allowed to stand overnight. The fact that the plants have produced more oxygen may be tested for in several ways, either by inserting a glowing splint or by having a cigarette lighter ignite a candle inside the bell jar. A general criticism of this method is offered by several investigators.[10] It has been shown that a flame in an enclosed space will not consume all the oxygen. ". . . An ordinary flame will not burn, as a rule, over about 3 per cent of the oxygen from a confined space before it goes out."[11] That there is a residual amount of oxygen has been demonstrated. A piece of lens paper, cotton, or a match head can be ignited by a spark from a spark gap within the bell jar after the candle flame has been extinguished. However, the candle enclosed with a geranium plant within a

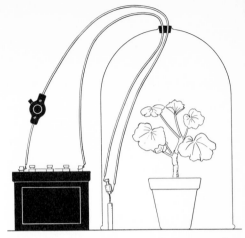

Fig. 1-14 Green plants give off oxygen: a cigar lighter from an automobile is wired through a switch to a 6-volt battery and used to ignite a candle; the control is the same but without the plant, or with different plants, for comparison.

bell jar, used with a control, can be valuable to show the difference in quantity of oxygen evolved by green plants.

An electric hot wire in the form of an automobile cigarette lighter with a 6-volt storage battery may be used to ignite a candle in this method. Prepare the apparatus shown in Fig. 1-14, but do not connect the battery. Use a healthy geranium plant. Place the demonstration on a glass plate so that Vaseline can be used to seal the rim of the bell jar to the glass. Set up the control in the same way, but omit the green plant. Cork the opening in the top of each bell jar. When the demonstrations have been in the sunlight for several days, connect the storage battery in series to the wires hanging outside of the bell jars. This battery supplies current for the cigarette lighter.[12] Then compare the burning time of the candle inside each of the enclosed jars. This

[10] B. C. Gruenberg and N. Robinson, *Experiments and Projects in Biology*, Ginn, Boston, 1925; A. Raskin, "A New Method for Demonstrating the Production of Oxygen by a Photosynthesizing Plant," *Sci. Educ.*, 21:231, 1937; W. F. Ganong, "The Erroneous Physiology of the Elementary Botanical Textbooks," *School Sci. and Math.*, 6:297, 1906.

[11] Ganong, *ibid.*

[12] F. Vaurio in "Photosynthesis Apparatus," *Sci. Educ.*, 22:6, 1938, p. 309, comments on the standing joke about cigarette lighters and suggests a 6-volt transformer, copper wire, and a nichrome wire loop to ignite the candle, or the use of storage battery or several dry cells.

demonstration is usually not very successful; but you may be able to turn a failure into a success by assigning a student the project of either explaining why it did not work or of designing modifications so that it will.

Developing skills in understanding the reports of scientists

Along with the skills of observing, demonstrating, and planning experiments, students need practice in another skill, the ability to read and interpret the writings of scientists. Many of the experiments or demonstrations that we have described here are a part of the history of biology and the fascinating story of how green plants make their food supply. In some classes you may want students to read small sections of the original papers of some of the workers in this field: van Helmont, Ingenhousz, Priestley, Sachs, or Blackman, among the hundreds who have contributed in this area.

In fact, some of the experiments may be elicited "afresh" from students as they think through the need for large numbers of experimental plants and for controls. In this way, students will come to appreciate the design of experiments.

We have selected a reading from the work of van Helmont to reproduce here. You may want to use a reading taken from a science journal or textbook, then prepare suitable questions based on the reading for students to answer. This is a valuable activity in giving practice in interpretation and reasoning.

Such a reading may be used as an introduction to a new topic; it might raise questions or give data related to the classwork; or it might introduce the need for experimental design in undertaking laboratory work. This is also one of the many ways a teacher may identify students with a high level of ability and interest in science. Such students read these passages with greater facility, appreciation, and understanding. In some classes,

readings may be included on an examination as a test for understandings and application in a new view.

Two examples follow; one is a historical paper and the other is devised by a teacher.

Early in the seventeenth century, Jan van Helmont undertook an experiment that has become a classic. Here is what he wrote about it.[13]

I took an earthen vessel, in which I put 200 pounds of earth that had been dried in a furnace, which I moistened with rainwater, and I implanted therein the trunk or stem of a willow tree, weighing 5 pounds, and at length, 5 years being finished, the tree sprung from thence did weigh 169 pounds and about 3 ounces. When there was need, I always moistened the earthen vessel with rainwater or distilled water, and the vessel was large and implanted in the earth. Lest the dust that flew about should be co-mingled with the earth, I covered the lip or mouth of the vessel with an iron plate covered with tin and easily passable with many holes. I computed not the weight of the leaves that fell off in the four autumns. At length, I again dried the earth of the vessel, and there was found the same 200 pounds, wanting about 2 ounces. Therefore 164 pounds of wood, bark and roots arose out of water only.

Answer these questions:
1. How long did van Helmont continue his experiment?
2. What was he trying to find out?
3. What was the gain in weight of this 5-pound willow stem?
4. How did van Helmont account for the increase in weight?
5. What would he have found if he had included the weight of the leaves over four years?

[13] From Leonard Nash, *Plants and the Atmosphere,* Case 5, Harvard Case Histories in Experimental Science, Harvard U. Press, Cambridge, Mass., 1952, p. 15.

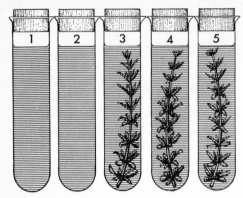

Fig. 1-15 (From E. Morholt & E. T. Smith, *Experiences in Biology*, Harcourt, Brace, 1954.)

6. What kind of control would you suggest to find out whether new plant tissue grows from water alone?

7. How do we explain the increase in weight of the plant nowadays?

You may find readings for similar purposes in scientific journals such as *Science* and *Scientific Monthly,* both publications of the American Association for the Advancement of Science (1515 Massachusetts Avenue, N. W., Washington 5, D. C.; *Scientific Monthly* merged with *Science* on January 1, 1958, but the old issues are still valuable sources); in the *American Scientist* (Sigma Xi, 56 Hillhouse Avenue, New Haven 11, Connecticut); or in *Scientific American* (415 Madison Avenue, New York 17).

The Harvard Case Histories in Experimental Science are a valuable set of booklets which are sources of readings in the history of science. Also, you may want to look into the readings edited by Gabriel and Fogel called *Great Experiments in Biology.*[14] This and others listed

at the end of this chapter are rich sources of reading materials.

You may also want to plan a test based on observations and reasoning rather than upon strict recall. For example, one type of test question might be of this kind.[15]

Experiment. A girl took five test tubes containing brom thymol blue and put elodea plants into three of them, as shown in Fig. 1-15. All the tubes were put in the dark. The next day she found that in the tubes containing the elodea (tubes 3, 4, 5), the brom thymol blue had turned to yellow. (Brom thymol blue changes to yellow when enough CO_2 is added.)

1. What is the best explanation of the girl's results?
a. Brom thymol blue turns yellow in the dark.
b. The plants gave off oxygen in the dark.
c. The plants gave off carbon dioxide in the dark.
d. There is insufficient evidence for any explanation.

2. Why were tubes 1 and 2 necessary or not necessary?
a. They were not necessary, because we know the action of brom thymol blue.
b. They were needed to match colors.
c. They were necessary to show whether any other factors change the color.
d. None of these.

3. What should the girl do to change the brom thymol yellow in tubes 3, 4, and 5 back to blue again?
a. Put the test tubes in the light.
b. Put a goldfish into the tubes.
c. Blow into the brom thymol yellow.
d. None of these.

4. What process, going on in the green plants in the dark, accounts for the color change?
a. assimilation
b. oxidation
c. photosynthesis
d. transpiration

[14] M. Gabriel and S. Fogel, eds., *Great Experiments in Biology,* Prentice-Hall, Englewood Cliffs, N. J., 1955.

[15] E. Morholt and E. Smith, *Experiences in Biology,* Harcourt, Brace, New York, 1954.

CAPSULE LESSONS
Ways to get started in class

1-1. Seal a snail in a soft glass test tube of pond water (Fig. 6-4). Ask the class: "How long might the snail live? Why?" By suitable questions lead the discussion toward the notion that green plants make food. And then the class is in a good discussion of how a green plant makes food and what materials it needs for food-making.

1-2. Perhaps you may prefer to begin with a film such as *Gift of Green* (New York Botanic Gardens), *Leaves* (Encyclopaedia Britannica), or *Photosynthesis* (United World).

1-3. Begin by testing a silver-edged geranium leaf for starch. Elicit reasons why the white portion does not contain starch. From here, you may have students design experiments to test the importance of light, of carbon dioxide, and so forth, as factors in food-making.

1-4. Develop a case study around the topic of photosynthesis using the reprint of the paper by Rabinowitch in *Scientific American* (see Bibliography). The reprint has been made available by the Atomic Energy Commission.

1-5. Introduce van Helmont's experiment with a willow twig and proceed from there. (See Brandwein, Hollingworth, Beck, Burgess, *You and Science,* Chapter 18, Harcourt, Brace.)

1-6. Begin with laboratory work. Have the class examine cells of the onion bulb under the microscope (Fig. 17-4). Compare these with elodea cells. Lead into a discussion of the function of chloroplasts.

1-7. Do green plants give off oxygen? Collect a tubeful of the gas which bubbles out of the cut stem of elodea twigs in the light (described on p. 22).

1-8. Have students design an experiment to show that green plants use carbon dioxide in light (see technique, p. 18).

1-9. Other suggestions for lessons may be found in these workbooks: Blackwood, *Experiences in Science* (Harcourt, Brace); Eckert, *Discovery Problems in General Science* (College Entrance Book Co.); Morholt and Smith, *Experiences in Biology* (Harcourt, Brace); Otto and Blanc, *Biology Investigations* (Holt); Vance, Barker, and Miller, *Biology Activities* (Lippincott).

1-10. Lessons may be devised by starting with any one of the demonstrations suggested in this chapter.

1-11. Keep a log of successful lessons. As these are revised each year (in the light of variations in classes and students) you will have a valuable piece of action research (see the companion volume, Brandwein, Watson, and Blackwood, *Teaching High School Science: A Book of Methods,* Harcourt, Brace, 1958).

1-12. Use a roll of cellophane or a clear plastic box to model a cell. Elicit from students information concerning the structures typical of all cells. As they suggest structures, build the cell. For instance, as your students suggest the structure "nucleus" insert a nucleus (made of modeling clay). Small balls of green clay might be chloroplasts, or a ribbon of green blotting paper the spiral chloroplast of *Spirogyra*.

You may have models of cells made by students (in previous years) to show new students. Models can be made of plaster of Paris or papier mâché (see model-making, p. 413). This making of models may be done in a club or it might be a student project. An attractive visual aids collection may be developed in a short time.

PEOPLE, PLACES, AND THINGS

There are times when a teacher may need help—equipment on loan, a special chemical for an experiment, an idea for a student project for a youngster with a high interest in science. Likely as not scientists in a college, university, or hospital nearby will want to be of help. Your colleagues in a nearby junior or senior high school may be of considerable help, too. Graduate students in nearby universities are often generous with suggestions for projects and new demonstrations. Many high school students have been sponsored in their project work in this way, and have thus been encouraged to continue in science.

You can get assistance from college librarians in hunting out an old or a new reference book on some specialty. A museum of natural history, botanic garden, or zoological park may have the information or equipment you need. And of course, the parents of your students (doctors, engineers, scientists) may be resource people in some aspects of special work going on in your school.

Books and Pamphlets

These are only a few of the books which are pertinent to the work discussed in this chapter. These and many other references classified by subject and with complete bibliographical data are given in the Bibliography at the end of the book.

Curtis, O., and D. Clark, *An Introduction to Plant Physiology,* 1950.

Gabriel, M., and S. Fogel, *Great Experiments in Biology,* 1955.

Gibbs, R., *Botany: An Evolutionary Approach,* 1950.

Hill, A., *Economic Botany,* 1952.

Meyer, B., and D. Anderson, *Plant Physiology,* 1952.

Nash, L., *Plants and the Atmosphere,* Harvard Case History Series, 1953.

Rabinowitch, E., "Photosynthesis," *Sci. American,* March 1949, Nov. 1953.

Films and Filmstrips

This partial list is intended only as a guide toward film and filmstrip selection. Refer to the more complete listing at the end of the book where films are classified by subject and where a key to abbreviations and addresses of distributors are given. The cost of film rental, of course, is subject to change. Films are sound and black and white unless otherwise specified.

The Atomic Greenhouse; Tagging the Atom (f), Handel Film Corp.; available free on loan from U.S. Atomic Energy Commission Field Offices.

Food from the Sun (fs), Sugar Information, free.

Gift of Green (photosynthesis) (f, c), N.Y. Botanic Garden, $1.00.

Leaves (f), EBF, $2.50.

Photosynthesis (f), UWF, $4.00.

Free and Inexpensive Materials

This is only a partial listing of free and inexpensive materials available to the teacher at this time. A more complete listing, including addresses, is given at the end of the book. Many of these materials are distributed to teachers without charge. Where there is a small fee, the cost is indicated, although the prices are subject to change. While we recommend the material for use in the classroom, we do not necessarily sponsor the products advertised.

How a Tree Grows (poster 16″ × 21″); *What We Get from Trees* (chart 28″ × 40″), U.S. Dept. of Agriculture, Forest Service.

Photosynthesis (reprint from *Sci. American*), U.S. Atomic Energy Commission, March 1949.

Some Applications of Atomic Energy in Plant Science, U.S. Atomic Energy Commission.

CHAPTER 2

Animals: food-takers

Ingestion

The devices used by animals, as food-takers, to capture or to ensnare their food are an essential part of the study of life functions of plants and animals.

The means of ingestion by protozoa, by small fresh-water invertebrates, including insects, and by some amphibia may be studied directly. Living animals to be studied in class might be cultured in the laboratory and be available throughout the year. The cultivation and maintenance of these animals are described in Chapters 18 and 19. Where facilities favor support of a marine aquarium (p. 356), interesting studies can be pursued on how ingestion takes place among small echinoderms, squids, other mollusks, crayfish, and others. Many suggestions for student projects are inherent in the subject area of this chapter.

Protozoa

Paramecium. Add a small pinch of carmine powder to a thick culture of *Paramecium* (or other ciliate). Students may prepare wet mounts of the protozoan-carmine mixture (pp. 307, 313) and watch how cilia create a current of water. They will note also the formation of a food ball in the oral groove and the passage of

the dark-red food mass into the cytoplasm, where a food vacuole is formed. You may substitute a drop of India ink for the carmine powder. (In this case, the food vacuoles appear black.)

As a special project a student might study digestion within the food vacuoles. He could stain a few drops of milk with a few grains of the indicator Congo red (indicators, p. 406), and then add this to an equal volume of a culture of *Paramecium*. He could prepare wet mounts and examine the ingestion of red butter-fat globules as food vacuoles. In a number of cases the food vacuoles become bluish in color as acid is secreted into the vacuoles, and finally change to red (alkaline).

An interesting but unsolved problem may be attempted by some students in class as a project. Do protozoa continue to take in carmine particles which cannot be digested, or do they "learn" to select their food types? One method of attack might be to count the number of food vacuoles formed during measured time intervals. Students may think of many more approaches. We have found this a good project.

Chaos chaos. Prepare several slides of thick cultures (see Chapter 18) of *Stentor,*

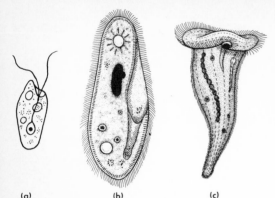

(a)   (b)   (c)

Fig. 2-1   Three common Protozoa: (a) *Chilomonas;* (b) *Paramecium;* (c) *Stentor.* (a, from G. G. Simpson, C. Pittendrigh, & L. Tiffany, *Life,* Harcourt, Brace, 1957; b, c, General Biological Supply House, Inc., Chicago.)

Paramecium, Blepharisma, or *Chilomonas* (Fig. 2-1). To each of these slides add some *Chaos chaos,* a large amoeba (Fig. 2-2). These may be purchased from a biological supply house (see the listing at the end of the book). Watch to see how a food cup is formed as the amoeba's pseudopodia close around the prey. Food vacuoles form, of different colors depending upon the food source (red with *Blepharisma,* blue-green with *Stentor*). At times you may see the captured prey moving within the vacuole. Circle the coverslips with Vaseline to prevent evaporation of the water. Students may study the change in the size of the food vacuoles during a period of several hours.

Blepharisma. Some *Blepharisma* are cannibalistic and contain deep-red food vacuoles of ingested, smaller *Blepharisma.* Mount several drops of *Blepharisma* culture for microscopic examination.

Trumpet-shaped *Stentor* (Fig. 2-1), mounted in a rich culture of *Blepharisma,* will soon show pink food vacuoles within the blue-green body.

Other microscopic invertebrates

For maintaining these invertebrates in the laboratory, see Chapter 18.

The microscopic annelid worm *Dero* or *Nais* (Fig. 2-3) may be mounted in a thick suspension of *Paramecium* for examination under the microscope. Watch how it ingests particles of food.

You may also want students to place some planarians (unfed for several days) in Syracuse dishes along with such annelid worms as *Dero* or *Aulophorus* (Fig. 18-13). The action of the proboscis of planarians during ingestion may be observed with a binocular microscope or hand lens.

The action of tentacles and stinging organs such as those in hydra (Fig. 18-8) makes interesting study. Select hydras which have not been fed for several days

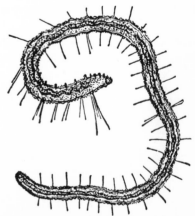

Fig. 2-3   An annelid worm: *Nais.* (From R. W. Hegner, *College Zoology,* rev. ed., Macmillan, 1930.)

Fig. 2-2   A large amoeba: *Chaos chaos.* (Photo: General Biological Supply House, Inc., Chicago.)

and add them to a Syracuse dish containing *Daphnia* or *Dero*. Students may be able to see the hydras grasp the food organisms and paralyze them with the nematocysts on the tentacles. Watch the movement of the food toward the hypostome. The gastrovascular cavity becomes distended and the captured organisms may be seen through the thin walls of this cavity. Under a binocular microscope or small dissecting lens you may see several organisms ingested in rapid succession.

Insects

Meal worms *(Tenebrio molitor)* may be raised in the laboratory (see p. 357). You may want to demonstrate the insect's mandibular mouth parts. A hand lens will show these chewing mouth parts.

In the fall, students may collect egg cases of praying mantis (Fig. 2-4), which appear as a frothy mass of tan material attached to twigs of trees and shrubs. Or egg masses may be purchased from supply houses or botanical gardens. They should be placed in a vivarium or large jar when they are received. When the mass is kept at room temperature, hundreds of nymphs hatch out and are available for study. Place several nymphs in small vials and watch the action of their forelegs and mandibles.

In contrast, the sucking mouth parts and the extensible and flexible proboscis of adult fruit flies may be observed by placing adults in slender vials of media

Fig. 2-4 Egg mass of praying mantis. (Photo: Hugh Spencer.)

(preparation, p. 200). Study the action of labrum, labium, and hypopharynx which terminate in a pair of soft padlike labellar lobes. On the other hand, the mouth parts of the larvae show only strong mouth hooks; the usual mouth parts are missing (Fig. 2-5).

Some vertebrates

The rapid, lashing tongue movements of frogs, toads, and salamanders may be demonstrated by placing one of these animals in a small container. Then empty a bottle of fruit flies into the container. (Earthworms may be substituted as food.) Similar demonstrations may be prepared using chameleons (a type of reptile), which will feed upon fruit flies (Fig. 2-6).

Fig. 2-6 Chameleon with tongue extended for feeding. (Photo: The American Museum of Natural History.)

Fig. 2-5 Larva of fruit fly (*Drosophila*) showing detail of mouth hooks. Also note the position of the salivary glands. (After M. Demerec & B. P. Kaufmann, *Drosophila Guide*, Carnegie Institution of Washington, 1945.)

Digestion

The food tube

The path of food through the digestive tract may be observed in microscopic many-celled organisms. Prepare wet mounts of *Tubifex* worms, *Dero, Nais,* the crustacean *Daphnia,* or the larvae of *Drosophila.* (Culture methods are described in Chapter 18.)

Also demonstrate the path of food along the digestive tract of frogs. First, pith to destroy the brain and the spinal cord as well (Fig. 9-3). Then pin down the frog on a dissection board and remove the skin and muscular layer to expose the digestive tube (see dissection, Chapter 16). Keep the organs bathed in Ringer's solution (p. 409). Note the slow, rhythmic contractions along the length of the intestine and rectum.

You may also want to demonstrate the ciliary action along the sides of the jaw and roof of the mouth of the frog. Use the same pithed frog; dissect away the lower jaw and the floor of the mouth. Then remove the viscera, leaving as much of the esophagus as possible. Sprinkle fine particles of cork or filings of lead or iron on the anterior part of the roof of the mouth. Watch how the particles are carried along the roof and through the esophagus. This is accomplished by ciliary motion. The particles reappear in the cut part of the esophagus and move into the coelom, since the stomach has been cut away. (Keep the tissue moist throughout.)

You may also prepare exceedingly interesting demonstrations by mounting bits of ciliated epithelial tissue from the roof of the mouth or the sides of the frog's jaw in Ringer's solution (Fig. 16-11). Examine under the high power and look for the rhythmic ciliary motion. You may, if you wish, slow down the motion with ice. Vaseline the coverslip if you plan to study the motion over some time. And after a study of cilia you may want to try a vital dye to bring out details (see Chapter 17).

A comparison of the adaptive devices among several organisms, small invertebrates as well as vertebrates, may be made through dissection followed by a careful study of anatomy (Chapter 16).

The need for digestion: diffusion through a membrane

We have studied ingestion among several food-takers, and we have compared their digestive systems. What happens to the food they consume? What is digestion and why is it necessary? Food materials must be made soluble; that is, they must be in a form which can pass through membranes. The process of diffusion may be shown in many ways. Probably all of us have used one or another of these methods to show diffusion of molecules from place to place.

You may want to drop a small piece of copper sulfate or several potassium permanganate crystals into water and leave them undisturbed. To do so, insert a few dry crystals into a section of glass tubing. Hold a finger over the top of the tubing as you insert the other end into water. When the tubing is at the bottom of the container of water, release the finger, and the crystals will fall to the bottom. Each day students will find that molecules of copper sulfate (or other substances) have moved from their place of greatest concentration and are becoming distributed throughout the water solvent.

Another striking demonstration of diffusion is the movement of a gas such as ammonia in another gas (air). Wet a circle of filter paper with phenolphthalein

phenolphthalein
in water

NH₄OH

Fig. 2-7 The water containing phenolphthalein in the tube turns red as molecules of ammonia evaporate and diffuse up through the membrane.

and insert it into the bottom of a large test tube. Now invert the test tube over a bottle of ammonium hydroxide. Students should be ready to explain the rapid change of the filter paper to red. The effect of the alkaline ammonia on the indicator phenolphthalein may be shown in a test tube. (Use controls with filter paper soaked in water.) Diffusion of gases may be shown in the spreading of illuminating gas, or of the volatile materials in perfume, around a room. Molecules move generally from their point of greatest concentration to a region of lowest concentration. This may also be demonstrated by pouring red ink or a dye carefully along one side of a container into water. Here it is demonstrated that a liquid diffuses through a liquid.

Now we may also show that some molecules diffuse through a membrane.

This makes an impressive class demonstration (Fig. 2-7). To a large test tube or cylinder of water add a few drops of a 1 per cent solution of phenolphthalein in alcohol. Cover the mouth of the tube with a wet goldbeater's membrane or wet cellophane (do not use the kind that covers cigarette packs, since an additional protective agent is added). Fasten with a rubber band and invert over a bottle of ammonium hydroxide. A pink stream will move rapidly up through the test tube. Since phenolphthalein turns deep red in an alkaline medium (ammonia in this case), "a stream of molecules in motion" is visible.

Diffusion of iodine through a membrane. Pour dilute iodine solution (p. 409) into a large test tube, cover with a wet goldbeater's membrane, and secure with rubber bands. Invert the test tube into a beaker containing a 1 per cent starch paste (Fig. 2-8).

Then prepare another test tube, but this time pour starch paste into the test tube and fasten the wet membrane over the mouth of the tube. Invert this test tube into a beaker half full of dilute iodine solution. Note that molecules of the

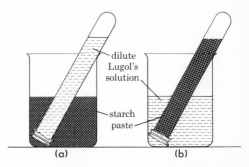

dilute
Lugol's
solution

starch
paste

(a)   (b)

Fig. 2-8 Diffusion through a semipermeable membrane: molecules of the Lugol's solution pass through the membrane; starch does not. Thus, the characteristic starch-iodine color appears in the starch suspension and not in the Lugol's; in the beaker in (a) and in the tube in (b).

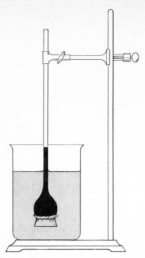

Fig. 2-9 Water diffuses rapidly through the membrane into the molasses, and the level in the tube rises.

iodine solution will pass through a membrane in either direction whereas starch molecules will not pass through; starch is insoluble.

Diffusion of glucose through a membrane. Fill large test tubes with glucose solution, molasses (dilute), corn syrup, or honey. Into other test tubes pour starch paste (1 per cent). Cover each test tube with a wet goldbeater's membrane. Fasten with a rubber band and invert each tube into an individual beaker containing a small volume of water. Within 15 minutes test for starch, with dilute iodine solution, the water in which the inverted tubes of starch paste stand. Then test the water in the other beakers for glucose with Benedict's solution (p. 405).

It may be desirable at this time to set up a test tube containing starch paste to which saliva (or commercial diastase) has been added. Demonstrate with dilute iodine solution that starch has not diffused and that there is now some simple sugar which has passed through the membrane (test with Benedict's). Of course, both the starch paste and the saliva should be tested for glucose before saliva is added.

Osmosis and osmotic pressure. Fill the bulb of a thistle tube by holding the finger over the tube opening; pour heavy molasses into the bulb portion of the tube. Instead of covering the tube opening with a finger, some teachers connect a short piece of rubber tubing with a clamp. Then cover the bulb with a wet semipermeable membrane (goldbeater's) or cellophane tubing and immerse in a beaker of water (Fig. 2-9). Soon the level of the liquid inside the thistle tube will rise. This special diffusion of molecules of water through the membrane is called osmosis.[1] As the water level rises in the tube, its pressure (hydrostatic pressure) will eventually halt the further upward diffusion of water. Some teachers connect extensions of glass tubing with rubber tubing to the stem of the thistle tube. You may get a considerable rise of fluid in the tube due to the diffusion of water molecules into the thistle tube.

Diffusion through the intestine of a frog. Dissect out the stomach and intestine of a freshly killed frog (dissection, p. 281). Clean out its contents by rinsing in Ringer's solution. Be certain the intestine is not perforated. Tie one end of the intestinal tube with thread; into the other end pour a solution of molasses diluted with Ringer's solution. Then tie this end off with thread and wash off the intestinal tract to remove excess molasses. Now suspend the intestinal tract in a beaker of water as shown in Fig. 2-10 by tying the ends to a wood splint or tongue depressor. Within a half hour, test the water in the beaker with Benedict's solution for glucose. For rapid, positive results use a small quantity of water in the beaker.

[1] *Osmosis* should not be confused with *diffusion*. Osmosis is a special case of diffusion, where pure water passes through a membrane permeable only to the water.

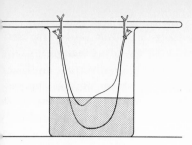

Fig. 2-10 If the intestine of a frog (or cellophane tubing) is filled with molasses and suspended in a beaker of water, molasses diffuses into the water; water also enters the tubing.

Intestinal casing purchased from a butcher or slaughterhouse may be used instead of the frog's intestine. Tubular lengths of semipermeable cellophane (dialyzing tubing) are available from some supply houses for the same purpose. Absorption of other soluble food products through the intestine is demonstrated using intestinal casing or tubular cellophane in Chapter 4.

Diffusion through a collodion membrane. Use large, clean, thoroughly dry test tubes. Into each test tube pour about 5 cc of collodion from a stock bottle. Rotate the test tube so that the collodion completely lines the test tube; then pour the collodion back into the stock bottle. Allow the film of collodion to harden slightly. Then loosen one edge of the film along the mouth of the tube with your fingers. Along this edge let water run down between the glass and the film of collodion so that more of the film is loosened (Fig. 2-11). Rotate the tube. By careful manipulation you can remove the collodion film intact. Test the bag of collodion for leakage by filling it with water. Then let it soak in water for a

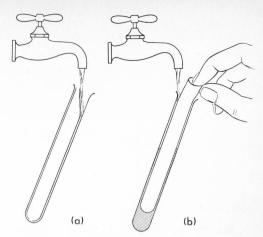

Fig. 2-11 Making a collodion bag: (a) pouring water between top of collodion film and test tube; (b) removing the film from the tube.

short time. Repeat the procedure until several collodion membranes are made.

You may fill these cylindrical bags with starch paste (as a control), glucose, or a 50 per cent solution of corn syrup or molasses. Close the tops securely by twisting and tying with thread. Wash off the overflow materials and immerse the bags in small beakers of water as shown in Fig. 2-12. After 10 minutes or so test the fluid in the beakers at intervals for the presence of molecules of glucose diffused into the water.

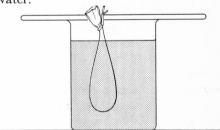

Fig. 2-12 Collodion bag, filled with starch paste or molasses, suspended in water.

Nutrients, nutrient tests, and nutrition

Most teachers think it desirable for students to understand how food is tested. While few consumers stop to test the nutrient content of the family diet, students should understand the general idea of *testing* that scientists use, and nutrient testing furnishes a very useful device. For example, iodine may be added to all nutrients in the pure form (in solution, of course). This establishes the specificity of the iodine test. Similarly, all tests should be tried on all nutrients.

Tests as tools for experimental work are therefore emphasized in this section. "Food nutrients" is the area selected for teaching the *idea* of testing.

Summary of nutrient tests

Starch. Add a few drops of a dilute iodine solution such as Lugol's solution (p. 409) to the substance to be tested for starch. A change to a blue-black color is a positive test. Dextrins give a red color with iodine. *Note:* Test pure nutrients to establish specificity.

Reducing sugars (glucose, fructose). In a Pyrex test tube boil 5 cc of Benedict's or Fehling's solution (p. 406) with a sample of the unknown. In a positive test for simple sugars (such as glucose or fructose), Benedict's or Fehling's solution is reduced so that a series of color changes results: green to yellow to orange. [*Note:* Pure sucrose (ordinary table sugar) is not a reducing sugar and will not give a positive test with Benedict's.]

Clinitest tablets[2] used for testing sugar in urine of diabetics do not require heating. The sample to be tested should be in solution.

Proteins. The xanthoproteic test consists of adding concentrated nitric acid to the unknown in solution. When proteins are present it turns yellow. As a further check, you may pour off the nitric acid and add a small amount of ammonium hydroxide. The yellow color should change to a deep orange. Or use the Millon test (p. 62). For partially digested proteins, use the Biuret test (p. 405).

Fats and oils. A simple test for fats and oils is to place some of the unknown substance on unglazed paper, such as wrapping paper. A permanent translucent spot through which light can pass indicates the presence of fats or oils. (Water spots will dry, but fat spots remain translucent.) In another test, ether or carbon tetrachloride may be mixed with a food, either liquid or crushed. After the solvent has evaporated, drops of fat or oil will remain in the dish.

Water. Insert the sample of food into a dry test tube. Heat gently over a Bunsen flame; look for drops of moisture which condense on the sides of the test tube in a positive test.

Minerals. Heat a sample of food such as bread or milk in a test tube or evaporating dish until it forms an ash or until the liquid evaporates. A whitish ash indicates that minerals are present. Students may be guided (in their club activities) into procedures in qualitative analysis. A pattern for such a procedure is suggested here for the qualitative analysis of bone ash.

Qualitative analysis of bone ash

Hawk, Oser, and Summerson[3] give a number of qualitative analyses of organic materials which can serve as a guide. A procedure such as this one may be worked through by a small committee or club. Add a small quantity of dilute nitric acid to a beaker containing about 1 gm of bone ash. Stir until most of the ash is dissolved, and then add an equal amount of water and filter. Now add ammonium hydroxide until the solution is alkaline and the phosphates precipitate out. Filter off the phosphates and test the solution for chlorides, sulfates, phos-

---

[2] These tablets, as well as Clinistix, are available from Ames Co., Inc., Elkhart, Ind.

[3] P. Hawk, B. Oser, and W. Summerson, *Practical Physiological Chemistry,* Blakiston (McGraw-Hill), New York, 1954.

phates, iron, calcium, and magnesium. For example, the addition of 1 per cent silver nitrate will cause a precipitation of silver chloride if chlorides are present. For further qualitative tests, see the above-mentioned reference.

Examining phosphates and magnesium in frog muscle

The same authors[4] describe Hurthle's method. Use a dissecting needle to tease apart a small bit of frog muscle on a glass slide. Then expose the slide to ammonia vapor for a few minutes. Cover with a coverslip and examine under the microscope. You should find large amounts of ammonium magnesium phosphate crystals distributed throughout the muscle fiber.

Vitamin content of foods

How have scientists learned to test for the vitamin content of foods? Students may be able to design an experiment with animals to discover whether foods contain vitamin B_1. Are there chemical tests for vitamins in foods? We shall first deal with experiments using animals to show the results of deficiencies, and then go on to demonstrate chemical tests for vitamin content of foods.

Effects of vitamin D on rats. Two groups of rats of the same age (about twenty-five-day-old albino rats, four to six days past weaning) might be used. At least two rats in each group should be used even for a comparatively short study of the effect of differences in vitamin D content. One group is fed a vitamin-D-free diet, while the second group receives the same diet with viosterol added. The diet which has been recommended is taken from *Turtox Service Leaflets*.[5]

[4] *Ibid.*
[5] General Biological Supply House, *Turtox Service Leaflet,* #49, Chicago, Ill.

Both groups are fed this diet:

Yellow corn, 76 parts
Gluten flour, 20 parts
Sodium chloride, 1 part
Calcium carbonate, 3 parts

For one group, supplement this diet with 20 drops of viosterol per 1000 gm of diet. Both groups should get adequate supplies of water daily. They should be housed in separate cages, and the cages should be kept away from direct sunlight.

Within 3 weeks, differences in weight should be apparent. As the animals are weighed every day and records kept, it should be found that the group lacking vitamin D in the form of viosterol stops growing. They show a general unhealthy appearance, they are somewhat wobbly in gait, and their fur appears ruffled.

When two groups of animals are fed the diet described above, the differences listed should be seen within 30 days. Then the animals on the deficient diet with visible symptoms of the deficiency disease should be placed on the more complete diet; i.e., viosterol should be added to the original diet. Almost immediately the affected animals will gain weight.

This experiment should not continue more than 4 weeks. At this time (when the affected animals are given viosterol) weigh them daily and record the rapid gain in the weight and the change to a healthy appearance.

Vitamin B_1 requirements of pigeons. When healthy young pigeons are fed a diet deficient in thiamin (B_1) they develop polyneuritis (beriberi).[6] Students who maintain pigeons at home may try this experiment, or it may be carried on in school.

Separate cages are needed for the

[6] Diets deficient in specific nutrients may be obtained from Nutritional Biochemicals Corp., Cleveland 28, Ohio, and General Biochemicals Inc., Chagrin Falls, Ohio.

experimental and the control pigeons. The cages should be kept free of droppings or pigeons will consume this along with food. Feed all the birds equal amounts of white polished rice, finely cracked egg shells, and water.

One group gets, in addition to this diet, a mixture of barley, hemp seeds, yellow corn, and some fresh vegetables such as shredded cabbage or lettuce.

In about 10 days the pigeons without the "extras" will develop a paralytic condition, since nerve-muscle connections are impaired. Then add the "extras" to the diet and watch how quickly the pigeons recover their health and activity.

Chemical test for vitamin C. A simple, quantitative test for the presence of vitamin C (ascorbic acid) in foods may be done as a class demonstration. Even better, it may serve as an excellent laboratory experience, a controlled experiment involving simple measurement.

Indophenol (sodium 2,6-dichlorobenzenone)[7] is an "indicator" which is blue in color, and is bleached in the presence of ascorbic acid or juices containing ascorbic acid. Prepare a 0.1 per cent solution of indophenol in water by dissolving 1 gm of indophenol in 1000 cc of water.

The test should first be demonstrated with pure ascorbic acid and later repeated with several fruit juices. You may purchase a 10 per cent ascorbic acid solution in a drugstore under the trade name "Cecon," and dilute it further with water as necessary.

Since this is a sensitive test, the ascorbic acid should be diluted enough so that the number of drops of ascorbic acid added to the indophenol may be counted accurately. If the ascorbic acid is too

[7] The indicator can be purchased from the Chemical Division of Eastman Kodak Co., Rochester, N. Y.

strong, one drop will immediately bleach the indophenol, so that a comparative study is difficult to make. About 10 cc of the indicator is added to a test tube. Diluted (1 per cent) ascorbic acid is added to this, drop by drop; count the number of drops needed to change the color from blue to colorless. (The intermediate pink stage should be disregarded.)

Now, diluted fruit and vegetable juices —canned, fresh, and frozen—may be tested. Test the juices beforehand so that you may dilute them sufficiently for students to add about 10 to 20 drops of juice to a given quantity of indophenol. Dilute them all equally, so that the ascorbic acid content of canned juices may be compared with that of fresh juices. In comparative tests the quantity of indophenol used should be standardized.

Some juices may be boiled, or left exposed to air for several hours and then tested again. The data collected may then be compared with the original readings.

Bicarbonate of soda, which is often added to vegetables to preserve their green color while cooking, may be added to samples of the same juices. Note the loss of ascorbic acid under these conditions. (The larger number of drops of juice needed to bleach a given quantity of indophenol is a measure of the small amount of ascorbic acid remaining in the juices.)

Calories

You may want to develop the need for calories in the diet here or in a study of respiration (p. 93). There are several approaches to this work which involve the use of the blackboard, charts, or paper-and-pencil techniques.

For example, you may put a chart such as Table 2-1 on the board. After a study

TABLE 2-1
Recommended daily dietary allowances*

	calories	protein gm	vitamin A I. U.	thiamin mg	niacin mg	vitamin C mg
Boys						
13–15 years (108 lb)	3200	85	5000	1.5	15	90
16–20 years (144 lb)	3800	100	6000	1.7	17	100
Girls						
13–15 years (108 lb)	2600	80	5000	1.3	13	80
16–20 years (122 lb)	2400	75	5000	1.2	12	80
Men (154 lb)						
Sedentary	2400	70	5000	1.2	12	75
Physically active	3000	70	5000	1.5	15	75
With heavy work	4500	70	5000	1.8	18	75
Women (123 lb)						
Sedentary	2000	60	5000	1.0	10	70
Moderately active	2400	60	5000	1.2	12	70
Very active	3000	60	5000	1.5	15	70
Latter half pregnancy	2400	85	6000	1.5	15	100

* Food and Nutrition Board of the National Research Council.

of the chart, students often ask why boys and girls have a higher caloric requirement than men and women. A minimum average of 1500 calories seems to be needed to keep a person alive.

For what kinds of activities does a person need more calories?

Why are some people overweight or underweight?

An activity which creates high interest is this one. Ask students to keep a list of all the foods they have eaten over three school days. Then in class distribute charts which give calories, mineral content, vitamin content, and the amount of proteins of many foods. One example of such a chart is the fine pamphlet *Facts About Foods* which is distributed by H. J. Heinz Company, Pittsburgh, Pa. (1952).

In this booklet, or a similar one, students may look up the number of calories, proteins, vitamins, and minerals in the foods they have consumed. Then total the list and divide by three; this is an average for one day. What number of calories is needed on the basis of body weight?

Students might compare their own diet with the recommendations given in Table 2-1. Are they getting an adequate diet, a balanced one? Plan a diet for a week for a person who needs to gain weight. Similarly, suggest a diet for a person who wishes to lose weight. Why should dieting of any kind be undertaken with the assistance of a doctor?

Using the library as a resource in the study of nutrition and health

The ability to gather facts from authoritative sources is one of the methods used by scientists. Students in science classes need practice in developing this skill. Intelligent use of the facilities of the library requires the same kind of planning that is needed in preparing for a field trip. Learning to find and organize information is time well spent.

Suppose the unit topic is "The Foods We Need for Good Health." The problems for study in this area may be elicited from students in class. Students' questions might be listed on the board. For example: What is food used for? Where do we get our food? Is it all right to go without breakfast? Why do some people gain weight? What are calories? What good are vitamins? Which vitamins do we need? Can your diet cause pimples? What's wrong with taking vitamin pills? What is a balanced diet? Must you have one every day? What should you eat to lose weight?

Then these questions may be selected by groups of three to six students working as committees for library "research." Allow time, possibly 10 minutes, for students to break up into their small groups to interpret among themselves the specific problems about which they want information. At the end of this time, the students reassemble and a spokesman in each group defines the areas his group will investigate. Perhaps the rest of the class can add suggestions.

You may want to bring textbooks, magazines, and vertical files of current clippings to class. Many teachers prefer to bring the students to the library for a period (or two) of reading.

While students are engaged in the library seeking references (on the stories of vitamin discoveries, of the "basic seven," of calories and food intake), there is opportunity to observe how well the students use a card catalog, *Readers' Guide,* or the index of a book, how they select a pamphlet they can read, how fast they read, and how well they take notes.

In sharing what they have learned with others, students may use many ways to present the information to their classmates. A panel group may elicit (by questioning) the facts from the class, another committee may dramatize a story of a vitamin discovery, another group may devise an experiment in nutrition, another committee may plan a review for the class on the unit of nutrition—particularly in preparation for an examination.

Several other areas lend themselves to this fruitful research by the group of students working in the library: "How Living Things Behave," or the topic of "Ancient Life on Earth," or the broad unit on "Diseases: Their Cause and Methods of Control," or some similar unit on maintaining health. In the last-mentioned unit, for example, students learn to classify diseases as to their causes or kinds, or glean the stories of how diseases have been brought under control, discover the men associated with major advances in medicine, vaccination, antibiotics, and so on. In this way students get practice in organizing and assimilating new reading material. The process is fruitful in that this kind of reading gives rise to a new awareness, and thus new questions arise for study in class.

CAPSULE LESSONS
Ways to get started in class

2-1. You may want to begin with a laboratory lesson. If you have many microscopic organisms available, students may examine food-getting in several protozoa (using carmine powder); also examine microscopic worms and crustaceans. Then lead to a discussion of food-getting.

2-2. If you have living frogs or chameleons, examine their way of ingesting food. Elicit from students the adaptations found in several kinds of animals for food-getting. Develop the uses of food to the body.

2-3. You may want to select this demonstration. In one test tube seal a snail, in another a green water plant such as *Cabomba* or *Anacharis* (elodea) along with a snail (p. 86). After developing the idea of their interdependence, you might compare the snail's dependence on plants with man's dependence on green plant foods.

2-4. In a laboratory lesson, have students dissect frogs (see Chapter 16) so that they may trace the path of food through the body. Compare this with the digestive system of man (as revealed in charts, or use a manikin).

2-5. Perhaps you may want to begin the work with a comparison of the kinds of animal diets. From here, develop a discussion of the need for digestion and the uses of food in the body.

2-6. Use one of the demonstrations of diffusion of materials through a membrane to develop the notion that foods taken into the digestive system are not "part of us" until they diffuse out of the digestive system into the blood.

2-7. You may want to begin with a film which reveals many of the ways animals get their food. Have you seen *How Nature Protects Animals,* or *Animal Life, Birds of Prey* (all Encyclopaedia Britannica)?

2-8. Ask students to list all the food they consumed the previous day. Develop the notion of nutrients (and balanced diet) and lead into a discussion of the "basic seven," then into tests for nutrients. Discuss animal experimentation and the use of chemical tests for the nutrients in foods.

2-9. At some other time, begin with a laboratory lesson testing the vitamin C content of some fruit juices (fresh and canned) with indophenol (description in this chapter).

2-10. Occasionally, you may want to have a supervised study lesson. Have you tested the reading and comprehension level of your students by having them read a chapter in their text? Or use supplementary readings to discover their interests. (See the companion volume, *Teaching High School Science: A Book of Methods,* P. Brandwein, F. Watson, and P. Blackwood, Harcourt, Brace, 1958.) With slow readers you may want to try a chapter in a general science textbook (see the list of general science texts in this same volume).

2-11. Discuss the significance of the Federal Food, Drugs, and Cosmetics Act. As an aid in this study have students examine and paste into their notebooks labels from food packages and from empty medicine bottles. What may be the danger in using additives?

2-12. Describe the diet of an average individual in the United States, Mexico, India, the Arctic, Spain, South America, China, Greece, and Germany. (See Gerard, *Food for Life,* in Bibliography.) Compare these diets as to the amount of proteins, minerals and vitamins as well as the other nutrients. Develop a discussion of what makes an adequate diet.

2-13. You might want to start a lesson this way: Let's examine what makes a good or a poor meal. A boy had this for breakfast: black coffee with a sugared doughnut. How would you improve this meal?

For lunch a girl had spaghetti, rolls and butter, custard pie, and black coffee with sugar. What's wrong with this lunch? What nutrients are in excess? Which nutrients should be added —and in what foods?

Ask the class to plan a good diet and develop a discussion of the kinds of food needed for a good diet.

2-14. A student might introduce a study of vitamins by reporting some historic discovery, for example, the story of how Dr. Goldberger discovered the cause of pellagra.

PEOPLE, PLACES, AND THINGS

Students may often get help in planning a project in nutrition from the nutrition or biology department of a nearby college or hospital.

Living materials may be collected in the field or borrowed from other schools; organisms for nutrition experiments, from protozoa to rats, may be purchased from biological supply houses (see the listing at the end of the book).

There may be a canning plant or a food processing plant in your community to which you may take your classes. Or possibly someone may come to speak to your classes on some aspect of nutritional research.

Your school dietician is another resource person. Perhaps she will describe to the class how balanced meals are planned in the school kitchen.

BOOKS AND PAMPHLETS

These are only a few of the books which are pertinent to the work discussed in this chapter. These and many other references classified by subject and with complete bibliographical data are given in the Bibliography at the end of the book.

Albritton, E., ed., *Standard Values in Nutrition and Metabolism,* National Research Council. Published by Wright Air Development Center, USAF, Wright Patterson Air Force Base, Ohio, 1953.

Asimov, I., *The Chemicals of Life,* 1954.

Borek, E., *Man, the Chemical Machine,* 1952.

Carlson, A., and V. Johnson, *The Machinery of the Body,* 1953.

Chatfield, C., *Food Composition Tables for International Use,* Food and Agriculture Organization of United Nations, Washington, D. C., 1949.

Davson, H., *Textbook of General Physiology,* 1951.

General Biological Supply House, *Laboratory Experiments in Nutrition,* S. Hoyne Avenue, Chicago, 1937.

Gerard R., ed., *Food for Life,* 1952.

Harrow, B., *Casimir Funk: Pioneer in Vitamins and Hormones,* 1955.

Hegner, R., *Parade of the Animal Kingdom,* 1955.

Hutchinson, R., and W. Krehl, "The Effect of Food Intake on Performance," *Borden's Review of Nutritional Research,* May—June 1954.

Jolliffe, N., *Vitamin Manual,* Upjohn Co., Kalamazoo, Mich., 1953.

Needham, J., and P. Needham, *Guide to the Study of Fresh-Water Biology,* 1953.

Sherman, H., *Chemistry of Food and Nutrition,* 1946.

Sproul, E., *The Science Book of the Human Body,* 1955.

Wooster, H., *Nutritional Data,* H. J. Heinz, P. O. Box 57, Pittsburgh, Pa., 1954.

———, *Present Knowledge in Nutrition,* Nutrition Foundation Inc., New York City, 1953.

FILMS AND FILMSTRIPS

This partial list is intended only as a guide toward film and filmstrip selection. Refer to the more complete listing at the end of the book where films are classified by subject, and where a key to abbreviations and addresses of distributors are given. The cost of film rental, of course, may be subject to change. Films are sound and black and white unless otherwise specified.

Citrus in Nutrition (f, c), through Visual Institute of U. of Calif., $1.00.

Digestion of Foods (f), EBF, $2.50.

Foods and Nutrition (f), EBF, $2.50; (fs), $3.00.

Hidden Hunger (f), Swift and Co., free.

Story of Human Energy (f), Modern Talking Picture, free.

Strange Hunger (f), Amer. Soc. Bakery Engineers, free.

Understanding Vitamins (f, c), EBF, $4.75.

FREE AND INEXPENSIVE MATERIALS

This is only a partial listing of free and inexpensive materials available to the teacher at this time. A more complete listing, including addresses, is given at the end of the book. Many of these materials are distributed to teachers without charge. Where there is a small fee, the cost is indicated, although the prices are subject to change. While we recommend the material for use in the classroom, we do not necessarily sponsor the products advertised.

The Basic 7 Food Groups; Food Charts (24″ × 36″), General Mills.

Care and Feeding of Laboratory Animals, Ralston Purina Co.

Eat and Grow Slim, Amer. Institute of Baking.

Facts About Foods, H. J. Heinz.

Food Values Charts (20″ × 30″), Nat. Livestock and Meat Board.

It's Smart to Eat Breakfast, Amer. Educational Publishers.

Milk, Borden Co.

Nutrition Charts (set of 10 in color, 19″ × 24″), U.S. Government Printing Office. $0.75 per set.

Nutrition Experiments, Turtox Leaflet #49, General Biological Supply House.

Nutritional Data, H. J. Heinz.

Nutritional Observatory (monthly), H. J. Heinz.

Overweight and Underweight; Vitamins and Health, Metropolitan Life Insurance Co.

Review of Nutrition Research (monthly), Borden Co.

Story of Oranges and Lemons, California Fruit Growers Exchange.

Vitamin and Mineral Facts, General Mills.

Vitamin Reviews, Merck & Co.

Vitamin Summary, Quaker Oats.

CHAPTER 3

Movement of water in plants

The techniques and materials in this chapter deal with those processes in plants commonly considered under the headings of conduction, transpiration, translocation, and diffusion.

How does water rise in plants? It is generally accepted that the best explanation of water transport is offered in the transpiration-cohesion-tension theory. Simply stated, this theory implies that a water column rises in the xylem tubes because of the cohesive tendency of water. Thus a continuous column of water exists from roots to leaves. Since evaporation of water goes on through stomates of leaves (during transpiration), there is a loss of water from the top of the water column of the plant. A tension is set up through which the column of water is lifted up through the plant to the leaves.

You may want students to demonstrate that water rises in certain regions of the plant, and that transpiration occurs in leaves. As a project a student, or a committee of students, might study the lifting power of transpiration in plants. A related but seemingly independent action, that of root or exudation pressure, is described here. Students might study this and also examine water absorption by seeds.

Path of water through a plant

One of the best plants for this purpose is jewelweed (*Impatiens*). Since the stem is clear, the fibrovascular bundles may be seen by holding the plant up to light. These plants may be maintained in the laboratory after they have been transplanted from the field. In fact they can be grown from seed in the laboratory if the seeds are first subjected to freezing temperatures for about 2 weeks, then followed by drying for another 2 weeks. Germination and rapid growth take place in moist or wet soil. Seeds or cultivated specimens of *Impatiens* may be purchased from florists.

When the plants are to be used for class demonstration of conduction, remove the plants from the soil, roots and all. Then wash the roots and immerse them in a colored solution such as dilute fuchsin, phenol red, eosin, methylene blue, or red ink in water. The path of the colored solution may be traced along the fibrovascular bundles.

It may be convenient for you to collect jewelweed in season, cut the stems into 3-inch sections, and preserve them in a mixture of equal parts of 95 per cent alcohol and glycerine. Then at any time in the school year, you will have material available to show xylem ducts. Cut the stems into longitudinal sections to reveal these ducts. Thin cross sections of stems may also be made by bundling a few stems tightly; then section them by hand with a razor blade (p. 315) for examination under a microscope. After mounting in water, parenchyma cells and epidermal cells, as well as the spiral markings of the xylem ducts, may be seen. Directions for the preparation of temporary and permanent stained slides are given in Chapter 17.

Where jewelweed is not available, other stems may be used effectively. For example, you may immerse the cut stalks of fresh celery, cornstalks, or bean seedlings, to suggest a few, in water colored by adding a few crystals of eosin, fuchsin, or red ink. After a few hours, the dye will have moved up to the stems and colored the fibrovascular bundles and the veins of the leaves. Shoots of beans or the leaves of celery or lettuce show red venation. Cross sections of the stems will show the red-colored fibrovascular bundles.

You may also want to have students grow seedlings to show root hairs. Grow soaked seeds of radish in covered Petri dishes for a few days. Or pin a soaked seed to the cork of each of several small vials (Fig. 3-1). (Add a few drops of water before closing the vials.) Each root will grow down into the vial if the vials are placed upright and the root hairs can be examined with a magnifying glass without removing them from the vials. In this way the root hairs will not dry out as many students examine them over the day.

Fig. 3-1 Germinating a seed in a vial, to show extensive growth of root hairs.

In summary, students should be ready to trace the entry of water and soluble salts from the soil into root hairs, up the stems of the plants to the leaves through the fibrovascular bundles.

Use of radioactive compounds and radioisotopes as tracers

Many teachers are using radioactive substances to show the way materials are rapidly absorbed and transported in living things. Techniques are in use for locating the site where residues of these chemicals are deposited. A Geiger counter, scintillation counter, incineration techniques, and radioautographs are used to locate these minute quantities of radioactive tracers.

While most of the procedures are not practical at the high school level for lack of equipment, lack of skill, or inability to provide safety precautions, many teachers are putting into practice activities of the sort described here.

Tracing circulation in a stem with uranium nitrate. In this demonstration students can trace the rate of upward movement of a water solution of uranium nitrate by means of a Geiger counter. Prepare a 10 per cent solution of uranium nitrate (which may be purchased from a chemical supply house). Stand the stems of geranium plants, stalks of fresh celery, or germinating bean seedlings in the solution.

Before using the Geiger counter, record the background count, which is the rate of clicking that is produced when the Geiger tube or probe is *not* brought near anything in particular. (This background count is due to cosmic rays and radiation from rocks and soil.) Then bring the counter near the plant after 1 hour, 2 hours, 4 hours. Students should find a high count in the leaves after a few hours. The correct count at any time is the registered count less the previously noted background count.

Radioautograph of a leaf. If a Geiger counter is not available, the demonstration can still be carried on; a radioautograph of the leaf can be made to show the accumulation of uranium nitrate. Dental x-ray film is excellent for this purpose, or use photographic film. Place a leaf from a plant which has been standing in a radioactive solution against unopened film (wrapped in lightproof paper—not aluminum foil). Similarly, place an untreated leaf against the same sort of film. Hold the leaves flat against the paper with a weight such as a block of wood, and keep them in a dark place for 2 weeks. Then remove the leaves and develop the film by placing it in developer, washing it in 3 per cent acetic acid (or pure white vinegar), and standing it in photographic hypo for 20 minutes. Students should see the outline of the treated leaf, with the veins the more prominent regions, in the radioautograph produced (Fig. 3-2).

Using radioactive isotopes as tracers. The Atomic Energy Commission makes available to high schools certain radioactive isotopes: potassium and sodium phosphate (radiophosphorus-32) and iodine chloride (radioiodine-131). When the ordinary caution suggested by the A.E.C. is used, there is no hazard in using these radioisotopes; for their strength is

Fig. 3-2 Radioautograph of leaf of coleus plant which has taken up radioactive phosphorus-32. (Photo: Brookhaven National Laboratory.)

approximately 10 microcuries, weaker than doses used in medicine.

Young tomato plants may be grown in a hydroponic solution (see p. 113) and radioactive phosphate may be substituted for the ordinary phosphate in preparing the solution. Use the method described above with uranium nitrate to trace the uptake and upward path of the radioisotope with a Geiger counter or the radioautograph technique.

You may want to write to the U.S. Atomic Energy Commission in Washington, D. C., to learn the location of distribution centers for your community. The A.E.C. provides suggested aids and rules for handling radioactive materials; in fact, a useful publication of practical demonstrations has been prepared under its auspices.[1] You may want to try some of the techniques given, such as using a

[1] S. Schenberg and J. Harley, eds., *Laboratory Experiments with Radioisotopes for High School Science Teachers,* rev. ed., U.S. Atomic Energy Commission, Supt. Documents, U.S. Govt. Printing Office, Washington, D. C., 1957, $0.30.

Geiger counter; making radioautographs of a fish skeleton, a leaf, colonies of bacteria and molds; the uptake of phosphorus-32 by goldfish. Safety precautions and health hazards are discussed in an appendix.

Evaporation of water through leaves (transpiration)

There are many techniques for showing that water is given off by leaves, specifically, through the stomates in the leaves.

Using collodion to locate the stomates. Spread a thin film of collodion over the upper surface of some leaves, and on the lower surface of other leaves, of a healthy plant. Do not remove the leaves from the plant. After several hours, students should see that collodion remains transparent over the regions of the leaves which remain dry; whereas moisture due to transpiration turns the film of collodion an opaque, whitish color.

The different patterns of distribution of stomates may be discovered by examining upper and lower epidermal layers under the low power of a microscope (see Table 1-1).

Using watch crystals to observe release of water.[2] Fasten small watch crystals to both sides of several different types of green leaves so that part of each leaf is sandwiched between the crystals (Fig. 3-3). These can be fastened with cellophane tape. Seal the glass edges on both sides of the leaves with a film of Vaseline. Since the leaves are not detached from the plant, photosynthesis continues and the leaves are not injured. Water vapor, released by the stomates in transpiration will condense on the cool surfaces of the watch crystals and form drops of moisture. Students should be able to see which surface of the leaf releases more water. Then they may compare, by microscopic examination, the relative number of stomates in the upper and lower epidermis of the different leaves studied (see Table 1-1).

[2] W. J. V. Osterhout, *Experiments with Plants,* Macmillan, New York, 1905.

Using cobalt chloride paper to demonstrate loss of water. Transpiration may be shown in leaves still on the plant in yet another way. Place a square of dry cobalt chloride paper (blue) on the upper and lower surfaces of the leaves. (Cobalt chloride paper is blue when dry but turns pink when moist.) Then fold a strip of cellophane across the leaves over the paper, to hold it in place and protect it from moisture in the air. Fix both with a clip as in Fig. 3-4. Elicit from students which surface of the leaves shows a greater degree of change in color of the paper.

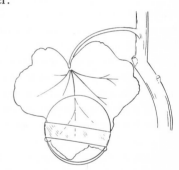

Fig. 3-3 Transpiration: on which watch crystal does water vapor condense?

Fig. 3-4 Transpiration: which surface of the leaf produces more color change in the cobalt chloride paper?

Cobalt chloride paper is easy to prepare. Soak strips of filter paper in a 3 per cent cobalt chloride solution. The water solution is red and the filter paper is red when wet. Dry the strips of filter paper and they will turn blue; then store the prepared paper in a closed container. Before using the paper, it may be necessary to dry the paper (to turn it blue) in an oven or over a flame since the paper turns pink in the presence of minute amounts of moisture in the air.

Loss of water from excised leaves.
Under a small bell jar or other closed container place a handful of leaves from geraniums, *Sempervivum,* maple, *Tradescantia,* or other plants. Let the container stand in bright sunlight. Use another small bell jar without leaves to serve as a control. Within 15 to 30 minutes, students may see moisture resulting from transpiration on the inner surface of the glass.

Or you may use single leaves. Punch a small hole in the center of a piece of cardboard. Then remove a leaf with its petiole from a plant and insert the petiole through the hole in the cardboard. Place this over a beaker of water so that the petiole is immersed in water (Fig. 3-5). Plug the hole in the cardboard in which the petiole is inserted with Vaseline or paraffin to prevent circulation of water vapor. Then cover the leaf with another beaker as shown. As a control, have a student prepare a similar demonstration, but cover both surfaces of the leaf with Vaseline. After several hours water vapor condenses on the inside of the upper glass tumbler of the experimental setup (the leaf that is free of Vaseline).

Loss of water from a growing plant.
Cover the soil of a small, healthy plant with rubber sheeting or plastic material so that the moisture from the soil and from the surface of the pot cannot escape by

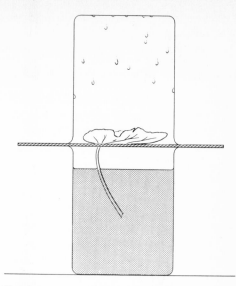

Fig. 3-5 Transpiration of cut leaf: what would happen if the leaf were covered with Vaseline?

evaporation. Then place the plant under a bell jar and keep it in bright sunlight. As a control, use a covered pot of soil, with no plant, under another bell jar. Within 15 minutes a film of moisture should appear on the inner surface of the bell jar covering the green plant.

Water loss in a whole plant. In this method, a whole plant is weighed periodically for a week. Grow sunflower or other rapidly growing plants (which have an active rate of transpiration) in glazed earthenware crocks or glass jars. Cover the surface of the soil with rubber sheeting or plastic to prevent evaporation from the surface of the soil.

You may want to have students weigh the whole plant in its crock or jar at the beginning of the preparation. Weigh the plant or plants at 24-hour intervals for a week. *Note:* Students might arrange to test many plants in this way so that they have a basis for comparison. (If the plants are watered during the experiment, the weight of the water added should be considered.)

Loss of weight in a leaf due to transpiration. Remove at least two leaves, approximately equal in size, from a rubber plant (*Ficus elastica*).[4] When the flow of latex has stopped, slip the petiole of each leaf halfway through a 1-inch length of tightly fitting rubber tubing. Fold over the ½-inch excess of rubber tubing (Fig. 3-7) and wire each securely to avoid evaporation from the petiole.

Coat the lower epidermis of one or more leaves with Vaseline; coat the upper epidermis of the other leaves. Now weigh each leaf with its attached tubing and mark each leaf for future identification. Hang these leaves by means of the wire in a dry room or outside the window. After a few hours, weigh both leaves again and compare the rate of transpiration. Students might return to class to weigh these leaves several times during the day. Remember that the stomates in *Ficus elastica* are found in the lower epidermis. Other succulent leaves may be substituted in this demonstration.

Potometer method for measuring water loss. Connect the bottom ends of two burettes with a short rubber tube, as shown in Fig. 3-8. Then fill the whole apparatus with water and plug one burette with a one-hole stopper through

[4] F. Darwin and E. H. Acton, *Practical Physiology of Plants,* Cambridge U. Press, New York, 1925.

Fig. 3-6 Transpiration of cut twigs: the flask above, which contains a leafy twig, shows quite a bit of water vapor condensed; a control with the leaves removed should show much less. (Photo: A. M. Winchester.)

Loss of water from twigs of trees. Get two freshly cut woody twigs and remove the leaves from one of the twigs. With a cork borer, punch a hole in two corks just large enough to permit the passage of the stems. Cork two flasks with the twigs inside, and the cut ends protruding. Spread paraffin or Vaseline around the joints of the cork and twig so the joints are airtight. Immerse the cut ends of the stems in water. A comparison may be made of the amount of condensation within each bottle;[3] Fig. 3-6 shows the experimental flask, with the leafy twig.

[3] B. C. Gruenberg and N. E. Robinson, *Experiments and Projects in Biology,* Ginn, Boston, 1925.

Fig. 3-7 Leaf of a rubber plant ready for demonstrating loss of weight due to transpiration.

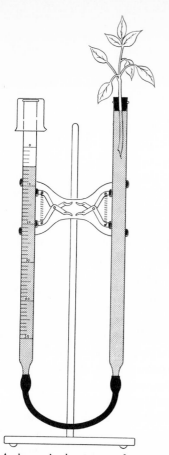

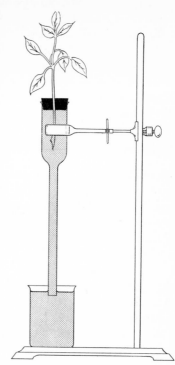

Fig. 3-9 True potometer: the rate of bubbles leaving the tube is measured.

Fig. 3-8 An improvised potometer for measuring water loss in transpiration: as the plant absorbs water, the level in the burette at the left will change; the change can be read from the scale.

which a woody stem has been inserted. Now seal the plant in place with paraffin. Invert a beaker over the other burette to prevent evaporation of water. The water level in this burette should be marked at the start of the demonstration so that as transpiration continues the amount of water absorbed may be measured by the change in the water level.

The method above is a modification of a true potometer method. Where a potometer is available, a quantitative measurement of transpiration may be made. Place a potometer, filled with water, into a small beaker of water (Fig. 3-9). Keep the bottom of the tube about 1 cm below the surface. Hold a leafy stemmed plant under water (to avoid air bubbles) and cut the stem near the bottom. Insert this stem into a one-hole rubber stopper and fit this tightly into the potometer bowl. Support the potometer with a stand and clamp. No air should remain anywhere in the potometer.

After 15 to 20 minutes, raise the end of the potometer out of the beaker and wait (for a few minutes) until a large bubble appears at the opening. Then lower the end into the water again and count the rate of movement of the bubble in the transpiration stream.

Simple U-tube to measure water loss. This method[5] is simpler than the previous

[5] George Atkinson, *A College Textbook of Botany,* Holt, New York, 1905.

ones used to measure the amount of transpiration. Place the cut end of a leafy shoot into a one-hole stopper and fasten this securely in one side of a water-filled U-tube. Plug the other side of the tube with a stopper through which a right-angle glass bend extends as shown (Fig. 3-10). Clamp the preparation to a stand to support it. As transpiration of water from the leaves of the shoot occurs, measure the movement of water in the extended delivery tube, by measuring how far the air bubble moves.

Lifting power of transpiration

Mechanics of the lifting power of leaves. A porcelain cup (called an atmometer cup) is used to simulate evaporation of water from leaves. The evaporation from the cup creates the conditions under which water is lifted up through thin tubes by capillarity. Boil the porcelain cup first in water to remove all air bubbles. Then insert a 30-inch length of 5-mm glass tubing into a one-hole stopper to fit the atmometer securely. Fill the atmometer and glass tubing with cooled, boiled water so that no air bubbles appear. Cover the end of the tubing with one finger and invert into a container of mercury (Fig. 3-11a). Or use the method shown in Fig. 3-11b, which uses water throughout, not mercury at all. In any case, clamp the preparation to a stand to support it. Then fan the porcelain cup or use an electric fan to stir the air to speed evaporation (water loss) from the porous cup. In (a) the mercury will soon rise in the tube; it will continue to rise higher than normal atmospheric pressure would lift it. The additional rise of the column of mercury is the result of a tension set up by rapid evaporation of water through the porous cup. In (b) the amount of water loss can be read from the calibrated burette. A similar demonstration using living plants may be developed (as below).

The lifting power of leaves in a living plant. Hold a plant under water to cut off a healthy leafy shoot; insert the shoot into rubber tubing. Then connect a section of glass tubing into the other end of the rubber tubing to make an airtight connection. Now completely fill the glass tubing with water, cover the end with a finger, and lower it into a dish of mercury. When the plant is supported by a clamp, the setup is similar to the previous demonstration, but in place of the atmometer, a living plant is used. Have students watch the gradual rise of mercury in the tube. In this demonstration a sizable rise in the mercury column is usually not observable because air bubbles often interfere.

A simple U-tube to show lifting power of transpiration. You may want to have students prepare the apparatus shown in Fig. 3-12. Here a leafy shoot is fitted into a stopper, airtight. Add some water to this arm of the U-tube; to the other arm add mercury so that the level is equal in both arms of the "U." In a short time (within the hour) students may see the mercury level displaced in the direction of the tube containing the shoot.

Exudation pressure (root pressure). You may have noticed that when a plant is cut off at the ground level, water exudes from the cut stem because of root pressure. Plants grown in the open may be used, but potted plants such as the geranium are more convenient for use in the classroom. Cut off the stem close to the soil level and use a short rubber tube to attach a long glass tube to the rooted part

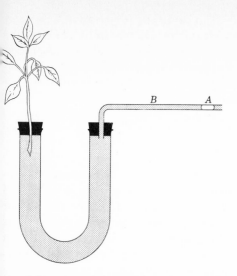

Fig. 3-10 A U-tube potometer: as transpiration occurs, the air bubble in the tube will recede a measurable distance from A toward B.

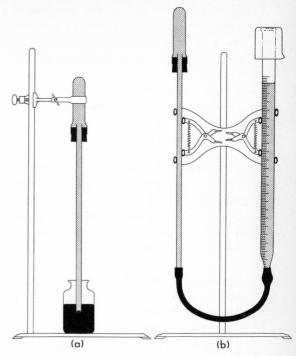

(a)   (b)

Fig. 3-11 Atmometers: (a) Porous cup (porcelain) atmometer with water and mercury; (b) porous cup (porcelain) atmometer with water-filled burette from which amount of evaporation can be read.

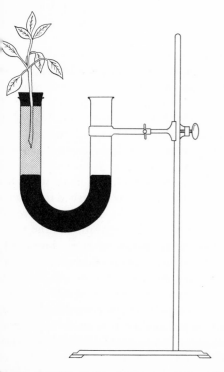

Fig. 3-12 Simple U-tube demonstration of the water intake of the woody twig.

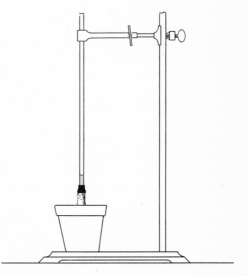

Fig. 3-13 Demonstrating exudation pressure of roots.

of the stem. Clamp the setup to a stand to keep it upright (Fig. 3-13). Now pour a small amount of water into the tube so that the stem remains moist. Within a short time (10 minutes or so) water begins to rise in the tube.

Palladin's method to show conduction of water up a stem. Both the ascent of liquids and the possible effect of transpiration on the rise of fluids in plants may be studied in this method[6] (Fig. 3-14).

Select a plant with forked stem or side branches; a branch of a bush or a tree with a side shoot will do nicely. Remove the leaves from the side shoot and attach the shoot to rubber tubing which leads to a glass tube. Be sure all joints are watertight. Then fill the glass tube with water and immerse it in mercury. For the best results, the shoot should be thin and the glass tube of narrow bore.

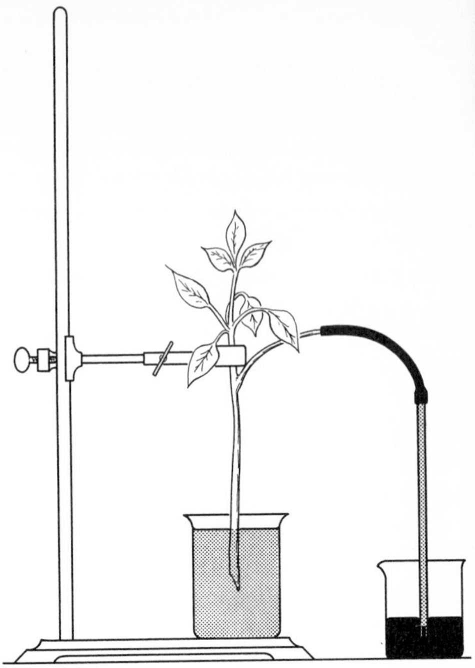

Guttation. When transpiration is retarded, and there is a free intake of water through the roots, exudation of water from the leaves occurs. This can be shown best by growing cereal seeds under a small bell jar. In this moisture-laden air, transpi-

Fig. 3-14 Demonstrating the movement of water in a woody twig.

ration decreases, and *drops* of water appear on the leaves (the process is known as guttation).

Passage of water from cell to cell

First, we shall need to make a clear distinction between osmosis and diffusion. *Diffusion* refers to the movement of any molecule. *Osmosis* is the passage or diffusion of molecules of *water* through a semipermeable membrane. The direction of motion (in nonionized substances) is from a region of higher to one of lower concentration of the particular molecule under study. Thus diffusion refers to the distribution of molecules of ammonia through a classroom as well as to the passage of glucose through a membrane.

Diffusion. Refer to the simple demon-

[6] Vladimar Palladin, *Plant Physiology,* Blakiston (McGraw-Hill), New York, 1926.

strations of diffusion described in Chapter 2, Animals: Food-Takers.

A diffusion model. You may want to set up a thistle tube as described in Chapter 2 and shown in Fig. 2-9, but with a 20 to 30 per cent sucrose solution in the thistle tube. This may be considered a model of the cell sap content of a cell. (It is not a good model of a cell, however, since it cannot show changes in turgidity.) Just as the water enters the thistle tube, so water molecules are thought to enter root hairs and diffuse from cell to cell along a diffusion gradient.

Osmosis through a raw potato. The living cells of a potato (or a carrot) may be used to show the passage of water through the semipermeable membranes which surround the cells (Fig. 3-15). You may want to use an apple corer to remove a center cylinder of a raw white potato. Do not plunge the corer through the entire length of the potato, but leave about ½-inch thickness at the bottom. Slowly pour a concentrated sucrose solution into the core, and close with a one-hole rubber stopper through which a piece of glass tubing has been inserted. Place this in a beaker of water; use a clamp to hold the tube upright. Then seal the stopper with melted paraffin so that there is no leakage.

Osmosis through a raw egg. This technique may be of interest to some teachers, although the results achieved may not be worth the time consumed in its prepara-

tion. Carefully crack and remove the shell at the blunt end of an egg to expose the underlying membrane. This is a semipermeable membrane (it permits the passage of water only). You may dissolve away the shell with dilute hydrochloric acid instead of cracking the egg. At any rate, the cut region of the shell must be smooth to avoid puncturing the membrane. Invert the egg and fit it into a bottle of water so that the egg is supported by the neck. Next, carefully break through the other end of the egg to make a narrow hole to fit a piece of glass tubing, which is to be inserted into the egg contents. Clamp the tubing in place, and seal it to the egg with melted paraffin (Fig. 3-16). You may need to replace the water level in the bottle when it falls below the level of the egg membrane.

For a demonstration of selectivity in the absorption of ions, see p. 114.

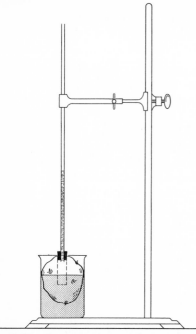

Fig. 3-15 Demonstrating diffusion of water (osmosis) through the cells of a raw potato: the cavity in the potato contains sucrose solution; water diffuses in through the membranes of the cells in the potato to the cavity, and rises in the tube along with some sucrose.

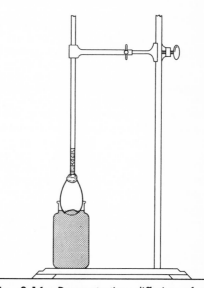

Fig. 3-16 Demonstrating diffusion of water through the membrane of a raw egg: water diffuses through the exposed shell membrane at the blunt end, up through the egg, out the hole in the top, and up the tube, along with some of the egg contents.

Absorption of water by seeds: imbibition and swelling

The rapid absorption of water by the colloids found in the seed may be illustrated simply. Fill a tumbler one third full with beans or peas, and the rest with water. Within a few hours students may see swollen seeds; they should notice that the seeds now almost fill the tumbler.

Imbibition pressure of seeds. Make a cardboard box mold about 1 inch in depth. Fill it with a thick paste of plaster of Paris, drop in a handful of dry oats, wheat, or peas, and allow the paste to harden. After an hour or so, cut away the cardboard box and place the plaster block into water.

The small capillary spaces in the plaster block absorb water, so that water is carried to seeds. The block is burst as a result of the swelling of the seeds due to imbibition. *Note:* You may want to refer to the structure of leaves, stems, and roots at this time. Free-hand sections for study under the microscope may be attempted (p. 315), or prepared, stained slides may be purchased. A description of the parts of plants is given in Chapter 16, Anatomy of Some Animals and Plants. The preparation of tissue for slide-making is described in Chapter 17.

CAPSULE LESSONS

Ways to get started in class

3-1. You may want to set up several demonstrations to show transpiration. Put them in the classroom where they may be watched and wait for students to ask questions. You are then in the topic: How is water transported in a plant?

3-2. Set fresh celery or bean seedlings or carrots into red-colored water. Ask students to trace the entrance of water up into the leaves. What is the water to be used for? How did the water get into the roots?

3-3. Distribute vials containing seedlings which show root hairs. Have students examine them with a magnifying lens. Ask them what advantage there may be in the increased surface provided by the extensive root hairs. What process goes on through these cell extensions?

3-4. Provide these materials for students: several plants, cobalt chloride paper, Vaseline, pins. Ask students to design a demonstration to reveal which surface of the leaves, the upper or lower surface, contains more stomates.

3-5. Have students examine fresh celery, jewelweed (*Impatiens*), or carrots so they may see fibrovascular bundles. Very thin sections of a carrot can be cut with a razor blade; if the edges of the slices are very thin, they can be examined under the microscope. Or study prepared, stained slides.

3-6. Have a laboratory lesson in which students examine the underside of such a leaf as *Sedum* or *Tradescantia*. Teach students how to strip off the lower epidermis for examination under the microscope as a wet mount (see p. 21 for wet mounts).

3-7. Have a student report to the class on the theories which have been elaborated to explain the rise of water in a tall tree. Almost any botany text will have a description of the different theories (see the list of books at the end of the chapter).

3-8. Perhaps you may want to show the film *Life of Plants* (United World) or *Roots of Plants* (Encyclopaedia Britannica). Use the film as a device for raising questions about the way plants get water and how it is transported through the plant. Other times, use a film as a review of the topic.

3-9. Begin with a demonstration of diffusion or any other activity described in this chapter.

3-10. Open a bottle of ammonia or perfume in class for a few seconds. Have students raise their hands when they can smell it. Elicit the facts that the liquid changed into a gas and the molecules diffuse among the molecules of gases in the air. Then lead into a discussion of diffusion of materials through a membrane. Refer to the passage of water through root hairs, and from cell to cell.

3-11. Sometimes you may want to include in a test one of the demonstrations of work done in class, with questions based on that principle or concept. For example, you might repeat a demonstration, or better still, show a modification of it (several are described in this chapter), which illustrates the same principle.

PEOPLE, PLACES, AND THINGS

Are you near an experimental station, an agricultural college, a nursery, or a farm? If so, you have many resource people to whom you may turn for assistance. Perhaps you may want to plan a field trip to one of them.

If possible, try to be in on the landscaping of the school grounds. Refer to some uses of the school grounds for field trips and work throughout the year in soil erosion, reproduction, interdependence, and other aspects of conservation (see Chapter 14).

A visit to an experimental station and several short field trips over the year around the school grounds to interpret some aspect of class work give meaning to the work at hand.

Books and pamphlets

These are only a few of the books which are pertinent to the work discussed in this chapter. These and many other references classified by subject and with complete bibliographical data are given in the Bibliography at the end of the book.

Bonner, J., and A. Galston, *Principles of Plant Physiology*, 1952.
Dunn, S., *Elementary Plant Physiology*, 1949.
Dutcher, R., C. Jensen, and P. Althouse, *Introduction to Agricultural Biochemistry*, 1951.
Smith, G., E. Gilbert, et al., *A Textbook of General Botany*, 1953.
Stanford, E., *Man and the Living World*, 1951.
Weatherwax, P., *Botany*, 1956.

Then make up five questions which test observation and also reasoning. This might be used as one test question. A sample of this type of question may be found on p. 26, Chapter 1.

Films and filmstrips

This partial list is intended only as a guide toward film and filmstrip selection. Refer to the more complete listing at the end of the book where films are classified by subject and where a key to abbreviations and addresses of distributors are given. The cost of film rental, of course, may be subject to change. Films are sound and black and white unless specified otherwise.

Hunger Signs in Corn (f), De Kalb Agricultural Assoc., free.
Leaves (f), EBF, $2.50.
Life Cycle of a Plant (f), UWF, $2.00.
Life of Plants (f), UWF, $1.50.
Roots of Plants (f), EBF, $2.50.

Free and inexpensive materials

This is only a partial listing of free and inexpensive materials available to the teacher at this time. A more complete listing, including addresses, is given at the end of the book. Many of these materials are distributed to teachers without charge. Where there is a small fee, the cost is indicated, although the prices are subject to change. While we recommend the material for use in the classroom, we do not necessarily sponsor the products advertised.

How a Tree Grows (poster, 16″ × 21″), U.S. Dept. Agriculture, Forest Service.
Some Applications of Atomic Energy in Plant Science, U.S. Atomic Energy Commission.

CHAPTER 4

Digestion in plants and animals

The independent green (holophytic) plant is the ultimate source of food, because, generally speaking and especially for our purposes, the green plant is the major converter of light energy.[1] Green plants make carbohydrates, fats, proteins, and use minerals in building foodstuffs. While a few animals can synthesize vitamins (and some fungi and bacteria have this ability too), most vitamins are derived from green plants.

Food nutrients must, in turn, be broken down chemically (digested) within the bodies of the plants and animals that consume them. The nutrients are then built into protoplasm in the pattern of the specific organism.

Digestion must take place within the green plant as well as in other organisms, for stored foods must be digested before they can be distributed and utilized within a plant. Digestion may be studied in seeds, which contain stored food materials.

Controlled experiments are described for investigating the role of enzymes and their specificity in the digestion of starch, proteins, and fats.

Digestion in plants

Starch

We may want to show that many seeds store carbohydrates in the form of starch. The starch is then digested to a simple form of sugar for use by the seedling.

Germinate several grains of corn in sawdust. In a few days the coleoptiles will appear; grind them in a mortar. To the macerated leaves or mash, add a few drops of water. Test the mash with Fehling's or Benedict's solution (p. 405) for glucose; test with Lugol's solution (iodine in potassium iodide, p. 409) for starch. Then test several dry, ungerminated seeds for simple sugar and starch. Compare the results with seeds which are germinating. What is the advantage to the growing plants in having a supply of soluble glucose rather than starch?

---

[1] We shall not cover the activities of the purple bacteria and similar organisms; these are far beyond the scope of the average high school course.

Extracting diastase from seedlings. Students may want to extract this starch-splitting enzyme as a project. Thoroughly grind up twenty-five germinating barley seeds with about three times as much water. Filter the preparation after it has been standing for about half an hour.

In the meantime, prepare a thin starch paste (0.1 per cent) by dissolving 0.1 gm of arrowroot starch in a little cold water, and adding this paste to boiling water; use 100 cc of water in all. (Stir to avoid lumps.) If it is easier to weigh out 1 gm of starch, prepare a 1 per cent solution with 1 gm of starch and 100 cc of water, as above; then dilute with water an appropriate quantity of this solution to 0.1 per cent.

Add 5 cc of barley extract to an equal amount of cooled starch paste. Let this stand in a warm place. Heat some barley extract to boiling, cool, and add to another test tube containing starch paste. This serves as a control (boiling destroys the activity of the enzyme). At intervals, test samples from each tube for starch with Lugol's solution. Starch disappears gradually as the diastase, extracted from the germinating barley seeds, completes the digestion of arrowroot starch. The test tube containing starch paste and boiled barley extract does not show this reaction; starch paste remains in the test tube.

As a project, a student or small group might explore this problem: Is there a difference in the quantity of the enzyme present during the first few days of germination and during the second week of germination, or is the same quantity produced at all times? Students might design an experiment such as this: test dried seeds, then test seeds after 1 day of germination, 2 days, and so forth. They may use the procedure already described for extracting diastase, as long as they use uniform quantities of water and seeds.

Using commercial diastase. The concept of digestion as the breaking down of a substance by an enzyme may be demonstrated in several ways with commercial powdered diastase: (1) as individual student experimentation; (2) as a demonstration, using large test tubes.

Prepare a 0.1 per cent solution of arrowroot starch as described in the preceding activity. While the starch paste is cooling, prepare a 0.1 to 0.2 per cent diastase solution in water. (The enzyme is available from supply houses, and it is always ready to use; simply dissolve a small quantity in a large amount of water.)

Each student needs a clean glass slide or a small square piece of glass. A student laboratory assistant in each row or group adds drops of different fluids to each student's slide in this way: (1) two separate drops of dilute starch paste; (2) a drop of very dilute Lugol's solution (light brown in color) to each drop of starch paste so that both drops become very light blue in color; (3) one drop of the diastase solution to only one drop of the combined starch and Lugol's solution. The other drop on the slide acts as a control throughout this demonstration.

Within a few minutes students should notice how the blue color of one drop disappears. Why? What is the reason that the other drop remains blue? In this experience students gain a notion of how rapidly an enzyme acts in splitting starch paste.

As a demonstration in class, using two large test tubes, prepare the same dilutions of the starch paste, diastase, and Lugol's solution as for the individual student work. Turn starch paste in each of the two test tubes light blue with dilute Lugol's solution. Then add the diastase solution, in the amount of ⅓ of the volume of solution already in the tube, to one test tube. The blue color should disappear within 1 to 15 minutes, depending on the quantities used and the temperature. Why doesn't the control test tube lose its blue color?

Some teachers prefer to add the enzyme to the starch paste, wait a short time, and then add iodine solution. This fails to produce a blue color, since starch is no longer present in the solution. This method is described on page 60 in an experiment in which students test their own saliva.

There are many extensions of this experiment which can be used by students as practice in designing an experiment. For example: (1) How could you show that this same change in starch goes on within the body (use saliva instead of diastase)? (2) How could you find out what the starch has been changed into? (3) How dilute a solution of the enzyme can digest the starch paste? (4) Is digestion independent of temperature, or would digestion go on faster at body temperature? (5) Does it make any difference whether large particles or finely chopped or chewed particles of food material are acted upon by an enzyme?

Students may use similar experimental designs using pancreatin (see p. 64).

Testing the effect of dilution on enzyme activity. You may want students to demonstrate how powerful the action of an enzyme is. This might be a small project. Use the enzyme diastase which was prepared earlier (p. 57). Have the students dilute a given volume of diastase in solution with an equal volume of water so that it has been diluted in half; to a given quantity of this dilution have them add an equal volume of water so that the diastase has been diluted to one-fourth its original strength. They may continue to dilute it many times. Is starch still digested when their most dilute diastase solution is added?

For another project, students may design a plan for an experiment to discover whether diastase acts as readily on starch paste at 40° F or 100° F as it does at 65° F (approximately room temperature) (also see p. 60). They may contrive many questions which can be answered by carrying through an activity in the laboratory or at home.

Proteins

Fresh pineapple juice contains the protein-splitting enzyme bromelin. (Another proteolytic enzyme, papain, may be purchased as a product derived from papaya.[2]) Students may make a mash of some slices of a fresh pineapple and collect the juice. Add a given quantity to two test tubes containing some chopped hard-boiled egg white. As a control, boil a similar volume of the pineapple juice and add this boiled juice to chopped egg white in two other test tubes. Add 2 to 4 drops of toluene to each test tube to inhibit spoilage. Notice the ragged, partially digested bits of egg white in the test tubes containing fresh pineapple juice.

Digestion in animals

Starch

There are several ways we may demonstrate that starch is changed into reducing sugar through the action of saliva.

Digestion of starch by saliva in a test tube. Collect saliva from a student into a large test tube (filter if necessary). Salivation can be increased by chewing soft paraffin or clean rubber bands.

[2] This product is sold as a meat tenderizing agent.

Prepare two or three test tubes each containing 5 cc of a 0.1 to 1 per cent starch paste suspension and 5 drops of saliva. Roll the test tubes between the hands to ensure thorough mixing. You may want to use a water bath with a thermometer for precise work (Fig. 4-1). At timed intervals, remove samples of the saliva and starch paste mixture and test with Lugol's solution for the presence of starch. Changes will occur gradually, until the blue-black reaction does not take place. At one point a reddish reaction may occur as the intermediate dextrins form. Finally, the color remains the light-brown tint of the dilute iodine. Now the starch has disappeared. What has happened to it?

At this point, test the mixture for a reducing sugar with Benedict's solution (or Fehling's reagent). A change from blue to green to reddish-orange gives evidence of the presence of varying amounts of reducing sugar (maltose or glucose).

Of course, students will want to demonstrate that the original starch paste did not contain glucose (or maltose), nor did the original saliva. Test both the starch paste and the saliva with Benedict's solution. These two tubes serve as controls. Other useful controls are two or three similar test tubes containing starch plus saliva.

You may find the form in Table 4-1 useful to put on the blackboard as a guide for students in recording their observations.

Digestion of a cracker in the mouth. This procedure may be used as a demonstration or an individual laboratory exercise. Collect saliva from a student into a clean test tube. Then ask the student to chew slowly on a piece of soda cracker (which has been tested previously to check whether reducing sugar was

Fig. 4-1 Test tubes of starch paste and saliva heated in a water bath with constant 98°F temperature.

absent or found in small amounts). Use a cracker that is all white; tan or brown patches may be indications of dextrins.

Have the student place this chewed mixture into a clean test tube. While this part of the experiment is under way, you may want a student to test the saliva for reducing sugar with Benedict's solution, for the student may have eaten sweets previous to this activity. Also test a whole cracker for the presence of starch (as another control).

TABLE 4-1
Blackboard diagram for salivary digestion demonstration

	result	interpretation
Starch paste		
plus Lugol's ⟶		
plus Benedict's ⟶		
Saliva		
plus Benedict's ⟶		
Starch paste and saliva		
plus Benedict's ⟶		

Within 5 minutes the chewed cracker may be tested with Benedict's solution; a color change from green to orange will be observed. Digestion goes on more rapidly here than in the preceding demonstration, since the process goes on at body temperature.

You may want to divide the chewed cracker mixture originally obtained from the student so that one half could be tested for reducing sugar and the other half for starch (should a student ask if all the starch had been changed to simple sugar). In most cases some starch remains. The quantity varies inversely with reaction time.

Students test their own salivary digestion. In this laboratory exercise students work alone or in pairs, depending upon available materials. Here we shall assume that students work in pairs. A small vial of dilute starch paste and a drop bottle of dilute Lugol's solution (with a pipette stopper) are given to each pair of students. Then *each* student gets a pipette, microscope glass slide, and an empty vial.

Each student now takes 10 drops of starch paste from the stock vial and places it into his own empty vial. Then each student puts 1 drop of the starch paste on the extreme left end of his microscope slide. To this he adds 1 drop of iodine (Lugol's) to check the starch content. Now each student adds his own saliva to the 10 drops of starch paste in his vial. Students warm the vial by rolling it between the palms of the hands. At 2-minute intervals the student puts successive drops along the length of the glass slide. Each is tested with iodine solution.

Gradually, the blue-black color fails to appear, the reddish color of dextrins may appear, and finally there is no color change. (Starch and dextrin intermediates do not generally appear.) A few tests may show no change in the starch reaction. (A very small percentage of the population seems to lack ptyalin, the salivary amylase. This is believed to be an inherited trait.)

One or two students should test the remaining saliva-starch mixture of the vials for reducing sugar. As controls, saliva as well as a sample from the original starch paste stock should be tested for reducing sugar. The main advantage in this procedure is that each student has the opportunity to test his own saliva, and each set of "experiments" acts as a control for the others.

Enzymes

Effect of temperature on enzyme activity. You may want to demonstrate the action of salivary amylase under different conditions. A committee of students may undertake this activity as a small project. Prepare six test tubes, each containing about 5 cc of a 1 per cent starch suspension. Leave two test tubes at room temperature. Chill two tubes in a beaker of water to about 5° C, and place two more in a water bath at 40° C.

Add an equal quantity of saliva to one of the test tubes at each of the three different temperatures. To each of the other matched tubes add an equal quantity of saliva which has first been boiled for 10 minutes. Test all the tubes for the presence of reducing sugar.

Effect of dilution of enzyme on digestion. Students may want to demonstrate the minute quantity of enzyme required to produce the hydrolysis of starch. Into one test tube pour 5 cc of saliva. Into a series of individual test tubes dilute saliva to the following dilutions: 10, 100, 1000, and 10,000 times. Each test tube should contain 5 cc of saliva of the different dilutions. To all test tubes add an equal amount of 1 per cent starch solution. In

15 minutes test for the presence of starch. Repeat in 30 minutes. Note that time is a factor in the hydrolysis of starch. Given more time, more digestion of starch will occur. Therefore limit the period of testing to 15 or 30 minutes. Record the time it takes for digestion to occur. You may want to test with Benedict's solution for the presence of a reducing sugar. Note the quantity of sugar produced in a given period of time.

Specificity of enzymes. At this point, a small committee or a student interested in an individual project may want to extend the work on enzymes (see procedure above). In so doing they will have the opportunity to learn how to design simple experiments with controls. Students may plan to investigate the effect of the amylase in saliva on starch, sugar, fat, protein, as well as on foods containing many nutrients (e.g., milk). Similarly, experiments may be devised to discover whether pepsin reacts with starch, sugar, fat, and protein.

This is one simple plan that students can develop into a small project. Does saliva act on starch alone? Dilute about 24 cc of saliva with an equal amount of water. Prepare eight test tubes so that each contains about 6 cc of the diluted saliva. Suppose we set up two test tubes for each kind of nutrient so that one may act as a check for the other. To the first set of two test tubes add 10 cc of 1 per cent starch paste. To the second set of two tubes add 10 cc of a freshly prepared 3 per cent cane sugar solution. To the third set of tubes add 2 drops of olive oil with 10 cc of 1 per cent sodium carbonate. To the last pair add a pinch of casein (or chopped hard-boiled egg white) with 10 cc of 0.2 per cent hydrochloric acid. Now put all the test tubes in an incubator or in a 40° C water bath for half an hour. Students may now test the

starch paste and cane sugar solutions for reducing sugar with Benedict's solution. Then they may want to test the casein-containing tubes for peptones (with the Biuret test, p. 62).

Proteins

A general test for a protein. Hawk, Oser, and Summerson describe a technique for testing the component elements of proteins.[3] These are carbon, nitrogen, hydrogen, and sulfur. In a dry test tube, heat some powdered egg albumin (see preparation below). Suspend a strip of wet red litmus paper in the tube. Across the mouth of the test tube place a strip of filter paper which has been moistened in lead acetate solution. If hydrogen and nitrogen are present, ammonia fumes are produced, and the litmus will be turned blue. The presence of sulfur is indicated by the blackening of the lead acetate paper. As the powder chars you know that carbon is present. If the powder and the test tube are dry at the beginning of the test, you can see drops of moisture condense on the sides of the test tube. This indicates the presence of hydrogen and oxygen (as water).

Preparation of albumin. Hawk, Oser, and Summerson also suggest this preparation of albumin. If you need albumin solution for immediate use, beat the white of an egg with about eight volumes of water. Strain through cheesecloth and filter if needed.

To prepare powdered egg albumin, beat the egg white with about 4 volumes of water and filter. Then evaporate the water from the filtrate on a water bath at about 50° C. Powder the residue in a mortar.

Specific tests for proteins. In demonstrating the xanthoproteic test, add 1 cc

[3] P. Hawk, B. Oser, and W. Summerson, *Practical Physiological Chemistry*, rev. ed., Blakiston (McGraw-Hill), New York, 1954.

of concentrated nitric acid to a few bits of hard-boiled egg white or to about 3 cc of an egg albumin solution. Gently heat the test tube over a Bunsen flame and note the yellow color (an indication of protein) resulting. When the solution has cooled, add an excess of sodium or ammonium hydroxide to the test tube. Watch the yellow color deepen into orange.

Biuret test for proteoses and peptones. Peptones and proteoses give a pink color reaction in this test. In a test tube place fresh egg white. To this add an equal volume of 10 per cent sodium hydroxide solution and shake to mix. Then carefully add a 0.5 per cent copper sulfate solution, drop by drop (it takes about 2 to 5 drops in a test tube of water), into the test tube. (Or use prepared Biuret reagent, p. 405.) Shake the tube as each drop is added and watch for a violet or pink-violet color.

Millon's reaction. This is especially useful in testing solid proteins. Dilute Millon's reagent (p. 409) with 2 to 3 volumes of distilled water. To chopped egg white or egg albumin solution add a few drops of Millon's reagent; then heat slowly. Notice the protein precipitates, which turn red. In this test the color reaction is due to the hydroxyphenyl group in the protein molecule. Any phenolic compound such as tyrosine, thymol, and phenol will also give this reaction.[4]

Gastric digestion

Digestion of proteins by pepsin. Take a hard-boiled egg and separate the albumin or "white," which is almost pure protein, from the yolk. Chop the egg white and place equal amounts into each of eight test tubes. Label the test tubes and add the following substances: (a) in two tubes about 10 cc of water; (b) in two more tubes, about 10 cc of 0.5 per

[4] Hawk, Oser, and Summerson, *op. cit.*

cent commercial pepsin suspension; (c) in two more tubes about 10 cc of 0.2 per cent hydrochloric acid; (d) in the last two tubes, about 10 cc of the pepsin suspension and 2 drops of the hydrochloric acid to make artificial gastric juice (lacking rennin, however). Or you may want to use another formula for the artificial gastric juice.[5]

Place all the test tubes in an incubator or into a water bath maintained at 37° to 40° C for a period of 24 hours. At the end of this time you will find digestion in (b) and (d). However, the increased activity of the enzyme in an acid medium (note the rapid digestion) should indicate the effect of an acid pH on the action of pepsin.

A more effective test of conditions affecting the action of pepsin can be shown if you add two more test tubes to the demonstration described above. To the two test tubes containing chopped egg white add about 10 cc of 0.5 per cent commercial pepsin suspension and 5 cc of 0.5 per cent sodium carbonate solution. Compare the rate of digestion in the test tubes containing pepsin and acid with those containing pepsin and alkali.

Effect of temperature on pepsin digestion. In this activity students should place 10 cc of a solution of pepsin and hydrochloric acid into each of eight or more test tubes. This is prepared by adding a few drops of hydrochloric acid to every test tube of 0.5 per cent pepsin solution. Students should immerse at least two test tubes in ice water; another set should be kept at room temperature; and a third set of two tubes should be placed in an incubator or water bath at 40° C. Have them boil the contents of another set of

[5] Bennett suggests this formula for preparing artificial gastric juice. Mix together 0.5 gm of pepsin with 0.7 gm of hydrochloric acid and 0.2 gm of lactic acid. Add these ingredients to 100 cc of distilled water. (H. Bennett, ed., *Chemical Formulary*, Chemical Publishing Co., New York, 1951.)

two test tubes for a few minutes, cool, and then place in the water bath. To each test tube, they should add equal amounts of hard-boiled egg white or albumin solution. Students can observe the rate of digestion in all the test tubes.

Fibrin may be substituted for egg albumin or egg white (boiled) whenever a practically pure source of protein is needed for testing digestion. Fibrin may be obtained from freshly drawn blood, as a clot forms, or commercial preparations may be purchased. Out-of-date whole blood stored in blood banks can also be used.

For a more quantitative test of digestion of egg white by pepsin suitable for a project, Hawk, Oser, and Summerson describe the preparation of Mett tubes.[6] In this technique egg white is drawn up into narrow-bore glass tubing. Subsequently measured lengths of this tubing are cut and added to flasks of digestive juice. The amount of digestion in the tubes can be measured in millimeters. Normally, human gastric juice is said to digest about 2 to 4 mm of albumin.

Antipepsin action of some worms.[7] Students may want to do a project on antipepsin action. They may get intestinal worms from a slaughterhouse. They should grind a few worms, such as *Ascaris,* in a mortar with sand. To this add some 0.9 per cent sodium chloride solution; this should be mixed well and filtered.

Into each of two test tubes pour 10 cc of a solution of pepsin and hydrochloric acid as described earlier, along with some fibrin or egg white. To one test tube add 4 cc of the worm extract, and to the other tube add 4 cc of water. Keep both tubes at 37° to 40° C. As the rate of digestion is studied the next day, it will be noted that the worm extract inhibits digestion of proteins.

[6] Hawk, Oser, and Summerson, *op. cit.*
[7] Ibid.

Action of rennin on milk. You may want to demonstrate the coagulating action of this enzyme. Crush a Junket tablet and add it to a test tube of milk. Warm, but do not boil, the milk. Notice how rapidly the milk solidifies in the test tube. Compare this with a duplicate test tube in which the milk has first been boiled for 5 minutes. Notice the destructive action of heat on enzyme activity. Some teachers prefer to prepare a rennin solution first by crushing a Junket tablet in water, and add this to milk.

Digestion by trypsin. You may want to show that proteins are digested by trypsin in the small intestine. Commercial pancreatin powder is useful for this purpose. Add chopped hard-boiled egg white or albumin solution (p. 61) to six test tubes; then add a pinch of pancreatin in proportion to a half test tube of water. Set two tubes aside, and to two others add 2 drops of phenolphthalein solution. Add a 0.5 per cent solution of sodium carbonate, drop by drop, until the first pink color appears. This will result in a pH (see p. 406) close to 8.3 (alkaline). To two other test tubes add 5 cc of a 2 per cent boric acid solution, which will result in a pH close to 5. Pancreatin contains the enzyme trypsin which digests proteins. This and the optimum pH for this enzyme's activity can be demonstrated. You will get more rapid results if you use a water bath kept at 40° C, or keep the test tubes in an incubator.

By following the pattern of experiments described for salivary digestion (p. 60), you may want also to show the effect of temperature on pancreatic digestion of proteins.

Digestion by an amylase. Prepare a pancreatin solution by adding a pinch of pancreatin to 10 cc of water. Then prepare two test tubes containing about 10 cc of thin starch paste, and add 5 cc of "pancreatic juice" to each. Keep the tubes at 40° C in a water bath for about half an hour. Test the contents of one test tube for simple sugar with Benedict's solution; test the other tube for starch with Lugol's solution. Is there an amylase in pancreatin? The digestion of starch begins in the mouth and is completed in the small intestine.

Emulsification of fats. In a test tube shake together a small quantity of water with a few drops of olive oil; an emulsion forms. On standing (for a short time), the oil separates from the water. To another test tube containing about 10 cc of water add 5 drops of a 0.5 per cent sodium carbonate solution. To this add 3 drops of olive oil and shake well. On standing, this emulsion does not separate as quickly (since an alkaline medium exists). To a third test tube of water, add a 5 per cent solution of bile salts such as sodium taurocholate (or add a soap solution). Then add a few drops of olive oil and shake well. Compare this more permanent emulsion with the preceding transitory ones. The size of the oil drops may be compared by placing a drop of fluid from each test tube on a slide for examination under low power of the microscope. Students may readily see the small size of the oil drops in an emulsion; in discussion these observations may be elicited, and their significance as a preliminary step in fat digestion by lipase in the small intestine should be apparent.

Digestion of fat by lipase in the small intestine. A small committee of students might undertake this demonstration. Prepare three test tubes containing 10 cc of water and a few drops of olive oil. To two of these tubes add 2 cc of a soap solution or 5 per cent bile salt solution (sodium taurocholate). Then prepare a pancreatin solution by adding a pinch of pancreatin to 10 cc of water. Or sub-

stitute an artificial "intestinal juice."

ARTIFICIAL INTESTINAL JUICE. Dissolve the following ingredients in 100 cc of distilled water:

pancreatin	1 gm
$CaCl_2$ (1% solution)	1 cc
K_2HPO_4 (0.2 M solution)	25 cc
NaOH (0.2 M solution)	11.8 cc

Add 5 cc of this pancreatin solution to one of the test tubes with soap solution or bile salts and to the one without this solution. Thus we have three test tubes: (a) a tube containing water, olive oil, soap solution, and pancreatin solution; (b) a control containing water, olive oil, and soap solution; (c) another control containing water, olive oil, and pancreatin solution.

At the start of this demonstration, check the pH with litmus or phenolphthalein or hydrion paper. The original solutions must be neutral, not acid, for the objective is to show that fat digestion results in the production of fatty acids. Demonstrate the formation of acid with litmus paper, or other indicator, after the test tubes have remained in a water bath at 40° C for at least half an hour.

Litmus milk test using pancreatin. You may want to show that pancreatin contains digestive enzymes which split fats into fatty acids and proteins into amino acids. Litmus can be used as an indicator to show the resulting acid reaction after digestion. First prepare litmus milk powder: to 50 parts of dried milk powder add 1 part of litmus powder. Then dissolve one part of prepared litmus milk powder in 9 parts of water.

To each of two test tubes add 10 cc of litmus-milk-powder solution, and to one test tube add a pinch of pancreatin powder. To the other test tube add only water, or boiled pancreatin solution. If the tubes are kept in a water bath, students may observe the change in litmus to pink, indicating the presence of acid.

Absorption in the small intestine. We have described demonstrations illustrating diffusion of substances through a membrane (see pp. 33, 52). Although the need for digestion was established in diffusion demonstrations, students may, with advantage, engage in this project. Students may fill a length of sausage casing or cellophane dialyzing tubing[8] (without holes—even pinpricks—or the demonstration will fail) with a variety of foods and pancreatin. Be sure to include sources of the common nutrients. For example, include molasses, egg white and yolk, salt, bread or a cracker, and some milk. (Mix these together in a mortar first, if necessary.) Tie each end of the tubing with thread and attach each end to a support as illustrated in Fig. 2-10. Wash off the outside of the tubing to remove traces of nutrients, and insert into a beaker of water. Place in a water bath at 40° C.

The next day students may test samples of the water in the beaker for reducing sugar, simple proteins, salt, and fatty acids. Use Benedict's solution to test for simple sugar (p. 405); the Biuret test for simple proteins (p. 62); litmus paper for acids. Add 1 or 2 drops of silver nitrate to a water sample; the formation of a white precipitate will indicate generally the presence of a chloride.

Absorption of potassium iodide. You may demonstrate the speed of absorption of certain substances through the small intestine (or possibly the stomach) on *yourself,* to the amusement of your students. Have a pharmacist prepare 0.2-gm gelatin capsules of potassium iodide.[9] Swallow one of these capsules before class begins. The iodide is absorbed quickly and appears in the salivary glands.

The saliva should be tested before the capsule is swallowed, or immediately afterward, by adding it to a starch paste suspension. Then test the saliva every few minutes. Shortly the blue-black color reaction occurs.

Student projects

There are many opportunities for individual student research work in this area.

(a) Individual students may want to learn to extract digestive juices from an organ. A club group may find this an introduction to the chemistry involved in the extraction of such proteins as enzymes. A reference such as Hawk, Oser, and Summerson's *Practical Physiological Chemistry* gives concise steps for more elaborate undertakings by a group working under a teacher's supervision. One technique is given here as an example.

Cut up a sheep or pig pancreas from which the fat has been trimmed and grind it in a meat chopper or in a mortar. Put the ground pancreas in a 500-cc flask, add 150 cc of 30 per cent ethyl alcohol, and let it stand for 24 hours, shaking it occasionally. Then strain this alcoholic extract through cheesecloth and filter it. Begin to neutralize the filtrate with potassium hydroxide. Use litmus as an indicator; near the endpoint slow down, by using 0.5 per cent sodium carbonate solution.

The pancreatic juice extract may be added to hard-boiled egg white or albumin solution to test whether it has retained its potency.

(b) One student might investigate the

[8] Dialyzing tubing made of unseamed cellophane may be purchased in rolls.

[9] G. Du Shane, and D. Regnery, *Experiments in General Biology,* Freeman, San Francisco, 1950.

kind of digestion and enzymes involved in insectivorous plants which trap flies or digest bits of meat. (See culture methods, pp. 233–34.)

(c) A student might devise a way to study extracellular digestion by molds, such as bread mold. In this case, enzymes are secreted into the bread (or other substrate) where starches are changed to simple sugars. These sugars then diffuse through the rhizoids of the mold. Is it possible to extract the enzyme? Is it possible to demonstrate that rhizoids do secrete enzymes?

(d) Here is an advanced research problem. A student may want to learn more about the way some molds and bacteria develop certain enzymes, adaptive enzymes, depending upon the kind of medium in which they are growing; i.e., starch-splitting enzymes are developed if the plants are grown in a medium containing starch. Sugar-splitting enzymes are developed by the molds or bacteria if they grow in a medium that is rich in a certain sugar. Look up the subject of adaptive enzymes in a book on physiology of bacteria. (See the references at end of chapter.)

CAPSULE LESSONS

Ways to get started in class

4-1. Have two students stretch out some 20 feet of clothesline. This simulates roughly the length of the intestine. How does food move along the digestive tract? What changes take place along the way? How does food material get out of this intestine into the blood stream, and finally to the cells?

4-2. Or set up a demonstration to show that a mixture of starch paste and Lugol's solution loses its blue color when a diastase solution or saliva is added (see techniques in this chapter). What has happened to the starch? Elicit the need for digestion.

4-3. As a laboratory lesson have students test the action of their own saliva on starch paste as described in this chapter. Or have one or two students demonstrate how saliva changes the starch (in starch paste or a chewed cracker) into soluble form.

4-4. Why do plants need a starch-splitting enzyme? Demonstrate the change from starch to sugars in germinating seedlings. Use non-germinating seeds as controls.

4-5. Have a committee of students report on the classic experiments in digestion done by Spallanzani, by Réaumur, and by Dr. Beaumont (on his patient, Alexis St. Martin). Lead into a discussion of the role of enzymes in making food materials soluble so they can diffuse through membranes out of the digestive system.

4-6. If you have not already demonstrated diffusion of molecules through membranes, you may want to begin this work on digestion with either starch paste or glucose in dialyzing tubing. Fasten each end to a tongue depressor or splint and suspend over a beaker of water. Or use a starch paste and saliva mixture (or diastase and starch paste). If you do not have this cellophane tubing, use test tubes across the mouth of which wet goldbeater's membranes are stretched as described previously (Fig. 0-1). Test the water in the beakers to find out which molecules pass through a membrane. Why didn't starch go through a membrane? Then you are in the topic of digestion.

4-7. Perhaps students will want to dissect a frog to show the digestive system (see directions, Chapter 16). Elicit from students the kinds of foods that are digested along the digestive tract.

4-8. Or prepare a demonstration to show which components of gastric juice digest proteins (described in this chapter). Better still, students may design the demonstration themselves.

4-9. You may want, at times, to use a film on the digestive system as an introduction, or as a summary of classwork. Have you seen *Digestion of Foods* (Encyclopaedia Britannica) or *Digestion* (*Mechanical, Chemical*) (United World)? There may be occasion to show *Plant Traps* (Encyclopaedia Britannica) or *Insect Catchers of the Bog Jungle* (U. California, Dept. Visual Instruction).

4-10. Perhaps you plan to teach *food-making* in crop plants as part of the need for soil conservation. What good farming practices are needed for a more nutritious food supply? Have you used the film made available by the Beet Sugar Development Foundation called *Feed the Soil and It Will Feed You*? Or see the films, *Hunger Signs* and *Life of the Soil* distributed by National Fertilizer Association. (A directory of film distributors is given on page 464.)

Or you may show a film describing how radioactive tracers are used in plant nutrition. (See the Magic of the Atom series, Atomic Energy Commission, which is listed at the end of this book.)

4-11. You may find it useful to have students summarize the work of the digestive system on the blackboard in this way.

Name of organ	Role in digestion
a. -----------------	-----------------
b. -----------------	-----------------
c. -----------------	-----------------
d. -----------------	-----------------
e. -----------------	-----------------
f. -----------------	-----------------
g. -----------------	-----------------

4-12. Perhaps you may want to plan a laboratory lesson on the examination of epithelial cells such as those in the lining of the mouth. Directions are given for scraping the lining of the cheek to get epithelial cells for mounting in Lugol's solution (p. 409).

4-13. Food-making by plants and food-taking by animals, along with digestion of insoluble materials, may be part of a broad study in interdependence among living things as developed in some activities in Chapter 14 on conservation. You may begin this study of digestion with activities in that chapter.

4-14. Begin, sometimes, with a discussion of molds and how they get their food supply. Then you are into a discussion of interrelations among plants and animals and the dependence on green plants as the food source.

4-15. Have a student report on the way termites get their cellulose food supply digested by flagellates (p. 311).

PEOPLE, PLACES, AND THINGS

When a student needs assistance in a research problem—either technical help or equipment—there may be an opportunity for him to work (washing glassware) in a laboratory in plant or animal physiology at a nearby college or university. There may be a part-time position in the college library for a student who wants to read in advanced areas of science. A government agricultural station or a biological testing laboratory may be in your community. In these places you'll find resource people who are willing to provide chances for mutual assistance between the junior or senior high school and the college. Perhaps you may plan field trips to these places.

Books and pamphlets

These are only a few of the books which are pertinent to the work discussed in this chapter. These and many other references classified by subject and with complete bibliographical data are given in the Bibliography at the end of the book.

Best, C., and N. Taylor, *The Living Body*, 1952.
Carlson, A., and V. Johnson, *The Machinery of the Body*, 1953.
Curtis, O., and D. Clark, *An Introduction to Plant Physiology*, 1950.
Davson, H., *Textbook of General Physiology*, 1951.
Dunn, S., *Elementary Plant Physiology*, 1949.
Fruton, J., and S. Simmonds, *General Biochemistry*, 1953.
Gerard, H., ed., *Food for Life*, 1952.
Harrow, B., and A. Mazur, *A Textbook of Biochemistry*, 1954.
Hawk, P., B. Oser, and W. Summerson, *Practical Physiological Chemistry*, rev. ed., 1954.
Meyer, B., and D. Anderson, *Plant Physiology*, 1952.
Oginsky, E., and W. Umbreit, *An Introduction to Bacterial Physiology*, 1954.
Prosser, C., F. Brown, et al., *Comparative Animal Physiology*, 1950.
Salle, A., *Fundamental Principles of Bacteriology*, 1954.
Stiles, W., *An Introduction to the Principles of Plant Physiology*, 1950.
Weisz, P., *Biology*, 1954.

Films and filmstrips

This partial list is intended only as a guide toward film and filmstrip selection. Refer to the more complete listing at the end of the book where films are classified by subject and where a key to abbreviations and addresses of distributors are given. The cost of film rental, of course, may be subject to change. Also refer to the films listed in the previous chapter. Films are sound and black and white unless otherwise specified.

Citrus in Nutrition (f, c), Visual Institute of U. of California, $1.00.

Digestion of Foods (f), EBF, $2.50.

Fungus Plants (f), EBF, $2.50.

Hunger Signs in Corn (fs), De Kalb Agricultural Assoc., Free.

Human Digestion (f), Athena, $3.00.

Rice and Health (f, c), Story of Bataan Experiment, available through U. of California, $2.00.

Story of Human Energy (f), Modern Talking Pictures, free.

This is only a partial listing of free and inexpensive materials available to the teacher at this time. A more complete listing, including addresses, is given at the end of the book. Many of these materials are distributed to teachers without charge. Where there is a small fee, the cost is indicated, although the prices are subject to change. While we recommend the material for use in the classroom, we do not necessarily sponsor the products advertised.

Atomic Energy and the Life Sciences, U.S. Atomic Energy Commission.

Land of Plenty, Farm Equipment Institute.

Food Facts; How to Conduct a Rat Feeding Experiment, Wheat Flour Institute.

Food for Life, Continental Baking Co.

Digestion, charts, Educators' Mutual Insurance Co.

CHAPTER 5

Circulation in animals

You may want to demonstrate the heart beat and the circulation of blood in several animals, invertebrate and vertebrate. There are also many opportunities for individual laboratory experiences and for group demonstrations. In this chapter some activities related to circulation and the heart, blood cells, and blood typing are described.[1]

Recording arterial pulse

Students learn easily to take their own pulse. They should place the index and middle finger of one hand on the inner side of the other wrist. About 1½ inches above the wrist joint, near the thumb, the pulse may be felt in the radial artery. Then students may want to take each other's pulse. They should count the pulse for several 15-second periods, find the average, and multiply this by four to get the average pulse rate per minute.

Now compare this pulse rate with the rate after exercise. Students might hop in place, or do knee-bending exercises, or run up a flight of stairs. Then count the pulse again. (*Note:* When teachers select students for any exercise they should be apprised first of their students' medical records. These may be obtained from the Health Education Department.)

The heart

Heart beat in the frog

Anesthetize a frog with chloretone or urethane (p. 314) or pith a frog (Fig. 9-3). Then open the frog to expose the heart. Remove the pericardial sac and bathe the heart (throughout the demonstration) in Ringer's solution (p. 409). In this way the heart will continue to beat for several hours.

For class demonstration you can amplify the contractions of the heart by making a lever arrangement (Fig. 5-1).

Altering the heart beat. The effect of temperature may be shown by bathing the frog's heart with water warmed to 40° C, then with iced water.

---

[1] Among many techniques, a teacher must select those which are best suited to his classroom situation. As a guide to selection, you may want to examine the *Biology Syllabus* of New York City Board of Education, 1957.

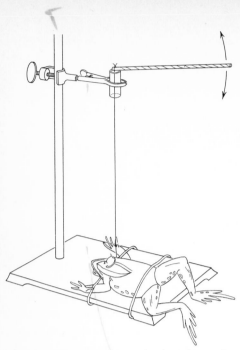

Fig. 5-1 Demonstrating the heartbeat of an anesthetized frog: a bent pin pierces the heart; from the pin leads a thin thread attached to a straw supported on a hollow glass tube.

The action of adrenalin may be shown by adding a minute quantity (0.01 per cent) to the Ringer's solution. A bit of experimentation may be necessary to determine the quantity needed to affect the particular frog's heart under study.

Effect of minerals on contraction. Ringer's solution is composed of ions of sodium, potassium, and calcium in definite proportions. You may want to show the effect of these ions when applied separately to the beating frog's heart. Suspend the heart of a freshly killed or pithed frog by means of a bent pin (like a fishhook) and thread attached to a tongue depressor in a beaker of Ringer's solution. Count the number of heart beats in a minute. Now transfer the heart into a beaker of 0.7 per cent sodium chloride solution. Count the number of beats now. The temperature of the solutions should be similar (room temperature). You will no-

tice that the heart beats are weaker and slower. Now replace the heart in Ringer's solution and note the recovery in rate of heart beat.

Next transfer the heart into a beaker of 0.9 per cent potassium chloride solution. Again count the heart beats until the heart muscle stops contracting. If the heart is now transferred into a 1 per cent calcium chloride solution you will find the heart contracting again. Replace the heart in Ringer's solution and watch the return to normal rate of heart beat. The ions in the Ringer's solution are balanced to effect the normal contraction of the frog's heart.

Heart beat in the clam

In many areas students may get hard-shelled clams from a fish market. Open a live clam by gently cracking one shell; then cut the anterior and posterior adductor or shell muscles with a sharp knife. Remove the mantle around the viscera and observe the beating heart in the pericardial cavity which lies below the dorsal hinge ligament (Fig. 16-3). Bathe the heart in clam juice or Ringer's solution. Watch the contraction of the ventricle.

Heart beat in embryo snails

Students may have the snail *Physa* (or other egg-laying snails) in their aquaria at home. Tease apart a developing egg mass in a drop of aquarium water on a microscope slide and examine under low power (without a coverslip). Students will find a beating heart in a developing embryo. (Also note the periodic muscular contractions of the body.)

Heart beat in Daphnia

Daphnia (water fleas) may be obtained from aquarium stores or from lakes and ponds (culturing, p. 351). Mount several for examination under low power of the microscope. Add a bristle to the slide be-

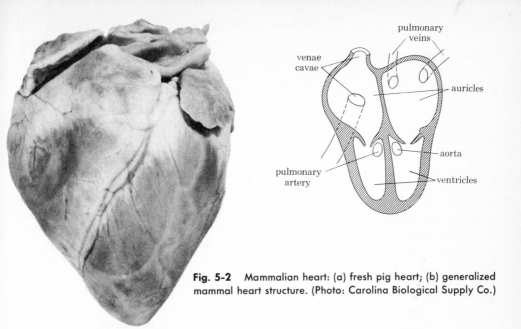

Fig. 5-2 Mammalian heart: (a) fresh pig heart; (b) generalized mammal heart structure. (Photo: Carolina Biological Supply Co.)

fore applying a coverslip, to prevent crushing the specimen. Look for the rapidly beating heart, which is situated in the dorsal region behind the eye. You may change the rate of the heart beat by warming the slide or by adding a trace of adrenalin (about 0.01 per cent). Since the heart beat is very rapid, this effect may not be a simple one to detect.

Heart beat in aquatic worms

Mount any of these annelid forms which may be obtained from an aquarium store or a lake or pond: *Dero, Nais, Aulophorus,* or *Tubifex* (culturing, pp. 349–50). Add a bristle to the mount before the coverslip is added. In *Tubifex* look for the single pair of aortic arches or loops, and note the movement of the dorsal blood vessel which pumps blood.

The worms may be anesthetized first by placing them in a drop of water to which a drop of very dilute formaldehyde has been added. (Other ways of anesthetizing small organisms are given on p. 314.)

Dissecting the heart

Students may get an untrimmed beef, sheep, or hog heart (Fig. 5-2a) from a butcher or slaughterhouse. They can locate the auricles, ventricles, aorta, venae cavae, and pulmonary vessels (Fig. 5-2b). Insert a soft metal probe, or use a fire-polished section of glass tubing as a probe, to explore the point of origin of blood vessels which lead into and leave the chambers of the heart. Note the semilunar valves in the blood vessels and determine the direction of blood flow.

Dissect the chambers of the heart and locate the bicuspid and tricuspid valves between the auricles and ventricles. Compare the thickness of the walls of the auricles and ventricles. Note especially the thickness of the left ventricle through which blood is pumped to the entire body. Look for the coronary arteries from the aorta and trace their paths as they spread over the heart. Students might cut cross sections of the aorta and a vena cava to compare their elasticity.

Circulation

Circulation in the tail of a goldfish

You may want to show circulation in the capillaries, arterioles, and venules in the almost transparent tail of a small goldfish. Wrap the body of the goldfish in wet absorbent cotton so that only the tail is exposed (Fig. 5-3). Place it in a Petri dish with a small amount of water. Cover the tail with a glass slide to hold it flat and expanded. Examine under low and high power of the microscope.

Watch the pulse and the swiftly moving blood in the arterioles. Contrast this with the more slowly moving blood which circulates in the opposite direction in the venules. Many criss-crossing capillaries are visible. Look for blood cells floating in the blood stream. Incidentally, irregular black patches of pigment in the skin (chromatophores) may be visible in the specimens (see p. 309).

Have students set up several similar demonstrations so that everyone may observe circulation within a 15-minute period. Then return the fish to the aquarium. At times the fish flip their tails vigorously and the demonstrations must be adjusted. When desired the fish may be anesthetized with chloretone or urethane (p. 314). However, circulation is sluggish in anesthetized fish.

Circulation in gills and tail of a tadpole

When very young tadpoles of amphibia are available, students can observe circulation of blood in their external gills. Later the gills are internal as epithelial cells of the skin grow over them. Nevertheless, in these older forms circulation can be observed in the almost transparent tail.

Mount a tadpole on a depression (welled) slide in a drop of aquarium water. Omit the coverslip or add a bristle to prevent the coverslip from crushing the specimen. Watch the circulation in capillaries under the low and high power.

Circulation in the frog

In the foot. The webbed skin between the toes of the frog is rich in capillaries. Wrap a live frog in wet cheesecloth, paper toweling, or absorbent cotton and lay the animal on a frog board made of cork. Or you may want to anesthetize the frog by injecting it with about 5 cc of a 2.5 per cent solution of urethane (p. 314). Inject into the lymph sacs under the loose skin along the sides and back of the frog. Frogs can be anesthetized without injection by putting them into a solution of chloretone. Add 1 part of a 0.5 per cent solution of chloretone in water, to 4 parts of Ringer's solution. Keep the frog in this solution for about half an hour. Avoid longer immersion.

Whether the frog is untreated or anesthetized, pin it to the board by fastening

Fig. 5-3 Demonstrating circulation in the tail of a goldfish.

it with cellophane tape. Punch a hole in one corner of the cork board and spread the web of one foot over this hole (Fig. 5-4); pin in place or use thread wound around the toes secured with pins to keep the toes immobile. Keep the frog's skin wet during the demonstration.

Place the board on the stage of the microscope and focus on the webbed foot. Observe capillaries, arterioles, and venules and the rate of blood flow. Notice the direction of the flow of blood and the pulsations of the blood vessels. Estimate the diameter of the capillaries (see below). Under high power compare the movement of red and white corpuscles. Notice the appearance and disappearance of capillaries. It may be possible to find, using high power, several white corpuscles moving through capillary walls.

A committee of students may want to study the effect of varying conditions on circulation of blood. For example, place a small piece of ice on the web and observe the effect on circulation. Then alternate with warm water (35° to 40°C) and observe the results. Watch the action of chemicals by adding a drop of dilute adrenalin (0.01 per cent) to the web.

In the tongue. Anesthetize a frog by placing it in chloretone or injecting it with urethane (p. 314). Wrap the body in wet toweling, cheesecloth, or absorbent cotton and place the animal, dorsal side up, on a cork board. Spread the unattached tip of the tongue over the hole in the cork board and secure with pins. Or cover the tongue with a strip of cellophane and fasten to the cork board with pins.

Place the board on the stage of the microscope, keep the tongue well lighted, and observe under low power a section revealing blood vessels of different sizes. Clamp the board to the stage of the microscope with a rubber band.

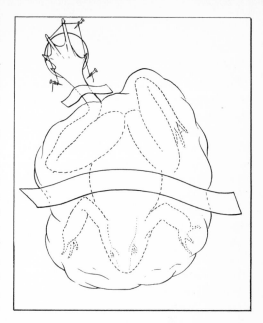

Fig. 5-4 Demonstrating circulation in the webbed foot of a frog: the frog is wrapped in wet gauze and secured in place on a cork board with cellophane tape.

Keep the tongue wet with Ringer's solution. Watch the pulsations in the arteries, the different direction of blood flow in arteries and veins, and the capillaries connecting the larger blood vessels.

Then under high power try to distinguish red and the larger white corpuscles. Estimate the diameter of the capillaries by using red corpuscles as reference. In the frog, these cells average 22 microns in length, 15 microns in width, and 4 microns in thickness.

Compare these effects on circulation: Apply slight pressure to the tongue by stroking it with a dissecting needle. Next apply, drop by drop, a small quantity of urethane to a small area of the tongue. Watch the changes in the capillaries. Then tie a string around a portion of the tongue to close off circulation for a short time. Observe the effect and watch the changes as the thread is released. Also try a small amount of adrenalin (0.01 to 0.1 per cent) applied to a small area of the tongue, and watch the changes.

In the lung. Anesthetize (p. 314) or pith (Fig. 9-3) a frog. Then pin the frog to a cork board or a waxed dissection pan and dissect to expose the lungs (dissection, p. 281). Inflate the lungs by blowing through a straw or glass tubing inserted into the glottis of the frog. Keep the lungs bathed in Ringer's solution. Examine the inflated air sacs and the rich network of capillaries in a bright light using a hand lens or binocular microscope. Observe circulation in the capillaries.

A small section of inflated lung can be examined under a compound microscope too. Spread a thin section over the hole in a sheet of cork similar to the one described previously. *Note:* You may also spread the capillary-rich mesentery supporting the intestine across the opening in the sheet of cork for observation of circulation. This is a dramatic demonstration.

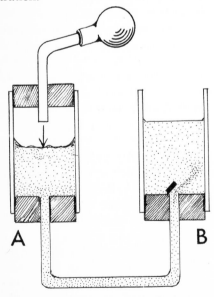

Fig. 5-5 Model of a valve. (From E. Morholt & E. T. Smith, *Experiences in Biology*, Harcourt, Brace, 1954.)

Circulation in the earthworm

Secure several live earthworms. Suspend them anterior end down for a few minutes or twirl them around so that the blood is concentrated into the anterior end. Anesthetize the worms by placing them in a shallow dish with enough water to cover them. To this add a small amount of alcohol, sufficient to immobilize the worms but *not* to kill them. Next wash off in water, and pin each worm to a waxed dissection pan or a sheet of cork. Make a lengthwise cut from the clitellum to the prostomium (tip of the head) cutting to one side of the middorsal line (dissection, p. 270). Cut through the body wall but avoid cutting into the viscera. Watch the five pairs of aortic loops or "hearts" beat. With a hand lens or a binocular microscope students may observe the circulation of blood more clearly.

Blood vessels

When possible have students get lengths of arteries and veins from a butcher and bring them to class. Compare their thickness in cross section and the difference in elasticity. Cut along the length of a vein, and open it to show the cuplike valves. Hold it upright and try to fill it with water to show the action of the valves.

Action of the valves.[2] Students may want to prepare the model shown in Fig. 5-5.

Attach a thin strip of rubber sheeting to one stopper with thumb tacks. This represents a valve in the one cylinder. Fill the glass cylinders with red ink. As the bulb is squeezed the increased air pressure forces the water through *A* into *B*. Why doesn't the water flow back into *A*? Then compare this with the flow of blood from the extremities back to the heart.

[2] Paul E. Blackwood, *Experiences in Science*, 2nd ed., Harcourt Brace, New York, 1955.

Devices to illustrate blood vessels. At times we may establish a concept with remarkably simple devices. Because they are immediately contrived before the eyes of youngsters they have additional impact.

Have you ever used these? Pull apart cheesecloth or gauze. This will represent the appearance of capillary beds. Or have you separated out the central strands of a coarse hemp cord (Fig. 5-6)? Dip one unfrayed end of the cord into red ink, the other into blue. Isn't this a standard representation of arteriole, capillaries, and venule?

Remove the insulation from the center section of a 4-inch length of electric wire. Spread apart the individual fine copper wires in the center. Imagine that these separated wires represent capillaries. Then the ends might represent an artery and vein.

When you want to show capillary cir-

Fig. 5-6 Demonstrating a capillary bed, using a piece of frayed cord.

culation around an air sac in the lungs, strands of cord wrapped around a Florence flask may give students the general idea. Or with a glass-marking pencil draw "capillaries" on the flask. And in similar fashion, show circulation in a villus of the small intestine. Wrap cord around a small test tube. Or draw capillaries with a glass-marking pencil. Now insert this into a larger test tube. This will serve as a villus with an outer epithelial layer. The smaller test tube within the larger one represents a lacteal.

The blood

Differences between blood in arteries and in veins

The effect of the amount of oxygen supply in the blood in arteries as compared with veins may be demonstrated. This technique is described in the section on respiration of animals (p. 89).

Blood cells

Fresh mounts of blood for examination under the microscope will be described here. Staining techniques using Wright's blood stain or Giemsa stain are described in Chapter 17.

Human blood cells. You may want to have students examine their own blood cells under the microscope.

Note: Whenever activities call for taking samples of students' blood, the following procedure should be followed:

1. *Get parental consent notes if your community or school requires them. A note might be obtained for the term or year to cover activities such as making blood smears and typing blood.*
2. *Apply alcohol to the area of the finger to be pricked. Use either the tip of the finger or the back of the finger about ¼ of an inch below the nail.*
3. *Sterilize the needle (whatever kind is used) immediately before use by passing it through a flame and then dipping it in alcohol. Some teachers prefer to use individually wrapped sterile needles which are disposable, or a needle inserted in a cork as described on p. 79.*
4. *After puncturing the skin and obtaining blood, clean the finger with alcohol again. If bleeding continues, have the student apply pressure by clenching a piece of sterile cotton.*

After following the procedure above, apply the blood to a clean slide. Add a drop of Ringer's or Locke's solution (pp. 408, 409) and a coverslip. Examine the vast number of red corpuscles in comparison to white blood cells. When red blood cells show crenation (wavy, irregular outline), the mounting fluid is hypertonic and should be diluted with distilled water.

White blood cells. White corpuscles may be studied more readily when red corpuscles have been destroyed. Prepare the slide as described above. Then put a drop of acetic acid at the edge of the coverslip so that it diffuses into the mounting fluid. Note the clear field of white blood cells that remains.

Blood counts. A small group of students, for example, a club, may want to learn to count red blood cells. For this technique micropipettes as well as special counting chambers are needed.

A measured volume of normal blood is taken from the finger or the ear lobe and drawn into a micropipette. This is diluted to a definite volume with a solution such as Hayem's (p. 406). Then the red blood cells become diluted and visible for counting. The blood in the pipette is mixed well and a drop is placed in the counting chamber. Specific details for these techniques may be found in such references

as Hawk, Oser, and Summerson *Practical Physiological Chemistry* or Todd and Sanford's reference listed at the end of this chapter. Or a doctor may demonstrate the technique.

Facts about human blood. For students who are interested in doing blood counts and similar work the information in Table 5-1 and Fig. 5-7 may be useful.

TABLE 5-1
Normal conditions of human blood

Coagulation time	3–5 minutes
Hemoglobin	90–100%
Red blood cells	4.5–5.5 million/cc
Platelets	300,000/cc
White blood cells	7,000–10,000/cc
Polymorphonuclear lymphocytes	60–70%
Small lymphocytes	20–25%
Large lymphocytes	5–8%
Eosinophils	1–2%
Basophils	1–2%

Blood cells of a frog. Mount a drop of fresh frog blood on a clean slide. Touch one end of a second slide to the drop; hold the second slide at a 30° angle to the first slide. Push the second slide along the first so that a thin film of blood is spread the length of the slide (Fig. 17-13). Let the slide dry. Examine without a coverslip or later stain with Wright's blood stain (p. 319) and mount in balsam with a coverslip.

A drop of blood may be examined in a drop of Ringer's solution as a wet mount instead of a dry smear. The red cells appear as oval, nucleated discs.

Blood cells of a mammal. Occasionally you may want students to compare the red blood cells of a frog with those of a mammal. Blood may be obtained from a slaughterhouse; usually ox blood is available. To prevent clotting, add 0.1 gm of potassium or sodium oxalate for every 100 cc of ox blood. Or you may prefer to

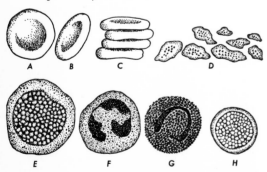

Fig. 5-7 Human blood cells: A–C, red blood cells; D, platelets; E–H, leucocytes: E, eosinophil; F, neutrophil; G, basophil; H, lymphocyte. (From W. G. Whaley, O. P. Breland, et al., *Principles of Biology*, Harper, 1954.)

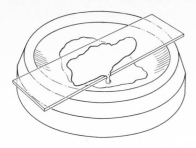

Fig. 5-8 Flooding a slide with stain. A Syracuse dish acts as catch-all.

add 1 part of 2 per cent sodium citrate solution to 4 parts of blood. The oxalate and citrate are both anticoagulants.

Then mount a drop of the ox blood as a wet mount or prepare a blood smear as for frog blood, above. Both white and red cells are visible. You may use Vaseline on the mount to prevent evaporation (p. 308).

Amoeboid movement of white corpuscles. In this technique described by Bensley and Bensley[3] vital dyes are added to blood cells on a slide. As the stains are absorbed the cells gradually die. However, the structures in the cells may be studied.

Prepare a number of slides with a coating of the stains described as follows: First prepare a *stock* solution of neutral red in absolute alcohol by adding 100 mg of neutral red to 10 cc of absolute alcohol. Then make a *dilute* solution from this stock solution by adding 10 cc of absolute alcohol to 4 cc of the stock solution. To this dilute solution add 1 to 2 drops of a saturated solution of Janus Green in distilled water.

Now support a chemically clean, dry slide on a Syracuse dish, and flood the slide with the diluted neutral red solution containing Janus Green (Fig. 5-8). Allow the excess stain to flow off by tilting the slide into the Syracuse dish. Set aside

to dry. Prepare a supply of such stained slides. (Protect them from dust.)

Mount a drop of fresh frog blood on this stained slide. Apply a coverslip. Examine under low power and under high power. As the dyes slowly dissolve notice that the mitochondria of the cells stain green and the cell inclusions become red. Amoeboid movements may be studied. As the cells gradually die, their nuclei absorb more of the stain.

Hemoglobin content of human blood

A comparison of color may be used as a simple, but somewhat inaccurate, method for the determination of the amount of hemoglobin in blood. One scale, the Tallquist scale, is made of strips of paper of different shades of red. Each strip is perforated in the center. A drop of blood from a finger which has just been pricked (see p. 75) is placed on special white absorbent paper which is provided with the Tallquist scale, and the resulting color is matched against the color scale. The approximate percentage of hemoglobin may be read from the scale. Students may be able to bring to class demonstration material of this type, for doctors use several of these scales for rough estimates of hemoglobin content.

A more accurate method involves using a hymacytometer (as described in physiology texts, such as those by Todd and Sanford and by Hawk, Oser, and Summerson listed at the end of this chapter). These books give complete detailed accounts of the commonly used techniques for determining the percentage of hemoglobin.

Hemin crystals in blood

This might be an activity for a small group of students interested in a more extensive study of blood.[4] Take a drop of

[3] R. Bensley and S. Bensley, *Handbook of Histological and Cytological Techniques,* U. of Chicago Press, Chicago, 1938.

[4] D. Pace and C. Riedesel, *Laboratory Manual for Vertebrate Physiology,* Burgess, Minneapolis, Minn., 1947.

blood from the fingertip (technique, p. 75), mount it, and allow it to dry in the air. To the dried blood add a crystal of salt, a drop of water, and finally a drop of glacial acetic acid. Now apply a coverslip. Gently heat one end of the slide until bubbles escape. Under high power locate the reddish-brown rhombic crystals of hemin.

Coagulation time

This is the time it takes blood to begin to form fibrin, to clot. The average coagulation time varies from 2 to 8 minutes depending on the method used and the amount of blood. Here are two ways in which you may show how rapidly blood clots.[5]

Using a glass slide. This is a convenient method. Obtain a few drops of blood from the finger (technique, p. 75), and place them on a clean slide. (Note the time at which the blood was taken.) Slowly pull a clean needle through the drop of blood at ½-minute intervals. When a fine thread of fibrin can be pulled up by the point of the needle coagulation has begun. Record the time interval between the flow of blood and the formation of fibrin (coagulation): this is called the coagulation time.

[5] War Dept., *Methods for Laboratory Technicians,* Tech. Man., 8-227, Supt. Documents, U.S. Govt. Printing Office, Washington D. C., 1941.

Using capillary tubing. For this method, pull out fine capillary tubing into capillary pipettes of even bore over a wingtop Bunsen burner. Clean the finger with alcohol, puncture the finger (see p. 75), and fill the pipette by placing it near the drop of blood exuding from the finger. Blood rises in the fine tubing by capillarity. At ½-minute intervals break off small sections of the capillary pipette. When fibrin forms at the broken edge, coagulation has begun. Record the time interval as in the slide method above.

Fibrin clot and plasma

Try to get fresh blood from a slaughterhouse or meat-packing house or "out-of-date" whole human blood from a hospital blood bank. If possible, keep it in a Thermos bottle. Some of the blood may clot in transit, but it may be possible to get fresh blood to class. Pour some into a beaker and whip it with straws or small sticks. Fibrin will form shortly. When some of the blood is allowed to stand undisturbed a clot also forms. As the clot contracts from the sides of the container, the clear, straw-colored plasma is visible.

Phagocytosis model

The movement of phagocytic cells, such as some kinds of white corpuscles and amoebae, is partially explained on the basis of surface tension; you may want to

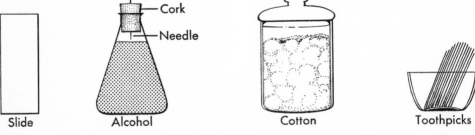

Fig. 5-9 Materials for typing blood. (From E. Morholt & E. T. Smith, *Experiences in Biology,* Harcourt, Brace, 1954.)

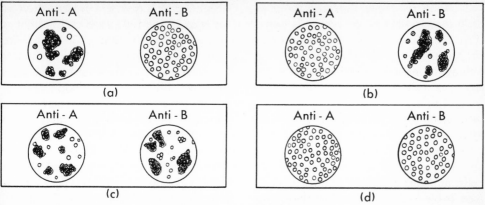

Fig. 5-10 Possible results after adding drop of "unknown" blood to each drop of serum. (From E. Morholt & E. T. Smith, *Experiences in Biology*, Harcourt, Brace, 1954.)

simulate such an action by preparing a "model." Place a drop of mercury in a bit of dilute acid in a Syracuse dish. Next to the mercury put a small crystal of potassium dichromate. Note the movement of the mercury and explain in terms of surface tension.

Typing blood

Students may type their own blood in the classroom. Laboratory space is not essential for this activity.

Divide the class into five or six groups and supply each group with a tray or box containing the materials illustrated in Fig. 5-9. Thus each student has access to a glass slide which he divides into two halves with a glass-marking pencil. Then there are cotton supplies and toothpicks. Each flask or bottle contains ethyl alcohol (rubbing alcohol) and has a needle inserted into the cork.[6] Notice that the needle has first been broken in half, then inserted with pliers so that only a quarter of an inch of needle protrudes from the cork. The preferred method is to use indi-

vidual needles which can be disposed of after each student has used one. In any event, be certain that each time the needle is used it is sterilized.

First, demonstrate the technique for the students. Divide a slide in half with a glass-marking pencil. At the left, place a drop of anti-*A* serum; on the right, a drop of anti-*B* serum. Make this a uniform practice to avoid confusion. Since the serum is expensive and youngsters may tip over the vials it is advisable for the teacher or one student to put the two drops of serum on each student's slide.

Demonstrate for the students how to obtain blood (technique, p. 75). (The flask of alcohol is inverted to maintain sterilization of the flamed needle; or use a sterilized, individually wrapped needle.) With one end of the toothpick, transfer a drop of blood to the drop of anti-*A* serum and stir it a bit. Now with the *other end* of the toothpick transfer a second drop of blood into the drop of anti-*B* serum. Tilt the slide back and forth a bit and note the immediate reaction (unless the blood is type *O*). Students may want to check their observation by examining the slide under a microscope or hand lens. Check the results against those illustrated (Fig. 5-10).

---

[6] Lancets are preferred by some teachers, but these must be checked within the class period to make certain that students have not inadvertently changed the adjustment so that the blade of the lancet gives a deeper puncture than the teacher had planned.

Students readily understand the principle upon which blood typing is based. The four blood groups are classified on the basis of the presence or absence of the two agglutinogens A and B found in the red blood cells. Both of these antigens are present in AB blood and both are absent in O blood type. However, when type A blood is added to type B blood it clumps. Therefore the plasma of type B blood contains a chemical which clumps "A" cells, and this is known as anti-A serum (see Table 5-2). In summary then, type B blood has a "B" chemical in the red blood cells and an anti-A chemical in the plasma. It is obvious that a person of B blood type couldn't live with anti-B in his own plasma, for it would clump his own blood.

TABLE 5-2
Summary for blood typing

blood group	in red blood cells	in plasma
A	"A" chemical	anti-B
B	"B" chemical	anti-A
AB	"A" and "B" chemical	no anti-serum present
O	no chemical present	both anti-A and anti-B present

And too, blood type A has "A" chemical in his red blood cells and anti-B in his plasma. (The anti-B serum which you use in blood typing in class has, of course, been extracted from blood of a person of type A.)

When students find that a drop of their "unknown" blood is placed into a drop of anti-A serum and clumping occurs, the unknown blood must be type A as in Figure 5-10a. Similarly, if the unknown blood clumps in anti-B serum, the unknown blood belongs to group B. Should the unknown blood clump in both drops of serum, anti-A and anti-B, the unknown blood belongs to type AB as in Figure

5-10c. O type blood, which lacks the two antigens in the red blood cells, will not clump in either serum. (There is some evidence for a separate O antigen, but this need not be considered here; it does not affect this method of blood typing.)

After students have typed their blood, compare the frequency of each blood group in the class. Type O is the most frequent, very roughly 45 per cent (the percentage varies among racial groups within a population). Then type A follows with about 42 per cent; type B is found in some 10 per cent of occidentals; type AB is the rarest in the western hemisphere, among the white population, about 3 per cent. (We repeat: these figures are very rough.)

Blood serum should be refrigerated when not in use. However, it cannot be stored indefinitely. It may be purchased already prepared from supply houses and certain biological laboratories (p. 479). Dyes are added to distinguish the two serums. Powdered serum is also available for purchase and is accompanied by explicit directions for preparing solutions. But it is easier to purchase the anti-A and anti-B serums already prepared, in solution.

The pattern of inheritance of blood groups is described in Chapter 12.

Hormones in the blood

You may prefer to include the role of hormones which circulate in the blood stream throughout the body in this topic rather than in a study of behavior. Hormones and their functions are described in Chapter 9.

Using a new laboratory tool, radioactive tracers, it is possible to follow the rapid uptake of iodine from the blood stream by the thyroid gland. Techniques for using radioactive substances have been described in Chapter 3. In essence, radioactive iodine is combined into an iodide compound. This is added to a sugary solution and fed by pipette to a white rat or rabbit 3 times daily for 2 days. Over the next day or days a high concentration can be located only in the region of the thyroid gland when a Geiger counter is moved over the body.

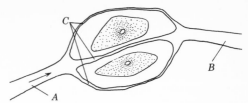

Fig. 5-11 Schematic drawing of two tissue cells surrounded by a network of capillaries.

Using the blackboard as a tool for summary

As a summary, students might outline the components of blood and their functions on the blackboard. Then a diagram such as Fig. 5-11 might be drawn on the board in colored chalk. A short review of the functions of blood might be established by this presentation "in a new view" at this time. What kind of blood vessel brings blood to the cells (i.e., what is *A*)? What kind of blood vessel is represented by *B*? By *C*? Then complete a chart such as Table 5-3 in class.

TABLE 5-3
What does the blood gain and lose in circulating through these organs?

organ	blood gains	blood losses
small intestines	. . . .	
liver	. . . .	
kidneys	. . . .	
lungs	. . . .	
bone marrow	. . . .	
muscle cell	. . . .	
thyroid gland	. . . .	
all cells	. . . .	

CAPSULE LESSONS
Ways to get started in class

5-1. Have students take each other's pulse. Develop the idea that the beating heart pumps blood through the body by way of blood vessels. Then compare the pulse after some kind of exercise; now the class is into a good discussion of the role of the heart in pumping blood and other aspects of circulation.

5-2. Perhaps you want to begin with the story of Harvey and his study of the circulation of blood. With advanced students you may want to read Harvey's original paper on circulation (obtainable from Regnery Publishing Co., Chicago, Ill.). Have students draw their conception of how blood circulates around the body.

5-3. Some teachers begin with a study of the contents of the blood. Have students examine a drop of their own blood. (In most school systems, parental consent notes are necessary.) Study either a drop of blood in Ringer's solution or a dried blood smear. A biology club might want to stain smears for the entire class (with Wright's blood stain, p. 319).

5-4. At some point show a film on the composition of blood. You may want to show *Blood* (Encyclopaedia Britannica), or in review, the complete circulation of blood as in *Circulation* (United World) or *Circulatory Control* (Encyclopaedia Britannica). If possible show the filmstrips, *The Work of the Blood* (Popular Science Publishing Co.) or *Heart and Circulation* (Encyclopaedia Britannica) or *Your Life Stream* (Harcourt, Brace).

5-5. Demonstrate how to prepare a goldfish for microscopic study of the circulation in its tail (see technique in this chapter). Then have several students prepare additional demonstrations so that all students may examine blood circulating through the arteries, capillaries, and veins of the tail. In which blood vessels does the blood move more quickly, and in spurts? Which are the fine connecting vessels? What are the large vessels in which blood flows the other way?

5-6. Bring in a fresh specimen of a beef heart for dissection in class. Elicit the uses of each chamber of the heart and of the valves. Develop a discussion, with diagrams, of a closed circulatory system from the heart and back again. Follow, the next day, with a development of the story of what materials the blood gains and loses in its trip around the body.

5-7. Have students report to the class on some blood disturbances (such as types of anemia or leukemia) and some heart conditions. Elicit a discussion concerning the factors which affect the circulatory system. Remember that the highest death rate is caused by circulatory diseases. (There are many free booklets available, see p. 83.)

5-8. As a laboratory lesson have students prepare wet mounts of the water flea, *Daphnia.* These are available from an aquarium shop. Examine the beating heart found in the anterior top end of the animal. Develop a discussion of the role of the heart in circulation. You may also see blood circulating in such microscopic worms as *Dero, Nais,* or the *Tubifex* worms students may be able to get from an aquarium shop (culturing, Chapter 18).

5-9. A very successful laboratory lesson is blood typing. Have students type their own blood. Demonstrate the technique and have students around the desk as you do it. Get anti-*A* and anti-*B* serums and prepare the materials listed in this chapter. Have a student report on the distribution of types *A, B, AB,* and *O* in the total population. Compare with the findings in your class. Warn students not to consider this exercise in blood typing as official, for this class work is subject to all the usual pitfalls of novices.

5-10. Begin the lesson with a question which arouses good discussion. These may be possibilities: How many know that food materials are sometimes injected into a person who is very ill? What kind of fluid is inserted into a vein? Why? Into which kind of a blood vessel? (Students might trace the path of this glucose solution through the body.)

5-11. You may want to use this little story as a means for getting attention focused on the day's lesson. A bad-tasting but harmless drug was injected into the leg of a man. In less than a minute he sensed a bitter taste on his tongue. Explain. From this elicit a discussion of circulation time around the body, the path of circulation, the need for blood's circulation.

5-12. Ask students if they know of the disease diabetes. Some students know a great deal about insulin injections and the precautions necessary. Here the topic of circulation is approached through the study of hormones. Of course, many other hormones might be used in this manner: role of thyroxin in metabolism; what causes a giant or a midget; a story of the adrenals and their role in stress. The role of the blood as a means for co-ordinating the chemistry of the body is developed in this manner. Or perhaps students may want to read from Cannon's classic *The Wisdom of the Body.*[7]

5-13. This may be the place you want to introduce the use of radioactive isotopes as tools in a study of functions of the body. Students might report to the class on how radioactive iodine, radioactive sodium chloride, and other isotopes are used (see the Bibliography at the end of the book and the films on uses of atomic energy also listed at the end of the book).

PEOPLE, PLACES, AND THINGS

Do students in a club need the assistance of a technician in learning how to make a blood count? Do you need advice as to where to take students on a field trip for living materials? Where can you get live frogs any time of the year? A beef heart? A film on circulation?

There are many resource people in your community: a lab technician at a hospital, or a parent. Neighboring high schools and colleges may provide you with a film or living material and possibly some suggestions for fruitful locations for a field trip. An aquarium shop and the local butcher can supply some materials suggested in this chapter. At the end of the book you'll find a listing of supply houses and a directory of film distributors. Are you looking for some information? Perhaps the books listed here or in the Bibliography include what you want.

BOOKS AND PAMPHLETS

These are only a few of the books which are pertinent to the work discussed in this chapter. These and many other references classified by subject and with complete bibliographical data are given in the Bibliography at the end of the book.

Best, C., and N. Taylor, *The Living Body,* 1952.
Comar, C. L., *Radioisotopes in Biology and Agriculture,* 1955.
Diehl, H., *Elements of Healthful Living,* 1955.

---

[7] W. Cannon, *The Wisdom of the Body,* Norton, New York, 1932, pp. 28, 302–03.

Gerard, R., *The Body Functions,* 1941.

Graff, S., ed., *Essays in Biochemistry,* 1956.

Hawk, P., B. Oser, and W. Summerson, *Practical Physiological Chemistry,* rev. ed., 1954.

Harrow, B., and A. Mazur, *Textbook of Biochemistry,* 1954.

Lawson, C. A., et al., *Laboratory Studies in Biology,* 1955.

Mitchell, P. H., *A Textbook of General Physiology,* 1956.

Romer, A. S., *The Vertebrate Body,* 1955.

Storer, T., *Elements of Zoology,* 1955.

Todd, J., A. Sanford, and B. Wells, *Clinical Diagnosis by Laboratory Methods,* 1953.

Films and filmstrips

This partial list is intended only as a guide toward film and filmstrip selection. Refer to the more complete listing at the end of the book where films are classified by subject and where a key to abbreviations and addresses of distributors are given. The cost of film rental, of course, is subject to change. Films are sound and black and white unless otherwise specified.

The Atom and Medicine (f), EBF, $2.50.

Atom and Biological Science (f), EBF; available free from U.S. Atomic Energy Commission field offices.

Blood Circulation in Marine Animals (f, si), Iowa State U., $3.00.

Circulation (f), UWF, $3.00.

Circulatory Control (f, si), EBF, $2.00.

Circulatory System (f, si, 2 rls), Bray, $3.50.

The Heart (f), Almanac, $2.00.

Nine Basic Functional Systems of the Human Body (f), Bray, $3.00.

Free and inexpensive materials

This is only a partial listing of free and inexpensive materials available to the teacher at this time. A more complete listing, including addresses, is given at the end of the book. Many of these materials are distributed to teachers without charge. Where there is a small fee, the cost is indicated, although the prices are subject to change. While we recommend the material for use in the classroom, we do not necessarily sponsor the products advertised.

The Story of Blood, Amer. National Red Cross; ask for additional materials for class use.

Your Heart; Rheumatic Fever, Metropolitan Life Insurance Co.

Your Heart and How It Works (chart), Amer. Heart Assoc.; ask for additional pamphlet information.

About Your Blood, John Hancock Mutual Life Insurance Co.

CHAPTER 6

Respiration and excretion in animals

The techniques described in this chapter are concerned with the exchange of gases in breathing, the production of heat (or other energy) and water, and the excretion of some wastes. (For demonstrations of respiration in plants, see Chapter 7; for mitochondria, p. 313.)

While the fascinating story of the role of respiratory enzymes is beyond the scope of this book, some students or classes of high ability may want to gain an introduction to biochemistry through reading a biochemistry textbook, Gerard's *Food for Life,* Upjohn Company's *Vitamin Manual,* or Heinz's *Nutritional Data.*

It is sometimes useful to make a crude comparison between the burning of foods in the body and the burning of a candle.

Burning a butter candle. Shape a mound of butter into a candle, in an evaporating dish or a Pyrex beaker, and insert a cotton string as a wick half way into it (Fig. 6-1). Then ignite the wick. Heat is produced.

Hold a cold glass plate or a mirror over the butter candle and look for drops of condensed water on the surface. Wipe dry. Then a student might breathe on the cold glass plate.

Test the air around the burning candle for carbon dioxide. To do this pour some limewater into the evaporating dish or beaker and cover with a glass plate. Shake slightly and note the cloudy appearance of the limewater formed by the precipitation of calcium carbonate.

Students recognize that water, heat, and carbon dioxide were released in oxidation. Do we exhale carbon dioxide? What instrument is used to measure the temperature of the body?

Respiration

Carbon dioxide released in exhalation

Students may breathe through a straw or glass tube into a beaker of limewater or water containing an indicator (such as brom thymol blue). When limewater is used, it becomes cloudy (as calcium carbonate is formed).

Since carbon dioxide added to water results in a weak acid (carbonic acid), we

Fig. 6-1 Burning of food: a butter candle.

may use several indicators to reveal the increase in acidity of the liquid. For example, pour dilute brom thymol blue (slightly alkaline and light blue in color) into a beaker (preparation, p. 18). When a student breathes into this it turns a light yellow or straw color.

At other times you may use phenolphthalein made slightly alkaline with sodium carbonate (or sodium hydroxide) so that it is pinkish (or red). When carbon dioxide is breathed into this, the medium becomes colorless as the acidity increases. Phenol red may also be made slightly alkaline with sodium carbonate. When exhaled air is bubbled through this indicator it turns from a red to a yellowish color (as the acidity is increased). For other indicators, see Table 21-1.

A comparison of exhaled and inhaled air

Students may know that there is a small percentage of carbon dioxide in air at all times. They may question the conclusion that limewater (or some other indicator) turned milky in the presence of exhaled air and claim the change indicated only that some carbon dioxide was in the air at all times.

A more valid way to show that exhaled air contains more carbon dioxide than inhaled air is diagramed in Fig. 6-2. To make this device connect a glass Y-tube to two sections of rubber tubing. Then fit one short and one longer piece of glass tubing into each of two two-hole rubber stoppers which fit two Erlenmeyer flasks.

Attach the rubber tubing to the *short* section of glass tubing in one flask and to the *longer* piece in the other flask.

Into each flask pour 100 cc of water to which alkaline brom thymol blue (p. 18) has been added so that the water is colored light blue. Compare your setup with the diagram again. Note that only one tube to which the rubber tubing is attached extends below the level of the fluid. Insert a short section of a straw into the mouth piece of the Y-tube. Have students inhale and exhale continuously without removing the lips from the straw. Watch the change in color of the indicator in flask *A*, the "expirator." Of course, phenol red, phenolphthalein, or limewater may be substituted for the brom thymol blue.

The principle upon which this "inspirator-expirator" works is relatively simple for students to understand. During inspiration, air from the bottle *B* is inhaled. As air is removed from this bottle the air pressure inside it is reduced, and more

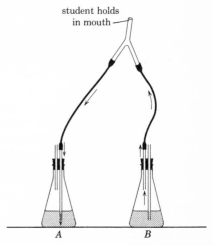

student holds in mouth

Fig. 6-2 Comparison of inhaled and exhaled air: student inhales (through mouth) air from flask B, exhales into flask A. A CO_2 indicator in the water will show one difference in the two types of air.

air is pushed into it and bubbles through the indicator. Now in exhalation, air is breathed into the indicator in flask *A*, and the indicator changes color rapidly.

Making a balanced microaquarium

You may want to call students' attention to a large "balanced" aquarium in the classroom. What is the need for green plants? From where do the animals get their oxygen supply? Or you may want to make a set of microaquaria for student examination.

In a test tube. Begin by asking students to predict what might happen if you were to seal a snail in a test tube. Seal a snail in one tube (Fig. 6-3). Into another place a snail and a green aquarium plant. You may prefer to "seal" each tube with a rubber stopper, and cover with adhesive tape or wax to prevent an exchange of gases.

However, the demonstration seems to be more effective when the test tubes are sealed in a flame. Hold the ends of a large, soft-glass test tube (not Pyrex) and rotate it in a Bunsen flame. As the central area of the test tube softens, remove it from

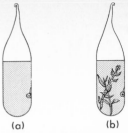

Fig. 6-3 What will happen in each of these sealed microaquaria: (a) a snail (*Physa*) in aquarium water; (b) *Physa* plus a green aquarium plant in aquarium water?

the flame and pull it out quickly so that a 1½-inch-long section is made (Fig. 6-4a). Make several of these and set aside until cool (3 minutes or so). Then add aquarium water to each test tube (not more than half full). To some of the tubes add green aquarium plants and a snail. Into others place a snail without the plants.

To seal each test tube, hold the tube at a 45-degree angle and heat the narrow part of the tube until the glass softens (Fig. 6-4b). Then remove it from the flame and pull it out quickly to form a fine strand of glass (still open for exit of gases). Place the center of this strand in

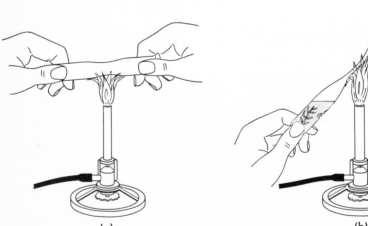

Fig. 6-4 Making a sealed microaquarium: (a) constricting the empty tube by heating and pulling; (b) making the constriction very narrow, after the materials are in the tube. When the expanded gases have escaped, the tube is completely sealed off.

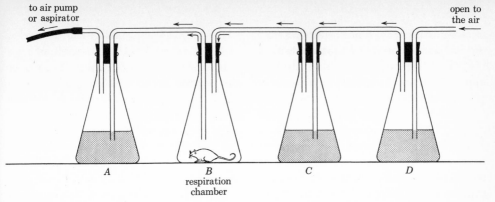

Fig. 6-5 Measuring respiration in small animals: flasks A, C, and D contain water with a CO_2 indicator.

the flame again in order to seal the tube. Be careful not to heat the liquid as you heat the glass tube, since the liquid will boil and expanded gases will cause the tube to crack. Stand the sealed micro-aquaria in a jar or test-tube rack in good light but not in direct sunlight.

You may want to use plastic bags instead of test tubes. These bags may be obtained in pet shops or department stores.

On a glass slide. The existence of the oxygen–carbon dioxide cycle among microorganisms may be shown on a sealed depression slide.[1] Into the depression place the growing tip and a small segment of an aquarium plant such as *Nitella* in several drops of a rich culture of mixed protozoa and possibly some microscopic worms (*Nais, Dero*) and a crustacean, *Daphnia.* Allow some space for several air bubbles to be trapped in the "micro-aquarium" as you apply the coverslip. Seal the coverslip to the slide with Vaseline or paraffin (to prevent evaporation). Keep the microaquaria in moderate light, not direct sunlight. These slides may be studied under a binocular or standard monocular compound microscope or with a microprojector. Also prepare a control without the *Nitella*.

[1] M. Rabinowitz, "A Balanced Microaquarium," *Teaching Biologist,* 7:5, Feb. 1938.

Respiration in small aquatic animals

Add enough brom thymol blue to a bottle or large test tube of water so that a light blue color results. To this add a goldfish, or guppies, or several tadpoles. Then stopper the container. Within 20 minutes (as carbon dioxide is excreted) a color change becomes apparent; the blue color changes to yellow. Similar preparations, without the experimental animals, should be used as controls.

As a short review in a new context, ask students how to reclaim the yellow brom thymol blue so that the blue color is regained. Some students may recall that green water plants carry on photosynthesis. What would happen if the plants were added to the yellow brom thymol solution and placed in strong light? In this process, carbon dioxide would be taken out of solution; thus the liquid would become less acidic and turn back to a blue color as it becomes slightly basic.

Respiration in small land animals

The increase in carbon dioxide content of exhaled air of land animals may be measured.[2] Make the apparatus shown in Fig. 6-5; be sure that the long and short

[2] D. Miller and G. Blaydes, *Methods and Materials for Teaching Biological Sciences,* McGraw-Hill, New York, 1938.

tubes are in the right place (note that they are reversed in the respiration chamber). Pour dilute brom thymol blue, slightly alkaline phenolphthalein, or limewater into three bottles, skipping the respiration chamber. Place some fruit flies, grasshoppers, or beetles, or a small frog, toad, or white rat into the respiration chamber. Be sure to fire-polish the ends of glass tubing before inserting into the rubber stoppers.

After connecting the apparatus, make it airtight. Connect an exhaust pump or aspirator to bottle *A*. As the pressure is reduced in bottle *A*, air will be forced from the respiration chamber into this bottle. If the organisms have been in the respiration chamber for a short time before the apparatus is used, carbon dioxide should have accumulated in the chamber. As this air is forced into bottle *A* the indicator changes color. Thus brom thymol blue becomes yellow, phenolphthalein becomes colorless, or limewater becomes milky. (The time in which this takes place will vary, of course, with the animal used—particularly in relation to its size—so that a change in the indicator may occur in an hour or it may take several hours.)

In this same way, reduced air pressure in the respiration chamber will cause air from bottles *D* and *C* to enter bottle *B*, the respiration chamber. Watch for a slight change in the color of the indicator in bottles *C* and *D* as the small amount of carbon dioxide in air gradually shows a cumulative effect.

Mechanics of breathing

Students may want to show that certain aspects of respiration are "mechanical" by preparing the bell-jar model shown in Fig. 6-6. Insert a glass Y-tube into the opening of a rubber stopper which fits into the top of the bell jar. Fasten two balloons of the same size by means of

string or rubber bands to the two arms of the Y-tube. Next cut a circle of thin rubber sheeting large enough to fit over the bottom of the bell jar, and tie it in place. In the center of the sheeting pinch out a piece, insert a small cork and tie it off as a "holdfast." Check to see that there are no breaks in the sheeting.

Now the balloons represent lungs and the rubber sheeting demonstrates the action of the diaphragm. When students pull out or push in the rubber "diaphragm" as shown, a change takes place in the size of the balloon "lungs."

What happens when the rubber sheeting is pulled down? Since we have increased the area within the bell jar by pulling down the "diaphragm," there is less pressure on the "lungs." Thus atmospheric pressure pushes outside air into the lungs,

Fig. 6-6 Bell jar model to show mechanics of breathing: when the rubber-sheet "diaphragm" is pulled down, air pressure around the balloon "lungs" is reduced, and atmospheric pressure pushes air into the "lungs."

or the balloons, in this case. When the sheeting is pushed inward the air pressure in the anterior of the bell jar is increased, the pressure on the lungs is increased, and the air in the lungs is forced out. Then the balloon "lungs" collapse.

Of course, in the body the size of the chest cavity is also changed through the action of intercostal muscles between the ribs. Students may want to make a movable model of wood with hinges, to show these changes in chest cavity.

Capacity of the lungs

A rough estimate may be made of the volume of air exhaled.[3] Make right-angle bends in glass tubing (½-inch bore) as illustrated (Fig. 6-7). Then fill a gallon bottle about four-fifths full with water to which some red ink or dye has been added. Insert the tubing into the two-hole stopper and seal the bottle with paraffin.

Cover the mouthpiece with paper toweling and have students exhale into it. The amount of water displaced into the cylinder will be equal to the volume of air exhaled. Use a graduated cylinder to facilitate measuring the volume of displaced water.

Effect of excess carbon dioxide on the rate of breathing

Students may determine their normal breathing rate while at rest. Count the number of times breathing occurs in half a minute and then multiply by two. In general, respiration rate varies with age:

At birth	30 to 50 per minute
First year	25 to 35 per minute
Four to fifteen years	20 to 25 per minute
Adult	16 to 18 per minute

Next, have students breathe into a paper bag held closely for several minutes over the nose and mouth. Determine the

[3] B. C. Gruenberg and N. E. Robinson, *Experiments and Projects in Biology*, Ginn, Boston, 1925.

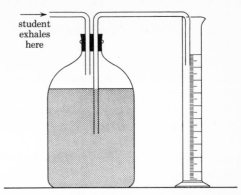

Fig. 6-7 Estimating the volume of air a student exhales. When he exhales into the glass tube, water roughly equal in volume to the air is displaced into the cylinder, where it can be measured.

rate of breathing while breathing into the bag, then again after breathing ordinary air. The increase in carbon dioxide in the air stimulates the medulla which in turn regulates the rate of breathing. However, this "experiment" yields very "rough" data.

Color difference between oxygenated and deoxygenated blood

Get several pints of fresh blood from a slaughterhouse, and add 1 part of sodium oxalate to 9 parts of blood to prevent it from clotting.

Prepare two flasks, each with a short piece of glass tubing and a right-angle bend of glass tubing in a rubber stopper. Rubber tubing leads from the bends to an oxygen generator for one flask and a carbon dioxide generator for the other (Fig. 6-8).

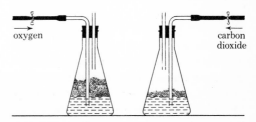

Fig. 6-8 Color change in blood: the effects of oxygen and carbon dioxide on oxalated blood.

Note the froth and the brilliant red color of oxygenated blood and the darker red color of blood rich in carbon dioxide.

Clamp the delivery tubes and reverse the attachments so that oxygen now flows into the flask of deoxygenated blood. Watch the change to bright red as oxyhemoglobin is formed in the blood.

Comparing respiratory systems in animals

How are different animals adapted for permitting a rapid interchange of oxygen and carbon dioxide? Students may study how surface membranes are increased by means of different kinds of gills (as in worms, fish, and amphibian tadpoles), tracheae in insects, and book lungs in some spiders and in king crabs.

Among vertebrate groups, examine gills of fish, which can be obtained from a fish market if there is one nearby. Also study the external gills of early amphibian tadpoles, and the lungs of mature frogs and toads. Observe the breathing movements of amphibia by watching the external nares and throat movements.

In the freshly killed frog, the lungs may be inflated by inserting a straw or glass tubing into the glottis and blowing gently as the small lungs begin to expand. Perhaps students have already studied the capillary circulation in the lungs as described on page 74.

Study of mammalian lungs

Have students bring to class the lungs and windpipe of a cow or sheep, which they may get from a slaughterhouse or the local butcher.

Drop the untrimmed lungs into a bucket of water and have students explain why they float. Dissect carefully to reveal the two bronchi and smaller bronchial tubes. Also examine the arrangement of cartilage rings in the trachea, or windpipe.

Oxidation in living cells

In the presence of oxygen the indicator methylene blue is blue in color. When oxygen is removed, methylene blue is bleached and becomes colorless. This change in color may be observed with living cells. Here are two methods described in the literature.

In the first method,[4] saturate an isotonic solution (0.7 per cent sodium chloride) with methylene blue. Then inject about 2 to 3 cc into the dorsal lymph sac of a living frog. Within 1 hour after injection place the frog under anesthesia (p. 132), dissect, and examine the organs for the presence of methylene blue.

As the cells use oxygen rapidly, the methylene blue will be bleached. When cells are exposed to air again, or when the cells die, the blue color returns. In this way it is possible to estimate the speed at which oxidation stops in the different organs of the frog (or the rate at which tissues die).

Oxidation in muscle cells

A student may want to do this as an advanced project,[5] making use of the fact that methylene blue is reduced so that it becomes colorless in living tissues.

Add a few drops of sodium hydrosulfite to a methylene blue solution. Note the disappearance of the blue color. In the presence of hydrogen peroxide or in shaking with air (so that oxygen is added) methylene blue is oxidized back to the blue color. This method may be used to show the disappearance of oxygen in muscle cells.

The student will need to dissect out two sartorius muscles from the leg of an anesthetized or freshly killed frog (p.

[4] D. Pace and C. Riedesel, *Laboratory Manual for Vertebrate Physiology,* Burgess, Minneapolis, Minn., 1947.

[5] R. Root and P. Bailey, *A Laboratory Manual for General Physiology,* 2nd ed., City College, New York, 1946.

130). These are stained with methylene blue–Ringer's solution (as described in the previous demonstration). Now each muscle strip is mounted on a slide and a coverslip is applied; use Vaseline around the rim to prevent evaporation. Within a short time, the center region of the muscle tissue may be examined; the methylene blue is colorless.

As the coverslip is raised, so that the muscle tissue is exposed to air, the blue color will return. As the coverslip is replaced, the methylene blue will again be reduced to the colorless form in the muscle. One of the slides may be steamed (over a beaker of boiling water) until the tissue is killed. After this slide has cooled, lift off the coverslip on both slides. Note any difference in the rate of reappearance of the blue color.

Oxidation-reduction illustrated

The fact that oxidation-reduction is a reversible process may be demonstrated by mixing a solution of the dye thionine with a solution of ferrous sulfate.

In the presence of intense light, the color of the dye disappears within a second. In the dark, the color reappears immediately. What happens is that in the presence of light the ferrous iron reduces the dye to the colorless form, and is itself oxidized at the same time to ferric iron; in the absence of light, the process is reversed. What is the applicability of this to living tissue?

Excretion

We have already described several indicators which may be used to show that carbon dioxide is excreted as a waste product of respiration. In brief, the method involves blowing into a water solution of an indicator in a beaker or other container. The following indicators may be used: phenolphthalein which has been made slightly alkaline (to a pink color) by adding sodium carbonate (or sodium hydroxide) will be decolorized; brom thymol blue will turn yellow; phenol red (alkaline solution) will turn yellow. We have described devices for enclosing small animals in a chamber so that exhaled air accumulates and can be tested (p. 87).

Excretion of water. To show that water is also excreted by lungs during exhalation, have students breathe against the blackboard or on a mirror. (Compare this with water vapor given off in the burning of a candle, early in this chapter.)

Study of kidneys. From a butcher, students may get an untrimmed kidney of a hog, sheep, or cow. Study the fat capsule which envelops the kidney. Remove this sheath and slice the kidney lengthwise. Distinguish the region rich in tubules and capillaries (cortex) and the collecting funnel which leads into the ureter.

Speed of action of an enzyme, urease. Urease is an enzyme which transforms urea into ammonia. Both urea and urease may be purchased from a supply house.

Dissolve some urea in water and divide the solution into two beakers. To each beaker add a bit of phenolphthalein so that the solutions are slightly milky. Then add a few crystals of urease to one beaker. Watch how quickly the solution changes to red (alkaline due to the presence of ammonia).

Using the blackboard as a visual device. Standard charts or models of a cross section of skin are useful but elaborate. A diagram drawn with the students participating may be as effective.

This is one suggestion. Draw a straight line on a blackboard to indicate the surface of the skin. From an opening on the surface (a pore), diagram a long shaft ending in a coiled tube. Elicit the kind of blood vessel which would be found encircling small groups of cells. Then, in the diagram, enmesh this sweat gland with capillaries. By means of arrows (use different color chalk) indicate the waste substances that the kidney or the skin receives from the blood.

Cooling effect of evaporation. Students can easily demonstrate the cooling effect of evaporation of sweat. They may wet some absorbent cotton with alcohol. Quickly apply it to one hand of each of several students in class. Do students notice that the hand wet with alcohol feels colder? When a liquid evaporates, it takes heat from the surface of the skin, thus resulting in a cooling effect. Using this demonstration as a guide, students can explain how evaporation of sweat cools the body.

Test for glucose in urine. Place 5 cc of Benedict's qualitative solution (p. 405) and exactly 8 drops of urine in a test tube. Boil for 1 to 2 minutes and allow to cool. A precipitate will form when there is about 0.3 per cent glucose. You may also want to demonstrate the use of commercial tablets used for testing sugar in the urine which do not require boiling over a flame. Show how Clinitest or Galatest or other such tablets are used by diabetics to test their own urine.

Test for albumin in urine. There are many tests for albumin in urine. The method described here is Heller's nitric acid ring test. Pour 5 cc of concentrated nitric acid into a test tube. Tilt the tube, and use a medicine dropper to add urine so that it flows slowly down the side of the test tube. Watch for the stratification of liquids with a white region of precipitated protein at the point of contact.

Some workers suggest that the urine be diluted in this test since concentrated urine will form a white ring due to the presence of uric acid. At times, bile pigments or other substances may give a colored ring, but the albumin ring is white in color. (See also glacial acetic acid test cited in Hawk, *et al.*)

Introducing a discussion about a reading in science

At some time you may want to use a "reading," a passage from a book or magazine, as a test or as a device for starting a discussion in some classes. For example, the following passage[6] summarizes the basic ideas about photosynthesis and respiration.

The process of photosynthesis has been described. This enables plants to make carbohydrates (later used by animals as food) as follows:

$$nCO_2 + nH_2O + \text{solar energy} \xrightarrow{\text{chlorophyll}} (CH_2O)_n + nO_2$$

In words, carbon dioxide plus water plus solar energy with the catalytic (enzyme aid) aid of chlorophyll give carbohydrate plus oxygen.

[6] R. Gerard, ed., *Food for Life*, U. of Chicago Press, Chicago, 1952.

Here $(CH_2O)_n$ represents carbohydrates in general.

The release of the stored solar energy from carbohydrates is the reverse of this reaction. It is essentially the combustion of the sugar or, more properly, its oxidation to carbon dioxide and water. In the laboratory that oxidation does not take place at ordinary temperatures. In the absence of catalysts it is necessary to heat sugar to more than 200° C. Only then does it release its stored energy:

$$(CH_2O)_n + nO_2 \xrightarrow{\text{heat}} nCO_2 + nH_2O + \text{energy}$$

But the animal organism is not obliged to ignite its fuel at such high temperatures. It makes use of enzymes to carry on the combustion of sugar at the temperature of the body, without accompanying noise or flame and at enormous speeds. This release of energy may be expressed by the following equation, quite analogous to the preceding one:

$$(CH_2O)_n + nO_2 \xrightarrow{\text{enzymes}}$$
$$nCO_2 + nH_2O + energy$$

This looks simple enough, but it is, in fact, a very intricate process, for the energy must be released in a succession of gradual steps and must be used where and when it is released, to accomplish directly such effects as muscular contraction or chemical synthesis.

Students might be asked to interpret this passage. Or a committee of students (or the teacher) might prepare five or ten questions based on the passage. The questions might be of this type: (1) What gas do plants use in photosynthesis? (2) What part does chlorophyll play in the food-making process? (3) How does respiration differ from photosynthesis? (4) Where did the energy given off in respiration originally come from? (5) If the direction of the arrow were changed, what process would be illustrated?

Many magazines and books contain passages which lend themselves to this kind of activity for class. The *American Scientist* (Sigma Xi, Yale University Press) and *Scientific American,* as well as *Science* or *Scientific Monthly* (both AAAS),[7] are especially fine for this purpose. Some texts are listed at the end of this chapter, and a more complete listing is given in the Bibliography at the end of the book.

CAPSULE LESSONS

Ways to get started in class

6-1. Begin with the inspirator-expirator apparatus described in this chapter and elicit an explanation for the color change in one flask from brom thymol blue to yellow. From this point on develop the need for, and the materials used in, respiration.

6-2. Fasten a candle to the bottom of a battery jar by heating the end of the candle. Pour a bit of brom thymol blue into the jar. Light the candle and cover the jar. Have students watch the candle become extinguished. (There is a value in observing and thinking in silence.) Then shake the jar to show that the brom thymol indicator has changed to yellow. Have a student blow into a small beaker of brom thymol blue. Now ask the class what the two cases seem to have in common. Develop a discussion of the details involved in burning or respiration.

6-3. Some other time begin with a film. There are several to select from in the field. Do you know the one on *Mechanics of Breathing* (Encyclopaedia Britannica) or the more general film *Respiration* (United World)?

6-4. You may want to begin with a reading from a book such as the example given in this chapter, and either ask questions or develop the meaning in class.

6-5. At another time, you may want to begin the work with a microaquarium (a snail sealed in a test tube of aquarium water) as described in this chapter. How long will it live? Develop the interrelationship between plants and animals and the oxygen–carbon dioxide cycle.

6-6. What effect does strenuous exercise have on breathing? Why is this so? From this point on, develop a discussion of the materials exchanged in respiration. Trace the path of oxygen throughout the body.

6-7. Ask students to hold their breath for some time. They will be forced to exhale and inhale in due time. Why? Then develop the need for respiration.

6-8. Have a student make the bell-jar model as a project. Demonstrate its use, and have the class develop from the animated model the mechanics of breathing.

6-9. Start a lesson with a dissection of untrimmed lungs which a student may bring to class. Also refer to a model of lungs (supply houses, p. 479). Have students trace the path of oxygen into the body and the path of carbon dioxide out of the blood and into air sacs.

6-10. Show the cooling effect of evaporation of perspiration from the skin in this way: Stroke the blackboard with cotton soaked in water and also with cotton soaked in alcohol (or ether). Notice which streak evaporates faster. Next wet one of a student's arms with water and the other with alcohol. Repeat on several students. Which arm is cooler? Why?

Ask for an explanation which should include

[7] American Association for the Advancement of Science, 1515 Massachusetts Ave., N. W., Washington 5, D. C.

the fact that heat must be removed from a surface in evaporation. Why do we feel cool on a windy summer's day? Why is a humid day uncomfortable?

6-11. Use a film to review the uses of the skin, kidneys, and lungs in excretion of liquid and gaseous wastes. You may want to use *Elimination* (United World), a film which discusses these three organs and also the function of the colon.

6-12. Have a student bring in a fresh kidney and dissect this in class. Or use a model and trace the path of nitrogenous wastes from the kidney tubules into the ureters and urinary bladder.

6-13. Use a Florence flask to represent one air sac in the lungs. With a glass-marking pencil draw interweaving capillaries on the glass. What materials would pass into the air sac from the blood? What would the blood gain from the air sacs? Develop the difference between inhaled and exhaled air and the path of air into the air sacs.

PEOPLE, PLACES, AND THINGS

There are many people who may be of help. A doctor may be invited to speak on how the body is affected in disease. A hospital technician may help a group of students in a demonstration. Students may solicit the help of a butcher for fresh materials such as organs or blood. Other science teachers in nearby schools and colleges may have models or living materials which you may borrow. There may be an opportunity to place a capable student in a position in a college or hospital laboratory on a part-time basis.

Models, slides, charts, and other illustrative aids are available from supply houses listed at the end of the book. Many students are talented and can make models or other devices which can be used in subsequent years as classroom demonstrations (Chapter 21).

BOOKS AND PAMPHLETS

These are only a few of the books which are pertinent to the work discussed in this chapter. These and many other references classified by subject and with complete bibliographical data are given in the Bibliography at the end of the book.

Best, C., and N. Taylor, *The Living Body,* 1952.
Davson, H., *Textbook of General Physiology,* 1951.
Gerard, R., *The Body Functions,* 1942.
———, ed., *Food for Life,* 1952.
Pace, D., and C. Riedesel, *Laboratory Manual for Vertebrate Physiology,* 1947.
Prosser, C., F. Brown, et al., *Comparative Animal Physiology,* 1950.
Romer, A., *The Vertebrate Body,* 1955.

FILMS AND FILMSTRIPS

This partial list is intended only as a guide toward film and filmstrip selection. Refer to the more complete listing at the end of the book where films are classified by subject and where

a key to abbreviations and addresses of distributors are given. The cost of film rental, of course, is subject to change. Films are sound and black and white unless otherwise specified.

Tagging the Atom; The Atomic Zoo (f), available on loan from the U.S. Atomic Energy Commission Field Offices, free.
Mechanics of Breathing (f), EBF, $2.00.
Control of Body Temperature (f), EBF, $2.50.
Elimination (f), UWF, $2.50.
The Human Skin (f), Bray, $1.50.
How the Respiratory System Functions (f), Bray, $3.00.
Respiration (f), UWF, $3.00.
The Urinary System (f, si), Bray, $2.00.
Work of the Kidneys (f), EBF, $2.50.

FREE AND INEXPENSIVE MATERIALS

This is only a partial listing of free and inexpensive materials available to the teacher at this time. A more complete listing, including addresses, is given at the end of the book. Many of these materials are distributed to teachers without charge. Where there is a small fee, the cost is indicated, although the prices are subject to change. While we recommend the material for use in the classroom, we do not necessarily sponsor the products advertised.

Nutritional Data, H. J. Heinz, 1954.
Nutritional Observatory (monthly), H. J. Heinz.
Review of Nutritional Research (monthly), Borden Co.
Food for Life, ed., R. Gerard, Continental Baking Co.
What to Eat and Why, John Hancock.
The Vital Story of Cereal Grain Products, Hoffman-La Roche, 1955.
So You're On A Diet! Amer. Can Co.
Vitamin Manual, N. Jolliffe, Upjohn, 1953.

CHAPTER 7

Respiration and excretion in plants

The fact that plants as well as animals oxidize food materials with a release of carbon dioxide, energy, and water may be demonstrated in many ways.

We begin with demonstrations of the production of carbon dioxide by plants, because these are the easiest to prepare.

These are followed by techniques for investigating the absorption of oxygen by plants in respiration and a comparison of rates of oxidation. The final demonstration shows the production of heat during respiration.

Production of carbon dioxide by living plants

In the presence of light, green plants absorb carbon dioxide in food-making. They also continuously give off small amounts of carbon dioxide as a result of oxidation, but this effect is masked by the large amounts absorbed for photosynthesis. Therefore a green plant must be put in darkness in order to demonstrate or ascertain the speed of production of carbon dioxide in oxidation.

Production of carbon dioxide by a leafy plant

Place a healthy, leafy green plant, such as a geranium or coleus plant, and a small beaker of limewater on a sheet of glass or cardboard. Cover this with a bell jar, and seal the glass rim with Vaseline. As a control, prepare a similar demonstration omitting the green plant. Then cover both bell jars with black cloth

for about 24 hours. At the end of this time the limewater with the green plant should be whiter than that with the control, due to the formation of carbon dioxide by the plant.

When a bell jar is not available, immerse cut stalks of plants in water in a large bottle or jar containing water. As shown in Fig. 7-1, suspend a vial of limewater from the tightly fastened stopper. Prepare a control with branches or stalks from which the leaves have been removed, and place both containers in the dark or cover with black cloth.

Production of carbon dioxide by an aquatic plant

You will recall that the indicator brom thymol blue is blue when alkaline; when carbon dioxide is added, the solution becomes more acid and turns yellow.

Fig. 7-1 Leaves give off CO_2 in the dark: the suspended vial contains a CO_2 indicator (brom thymol blue or limewater).

This indicator was used previously to show the absorption of carbon dioxide by a green plant in photosynthesis (p. 18). Now we shall use the blue solution again. If aquatic plants produce carbon dioxide during oxidation, the solution should become yellow. (This must be done in the dark where photosynthesis will not obscure the effect.)

Prepare a 0.1 per cent solution of brom thymol blue in tap water (p. 18). Add about 20 cc of this to some 50 cc of aquarium water. Set up several test tubes containing this blue solution; to each add a sprig of elodea with a growing tip. As controls, prepare other test tubes without elodea plants. Then place some of the tubes in the dark (or cover them with carbon paper). Let one control (containing the indicator, without a plant) remain in light. Which tubes show a color reaction? How long does it take for the solution to turn from blue to yellow as a result of oxidation?

Using the blackboard as a device for summary

Students might diagram a large cross section of a leaf. (You may want to examine leaves, stems, and roots at this time; see Chapter 16.) Then students

might draw a comparison between photosynthesis and respiration, perhaps in the form of Table 7-1.

TABLE 7-1
Photosynthesis vs. respiration

	photosynthesis	respiration
Check one column:		
Process in which food is used		
Process in which food is made		
Process which uses energy		
Process which releases energy		
Fill in one or both columns, as appropriate:		
Gas taken in		
Gas given off		
Gas entrance		
Gas exit		
Water entrance		
Water exit		
Time of day process goes on		

Production of carbon dioxide by roots

The excretion by roots of carbon dioxide as carbonic acid can be demonstrated by using an indicator in this way. Support several vigorously growing seedlings (such as lima beans) on wet absorbent cotton with their roots submerged in test tubes containing water and a dilute indicator.

One indicator may be phenolphthalein (add a bit to the water, then introduce the small amount of sodium hydroxide needed to turn the water slightly pink). Other times you may vary the demonstration by using another indicator, such as litmus powder or brom thymol blue (turn the litmus powder blue by adding a small amount of limewater).

Within a few days, watch the change as the seedlings grow with their roots in the water (with indicator). The phenolphthalein solution will turn from pink to colorless; the litmus solution from blue to red.

You may improve upon this demonstration if you wish by using a solid medium. Prepare some unflavored gelatin. Before it solidifies, add a small quantity of litmus and limewater to tint the gelatin blue. (Or add phenolphthalein and enough sodium hydroxide to color the gelatin red.)

Fill test tubes about one-third full of the liquid gelatin. Then insert the roots of vigorously growing seedlings, such as sunflower or lima beans, into the cool, solidifying gelatin. Loosely cork the test tubes. Within 2 days you should detect increased acidity. The litmus should be red; the phenolphthalein should now be colorless. (Of course, brom thymol blue might be used; in this case the change in color would be from blue to yellow.)

Production of carbon dioxide by germinating seeds

Rapidly oxidizing tissues such as those of growing seeds produce appreciable amounts of carbon dioxide.

Place a dozen soaked peas, beans, or corn kernels into a test tube, or fill a bottle not more than one-third full of soaked seeds. As shown in Fig. 7-2a, connect this to another test tube or bottle containing limewater, brom thymol blue, or other indicator. Where space is limited, use the apparatus in Fig. 7-2b as a substitute. In this case, a small test tube containing seeds is placed on a support inside a larger test tube containing the indicator solution.

It is advisable to first disinfect the seeds by putting them in dilute formalin (1:500) or in dilute potassium permanganate for about 20 minutes. Then wash the seeds and soak them (see also p. 109). Controls can be set up by using seeds killed with formalin, p. 330 (to prevent decay or mold).

While the previous demonstration is

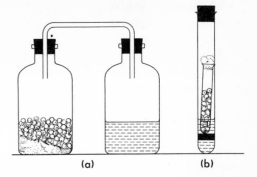

Fig. 7-2 Germinating seeds give off CO_2: (a) one bottle contains seeds, the other, indicator; (b) a small tube of seeds is supported inside a large tube containing indicator.

effective, a simpler one may be used. In fact, this demonstration as well as the previous one may be used to show respiration in flower buds, tips of growing stems, small insects, or insect larvae. Put a grain of barium hydroxide (or limewater, brom thymol blue, or other indicator) into a test tube containing approximately 10 drops of water. Then put a small wad of cotton in the tube about 1 inch above the water level. On this cotton surface lay six germinating seeds of peas or beans, or about two dozen oat seeds; seal the test tube. Then set up several such tubes using different seedlings, as well as controls using either killed seeds or none. The rapidity with which a precipitate forms (or the color changes) is a rough indication of the rate of carbon dioxide formation.

Throughout this section a variety of indicators as well as of demonstration techniques are given. The teacher can select from these and use many different means for bringing variety into classroom demonstrations. The possibility that students may have memorized the results instead of understanding basic principles can be ascertained through using demonstrations which have not been described in the text or workbook used.

Measuring the volume. Now that the gas has been identified as carbon dioxide, you may want to measure the volume produced in respiration. Several techniques are described below. Frequently students want to find answers to questions which involve a need for effective ways to measure volumes of a gas absorbed or a gas released in a specific life activity. The suggestions described may serve as guides in planning the tools to use in a project.

Using water. Place a quantity of germinating seeds such as beans or peas, or kernels of corn, on a pad of moist absorbent cotton in a bottle or test tube. Connect the bottle to a delivery tube that runs to another bottle (Fig. 7-3). Set up similar demonstrations using seeds which have been killed, as controls. Students will see a substantial rise in the level of water in the delivery tube take place within a few hours. The rise is a measure of the volume of the carbon dioxide produced by the seeds.

Using mercury. A committee of students might want to use this device as a demonstration of the evolution of carbon dioxide. Soak a quantity of seeds and let them begin to germinate. Then place a wad of wet cotton on the bottom of a bottle and add the germinating seeds until the bottle is about one-third full. Seal off one end of a short piece of glass tubing. Into the open end of the tubing insert a pellet of potassium hydroxide; hold this in place with a bit of cotton. As in Fig. 7-4, insert this into a two-hole stopper. Into the other hole insert one end of a delivery tube. Place the stopper in the bottle and seal it with paraffin. Immerse the other end of the delivery tube into a dish of mercury.

As carbon dioxide is produced in respiration, it is absorbed by the potassium hydroxide pellet. As a result, air pressure within the bottle is reduced and normal

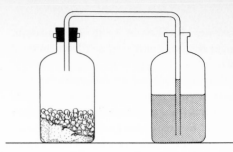

Fig. 7-3 Measuring the CO_2 given off by seeds: it dissolves in the water in the second bottle, and atmospheric pressure pushes water up the tube.

air pressure pushes the mercury up the delivery tube arm. This serves to give an approximate measure of the volume of carbon dioxide produced by germinating seeds.

The negligible amount of carbon dioxide within the bottle at the start of the demonstration can be measured in a control; the same materials are used except that the seeds have been killed.

Using a thistle tube. Soak some wheat seeds, or oat seeds for 24 hours in water and allow to germinate in folds of damp paper. Then fill the bulb of a thistle tube with these germinating seeds. Support the tube upright so that the stem of the tube stands in a strong solution of potassium hydroxide (one stick of caustic potash in ⅔ of a glass of water). This hydroxide will absorb carbon dioxide. Red ink may be added to the liquid to

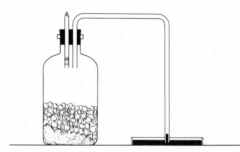

Fig. 7-4 Measuring the CO_2 given off by seeds: the pellet of KOH absorbs CO_2; as the air pressure is reduced, mercury rises in the tube.

increase visibility in a large classroom. Cover the bulb with a glass plate and seal with Vaseline (Fig. 7-5). Prepare several of these devices, using different types of seeds, as well as killed seeds as controls.

Within a few hours students may watch the rise of potassium hydroxide solution in the tube. In about 6 hours the liquid will rise halfway up the tube. This serves to demonstrate that some gas in the thistle tube has been absorbed and that more carbon dioxide has been formed. The carbon dioxide in turn was absorbed by the potassium hydroxide.

Burette technique. This technique is similar to the previous one. Place some germinating seeds into the constricted end of a 100-cc burette. Hold them in place with wet cotton. Now invert the burette into a large test tube of saturated potassium hydroxide solution (Fig. 7-6). Adjust the level of the solution to the zero mark. When the burette clamp is closed, there will be 100 cc of air in contact with the germinating seeds. Students might prepare a control with dead seeds or without seeds. (Saturated KOH is corrosive.)

There will soon be a difference in the rise of potassium hydroxide in the two burettes. This will be a rough measure of the carbon dioxide evolved in respiration, since carbon dioxide was absorbed by the hydroxide.

Respiration chamber. The demonstration using a series of bottles with a respiration chamber and an aspirator as described for animal respiration (Fig. 6-5) applies here as well. Fill the respiration chamber two-thirds full of germinating seeds. Then prepare a control with either killed seedlings or none.

Production of carbon dioxide by fruits and tubers

You may want to use the apparatus shown in Figs. 6-5 and 7-1 to show pro-

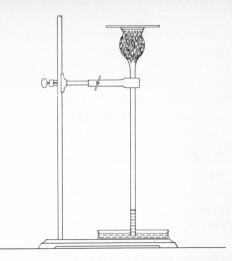

Fig. 7-5 Measuring the CO_2 given off by seeds: it is absorbed by the KOH solution in the dish; as the air pressure is reduced, liquid rises in the tube.

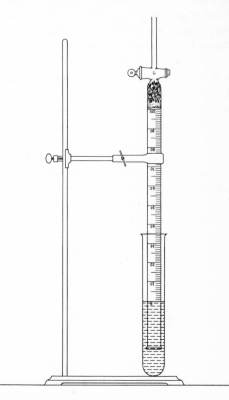

Fig. 7-6 Measuring the CO_2 given off by seeds: it is absorbed by the saturated KOH solution in the test tube; the volume can be read from the burette.

duction of carbon dioxide in respiration of tissues of tubers such as potatoes, and in fruits like apples. Place a portion of the apple or potato in a jar or tube, and line the jar with moist filter paper. Then use an indicator or limewater to show that carbon dioxide is evolved in respiration.

Production of carbon dioxide by fungi

You may want to use a rich culture of yeast or bread mold to demonstrate the evolution of carbon dioxide.

Such forms as the edible mushroom (*Agaricus campestris*) give excellent results, because they do not readily decay. Prepare the demonstration as in Fig. 7-1. Within an hour enough carbon dioxide to change brom thymol blue to yellow (or to make limewater milky) is produced. Include a control in which the organisms are omitted.

Role of yeast in bread-making. Students may want to show that dough rises because bubbles of carbon dioxide are trapped within it. Mix flour with water, place this in a jar, and sprinkle the paste with yeast (Fig. 7-7a). The indicator (brom thymol blue or limewater in the cylinder) will show the evolution of carbon dioxide. (The addition of sugar to the dough will speed up fermentation.)

Prepare a similar jar; this time thoroughly *mix* the yeast with the dough.

Note how quickly the dough rises (temperature is a factor); but the limewater or brom thymol blue does not react readily since the carbon dioxide is trapped within the dough. Now arrange a glass rod as in Fig. 7-7b so that the dough can be punctured as it rises. Place the rod within a glass tube and make the connection airtight with clay or with wired rubber tubing. Then fit the glass tube containing the rod into the rubber stopper. (Prepare a control similar in all details except that yeast is not added.) Why does the indicator change when the dough is punctured?

Fermentation tubes. Fill the closed tubular portion of a fermentation tube with a dilute solution of molasses (Fig. 7-8a). Leave the bulb side partly empty. Prepare another fermentation tube in which yeast is added to the molasses. Then plug with cotton and keep the tubes in a warm place. Within 24 hours students may see bubbles of gas rise in the fermentation tube which contains yeast cells. Now a small piece of potassium hydroxide may be put in the liquid, where it will soon dissolve. Watch the liquid rise again into the tubular arm as the carbon dioxide gas is absorbed by the caustic potash.

Alcohol production by yeast cells. Fermentation results in two main products, carbon dioxide and alcohol. This method indicates the production of alcohol. Since

 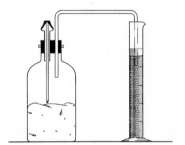

Fig. 7-7 (a) CO_2 is given off by yeast sprinkled on top of a flour-and-water "dough"; (b) the CO_2 given off in a well-mixed "dough" of flour, water, and yeast is trapped; punching the dough several times with the glass rod will release it.

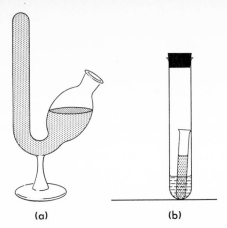

(a)   (b)

Fig. 7-8 (a) Fermentation tube containing yeast cells in a molasses (or 10% glucose) solution; (b) yeast culture growing under anaerobic conditions—oxygen is removed from the outer tube by potassium pyrogallic acid.

fermentation proceeds rapidly under anaerobic conditions the apparatus shown in Fig. 7-8b may be preferable to fermentation tubes.

Prepare a rich culture of yeast plants by adding yeast cells to a solution made of equal parts of molasses and water, or to a 10 per cent glucose solution. Let the yeast culture grow for at least 24 hours, and then pour it into the inner tube in the diagram. Then fill the outer tube to the level indicated with alkaline pyrogallic acid (prepared by mixing equal volumes of 5 per cent solutions of pyrogallic acid and potassium hydroxide) or any other oxygen absorbent; stopper tightly. From time to time, test the contents of the inner tube for the presence of alcohol, as follows.

Testing for alcohol production by yeasts. In anaerobic respiration or fermentation, yeast plants ultimately break down sugars into carbon dioxide and alcohol. The odor of alcohol is evident in both of the previous demonstrations. If the odor of alcohol is not characteristic in itself, the presence of ethyl alcohol may be detected in this way: Pour about 5 cc of the fermenting molasses or glucose solution into a clean test tube. To this add 4 drops of a 10 per cent solution of sodium hydroxide. Then add iodine potassium iodide solution (Lugol's solution, p. 409), drop by drop, until the liquid remains faintly yellow. Let it stand for 2 minutes and then shake the tube. Note the separation of a layer of iodoform settling to the bottom of the tube.

Absorption of oxygen by living plants

There are many ways to show that oxygen is absorbed by a living plant.

Oxygen absorption by germinating seeds

Students might prepare this demonstration (Fig. 7-9). Place a quantity of germinating seeds on a cushion of moist absorbent cotton in a 250-cc bottle so that it is about one-third full of seeds. Make the long arm of the delivery tube about 50 cm long. Insert the short arm into a one-hole stopper, with a small vial of 10 per cent potassium hydroxide suspended from it by means of a string and a bent pin, and stopper the bottle. Immerse the

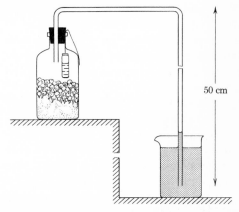

50 cm

Fig. 7-9 Indirect measure of the oxygen absorbed by germinating seeds: the CO_2 evolved by the seeds is removed by KOH in the vial from the atmosphere of the bottle. Since the seeds absorb as much O_2 as they evolve CO_2, the decrease in pressure, indicated by a rise of water in the tube, is an indirect measure of O_2 absorbed.

other end of the tube in a beaker of water colored with a few drops of red ink.

Then set up a control using killed seeds. Keep both preparations at the same temperature. Potassium (or sodium) hydroxide absorbs carbon dioxide immediately, and since there is an approximate 1:1 ratio between the amount of oxygen taken in and the carbon dioxide given off in respiration, the rate of oxygen consumption will be indicated by the water level in the delivery tube.[1]

Or students might set up the demonstration in Fig. 7-10 using sprouting seeds held in place with moist cotton. The graduated cylinder should then be inverted into potassium or sodium hydroxide. Prepare a duplicate demonstration using killed seeds. As in the previous preparation, seedlings absorb oxygen and an equal quantity of carbon dioxide is produced. Here, the carbon dioxide is absorbed by the hydroxide, which rises in the cylinder.

Burning splint. In this method you may want to show that oxygen is used up in a container in which germinating seeds are growing. The decrease in oxygen content may be shown by testing with a burning splint. Soak bean, wheat, or oat seeds or corn kernels. Fill several jars about one-third full of germinating seeds; cork the jars securely. Also prepare replicas as controls using seeds which have been killed with formalin.

After 48 hours, insert a burning splint into the bottles. The splint will burn more brightly in the control bottles than in the jars containing living germinating seeds.

This demonstration is generally unsatisfactory because there is little difference in the glow of the burning splint in the two jars.

Using fermentation tubes. Place a quantity of soaked seeds (wheat, oats, or corn kernels) into the tube-part of each of four

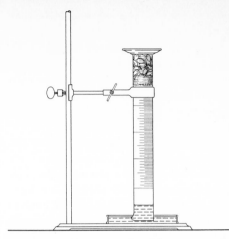

Fig. 7-10 Measuring the CO_2 generated by germinating seeds: it is absorbed by the KOH solution, and air pressure forces liquid up the graduated cylinder.

fermentation tubes. Then fill this tube-part with water.[2] Generate carbon dioxide and let it pass into the first tube; add oxygen to the second tube, and nitrogen (if available) to the third tube. Let the gases displace nearly all the water in each tube. Then insert a rubber stopper into the open end under water. Take out the tube, placing the corked end into a beaker containing water so that air is prevented from entering. In the control tube, the fourth tube, seeds are placed in a small quantity of water and the fermentation tube is stoppered. Within 24 hours, germination will be found in the control tube and in the tube containing oxygen.

Comparing oxidation in different seeds

A small group of students might undertake a project to compare the quantity of oxygen absorbed by seeds rich in fats as contrasted with seeds rich in starch. In other words, is there a 1:1 ratio of oxygen to carbon dioxide when fats are oxidized? For instance, students might germinate

[1] P. B. Leach, *Practical Botany,* Methuen (Wiley), New York, 1935.

[2] L. J. Clarke, *Botany as an Experimental Science,* Oxford U. Press, New York, 1931.

soy beans and wheat seeds which have been soaked for 24 hours in advance. Prepare the device shown in Fig. 7-11, using soy beans (rich in fats) in one setup, and wheat seeds (rich in starch) in the second. Put mercury into the U-tube in each preparation and seal the bottles so they are airtight. Students should observe some differences in 24 hours. Do the two arms of the U-tube remain about the same in the case of the wheat seeds? This would indicate that the volume of oxygen consumed equals the volume of carbon dioxide given off. What happens in the device using soy beans? The additional amount of oxygen consumed is indicated by the higher column of mercury in the tube nearer the bottle.

Oxygen absorption by aquatic plants

A simple modification of Warburg's manometric method previously used to show that oxygen is given off in photosynthesis (p. 23, using a U-tube) may be used here to show that oxygen is absorbed during respiration.

Effect on seedlings of oxygen shortage

Using potassium pyrogallate to remove oxygen. Soaked oat, wheat, or other small seeds or corn kernels should be placed on moist absorbent cotton in a jar or wrapped in a small cheesecloth bag, tied with string and suspended as shown in Fig. 7-12. Prepare two demonstrations. Pour fresh potassium pyrogallate solution (prepared by mixing equal volumes of 5 per cent solutions of pyrogallic acid and potassium hydroxide) into the two bottles. Then prepare two replicas as controls, using water instead of potassium pyrogallate solution. Students may observe the small amount of germination in the bottles which contain

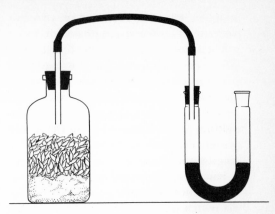

Fig. 7-11 Germinating seeds consume oxygen: apparatus for measuring the volume.

potassium pyrogallate. There may be a small residue of air containing oxygen trapped within the seed coats so that a little germination occurs; yet there should be an appreciable difference in germination between the jars with water and those with potassium pyrogallate solution.

Drowning the seedlings. The fact that drowned seedlings stop growing is a very indirect kind of evidence for the lack of oxygen. (Although this approach is described in the literature, it is not satisfactory to our way of thinking.) In this method, bean seeds or corn kernels are germinated until the root tips are about

Fig. 7-12 Germinating seeds need oxygen: seeds suspended over potassium pyrogallate solution should not grow.

10 mm long. Then the root tips are marked at uniform lengths with India ink. Test tubes or jars are lined with blotting paper, and the seedlings are inserted between the blotter and the glass walls. Let several jars stand with seeds drowned by water. In other jars, only moisten the blotting paper. Then cover all the jars to prevent evaporation. Measure the root-tip lengths after 1 day and after 2 days.

Immersing the seedlings in mercury. In this method mercury is used to displace air which would otherwise be available to seedlings. Completely fill a large test tube with mercury and invert this into a dish of mercury; fill another test tube nearly full with mercury and invert it into the same dish. By this procedure, the second test tube contains a small amount of air. Now support both test tubes with clamps on a stand (Fig. 7-13).

Students will need peas or beans germinated until the roots are about 25 mm long. After first removing the outer seed coats (to eliminate air pockets) measure the lengths of the roots. Then insert six of the seedlings into each of the two inverted test tubes so that they float to the top. Place this preparation in a warm place and measure each root after 24 hours. Students should learn from the results that seeds which receive some air show greater growth.

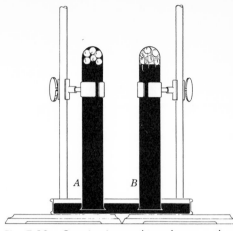

Fig. 7-13 Germinating seeds need oxygen: those in tube B, with an air pocket, should grow; those in tube A should not.

Overcrowding. You may want students to soak a large quantity of beans, peas, corn kernels, or oat seeds in water. Place some of the seeds in a small bottle, then pack the remainder of the bottle with moist sand so that every space is filled; stopper this bottle tightly. Then prepare another bottle with about the same amount of soaked seeds. Fill this bottle only halfway with moist sand; do not seal this bottle.

Students may compare the degree of germination of seeds in both bottles after the bottles have been exposed to the same temperature conditions for a few days.

Production of heat by living plants

The evolution of considerable heat by seedlings during respiration may be demonstrated by preventing its escape, and noting the substantial difference in temperature (Fig. 7-14). Fill a pint vacuum bottle nearly full with germinating beans, corn grains, peas, wheat, or oats on a bed of moist absorbent cotton. Insert a thermometer through a one-hole stopper and seal it in place with modeling clay to make it airtight. Prepare a control containing seedlings killed in formalin. Unless the seeds in the control are properly killed and disinfected (p. 97), there will be evidence of temperature change due to heat generated through bacterial decay.

When Thermos bottles are not available an effective substitute can be made by using two bottles with thermometers as above (one experimental, one control) and packing them into rockwool insulation or excelsior to provide insulation.

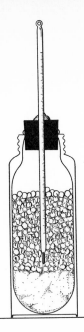

Fig. 7-14 Germinating seeds generate heat: the thermometer in this vacuum bottle should show a temperature rise within 24 hours; the same setup, without seeds or with killed seeds, should not.

CAPSULE LESSONS

Ways to get started in class

7-1. Recall this previous activity and introduce a new relationship. Seal an aquarium plant and a snail in a large test tube (p. 86). Have students describe the oxygen–carbon dioxide cycle. Extend this to life on land as well as plant-animal relationships in a lake or ocean.

7-2. Prepare a demonstration ahead of time, using elodea plants and brom thymol blue in test tubes placed in the dark (p. 96). Ask students to explain why the brom thymol blue turned yellow in the dark. This should raise many questions. Then have students set it up again as an experiment with controls. This may help clarify one difference between photosynthesis (in which carbon dioxide is absorbed) and oxidation, or respiration (in which carbon dioxide is given off).

7-3. Provide the class with jars and germinating seeds. You may want to ask students to design an experiment, after they have established the fact that respiration may be measured by testing either the amount of oxygen used or the amount of carbon dioxide given off.

7-4. You may want to begin a lesson with a demonstration showing that growing seedlings give off enough heat to raise the temperature above that of the room. Elicit from students a discussion of the process going on: respiration. What materials are used? What happens when food is oxidized?

7-5. You may want to begin with a film such as *Seeds and How They Grow* (William Cox Enterprises). Or show *Life of a Plant* or *Plant Growth* (both by Encyclopaedia Britannica). Use the film to focus attention on the life functions of plants.

7-6. Begin with any of the demonstrations described in this chapter.

PEOPLE, PLACES, AND THINGS

Have you discovered the people in neighboring schools, colleges, experimental stations, and nurseries who can help you when assistance is needed? Nurserymen, for instance, can supply young plants.

BOOKS AND PAMPHLETS

These are only a few of the books which are pertinent to the work discussed in this chapter. These and many other references classified by subject and with complete bibliographical data are given in the Bibliography at the end of the book.

Bonner, J., and A. Galston, *Principles of Plant Physiology,* 1952.

Gibbs, R. D., *Botany: An Evolutionary Approach,* 1950.

James, W. O., *An Introduction to Plant Physiology,* 1955.

Meyer, B., and D. Anderson, *Plant Physiology,* 1952.

Sinnott, E., and K. Wilson, *Botany: Principles and Problems,* 1955.

Stiles, W., *An Introduction to the Principles of Plant Physiology,* 1950.

FILMS AND FILMSTRIPS

This partial list is intended only as a guide toward film and filmstrip selection. Refer to the more complete listing at the end of the book where films are classified by subject and where a key to abbreviations and addresses of distributors are given. The cost of film rental, of course, is subject to change. Films are sound and black and white unless otherwise specified.

Life Cycle of a Plant (f), UWF, $2.00.

Life of a Plant (f, c), EBF, $4.00.
Life of Plants (f), UWF, $1.50.
Plant Growth (f), EBF, $2.50.

FREE AND INEXPENSIVE MATERIALS

This is only a partial listing of free and inexpensive materials available to the teacher at this time. A more complete listing, including addresses, is given at the end of the book. Many of these materials are distributed to teachers without charge. Where there is a small fee, the cost is indicated, although the prices are subject to change. While we recommend the material for use in the classroom, we do not necessarily sponsor the products advertised.

Turtox News (monthly), *Turtox Service Leaflets* (set of "How to Do" pamphlets), General Biological Supply House, Inc.

Ward's Natural Science Bulletin (periodical), Ward's Natural Science Establishment.

The Welch Biology and General Science Digest (periodical), Welch Scientific Co.

Some Applications of Atomic Energy in Plant Science (use of radioisotopes in study of life activities) U.S. Atomic Energy Commission.

CHAPTER 8

Growth of plants

The rate of growth of leaves, stems, roots, and of the total plant may be recorded from day to day. When the *amount* of growth is plotted against *time,* a typical sigmoid growth curve results (Fig. 8-1).

In this chapter several aspects of plant growth are described. First, a number of ways to germinate seeds is given. Second, these methods are followed by specific techniques for measuring the growth of parts of plants, including the regions of growth in leaves, stems, and roots of seedlings. Third, a description is presented of the mineral requirements of plants along with certain culture solutions. This is an introduction to hydroponics (the soil-less growth of plants). Fourth, there is an introduction to some of the simpler techniques for a study of plant hormones.

And fifth, a brief description is given of some practical aspects of the study of the growth of bacteria and the effect of antibiotics. These last are especially excellent for class demonstration.

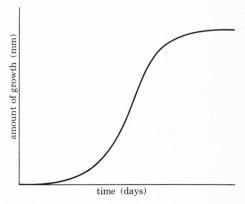

Fig. 8-1 Most growing things follow a sigmoid curve like this one.

Growth of seedlings in relation to stored food

Generally, the growth of seedlings is dependent upon the amount of stored food available to the embryos. You may want students to germinate several bean seeds which have been soaked in water overnight. When the rudimentary roots, or radicles, become visible, students may

select several seeds at the same stage of germination and treat them as follows: (a) remove one cotyledon from several seeds; (b) remove both cotyledons from other seeds; (c) as controls, leave the cotyledons intact on some seeds. Then suspend the seeds on a wire mesh with

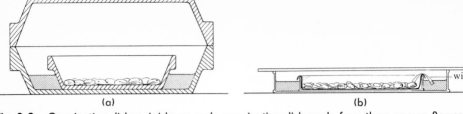

Fig. 8-2 Germination dishes: (a) large-scale germinating dish made from three porous flowerpot saucers; (b) smaller dish made from glass dishes, a blotting-paper lining for the smaller one, and a filter-paper wick dipping into the water.

their roots in nutrient solution (p. 111), or plant them all in clean, moist sand. Students may watch their growth at regular intervals over the next few weeks.

This preliminary classroom or laboratory activity might serve to stimulate further activities which are developed in this chapter. Some of these questions will arise: Can we substitute nutrient solutions in place of the stored food in the seeds? How do roots grow? What substances are responsible for the growth of roots or the bending of stems? How do leaves grow into different patterns? What environmental factors affect the growth rate of parts of plants? Can we speed up the growth of roots on cuttings by using growth substances? What conditions do bacteria need to grow? How does penicillin affect the growth of bacteria?

Ways to germinate seeds

Seeds may be sown on paraffined cheesecloth drawn taut over a container of water, or in moist sand, sawdust, excelsior, or sphagnum moss. Methods vary with the purpose and the type of seeds. Several methods which have proven successful are described.

Growing seeds to show root hairs. This is a rapid method for use by students in the classroom. Students might line several test tubes with wet blotting paper, and place radish seeds between the wet blotter and the glass walls of the test tubes. Enough test tubes for the entire class may be prepared. In a few days, students may examine the root hairs with a hand lens without disturbing their growth. Occasionally, add a few drops of water to the bottom of the test tubes; this will be absorbed in the blotter by capillarity.

When seeds larger than radish seeds are used, soak them first and pin the germinating seeds to the cork of a vial, one seedling per vial. When the vials stand upright the root with the root hairs grows down into the vial (Fig. 3-1).

Large-scale germination. Prepare a germinating dish with two 12-inch porous flower-pot saucers and a smaller one (Fig. 8-2a). Wash all the porous plates in hot water at the start to reduce fungus growth. Place the smaller plate containing germinating seeds inside one of the 12-inch plates; fill the peripheral moat with water. Now cover the large plate with the other 12-inch plate.

In some cases, you may want a glass germinating dish so that growth stages of seedlings are visible without removing the cover. As shown in Fig. 8-2b, fit a small flat dish within a larger glass dish and fill the outer moat with water. Then line the inner dish with moistened filter paper; two pieces of blotting paper are bent from the inner dish into the water of the outer dish to form a wick. Cover the dishes with a plate of glass or a bell jar. The whole device may be covered with dark paper, aluminum foil, or heavy cloth to aid germination.

Seed viability test. This is a rapid method[1] for testing large numbers of seeds. The usual germination tests take up to 10 days, but the use of the indicator 2,3,5-triphenyl tetrazolium chloride reduces the test time to 24 hours or less. Soak 100 barley seeds in water for about 18 hours and then germinate 50 seeds on moist filter paper in Petri dishes kept in the dark. Cut the remaining 50 seeds in half lengthwise; cut through the embryo plants as well. Place these seeds in Petri dishes. Add a 0.1 to 1.0 per cent solution of the tetrazolium chloride to the dishes so that the seeds are just covered. Let them soak for 2 to 4 hours in the dark at 20° C.

The tetrazolium salt is colorless, water-soluble, and nontoxic. By chemical or phytochemical action this indicator is reduced to triphenylformazan, an insoluble bright-red dye. As germination starts, chemical action changes the colorless solution into the insoluble red dye. The viable seeds may be identified by the staining of at least half of the scutellum, the whole of the shoot, and the regions where the adventitious roots will later develop (Fig. 8-3).

Some days later, have students compare the number of viable seedlings which germinated in the untreated dish with the number obtained in the rapid test using the indicator.

Sterilization of surfaces of seeds. The conditions favorable for germination of

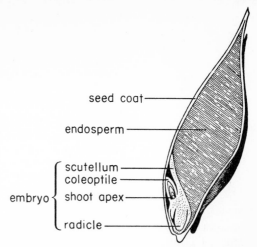

Fig. 8-3 Lengthwise section through a barley seed. (From L. Machlis & J. G. Torrey, *Plants in Action*, W. H. Freeman, 1956.)

seeds also enhance bacterial or mold germination. To prevent this, the surfaces of the seeds may be sterilized; three methods are suggested here.

1. Place seeds in a dilute formalin solution (1:500) for about 20 minutes. Then rinse off in water.

2. In a glass container prepare a 1 per cent solution of bichloride of mercury (1 gm to 100 cc of water). (*Caution:* This mercury salt is very poisonous to mucous membranes. Avoid having students handle it.) Soak the seeds in this solution for about 10 minutes and rinse in water.

3. Soak the seeds for about 15 minutes in a 1 per cent solution of chlorine, prepared by adding 21 gm of pure sodium hypochlorite to 100 cc of water. Or use Clorox (5 per cent sodium hypochlorite); add 1 part of Clorox to 4 parts of water.

Measuring the growing regions of a plant

Finding the region of greatest growth in roots. Germinate bean, pea, or lupine seeds in a germinating dish. When the

[1] H. Bennett, ed., *Chemical Formulary*, Chemical Publishing Co., New York, 1951; L. Machlis and J. Torrey, *Plants in Action*, Freeman, San Francisco, 1956.

rudimentary roots are about 1 inch long, mark equal intervals along the length of the root with India ink. To do this, students should first dry the roots with blotting paper, then place a ruler alongside the root and mark off intervals ⅛-inch

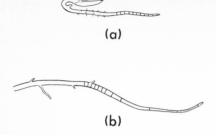

(a)

(b)

Fig. 8-4 Demonstrating the regions of growth in a young root: (a) marked root; (b) same root after growth.

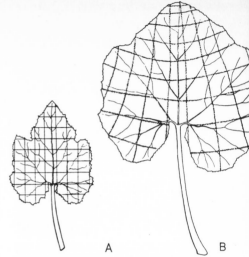

A   B

Fig. 8-5 Growth of a squash leaf: When the leaf was as shown in A it was marked with India ink into equal squares; note that in B all squares have increased in size, but some more than others. (From R. M. Holman & W. W. Robbins, *A Textbook of General Botany*, 4th ed., Wiley, 1939.)

or 1 mm apart (Fig. 8-4). Replace the seeds in the germinating dish and examine after 24 hours, 48 hours, and so on.

Growth of stems. Shoots of seedlings of beans, oats, wheat, or peas are suitable for marking with India ink. Blot the stems dry and mark intervals ⅛-inch apart.

Growth of leaves. Germinate bean or pea seeds in moist sand or sawdust. When small leaves are visible, flatten them against a glass plate or similar support which has been marked off into boxes like graph paper. Trace these equidistant markings on the leaves with India ink (Fig. 8-5). Examine the leaves from day to day and watch the changes in the pattern of the boxes.

An interesting variation of this demonstration may be undertaken as a project. A student might grow these seedlings with marked roots, stems, and leaves, under different colored lights, or with different conditions of moisture and atmospheric pressure.

Growth in height of total plant. Use a ruler to measure the total vertical growth of a plant. For more accurate work you may want to use an auxanometer (Fig. 8-6). Measure growth in width of stems or roots with a caliper. Also weigh the total plant; an increase in weight is an index of growth. (If a truer index of growth is desired, the dry weight of the plant should be taken.)

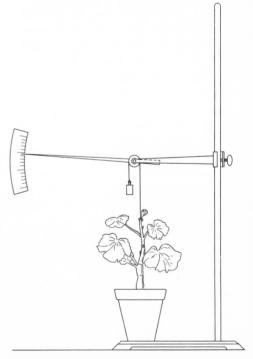

Fig. 8-6 Auxanometer, for measuring vertical growth of a plant.

Mineral nutrition in plants

While green plants can manufacture food (simple sugars) in photosynthesis, for growth of the plant certain minerals are necessary. As a group project, students may grow plants in soil-less cultures (hydroponics). They may also want to show the effects upon plants of a deficiency of certain minerals.

Although the term "hydroponics" was originally applied to water-culture methods, the term has been extended to water, sand, and gravel cultures. While detailed care is not possible in the classroom, emphasis may be given to the need for balanced solutions for the growth of plants. In our experience, these activities are successful if the following conditions are observed.

Provision should be made for roots to receive adequate aeration (by using an aerator pump). Glazed crocks are excellent containers; enameled pails may also be used. Metal cans or Mason jars (soft glass) may be used if a paraffin or asphaltum lining is applied to the metal or glass to prevent the solution from making contact with the fairly soluble surface. Glass jars may be painted black or covered with black oilcloth or paper to inhibit the growth of algae in the solution.

Growing seedlings in solution

Begin with a simple method successful with small fast-growing seeds, especially cereal plants, which require little support.

To prepare support for the seedlings several methods are useful. You may want to immerse a layer of cheesecloth or mosquito netting in hot paraffin and spread it across the top of a container of fluid. Allow a little slack in the center to dip into the solution. (This depression is where the seeds will be planted.) Other times, you may prefer to add sterile sand to the bottom of the container. This gives some support to plants rooted in the sand. Or you might bore holes into a wooden block (or cork), which can be fitted over a container to give support to stems (Fig. 8-7).

Make a more substantial support for larger plants from zinc (or galvanized iron) mesh troughs. These must be given several coats of paraffin or asphaltum to prevent toxicity. You may try to use nontoxic stainless steel mesh. As shown (Fig. 8-8), shape ¼-inch mesh into a trough with flanges to support it against the sides of the jar.

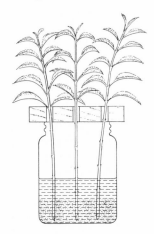

Fig. 8-7 Seedlings or cuttings growing in glass jar containing a layer of sterile sand and nutrient solution; plants are supported in holes in wooden block or cork.

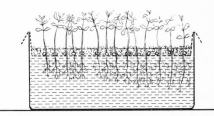

Fig. 8-8 Seedlings bedded in glass wool or excelsior in a paraffined zinc mesh trough; roots grow down into nutrient solution.

Fig. 8-9 Single plant or cutting grown in low porous flowerpot immersed in container of nutrient solution.

Most plants need a surface area of about 4 square inches of nutrient solution and about 2 square inches of air space. When large numbers of seedlings are planted in crocks, use a fish-tank aeration pump to provide a stream of air through the solutions. Other specialized devices to ensure aeration and circulation of nutrient solutions are described in many of the texts specializing in this area; the text by Ellis and Swaney gives many methods (see listing at the end of this chapter).

First cover the mesh trough with a 2-inch layer of straw, glass wool, coarse sawdust, excelsior, or sphagnum moss; plant the seedlings in this. As a preliminary step, you might want to test the possible toxicity of the bedding by first germinating some seeds in the specific material you plan to use.

Use enough solution to cover half of the roots of the seedlings. Then cover the other half of the roots with another 2-inch layer of bedding to exclude light. This also provides a moist air space around the roots. Keep the jars in medium light. As the plants grow, support them with stands. Change the nutrient solution weekly.

Growing cuttings in solution

When single plants are used, plant them in wide, porous flower pots as shown in Fig. 8-9. Wash the pot thoroughly in hot water. Choose a jar into which 2 inches of the pot will fit. Fill the jar with the nutrient solution and fit the pot into this. Plant the cutting in the pot in excelsior, glass wool, or sphagnum moss. As the cutting grows, supports may be made of sections of plywood through which holes have been bored. Instead of wood supports you may find it useful to make supports for cuttings by molding paraffin sheets to fit as covers on the pot; then make holes in the paraffin by means of a hot iron rod.

Seedlings or cuttings need not be grown in solution alone; they can be grown in coarse sand cultures. For this method, use a mixture of peat moss (about 30 per cent by volume) and clean sand. Peat moss (sphagnum) retains moisture and also reduces the alkalinity of the medium. Fill a small flower pot with the sand–peat moss mixture and fit it into a container of solution. Run glass wool, placed in contact with the roots of the plants, through the drainage hole in the flower pot, into the nutrient solution. This wick transports nutrient solution to the roots with less evaporation than would result if you watered the sand from the top of the mixture.

Although most plants can be grown by these methods in the classroom, certain plants are especially resistant to poor environmental conditions. Good results should be forthcoming with wheat, rye, corn, radish, sunflower, castor beans, peas, beans, pepos, tomatoes, and potatoes. *Precaution:* Avoid growing these plants in a laboratory where illuminating gas or bottled gas is used, since this causes wilting and loss of leaves.

Some nutrient solutions

Plants seem to have a wide tolerance for different salts, so there is actually no one solution of nutrient salts which serves all plants.

Some of these solutions date back to the original ones of Knop, Sachs, and Pfeffer, which were developed nearly a hundred years ago. Other solutions show modifications which include varying quantities of trace elements. Some trial-and-error activity may be needed to learn which of these solutions is the most fruitful in a specific school situation.

KNOP'S SOLUTION. Weigh out the following materials and dissolve them in a liter of water.

	grams
$Ca(NO_3)_2 \cdot 4H_2O$	0.8
KNO_3	0.2
KH_2PO_4	0.2
$MgSO_4 \cdot 7H_2O$	0.2
$FePO_4$	trace

SACHS' SOLUTION. Dissolve these salts in 1 liter of water. (The calcium phosphate is only partially soluble.)

	grams
KNO_3	1.0
$NaCl$	0.5
$CaSO_4$	0.5
$MgSO_4$	0.5
$Ca_3(PO_4)_2$	0.5
$FeCl_3$ (1 % solution)	trace (one drop)

PFEFFER'S SOLUTION. Weigh out and dissolve in 1 liter of water the following salts. (This is similar to Knop's solution.)

	grams
$Ca(NO_3)_2$	0.8
KNO_3	0.2
KH_2PO_4	0.2
$MgSO_4 \cdot 7H_2O$	0.2
KCl	0.2
$FeCl_3$	trace

SHIVE'S SOLUTION. Dissolve these salts in 1 liter of water. Iron and phosphate salts should be added first to the water, since they precipitate readily. (Enough of the minerals will remain in the solution, however.)

$Ca(NO_3)_2 \cdot 4H_2O$	1.23 gm
KH_2PO_4	2.45 gm
$MgSO_4 \cdot 7H_2O$	3.70 gm
$FePO_4$ (0.5 % solution)	1 cc

HOAGLAND'S SOLUTION. Weigh out these salts and dissolve them in 1 liter of water.

	grams
$Ca(NO_3)_2 \cdot 4H_2O$	0.95
KNO_3	0.61
$MgSO_4 \cdot 7H_2O$	0.49
$NH_4H_2PO_4$	0.12
ferric tartrate	0.005

Agricultural experimental stations may vary the ingredients of some of these well-known solutions. Yet most of the nutrient solutions contain six of the essential elements for plant growth: phosphorus, nitrogen, sulfur, potassium, calcium, and magnesium.

Most workers in this field advise the addition of trace elements to all the nutrient solutions. These trace elements needed in minute quantity include boron, manganese, copper, zinc, and probably molybdenum. Curtis and Clark recommend the addition of 1 cc of Haas and Reed's "A to Z solution" per liter of nutrient solution. This should fulfill the requirement of trace elements for plant growth.

HAAS AND REED'S A TO Z SOLUTION. Weigh out these ingredients and dissolve in 1 liter of water.

	grams
H_3BO_3	0.6
$MnCl_2 \cdot 4H_2O$	0.4
$ZnSO_4$	0.05
$CuSO_4 \cdot 5H_2O$	0.05
$Al_2(SO_4)_3$	0.05
KI	0.03
KBr	0.03
$Co(NO_3)_2 \cdot 6H_2O$	0.05
$LiCl$	0.03
TiO_2	0.03
$SnCl_2 \cdot 2H_2O$	0.03
$NiSO_4 \cdot 6H_2O$	0.05

Acidity of solutions. Students may want to learn to check the pH of the solution with an indicator (as described on p. 406), pH meter, or Hydrion pH paper. Most plants grow best within a range between 4.5 and 6.5 (acid); a pH over 7 (alkaline) may cause plant growth to be retarded. Further, when the solution is slightly acid, iron salts are more soluble. Check the pH every few days, since the solution may become alkaline as nitrogen-bearing ions are absorbed. If potassium ions are absorbed rapidly, sulfate ions accumulate and produce an acid solution.

To avoid these changes in pH, some workers prefer a drip method rather than immersion of the plants directly in the solution. It may be possible to get an intravenous drip bottle like the kind used in hospitals to administer glucose. To make one, fill a bottle with nutrient solution and seal a siphon with a clamp to the stopper. Invert the bottle, and at intervals release the clamp to moisten the bedding in which the plants grow. However, it is easier to change the solution when there is no bedding.

Effect of mineral deficiency

This is a useful group project. Students may prepare a series of containers, each supporting a growing seedling held fast in a one-hole stopper. In each of the containers in the series, students might omit a different salt from the solution. Later on, they may compare the plant growth with the control, plants grown in the normal nutrient solution. They may also want to test the effect of different degrees of acidity on plant growth. For example, while potassium dihydrogen phosphate, KH_2PO_4, gives the solution a slightly acid reaction, potassium monohydrogen phosphate, K_2HPO_4, produces an alkaline solution. What effect do these salts have on plant growth?

There are several valuable keys for identification of nutrient deficiencies of plants. In these keys, the main traits described refer to changes in chlorophyll and types of plant growth. All these observations may be made by students. In addition, the work has a practical application in some school areas. Useful keys may be found in Curtis and Clark's reference and in Stuart Dunn's physiology text (see listing at end of chapter). Color slides showing symptoms of specific mineral deficiencies are available from National Plant Food Institute (see the directory of film and filmstrip producers at the end of the book). Excellent suggestions are given to guide students in preparing apparatus for hydroponics in the book by Ellis and Swaney, 2nd edition (revised by Eastwood).

Effect of darkness upon the growth of seedlings

Light seems necessary for several of the formative processes as well as for photosynthesis. Seedlings in darkness generally grow tall and spindly, because they lack adequate supporting tissue and have long internodes. Most plants do not develop chlorophyll in the dark. Students may test this by growing some bean or pea seedlings in the dark and others in the light. About a week later, the seedlings grown in the light should be sturdier, shorter (since there are short internodes), and greener than the etiolated plants grown in the dark (see Fig. 13-4). A few days of exposure to light should cause the development of chlorophyll in the pale leaves.

Growth-promoting substances in plants

Many substances have been found to affect growth in plants. Individual students, or a group, may want to repeat some of the classic experiments of Went and those of Boysen-Jensen[2] with oat coleoptiles to demonstrate the production

[2] P. Boysen-Jensen, *Growth Hormones in Plants*, McGraw-Hill, New York, 1936.

of hormones from oat tips. These growth-promoting substances *stimulate* the elongation of stems and, conversely, *inhibit* the growth or elongation of cells of roots.

Introductory approach to a project using auxins

Growth of shoots. Students may germinate soaked oat seeds in paper cups of moist sand kept in the dark. When the coleoptiles emerge and are about 1 to 1.5 cm high, cut off some 3 mm of the tips of several with a sharp sterile razor or the edge of a coverslip. Then apply a bit of lanolin paste to the cut surfaces. Decapitate an equal number of coleoptiles; this time apply lanolin to which 0.1 per cent indoleacetic acid has been added. (Prepare this by dissolving 100 mg of indoleacetic acid in 2 cc of absolute ethyl alcohol. Add this to 100 gm of lanolin paste and mix thoroughly so that the auxin is evenly distributed in the paste.[3]) Set aside a third batch of coleoptiles from which the tips are not removed. Place all the shoots (that is, cut tips with lanolin, cut tips with lanolin plus indoleacetic acid, normal tips) near a source of light. After 24 hours, students should measure the angle of curvature in all three sets of plants. Which part of the coleoptile seems to produce a growth-regulating substance? Which part of the coleoptile seems sensitive to light?

Growth of roots. In a similar approach, students may repeat the previously described technique for growing oat seedlings. This time the aim is to show the inhibitory effect of growth-regulating substances on root growth. In this case students should cut off the 2-mm tip of several roots. Prepare untreated roots and treated roots with the lanolin paste and lanolin-plus-auxin preparation, respectively. Then set up the seedlings in

[3] Machlis and Torrey, *op. cit.*

Petri dishes for a geotropism demonstration as shown in Fig. 10-5. Students may observe in subsequent demonstrations that auxins initiate root formation, but in this case, after the root primordia are formed and the roots elongate, then auxin inhibits further growth of roots.

Some students may also plan experiments to find out whether terminal buds produce a substance that inhibits the growth of lateral buds, or they may plan activities to show the effect of leaves on stimulating root formation. Under which conditions does root initiation proceed faster—when stem cuttings have leaves or when the leaves have been removed?

Effect of leaves and buds on the growth of cuttings

Select healthy coleus, geranium, or other herbaceous cuttings which have several internodes. In some, remove all the leaves; in others, remove the terminal buds and the growing tips; in a third group, remove only the lower leaves. Set aside several others as controls. Then compare the rate of root formation after planting the cuttings in moist sand. Better results should be forthcoming if cuttings are grown in nutrient solutions to which thiamine, pyridoxine, and other vitamins of the B group are added.

Students may use soaked seeds—garden beans or lima beans—rather than cuttings. After they have germinated in the dark for about 2 weeks, or until a pair of leaves is formed, cut off the roots, leaving only a stem portion about 8 to 10 cm long. Stand several of these young plants in containers of the following solutions: a nutrient solution such as Shive's or Hoagland's (p. 113) to which micronutrients have been added; nutrient solution plus 0.1 mg of indoleacetic acid; nutrient solution plus 1.0 mg of indoleacetic acid;

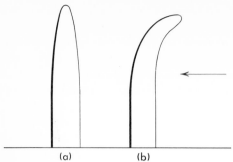

(a)   (b)

Fig. 8-10   Growth hormone applied to one side of shoot (a) causes elongation of cells on that side and consequent bending of the shoot (b). This gives the same effect as if light were shining from the opposite (right) side; light deflects auxins to the shady side.

distilled water. Under which conditions does root initiation occur?

There is some indication that root-forming substances may be made in buds and leaves and transported to the region where new growth is stimulated. Demonstrations may be devised in which there is a unilateral application of growth hormones. One side of the stem (the side to which the hormone has been applied) elongates to a greater extent than the other side (Fig. 8-10). This activity may be tried with the growth-promoting substances to be described. Of course, when the hormones are applied to cuttings they stimulate good root formation.

Growth-promoting substances

The growth-promoting substance which has been shown to be elaborated by the plant is indoleacetic acid. However, there are substitutes for this substance which are less expensive and which are not quickly destroyed by the enzyme systems of plants. Two successful ones are beta-indolebutyric acid and alpha-naphthaleneacetic acid. In fact, small amounts of the latter are active in duplicating the entire range of activities initiated by the growth substances, or hormones, native

to the plants. A general name for these growth-promoting substances is *auxin,* which we shall use for a whole group of chemicals which stimulate growth or elongation of cells, not just one particular chemical compound.

Other related compounds have practical applications. In minute amounts, the herbicide 2,4-D (2,4-dichlorophenoxyacetic acid) is effective in reducing fruit drop in citrus fruits. Yet at higher concentrations it is toxic to broadleaved plants and thus acts as a selective herbicide for such weeds as plantain, dock, thistle, dandelion, and others. In fact, Mitchell and Marth[4] offer explicit directions for preparing large quantities of 2,4-D to be used on lawns or fields. In their text they give tables to indicate the effect of 2,4-D on several hundreds of weeds, crop plants, and ornamental shrubs.

In some communities actual field experiments may be undertaken to compare treated and untreated fields or lawns. Other projects may use refined techniques to find the stage in growth at which the chemicals are most effective. Perhaps some students want to demonstrate the specific physiological effects of auxins; for instance, it is thought that 2,4-D interferes with the sugar transport from leaves to stems and roots.

Rooting preparations may be applied as liquids, powders, or pastes.

Liquid form. Mitchell and Marth[5] suggest these concentrations for soaking stem cuttings. Dissolve ⅓ of a level teaspoon of indolebutyric acid in ½ teaspoon of grain alcohol. Then stir this into 5 quarts of water, making a 0.01 per cent solution. This solution remains effective even after refrigeration for several months. The time needed for soaking stem cuttings

[4] J. Mitchell and P. Marth, *Growth Regulators for Garden, Field, and Orchard,* U. of Chicago Press, Chicago, 1947.

[5] Ibid.

varies with the kind of plant used (from 2- to 24-hour periods). For example, young leafy cuttings may take root quickly after soaking for some 1 to 2 hours in a 0.005 per cent solution of indolebutyric acid. More woody cuttings of herbaceous plants may need a soaking from 6 to 24 hours in the same dilution. Woody cuttings of trees such as dogwood or elm will root best if the leaves are still attached. They should be soaked for 1 to 2 hours in 0.01 per cent indolebutyric acid. Consult the tables in the text mentioned above.

At times you may need a more rapid method. Dip the cuttings (about 1 inch of the stem) into a stronger solution (0.05 to 0.1 per cent for about 1 second. Prepare the 0.1 per cent solution by dissolving 1 ounce by weight of indolebutyric acid in 1 ounce by volume of 50 per cent (100 proof) grain alcohol. Students may make more dilute solutions by adding more of the alcohol.

Powder form. Probably the easiest method is to dip the cuttings in a powder mixture. One method suggests rolling succulent stem cuttings in a mixture of 1 part of growth hormone powder to 1000–5000 parts of clay or talc. Stronger mixtures are needed for stems of woody plants, that is, 1 part to 500.

There are several commercial products on the market called by such names as *Auxilin, Hormodin, Quick-root, Rootgro,* and *Rootone* (among many others). *Hormodin* was developed at the Boyce Thompson Institute for Plant Research and is easy to use. Powder seems simpler to use than the liquid form, although both are available.

This experiment may be useful to demonstrate how growth hormones stimulate rooting. Select several cuttings of privet or willow which are about 4 to 6 inches long. Wet the cut ends of several of the stems in water and dip them into *Hormodin* powder (or a similar preparation). Shake the twigs to remove excess powder; the amount of powder sufficient to produce results is that amount which just adheres to the wet tip. Plant the cuttings, the treated and several untreated controls, in separate pots of sand. Examine the growth of roots each week.

Paste form. A paste is made by mixing indolebutyric acid or other growth-promoting substance in lanolin. The advantage of a paste is that the substance can be placed on a localized region of the plant. First, prepare a solution (0.01 to 0.05 per cent) of a growth-promoting substance such as indolebutyric acid or naphthaleneacetamide. Use the directions given above under "Liquid form" for the preparation of a 0.1 per cent solution and dilute this. Then mix 1 teaspoon of the solution in 1 tablespoon of melted lanolin. The small amount of alcohol used as a solvent for the growth substance evaporates in the heated lanolin. After a thorough mixing, apply this paste with a toothpick to different parts of several plants. For example, apply a circle of paste around the stem, to the upper leaves, to the lower leaves, to cuttings. During the next few weeks, compare the treated parts with untreated controls. Keep both sets of plants under similar conditions of temperature and moisture. Indoleacetic acid may be used in some tests, naphthaleneacetic acid or naphthaleneacetamide in others.

Another easily prepared auxin formula suggested in the literature uses indoleacetic acid in this way. Mix thoroughly 0.1 gm of beta-indoleacetic acid with 1 cc of 70 per cent ethyl alcohol and then add this to 50 gm of hydrous lanolin. A smooth paste should be made. Heat the lanolin a bit. If you wish to have a color for identification, add a pinch of carmine powder to tint the paste red.

In other project work, students may

want to use beta-naphthoxyacetic acid, which is effective in stimulating the formation of parthenocarpic fruits (seedless fruits, formed without pollination).

There are several other growth-regulating substances besides the auxins. The work of Overbeek on the growth-stimulating substances in coconut milk (1941), more recent work on the inhibiting action of lactones, and the exciting work with gibberellin (extracted from a fungus) are beyond the scope of this book. However, students with high-level ability and deep interest in science may find suggestions for individual long-term research projects by examining copies of *Science* or *Biological Abstracts*. In the section on "botany" or "plant physiology" in the *Abstracts* students will come across current research on many of the growth regulators.

Conditions required for growth of bacteria

The optimum factors for bacterial growth may be rediscovered by a committee of students. We are thoroughly acquainted with the conditions bacteria need for growth, and we sometimes forget that for children this work presents a fresh experience in learning. Our emphasis is not so much on the end results, but on providing practice in devising experiments.

Does temperature affect the growth of bacteria? Prepare a nutrient agar medium (p. 380) and plan to plate several Petri dishes (p. 383). Inoculate the cooling nutrient agar with a pure culture of harmless bacteria such as *Bacillus subtilis,* or the bacteria in sour milk. Then plate the Petri dishes so that each dish has about the same quantity of bacteria in the beginning.

Place two or more dishes in a refrigerator at 4° to 8° C. Keep two at room temperature (20° to 25° C), and put two in an incubator at 37° C. If you have a second incubator, keep two more Petri dishes at approximately 55° C. Check the temperature each day with a thermometer and observe the rate of development of visible colonies.

Where are bacteria found? To determine whether bacteria are present optimum conditions for their growth must first be provided.

Prepare nutrient agar medium and plate several sterile Petri dishes (p. 383).

Set aside a few unopened plates as controls. Then carefully lift the cover on each of several Petri dishes and inoculate in the following ways. Into one dish place several coins. Have a student touch the surface of the agar of another dish lightly with his fingertips. In another dish add a film of yoghurt, milk, or sauerkraut. A student might cough into still another dish; expose the remaining dish to the air of the classroom. Incubate all the Petri dishes. Students should recognize that the absence of a full growth of bacterial colonies on a window sill is due not to the lack of bacteria, but to the absence of optimum conditions for growth.[6]

Students may begin to ask how antibiotics interfere with the growth of bacteria, and inquire about the role of antiseptics in affecting bacterial growth.

Effect of penicillin on bacterial growth. Prepare a nutrient agar culture medium (p. 380). While the medium is cooling but still liquid, inoculate it with a pure culture of harmless bacteria. Then plate into several sterile Petri dishes. In this way the agar medium has a uniform distribution of bacteria. Inoculate some culture media with a pure culture of nonpathogenic, Gram-positive bacteria

[6] You may want to read how teachers in Indianapolis Schools do this: *A Guide for Teachers in Junior High Schools,* Science Curriculum Bull. 20, Indianapolis Schools, Ind., 1955.

(*Bacillus lactis* found in milk, or *Bacillus subtilis* found in hay and soil), others with nonpathogenic, Gram-negative bacteria (*Pseudomonas hydrophilus* found on frogs suffering from red leg, *Achromobacter nitrificans* found in soil, or *Escherichia coli* var. *acidilactici*).

Now set two inoculated Petri dishes aside as controls; to the other inoculated dishes add a few discs of filter paper, about ¼ inch in diameter, which have been soaked in a solution of penicillin, prepared by dissolving a penicillin lozenge in cooled, sterile water; or soak the filter paper in a culture of *Penicillium* mold. After incubation of all dishes students should find abundant growth of colonies in the cultures. On the other hand, the Petri dishes containing discs of the antibiotic show a clear zone, a "zone of inhibition" around the discs in some cases. Penicillin shows greater activity against Gram-positive bacteria, mainly cocci.

At times you may want to show a comparison of the action of several antibiotics at one time, or a quantitative difference in the use of a single antibiotic. Bacto-Unidisks[7] are sterile preparations containing specific amounts of commonly used antibiotics and sulfa drugs.

Effect of antiseptics on bacterial growth. Prepare nutrient agar culture medium as just described and inoculate the cooling nutrient medium with a pure culture of harmless bacteria. Then plate the seeded agar in Petri dishes; in this way bacteria are distributed throughout the medium.

Now set aside several dishes as controls. To the other dishes add several selected antiseptics. To some dishes you may add a film of 2 per cent tincture of iodine, or use filter-paper discs which have been soaked in the antiseptic. To others add a film of 70 per cent alcohol, to others a film (or discs) of full-strength *Lysol*, and to others diluted *Lysol*. You may want to include household mercurochrome (1 per cent), as well as witch hazel and 3 per cent hydrogen peroxide.

Incubate all the Petri dishes, including the control dishes. Look for the appearance of colonies. Students may compare the effectiveness of the various antiseptics used by counting the number of colonies and the size of each colony. Which chemicals were effective in a 24- to 36-hour period? Which chemicals were still effective after 72 hours?

Suggestions for student projects

Students of high ability may be guided into long-range projects which can develop into "independent research." Tissue culture techniques require patience and practice to avoid contamination, but these skills open the door to the creative ability of young people. Devising experiments to explore the role of special hormones in photoperiodism is an area of biology rich in problems. Tissue culture methods offer one technique to use in finding answers and raising more problems.

Tissue culture techniques

Some students may want to learn aseptic tissue techniques. In this method the apical tips, about 2 to 5 mm of root tips of seedlings (tomato seedlings are desirable) are removed and transferred under sterile conditions from Petri dishes in which the seedlings are grown into sterile flasks of culture medium. Transfer methods used in bacteriological technique are recommended (see p. 384). Philip White's book is a fine guide for this work and offers suggestions for student work.[8]

[7] Available from Difco Laboratories, Detroit 1, Mich., among other supply houses.

[8] P. White, *The Cultivation of Plant and Animal Cells*, Ronald, New York, 1954.

White's medium is time consuming to prepare but it is necessary; for it contains macronutrients and micronutrients needed for growth. Prepare each of the following five stock solutions, each in 1 liter of distilled water.

SOLUTION 1	grams
$Ca(NO_3)_2$	2.0
KNO_3	0.8
KCl	0.65
NaH_2PO_4	0.165

SOLUTION 2	
$MgSO_4$	36.0

SOLUTION 3[9]	
$MnSO_4$	0.45
$ZnSO_4$	0.15
H_3BO_3	0.15
KI	0.075
$\begin{bmatrix} CuSO_4 \\ Na_2MoO_4 \end{bmatrix}$	$\begin{bmatrix} 0.002 \\ 0.021 \end{bmatrix}$

SOLUTION 4 (MUST BE FRESHLY PREPARED)	
$Fe_2(SO_4)_3$	0.25

SOLUTION 5	
glycine	0.3
thiamin	0.01
pyridoxine	0.01
nicotinic acid	0.05

In preparing White's solution, only small amounts of the stock solutions are used. For example, begin with 500 cc of distilled water; to this add 100 cc of stock solution 1, and 10 cc each of solutions 2, 3, 4, and 5. After these have been thoroughly mixed by shaking, add 20 gm of sucrose and make up the quantity to 1 liter by adding distilled water. Now divide the solution by pouring 50-cc amounts into smaller flasks, plug with cotton, and place in an autoclave for 15 minutes at a pressure of 15 pounds per square inch. These flasks may be stored for a few days in a refrigerator until transfers can be made. Since the solution contains organic compounds the solution cannot be stored indefinitely.

[9] Mo and Cu (as the salts bracketed) have been added by Machlis and Torrey to the original formula developed by White.

Once they have mastered this tissue-culture technique, students may try to grow isolated sections of roots, stems, and leaves in nutrient solutions to examine how differentiation and growth take place.

Photoperiodism

Where space is available, for example a greenhouse or an outdoor plot of ground, students may find out firsthand the effects on flowering in plants when the number of hours of light and dark is altered. For example, they may grow "short day" plants, such as chrysanthemum, ragweed, or poinsettia, which need only about 10 hours of light in every 24 hours in order to flower. These plants need long periods of dark to flower normally; if this dark period is interrupted by even a short exposure to light, the plants remain in a vegetative stage. It is believed that the hormone which controls flowering is made in the leaves and transported to the sites of flower formation. An advanced project for a competent student might involve designing experiments to learn more about the effect of covering leaves, rather than the total plant; the possible effect of covered leaves and exposed leaves on flower development of grafted branches of shrubs or trees; the effect of temperature on photoperiodism.

Similar projects may be undertaken using sturdy "long day" plants (light for 14 hours) like aster or barley plants. Plan to use plants which are about 4 to 5 weeks old and expose them to changed light conditions for a week. Students should provide for controls. Also use tomato plants as examples of plants not affected by fixed periods of light and dark.

Other projects

A study of chlorophyll extracts, or the properties of chlorophyll in transmitted light and in reflected light, can be used for individual study, or as part of a larger project. The separation of carotinoids from the leaves of plants, as well as the types of chlorophyll, may be done with paper chromatography (p. 16).

Committees of students may devise experiments to test which wave lengths of light are most effective for photosynthesis. Small land plants or test tubes of elodea plants (or others) may be covered with different-colored sheets of cellophane. The plants are later tested for starch, as are leaves from control plants kept in sunlight and in the dark. Have students develop a comparison scale for use in making a judgment concerning the amount of starch present in leaves. It will be found that the most active region ranges in the yellow to red region of the spectrum.

Other committees may design experiments using colored cellophane to study the wavelength in which auxin activity is most effective.

Some students may study the causes of dormancy in seeds. They may devise ways to show how dormancy may be broken. Some hard surfaces of seeds may be filed or cut, others placed in acid, and so forth. Controls should be included in these experiments.

In this chapter we have included many aspects of the whole area of growth in plants. Much of this work may be considered extensions of the classwork. Many of the topics in other chapters—reproduction, mitosis, nutrition diseases, photosynthesis, and vegetative propagation—include some aspect of the work described in this chapter. The techniques and the subject areas may be co-ordinated effectively, as the teacher sees fit, into specific classroom learning experiences.

CAPSULE LESSONS
Ways to get started in class

8-1. Many of the activities of this chapter are techniques which are useful in illustrating all the life activities of plants. As such, these skills may be developed through club work, laboratory experiences, or home activities, in the form of projects of one kind or another.

For example, begin with a handful of dried beans and another of germinating beans. You may develop a lesson on respiration and the use of the stored food supply. Or you may ask, what are the characteristics of living things? Are the dried beans living? This is one way to develop the notion of organization of materials in living systems.

Perhaps you may want to show tropisms suggested by students. Or possibly you plan a study of plant functions beginning with seedlings, which are so adaptable for class demonstrations.

8-2. Have students grow seeds of beans, sunflowers, squash, or other plants at home. Show them how to soak and place the seedlings between wet blotters and the glass walls of baby-food jars or other containers. This activity may lead into growth hormones, or a study of the way plant embryos grow, or a study of root hairs and the conduction system of seedlings.

These are the times when a firsthand experience is easier to provide, and more meaningful and exciting, than showing a film of a growing seed. For this is a remote, secondhand experience, far removed from daily living. However, there may be likely times to show time-lapse photography of plant growth.

8-3. If you introduce the concept of a hormone as a substance made in one part of a body which produces an effect in other parts, you will find studies with auxins of plants a fruitful approach to the topic. Have the students offer explanations. Perhaps students will report to the class on some of the classic experiments in the field.

8-4. Introduce the notion that bacteria are present in the air and on the body (also in the body) by having students inoculate prepared Petri dishes. Develop the conditions needed for their growth. Establish from this discussion ways to preserve food, that is, ways to prevent bacteria from growing in our food. For if we know the conditions for bacterial growth, we can protect our food supply by removing at least one of the conditions required for their optimal growth. Students may devise an experiment at home testing the effectiveness of vinegar, sugar, and salts as preservatives (see p. 10).

8-5. In lessons on control of diseases, demon-strate the effect of penicillin on the growth of bacteria; use Gram-positive and Gram-negative organisms. Also devise ways to test the effective-ness of antiseptics. Compare antiseptics and antibiotics and the role they play in control of diseases.

PEOPLE, PLACES, AND THINGS

Is there an agricultural experimental station, a plant nursery, or a botanical garden in your community? You may want to plan a field trip to learn the kind of research work going on with plant hormones, photoperiodism, aspects of soil-saving and conservation, the soil-less growth of plants, and so on.

Students may glean ideas for individual research projects which may be carried on at home or on the school grounds (p. 265). Possibly you may borrow from a nearby hospital or college bacteriology department sterile Petri dishes or a dye for staining slides.

You may want to invite a guest speaker to help your students discover what is being done in the field of antibiotics (or some other field of biology). Possibly a parent doing research of some kind is willing to visit with the class.

The librarian of a college may help you find some books (such as those in the Bibliography) which furnish information in specific subject areas. Science teachers in other schools may have books, films, and equipment to share with you. You will want to look into Goldstein's *How to Do an Experiment* for ways to guide students.

Be sure to use the Yearbooks of the Department of Agriculture (Washington, D. C.). Recent advances are given in these books, which report on the work of research teams: *Crops in Peace and War, Science in Farming, Plant Diseases, Soils and Men, Keeping Livestock Healthy, Farmers in a Changing World, Water, Trees, Soil,* and so on.

Some universities have experimental stations from which you may get help in your specific problem. You'll want to look into the opportunities to place interested, able students in voluntary or part-time jobs in experimental stations, plant nurseries, experimental farms, or research departments of a hospital.

BOOKS AND PAMPHLETS

These are only a few of the books which are pertinent to the work discussed in this chapter. These and many other references classified by subject and with complete bibliographical data are given in the Bibliography at the end of the book.

Avery, G., and E. Johnson, *Hormones and Horti-culture,* 1947.

Boysen-Jensen, P., *Plant Hormones,* 1936.

Curtis, O., and D. Clark, *An Introduction to Plant Physiology,* 1950.

Dunn, S., *Elementary Plant Physiology,* 1949.

Dutcher, R., C. Jensen, and P. Althouse, *Intro-duction to Agricultural Biochemistry,* 1951.

Ellis, C., and M. Swaney, *Soilless Growth of Plants,* 1947.

Gilbert, F., *Mineral Nutrition of Plants and Animals,* 1953.

Goldstein, P., *How to Do an Experiment,* 1957.

Hill, A., *Economic Botany,* 1952.

Machlis, L., and J. Torrey, *Plants in Action* (lab manual), 1956.

Miller, E., *Within the Living Plant,* 1953.

Mitchell, J., and P. Marth, *Growth Regulators for Garden, Field, and Orchard,* 1947.

Salle, A., *Fundamental Principles of Bacteriology,* 1954.

Silverman, M., *Magic in a Bottle,* 1951.

Sokoloff, B., *The Miracle Drugs,* 1954.

Spector, W. S., ed., *Toxicology: Antibiotics,* 1957.

U.S. Dept. of Agriculture, Yearbooks, U.S. Government Printing Office.

Walker, J., *Diseases of Vegetable Crops,* 1952.

White, P., *The Cultivation of Plant and Animal Cells,* 1954.

FILMS AND FILMSTRIPS

This partial list is intended only as a guide toward film and filmstrip selection. Refer to the more complete listing at the end of the book where films are classified by subject and where a key to abbreviations and addresses of distributors are given. The cost of film rental, of course, may be subject to change. Films are sound and black and white unless otherwise specified.

And the Earth Shall Give Back Life (antibiotics) (f), Squibb, free.

Antibiotics (f), EBF, $3.00.

Bacteria: Friend or Foe (f, c), EBF, $4.00.

Body Fights Bacteria (f), McGraw-Hill, $3.00.

Chemical Weed Control (f, c) Dow Chemical, free.

From One Cell (f, c), Amer. Cancer Society, free.

Hidden Hunger (f), Swift and Co., free.

Hunger Signs in Corn (fs), De Kalb Agricultural Assoc., free.

Man Against Microbe (f, c), Assn. Films, free.

Plant Growth (f), EBF, $2.50.

Plant Speaks Through Leaf Analysis; Soil Tests Tell Us Why; Plant Speaks Through Deficiency Symptoms (f, c), American Potash, free.

Seeds and How They Grow (f, c), William Cox Enterprises, inquire about rental.

Killing Weeds with 2,4D; Stem Rust (f), U.S. Dept. Agriculture, distributed through state universities, nominal fee.

FREE AND INEXPENSIVE MATERIALS

This is only a partial listing of free and inexpensive materials available to the teacher at this time. A more complete listing, including addresses, is given at the end of the book. Many of these materials are distributed to teachers without charge. Where there is a small fee, the cost is indicated, although the prices are subject to change. While we recommend the material for use in the classroom, we do not necessarily sponsor the products advertised.

Turtox Leaflets ("How to Do" pamphlets), General Biological Supply House, Inc.

Our Smallest Servants, Chas. Pfizer and Co.; write to large pharmaceutical firms which make antibiotics and ask for literature.

Soilless Culture of Plants, U. of Illinois, Dept. Horticulture.

Some Applications of Atomic Energy in Plant Science, U.S. Atomic Energy Commission.

Story of Farm Chemicals, DuPont de Nemours and Co.

CHAPTER 9

Responses of animals

There are many ways to demonstrate reactions among animals. In this chapter we describe some ways to show simple tropisms in the lower animals, and reflex behavior, conditioning and learning among higher animals (including man).[1]

Responses in lower animals

Response to gravity

Paramecium. These forms show a negative geotropic response; they swim up to the top of a container. You may show this by pouring a thick culture of the animals into a stoppered test tube or vial. Students may want to check whether light or other factors also influence this response. Set up several types of controls. For example, several tubes might be prepared; some might be placed in a horizontal position, some two-thirds covered with carbon paper, and so on. Do the protozoa respond to light? To gravity?

You can put this tropic response to use in concentrating a culture when you plan a laboratory lesson on *Paramecium* (see Fig. 17-11; culturing, p. 340).

Response to light

The fact that animals respond to light may be shown in several ways.

Euglena.[2] Pour a concentrated culture of *Euglena* into a finger bowl or Petri dish (culturing, p. 375). Cover half the dish with a library card, so that light shining down on the dish falls on one half of the dish. Within ten minutes remove the cover. Observe the concentration of these organisms in large numbers in the lighted half of the dish. This is a splendid example of positive phototropism.

Students may show this phototropic response under the microscope. Cut a library card to the size of a glass slide. In the center cut out a slit about $\frac{1}{16}$ inch wide. Prepare a wet mount of *Euglena*,

[1] You may want to examine syllabuses from other schools to learn which concepts they develop in the broad topic of behavior. For instance: R. Putnam, *Science for Oregon Schools*, Part 2: High School Science, Oregon State Educ. Dept.; *Course of Study in Zoology*, Curriculum Bull. 197, Cincinnati Public Schools, 1950; *Course of Study in Science for Secondary Schools*, Bull. 400, Dept. of Public Instruction, Harrisburg, Pa.

[2] You may prefer to classify *Euglena* as a member of the plant kingdom.

focus under low power, and place the library card under the slide. Examine the organisms visible through the narrow slit and quickly remove the library card. Observe that the majority of the micro-organisms congregate in the region of the narrow slit in the card through which light passes.

Flatworms (Planaria). Planarian worms are found in streams on the underside of rocks or leaves of water plants. In the laboratory they thrive best when kept in shallow, darkened jars of pond water containing some small stones under which they can hide (culturing, p. 346). Remove the cover of the containers holding planarians and watch their movement away from a source of light. They exhibit a negative response to light.

Earthworms. Students may keep earthworms in wet sphagnum moss in a dark box or covered dish. Or they may use a layer of humus to line the container.

Suddenly lift the cover and direct a beam of light from a flashlight on the anterior region of the worms. Observe the way they avoid the light by contracting or burrowing into the moss.

Fruit flies. Transfer a fairly large number of adult fruit flies (*Drosophila*) from a culture bottle into a long test tube; stopper the test tube with cotton. Then cover one half of the test tube with black paper. Direct a beam of light at one end of the tube and observe the attraction of the flies to the light. This is a positive response to light. If the position of the carbon paper is reversed and the beam of light is shifted to a new position, you will find that the flies again orient themselves in the lighted part of the tube.

Response to electricity

The electrical charge on the surface of microorganisms may be demonstrated in this way. (Some people call the re-

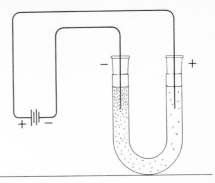

Fig. 9-1 Clustering of *Paramecia* move toward the negative arm of U-tube.

sponse of these "charged" organisms a galvanotropism; whether it is a tropic response is questionable.)

Partially fill a U-tube or a flat-sided glass container with a thick culture of *Paramecium*. Connect two dry cells in series and insert the two wires from the cells into opposite ends of the container or U-tube containing the animals (Fig. 9-1). Notice the clustering of the microorganisms around the negative pole. This seems to indicate that the surface of the microorganisms is positively charged.

You may throw a shadow picture of this reaction on a screen or wall. Use a flat-sided container which fits into the slide compartment of a lantern slide projector or a projection cell. Show the clustering effect. Then reverse the current and show the migration of the organisms to the other electrode, which is now the negative pole.

Response to chemicals

Organisms react to chemical stimuli by moving toward some chemical substances, such as desired food. Other chemicals, such as strong acids, cause a negative response.

Positive chemotropism in Paramecium. As food materials diffuse through the culture medium, the *Paramecium* responds by swimming toward the food. Mount a drop of culture fluid containing some debris. Examine under the microscope to find clusters of protozoa gathered around the food material. This response to "food chemicals" is considered a chemotropism.

Negative chemotropism in Paramecium. Prepare a wet mount of a concentrated culture of *Paramecium*. Add a drop of dilute acetic or hydrochloric acid (1 drop of concentrated hydrochloric acid in 20 drops of water) or 1 drop of Waterman's ink[3] to one side of the coverslip. Observe the movement away from the incoming acid. Often the trichocysts of *Paramecium* are extruded.

Another way to show negative chemotropism in protozoa uses a bit of cotton thread soaked in dilute hydrochloric acid. This thread is placed across a drop of thick culture of *Paramecium* on a slide. Hold the slide against a dark background or view it under the microscope. Students will see a cleared area around the thread. The animals have moved away from the dilute acid.

Response of Hydra to acid. Mount several specimens of *Hydra* in a drop of the aquarium or pond water in which they were found. They will elongate when not disturbed. Place a bristle under the coverslip so that the organisms will not be crushed by the weight of the coverslip. Then introduce a drop of weak acetic acid to one side of the coverslip. Observe the discharge of nematocysts on the tentacles of the animals as the acid diffuses through the water. This makes an especially fine demonstration of nematocysts (p. 311). (This reaction is not considered a tropistic response.)

Response of Planaria to chemicals. Place small strips of raw liver in the cul-

ture dishes of planarians and watch the rapid aggregation of these forms around the liver. In fact, you may collect planarians from a lake or brook by suspending a bit of raw liver in the water for a few hours. If planarians are present large numbers will be found collected around the liver. This may be considered a positive chemotropic response.

On the other hand, place a drop of ammonium hydroxide or acetic acid near the planarians and watch the negative chemotropic response.

Response to contact

You may want to show how large protozoan forms like *Spirostomum* or *Stentor* respond to contact or disturbance. When a drop of a rich culture of these organisms is mounted on a slide and the slide is tapped, these large organisms will contract. This is visible to the naked eye. You need a microscope, however, to see similar contractions in *Vorticella*, a stalked form (Fig. 9-2).

Students may recall that whenever *Paramecium* or other microorganisms run into each other they respond by altering the direction in which they are moving. This,

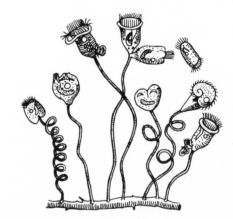

Fig. 9-2 *Vorticella* (diagrammatic), showing expanded and contracted forms. (From G. G. Simpson, C. Pittendrigh, & L. Tiffany, *Life*, Harcourt, Brace, 1957.)

[3] Not every ink contains enough tannic acid to give this response. Some preliminary experimentation may be necessary.

too, may be considered a tropic response to contact (thigmotropism).

Similarly, when hydras, earthworms, insect larvae, planarian worms, and many microscopic worms are touched with a dissecting needle they contract.

Responses in higher animals

Reflexes in the frog

A living frog is an excellent specimen for the study of reflexes. Here are a few reflex responses which can be shown in class.

Blinking. Hold a live frog securely in one hand by grasping the hind legs. Bring a blunt probe or a glass rod near one eye. Students should observe that the frog blinks. In fact, the response at times is so strong that the eye may be pulled into the throat region. Observe, also, the lids covering the eyes.

A student may show the blinking response in another way. Dip a cotton-tipped toothpick into ammonium hydroxide and bring it near the eye of the frog.

Other reflexes. Touch the "nostrils" and watch the response. Stroke the throat and belly regions. When these regions are first stroked in males, watch the distinct clasping reflex in the forelimbs. When the frog is placed on its back and stroked longer, students will not fail to notice the quieting, almost hypnotic effect on the frog. Stroke the back and sides of a male frog to make it croak. Watch the extension of the vocal sacs and note the closed "nostrils" which prevent the escape of air.

"Scratch" reflex. Demonstrate the "scratch" reflex in this way. Grasp the head and hold the forelimbs securely in one hand. Wash off any mucus present on the back of the frog. Now touch its dorsal skin with a cotton-tipped toothpick or glass rod dipped in dilute nitric acid. Notice how the hind leg attempts to brush off the irritant. With a stronger acid, a more violent response occurs. In fact, the animal may try to use both legs to brush off the irritating substance. Wash off the acid with water. (You may also want to show the same response in a spinal frog at this time. See Fig. 9-3 and p. 130.)

Other responses. Place the frog back in water. Notice the resting position. Watch the normal breathing movements. Suddenly tap the jar and watch its reactions. Now watch the motion of the limbs in swimming.

Perhaps a student will demonstrate changes in the size of chromatophores in the frog's skin in response to light. Put one frog in the dark (several would be preferable) and set others in the light for several hours. Which frogs are darker in color? These responses are due to reactions of the nervous system as well as the effect of a hormone from the intermediate lobe of the pituitary, called intermedin. (See also chromatophores of fish, p. 309.)

Show the feeding reactions of a live frog by dangling earthworms before it. Note the position of the eyes in swallowing.

Locating responses. Which region of the nervous system is responsible for these reflexes? If we destroyed only the brain of a frog, would the blinking reflex or the scratch reflex remain in this "spinal frog"? What if we also destroyed the spinal cord? Do any reflexes remain in this "pithed frog"? For destroying (pithing) the brain and spinal cord of a frog, see the photographs and description in Fig. 9-3. A longitudinal section of the frog's head is shown in Fig. 9-4, as a guide to demonstrating the procedure.

Spinal frog

Hold the frog securely with the left hand (if you are right-handed) with its legs extended. Bend its head down by pressing its snout with the index finger.

Rest the dissecting needle on a line bisecting the head. Slide the needle down until the point is at the cranial opening (foramen magnum) just below the cranium and above the spinal column (see Fig. 9-4 for diagram of frog's head); this is about in the middle of the posterior line of the tympanic membranes.

Insert the needle without changing its direction and move it from side to side to sever the brain from the spinal cord (hold the frog firmly, for it will wriggle); tilt the needle forward, insert it into the brain case, and move it around to destroy the brain. You now have a "spinal frog." (*Note:* we call this a spinal frog for ease of reference; different authors apparently accept different terms.)

Pithed frog A pithed frog has not only its brain but its spinal cord destroyed. Take a spinal frog and insert the needle into the same opening, but this time tilt it downward through the length of the spinal column and scrape a bit. Observe the extension and relaxation of the hind legs. Notice the difference between a spinal frog (swimming peculiarly) and a pithed frog (as if dead) in the tank above.

One reflex of a spinal frog
When the toes of a spinal frog are pinched, its legs jerk up close to its body. See the text for other reflexes to test for in spinal and pithed frogs.

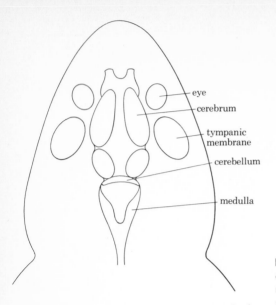

Fig. 9-4 Longitudinal section of the head of a frog, showing the parts of the brain in relation to the tympanic membranes.

eye
cerebrum
tympanic membrane
cerebellum
medulla

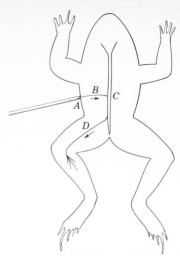

Fig. 9-6 Diagrammatic representation of reflex arc in a frog: acid applied at A is the stimulus, received by sense receptors in the skin; the impulse is carried by sensory neuron B to the spinal cord C; motor neuron D transmits an impulse to the muscles and the leg contracts to brush off the irritant.

The "scratch" reflex in a spinal frog. Is the brain of the frog necessary for the scratch reflex to occur? Is the spinal cord necessary? If the brain is the center for the scratch reflex, then the frog should lose this response when the brain is destroyed. Use a spinal frog (brain removed or destroyed) for this demonstration.

Destroy the brain of a frog as shown in Fig. 9-3; avoid injuring the spinal cord. In fact, some teachers prefer to cut off the entire head to be sure they have removed the brain: insert a sharp dissecting scissors into the mouth and cut off the head by cutting behind the tympanic membranes; place a bit of cotton over the cut end. (*Note:* This should not be done in front of the class.) Whether the brain is destroyed or severed from the body, suspend the frog from a ringstand by clamping the lower jaw (Fig. 9-5).

Wash off the mucus covering, which may be quite thick, but remember to keep the skin moist. If spinal shock has occurred the animal gives no response;

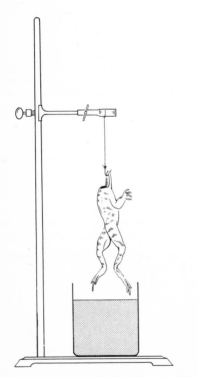

Fig. 9-5 Spinal frog with head removed, suspended from a clamp by lower jaw.

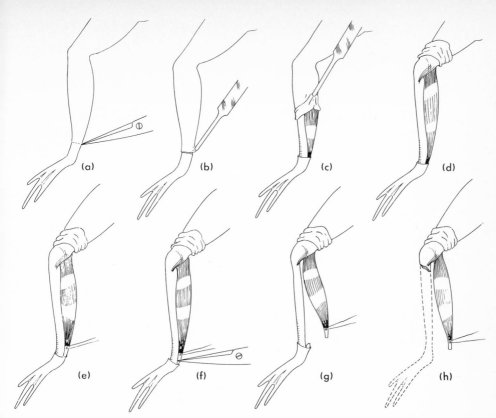

Fig. 9-7 Dissection of the gastrocnemius muscle of the frog in preparation for study: (a) the skin is carefully cut with sharp scissors near the insertion of the Achilles' tendon; (b), (c), and (d) the loose skin is rolled back with tweezers; (e) a hole is made with a dissecting needle through the tendon and a copper wire is inserted; (f) and (g) the tendon is cut *below* the wire; (h) the bone and other muscles are cut away. The loose skin can be pulled down over the muscle to keep it from drying. (After D. M. Pace & C. C. Riedesel, *Laboratory Manual for Vertebrate Physiology*, Burgess, 1947.)

wait 5 or 10 minutes for recovery before proceeding. Now dip a glass rod into dilute acetic or nitric acid and apply it to the back of the frog. The "scratch" reflex takes place even though the brain has been destroyed. Wash off the irritating acid by raising a battery jar of water up to the suspended frog and immersing the frog's body in the water. Repeat.

Release the frog from its suspended position; now destroy the spinal cord (see Fig. 9-3). Suspend the frog once more and apply acid to the body again. Why is there no response this time? Apparently the spinal cord is the center for this body reflex.

You may now want to trace the path of the stimulus in the body. For example, when acid is placed on the skin of the back, why is the response given by the hind leg? Develop a simple pattern of a reflex arc on the blackboard as a summary activity (Fig. 9-6). Students might represent sensory neurons with one color chalk and motor neurons with another color.

Nerve-muscle pathway. You can readily show how a nerve transmits a stimulus to a muscle and how this muscle tissue contracts to produce movement. Use a pithed frog. Dissect the hindlimb to expose the gastrocnemius muscle (Fig. 9-7).

Then dissect the thigh to expose the sciatic nerve. (You may wish to remove the muscle and its nerve connection and put it in a dish of Ringer's solution.) What happens when the nerve is pinched with a forceps? When the nerve, or muscle, is stimulated by a very mild electric current (copper electrodes attached to a dry cell)?

Anesthetizing a frog. There are times when you want a frog anesthetized so that you may prepare it for a demonstration, such as circulation in the webbed foot. You may immobilize a frog by putting it in a covered jar with some cotton saturated with ether, but this effect will not last very long.

A more effective way[4] is to inject a 2.5 per cent solution of urethane (ethyl carbamide) into the ventral lymph sac. As a guide, inject about 0.1 cc for every 10 gm of the frog's weight.

There may be other occasions when you want to inject drugs of various sorts into a frog. Drugs are usually injected into the anterior lymph sac,[5] which is found in the floor of the mouth. Hold the animal in your hand so that its ventral surface is toward you. Draw the drug into the hypodermic syringe. Open the frog's mouth; avoid the tongue and point the needle toward the floor of the mouth. When you press the needle into the skin, the needle enters the lymph sac; then inject the drug.

Conditioning and learning

Conditioning earthworms. With some patience, students may show that "learning" of a sort takes place among earthworms. They can build a T-shaped maze of wood or other materials (Fig. 9-8). At one end of the T-bar, place a

[4] D. Pace and C. Riedesel, *Laboratory Manual of Vertebrate Physiology*, Burgess, Minneapolis, Minn., 1947.
[5] *Ibid.*

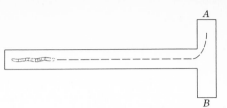

Fig. 9-8 T-maze for training earthworms: at A place rich garden soil; at B, coarse sandpaper, weak acid, or a weak electric current.

rich sample of organic soil. At the other end place a piece of filter paper or cotton soaked in a dilute acid, or cover the area with coarse sandpaper. Place a hungry earthworm at the beginning and watch its trail along the length of the path. As a project students might keep a record of the number of times the same worm (or worms) turned toward the humus and avoided the acid or sandpaper. Identify the worms with India ink (or some similar device) so that the records of trials and errors may be identified. Repeat the experiments daily. It may take some 50 trials before the earthworms "learn" to avoid the irritating substances and turn to the humus where the food is located.

Conditioning goldfish. Goldfish, unlike earthworms, have a definite brain in the acknowledged sense of the term. If you feed the fish from one end of the aquarium regularly, and at the same time introduce another stimulus, the fish will associate the two stimuli. Flash a light each time the fish are fed, or tap on the tank. Students might take over this activity as a learning experience. It may take 3 weeks or more to condition the fish. After conditioning, the fish will rise to one end of the aquarium when the tank is tapped (or when a light is on), although food may not be given. The original stimulus, food, has been removed. The fish respond to a substitute stimulus (tapping) associated with the food stimulus.

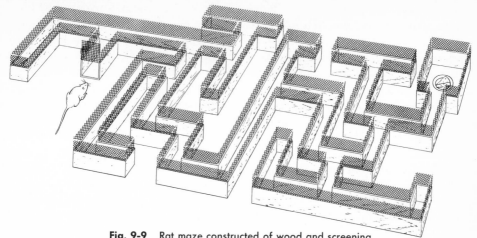

Fig. 9-9 Rat maze constructed of wood and screening.

We may consider the original response to food a reflex, an inborn behavior pattern. As a result of conditioning, a conditioned reflex has been established.

Learning in the white rat. Construct a rat maze using wood and window screening (Fig. 9-9). Trace out a maze and nail down strips of wood topped with screening (6 inches high) so that the animal moves along channeled paths.

Select a hungry white rat for training. Lead it through the maze several times. When it is successful in running the maze, reward it by giving it food and fondling it. In this way the rat comes to associate food and petting with a completed task.

Keep a record from day to day or several times a day, as the animal (when hungry) is put through the maze. Students might want to compare the number of trials needed for learning the maze among several rats, some young, some older.

As a project, a committee of students may want to compare the learning rate of rats which have a thiamin (or other) deficiency with normal controls. Perhaps they may want to study the effect of drugs (caffeine) on speed of learning.

Learning seems to go on faster when a reward rather than punishment accompanies the learning task at hand. What would happen if we slapped the rat each time it failed to complete the maze? (Do not try this in class, for the animal may become vicious.)

Behavior in man

Reflexes in man

Have students observe their own reactions in the following situations:

Blinking. Have one student stand and hold a sheet of glass in front of his face. Then ask a second student to throw cotton balls or crumpled paper at the glass. The student cannot avoid blinking even though he is protected by the glass.

Contraction of the iris. Have students cover one eye for a minute. When they remove the hand have them look at once into a mirror. Note the dilation of the pupil of the eye that was covered. As light strikes the eye observe the change in size of the pupil (as the iris contracts in bright light). Students will need to try this several times.

Or darken the room for a minute. Have students observe their eyes in a mirror as the light is suddenly turned on. The contraction of the iris is marked. Also note the size of the pupil when the eye accommodates for close and distant vision.

Flow of saliva. Slice a lemon in front of the class, or describe its sour taste. Recall a favorite food by means of a full description (or pictures). Ask students to describe the results of a reflex that occurs within them.

Cilio-spinal reflex. Watch the pupils of the eyes of several students when the skin of the back of the neck is pinched.

Patellar reflex (knee jerk). Have a student sit on a chair or a table with legs crossed or freely suspended. When the subject is completely relaxed, strike a blow just below the patella bone with a rubber hammer or with the side of the hand.

Reception of stimuli by sense organs (skin receptors)

You may want to have students map the location of several of the sense receptors in the skin (and errors in sensing the location of these receptors) in the following ways.

Localization of touch. Have a student keep his eyes closed throughout the experiment. Show another student how to touch the skin of the hand of the subject with the pointed end of a soft pencil (leaving a mark). Remove the pencil, give the subject a blunt probe, and ask him to locate the place on the skin where he received the stimulus. Use a millimeter ruler to measure his error in locating where the stimulus was applied. Try this on several subjects.

Here is another method for localizing these receptors. Insert two pins closely spaced in a cork, or use pointed calipers. Then gently bring the pin points to the surface of the hand, forearm, and fingertips. When the pins are placed closely the sensation received by the subject is that of one pin point. When the distance between the pin points is increased a bit the subject receives two sensations. This approximates the distance between the two sense receptors in the skin. Are the receptors grouped more closely on the forearm or at the fingertips?

Temperature contrast. Have students immerse one finger in water at 40° C, and at the same time put a finger from the other hand into water at 20° C; after 30 seconds they should transfer both fingers into water at 30° C. What is the sensation? Use the same procedure but this time have students first immerse one finger in water at 45° C and the other finger in water kept at 30° C, and finally shift both fingers into water at 10° C. Have them describe the sensation.

Temperature response. Draw out a glass rod to form a blunt point. Prepare several, fire-polish the ends, and allow to cool. Chill the rods in ice water and then have students apply one to the skin of the back of the hand, and also to the forearm. Locate the receptors. Use washable ink to mark the receptors on the skin.

Repeat the procedure, but this time with a rod warmed in hot water. (*Warning:* not too hot.) Locate the receptors which sense the stimulus of heat. Mark these receptors on the skin with different colored ink.

Chemical response. Map the areas of the tongue which are sensitive to salt, sweet, sour, and bitter substances. Apply the solutions with a sterilized camel's hair brush, toothpick, or glass rod drawn out to a blunt point and fire-polished. Wash out the mouth between testings. First use a solution of two parts of water and one part of vinegar. Apply it to the tip, the sides, the center, and the back of the tongue. Locate the area of the tongue that is sensitive to sour substances.

In testing for the salt-sensitive area of the tongue, use a 10 per cent solution of sodium chloride. Apply it to the same regions of the tongue as before. Remember to wash out the mouth between tests.

For a bitter substance, use a weak solution of aspirin in water, or quinine sulfate. Use a 5 per cent cane sugar solution as a sweet substance. Use coded bottles so that students do not know the true contents. Also test students with tap water to eliminate the factor of suggestion. Compare your findings with the areas mapped in Fig. 9-10.

Confusing the senses. Ask students to cross the middle finger and the index finger of one hand. Then have them roll a small pill or bean in the palm of the other hand with the crossed fingers. The students should be able to describe the sensation.

Conditioning in human beings

You may want to demonstrate how conditioning occurs. Stand at the rear of the classroom so that your students are not facing you. Ask them to try an experiment with you and to follow what you say. Direct them to mark a tally line on a sheet of paper each time you say *WRITE*. Use a ruler to tap on the blackboard or on a desk each time you say *WRITE*, so that the two stimuli are associated with the students' response (the drawing of a line on the paper).

After some 20 times of repeating these signals (about two every second) continue to rap with the ruler but stop using the stimulus word *WRITE*. Many students will continue to draw lines at the sound of the rapping. They have been conditioned temporarily so that they draw a line in response to the stimulus (the sound of the tap). Students will vary in

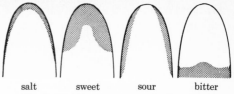
Fig. 9-10 Taste receptors in the tongue.

this experiment. Some stop immediately when you omit the oral command. Others may continue to write extra lines 10 times longer than the rest of the students. Have the students explain the factors needed for conditioning.

Habits in human beings

Show the value of making certain kinds of behavior habitual. Here are two methods to show that habits are time-saving and require little conscious thought.

Have students write their full name in the usual manner as often as they can in half a minute. Then have them write their name with the other hand at least five times. Record the time it takes. Why does it take so long to write with the other hand? What is one value of a habit?

Direct students to copy as quickly as possible an oral paragraph of material. Read at a fair pace and record the time it takes for students to copy the material you dictate. Then read another paragraph with one change in directions. Students are not to dot any *i* or cross any *t* in the words they copy. Select material with many words containing *i*'s and *t*'s; read at the same fair pace. Have students score the number of dotted *i*'s and crossed *t*'s.

Have a boy describe in detail how he ties a shoelace. Have someone describe the details of the kinds of houses, trees, store signs, and so forth that he passes on the way to school. Why must the students stop to think when they pass the same way to school daily? when they tie shoelaces daily?

Learning

Considerable time should be spent on gaining some experimental evidence with young people. Many students lack proper study habits; they fail to get the "big idea" in their assignments, in reading, in work in class. Some of these "experiments" may help to change students' work habits.

Comparing the rate of learning under differing conditions

Learning sense and nonsense rhymes. On the blackboard list in two vertical columns the words in Column A and in Column B. Cover the lists so that students cannot see them.

Column A	Column B
thing	Its
whatever	a
a	very
as	odd
odd	thing
eats	as
its	odd
very	as
Miss T	can
can	be
Miss T	that
odd	whatever
as	Miss T
be	eats
turns	turns
that	into
into	Miss T[6]

Now uncover the list of words in Column A. Direct students to memorize the list in vertical order. Record the time. Ask students to raise their hand when they have memorized the list. Allow this activity to go on for five minutes.

Now uncover Column B, and have students memorize it. Keep a record of the time and the number of students who quickly raise their hands when they have memorized the words. Students readily

Fig. 9-11 A simple puzzle students can make: use this shape as a pattern to cut four pieces; these can be fitted together to form a perfect square.

explain that Column B made sense and that Column A was meaningless. From here it is not difficult to guide the class toward the need for understanding main ideas so that most work and reading in school does not fit into the category of "nonsense."

Learning under distraction. Have students copy a stanza of poetry which is dictated. Better still, distribute mimeographed sheets containing two stanzas of a poem.

Ask students to memorize the first stanza as quickly as possible. Students might raise their hands when they have memorized the stanza. Keep a record of the time it takes for the first hand to be raised until some dozen or so students raise their hands.

After complimenting them on their success, ask them to memorize the second stanza. However, occupy yourself by making noise which is distracting. Turn on a portable radio and find a nonmusical program. Also slam drawers or metal lockers from time to time. Keep a record of the time it takes for the first student to indicate success in memorizing the second stanza. Count others. Ask for an explanation of the relative slowness or even failure to memorize the second stanza. There is an opportunity here to stress the

---

[6] Walter de la Mare, "Miss T." By permission of the Society of Authors as the Literary Representative of the estate of the late Walter de la Mare, and Faber & Faber, Ltd.

need for a quiet place for work and study.

Learning by trial and error. One of the simplest and most time-consuming ways to learn something is by trial and error. Give students a simple puzzle to solve, without pictures as a guide. Use the exact shape shown in Fig. 9-11 as a guide. Draw it on onion-skin paper, and have a group of students volunteer to cut out sets of four cardboard or oaktag pieces from this pattern. Place four of these pieces in each one of enough envelopes for all the students in class.

Distribute an envelope to each student (note the time). Tell the students to put together the four pieces to form a perfect square, with no spaces. Allow 10 minutes. When a student is successful have him raise his hand; keep a record of the time. Then have him take apart his puzzle and put the pieces back in the envelope. After 5 minutes, tell each of the successful students to try solving the problem again.

Why is it that most students have difficulty in solving the puzzle? Why is it that some students who successfully completed the puzzle the first time cannot repeat their performance? Elicit from students that this is hit-or-miss learning, as they say, or trial-and-error learning.

Show that when something has meaning, learning goes on faster. Have a student who was successful show the rest of the class, in great detail, how to put the puzzle together. Then time the students in their performance in learning to solve the puzzle.

These experiences help the students gain insight into some methods of improving study habits. Many, who worry about their poor study habits, appreciate this help. Naturally, these are suggestions only and need to be personalized through individual guidance.

Structure of the brain. Students may get the brain of a sheep or calf from a butcher.

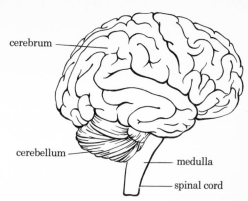

Fig. 9-12 Schematic drawing of human brain. (From J. W. Clemenson, T. G. Lawrence, et al., *Your Health and Safety*, 4th ed., Harcourt, Brace, 1957.)

In class, identify the cerebrum, cerebellum, and medulla. A student may report on a comparison of brains in different groups of animals. Develop the notion that the cerebrum has become larger in the higher animals, with more convolutions in the cortex.

A student might diagram the human brain on the blackboard (Fig. 9-12). Then associate these activities with the region of the brain or spinal cord which controls them. For example:
(a) Region where thinking occurs
(b) Controls sneezing and swallowing
(c) Coordinates body movements and equilibrium
(d) Center for sight, hearing, and speech
(e) Controls heart beat
(f) Center for reflexes of the body, such as pulling away from a hot object
(g) Controls breathing
(h) Center for making decisions and other voluntary behavior

If you study sense organs at this time, you may want to study the structure of the eye of a sheep, or that of a frog. Students may try to trace the optic nerve to the brain. Some teachers like to use a sagittal half of a sheep's head. (Refer to

Chapter 16 for instructions on dissecting a frog and other vertebrates if you want to study the nervous system in more detail.)

Behavior and ductless glands

How do ductless glands coordinate the functions of the body and affect behavior? Use a manikin or a chart to show the position of the ductless glands in the body. Students may bring to class the pancreas, the adrenal glands located above the kidneys (which may have been identified previously). You may plan to dissect a frog or a bird, such as a pigeon, to locate some of the ductless glands (dissections, Chapter 16).

Students may feel thyroid gland tissue by lightly putting their fingers against their windpipe. Then swallow and try to locate the thyroid tissue, which seems to move up and down in front of the windpipe.

Students may report on the classic work of Bayliss and Starling regarding ductless gland hormones. Describe the effects of the hormones secreted into the bloodstream. Many students have a background of information based on experience upon which you can draw. For example: Who has had a basal metabolism test? What is

done in the test? Why is it given?

In season, a group of students may treat tadpoles with thyroxin or an iodine salt or use pituitary hormones to induce ovulation in the frog (as described in Chapter 11).

Ask students: Under what conditions is insulin given to a person? What caused the size of the giant in the circus? Which gland is considered the master gland in the body?

In summary, students might use the basic information about the endocrine glands to plan a table such as Table 9-1. This might be developed using the blackboard as the device for focusing the attention of the class.

TABLE 9-1
Endocrine glands and behavior

ductless gland (and location)	hormone	normal function	undersecretion or oversecretion
pituitary			
thyroid			
parathyroids			
adrenals			
pancreas (Islands of Langerhans)			
ovaries			
testes			

CAPSULE LESSONS
Ways to get started in class

9-1. Ask students to name activities their bodies perform unconsciously (i.e., reflexes). List a series of examples of reflexes on the blackboard. Develop a definition of a reflex. What is the path of the reflex arc within the body?

9-2. Or begin by asking the class what behavior a child has from birth. List the reflexes on the board. As students mention them, ask how these activities differ from the behavior involved in dressing, riding a bike, dancing, or writing a composition.

9-3. Or ask a student to hold up a glass in front of his face. Have another student throw

paper balls at him. Ask the class to note the student's behavior. Why does he blink even though he is protected by the glass? Develop the idea that some behavior is inborn, and takes place without any thought.

9-4. Start a discussion of study habits by using the activity described in this chapter wherein students memorize stanzas of poetry in quiet and with distractions. Or use a list of nonsense words first, and let children develop the conclusion that problems can be solved faster when one knows what the problem is, and how to tackle it.

9-5. Have a student describe how to knot a tie without using gestures. Why is the description slow and stumbling? Develop the notion that our habits are now activities done without thinking.

9-6. Have students write their names five times. Then have them shift their pens into the other hand and again write their names five times. Why is it so much longer, so difficult? Elicit from students that each letter must be thought through in spelling a word. What is the value of having a habit?

9-7. Use the puzzle referred to in this chapter. Students take from 5 to 15 minutes to solve it. After 10 minutes, have one student explain how to put the pieces together. Then time the class again. Why is it easier to solve the puzzle now? Keep a tally of the number of students who get the puzzle in each case. How does this apply to doing a school assignment?

9-8. A student might want to give a report of the kind of learning that Wolfgang Kohler described in his book *Mentality of Apes* (Harcourt, Brace, 1927). Was the putting together of two sticks to make a longer one for reaching food an example of an instinct or insight?

9-9. You may want students to describe instincts in animals, such as nest-building, spinning of a spider's web, migration of some birds and fish, behavior in a beehive, and many others. How do these behavior patterns differ from problem-solving behavior in man? (A description of an ant-observation case is given on p. 358.)

9-10. What are some successful ways to study? Students might contribute answers from their own experience. Then you may want to try some of the "experiments" described in this chapter. Include a discussion of the role of insight in their problem-solving activities.

9-11. Begin with a film showing instinctive behavior, such as *Dance of the Bees* (a description of Von Frisch's work), available from Wilner Films and Slides. Or show *Bee City* (Almanac). What is an instinct? Or show *Behavior in Animals and Plants* (Coronet).

9-12. Ask students to list their fears. Discuss the questions: Are fears inherited? How are fears developed? Perhaps some students can recall what situations were associated with the development of their fears.

9-13. You may have time in class to read or discuss a student's report on some of the booklets published by Science Research Associates, 57 West Grand Avenue, Chicago, Ill. For instance, these may be useful: *You and Your Mental Abilities, Getting Along with Brothers and Sisters, Why Stay in School?, What Is Honesty?, Choosing Your Career,* and others.

Students in high school give much time to the problems discussed in these booklets; they often wonder if they are normal or if others feel the way they do. The stress should be on the fact that all young people growing up have similar problems to face and to solve. What are the best ways to solve problems of living?

9-14. There are many films on learning in rats, cats, chimpanzees, and children. Some of these may be suitable for class. For instance, *Preface to a Life* (United World), *Behavior Patterns at One Year* (Encyclopaedia Britannica), *An Analysis of the Forms of Animal Learning, I and II* (Penn. State College Psychological Cinema Register), *Fears of Children* (International Film Foundation), *Problem Solving in Monkeys, Problem Solving in Infants* (International Film Bureau), *You and Your Attitudes* (Association Films), *Self-Conscious Guy* (Coronet), *Shyness* (McGraw-Hill), and others.

9-15. You may want to show a film on the structure of the nervous system and the function of such sense organs as the eye and ear. For example, there are *Nervous System* (Encyclopaedia Britannica), *How the Ear Functions, How the Eye Functions* (Knowledge Builders), *Science of Seeing* (filmstrip, General Electric).

9-16. In a panel discussion, students might describe some of the problems facing adolescents: in school, in getting a job, in getting along with others.

9-17. You may want to show a film on hormones such as *Endocrine Glands* (Encyclopaedia Britannica). This might serve as a summary of the work in that area. How do ductless glands affect behavior?

9-18. Begin by asking students how they would train a new puppy to answer to its name. Develop the steps in habit formation: desire, repetition, and satisfaction.

9-19. You may want students to list the traits they admire in other people. Then have them check themselves against this yardstick. Develop a discussion of ways to improve oneself. What are the characteristics of a pleasant personality?

9-20. In planning a test, you may want to include some questions with this pattern:
A. In which part of the nervous system is each of these behavior patterns centered?
Learning to drive a car, pulling away from a hot object, swallowing, breathing, touch typing, solving a puzzle, dilation of the iris of the eye, doing your math homework,

dancing, suspending judgment until you have the facts.

B. Identify a possible cause of each kind of behavior:

Increased flow of adrenin, sluggish metabolism, sudden increase in glucose in the blood, rapid growth of long bones in the body, flow of saliva when you see a picture of certain foods, fear of the dark, finding the right key among those on a key ring, ducking when a ball is thrown your way, ducking a clothesline which has recently been removed.

You may also want to include a reading from the works of William James, Walter Cannon (*The Wisdom of the Body*), or Bayliss and Starling. Then prepare several questions based on the reading.

PEOPLE, PLACES, AND THINGS

Where, in your community, can you get living material to demonstrate behavior patterns? Ask a teacher in another school or a member of the biology department of a nearby college for fruitful places to take a class on a field trip.

Living materials out of season may be purchased from a biological supply house. Then you may culture many kinds of living things the year around in the laboratory (see methods in Chapters 18, 19, and 20).

Students may bring in organs of animals, such as a brain, endocrine glands, or an eye, which they can get from a butcher. You may need to borrow a model of an eye or a brain from a college department, a doctor, or another school. Perhaps you may be able to borrow films from a nearby school or college (psychology department).

When possible, invite a guest speaker from a child guidance bureau to talk about getting started toward a vocation, or about setting goals. It might be advisable to inform students early about the requirements for college entrance and the requirements for specific vocational opportunities.

BOOKS AND PAMPHLETS

These are only a few of the books which are pertinent to the work discussed in this chapter. These and many other references classified by subject and with complete bibliographical data are given in the Bibliography at the end of the book.

Buchsbaum, R., *Animals Without Backbones,* 1948.

Carlson, A., and V. Johnson, *The Machinery of the Body,* 1953.

Clemenson, J., T. Lawrence, et al., *Your Health and Safety,* 1957.

Curtis, W., and M. Guthrie, *Textbook of General Zoology,* 1947.

Gabriel, M., and S. Fogel, eds., *Great Experiments in Biology,* 1955.

Garrett, H., *Great Experiments in Psychology,* 1951.

Gray, J., *How Animals Move,* 1953.

Hegner, R., *Parade of the Animal Kingdom,* 1955.

Kohler, W., *Mentality of Apes,* 1927.

Munn, N., *The Evolution and Growth of Human Behavior,* 1955.

Pace, D., and C. Riedesel, *Laboratory Manual of Vertebrate Physiology,* 1947.

Prosser, C., F. Brown, et al., *Comparative Animal Physiology,* 1950.

Roeder, K. D., *Insect Physiology,* 1953.

Romer, A., *The Vertebrate Body,* 1955.

Sproul, E., *The Science Book of the Human Body,* 1955.

Turner, C. D., *General Endocrinology,* 1955.

FILMS AND FILMSTRIPS

This partial list is intended only as a guide toward film and filmstrip selection. Refer to the more complete listing at the end of the book where films are classified by subject and where a key to abbreviations and the addresses of distributors are given. The cost of film rental, of course, may be subject to change. Films are sound and black and white unless otherwise specified.

Action and Reaction (instincts, trial and error) (f), Almanac, $2.00.

Behavior in Animals and Plants (f, c), Coronet, inquire about rental.

Can Animals Think? (f), Almanac, $2.00.

Conditioned Reflexes and Behavior (f, si), Brandon, $8.00.

Do Better on Your Examinations (f), Coronet, $2.00.

Development of the Nervous System in Vertebrates and Invertebrates (f, si), Brandon, $4.00.

Endocrine Glands (f), EBF, $2.50.

Embryology of Human Behavior (f), Int. Film Bur., inquire about rental.

Growth of Motor Behavior (Gesell's work) (f, si); *Behavior Patterns at One Year* (f), EBF, $2.50.

How the Ear Functions; How the Eye Functions (f),

Knowledge Builders, $2.00.

Human Brain (f), EBF, $2.50.

Motivation and Reward in Learning (f, 2 rls), New York U., $5.00.

Nervous System (f), EBF, $2.00.

The Nervous System; The Glandular System (fs), Bowmar, $3.00.

Problem Solving in Monkeys; Testing Animal Intelligence (f, si), Int. Film Bur., $2.50.

Mental Health (f), EBF, $2.50.

Preface to a Life (f), United World, $4.00.

Reactions in Plants and Animals (f), EBF, $2.50.

Science of Seeing (fs), Gen. Electric, free.

Shy Guy; Self-conscious Guy (f), Coronet, $2.00.

Shyness (f), McGraw-Hill, $3.00.

You and Your Attitudes (f), Assoc. Films, $2.50.

FREE AND INEXPENSIVE MATERIALS

This is only a partial listing of free and inexpensive materials available to the teacher at this time. A more complete listing, including addresses, is given at the end of the book. Many of these materials are distributed to teachers without charge. Where there is a small fee, the cost is indicated, although the prices are subject to change. While we recommend the material for use in the classroom, we do not necessarily sponsor the products advertised.

Studying Ants in Observation Nests, Turtox Leaflet, General Biological Supply House.

Hale and Hearty, N. Y. City Board of Health.

School Days; Teen Time; Your Job (Guideposts to Mental Health Series), N. Y. State Dept. Mental Hygiene.

Study Your Way Through School; Understanding Yourself; many others; Sci. Research Associates, $0.60.

Catalog of Mental Health Pamphlets, U.S. Govt. Printing Office, $0.25.

Your Child from Six to Twelve, Children's Bur., Supt. Documents, U.S. Govt. Printing Office, $0.20.

Helping Children Grow in Friendly Ways, Amer. Friends Service Committee.

Guiding Children—Dealing with Fear and Tension, Assoc. for Childhood Educ. International, $0.50.

Understanding Children's Behavior, Fritz Redl, Bur. Publications, Teachers College, Columbia U., $0.60.

Career Series (many titles), N. Y. Life Insurance Co.

Emotions and Physical Health, Metropolitan Life Insurance Co.

Eye; ear; brain (set of charts), Educators' Mutual Insurance Co.

CHAPTER 10

Responses of plants

There are many ways to demonstrate responses of plants to various stimuli. A number of these methods are described here.

Response to light

Leaves. Observe plants growing in the field. Note the mosaic of leaves formed as the leaves are oriented in relation to the angle at which light strikes. Few leaves are shaded by others. Notice the leaves of vines in particular. Indoors, healthy, full-grown geranium and coleus plants show the same tilting of leaf petioles as a positive response to light.

Stems. Shoots of growing seedlings show a positive reaction to light more readily than fully grown plants. Soak seeds of radish, oats, wheat, or bean, or kernels of corn overnight and plant them just under the surface of moist, clean sand in paper cups or flowerpots. Students may place several of these cups of seeds under a box to exclude light. Arrange a second box covering similar cups of seeds, but with a slit on the side at about the level of the cups, and set the boxes where moderate light can enter the slit.

Within a few days, depending on the kind of seeds used, a marked growth or bending of the stems of the shoots should be apparent in the box in which light enters from one side. In the other box, seedlings grow upright in random fashion.

A more elaborate version of this demonstration can be constructed which provides standard conditions of humidity and ventilation. Students might build inside a suitable wooden box a partition reaching within ¼ inch of the top of the box. They can also make a hinged cover for convenient handling if the box is to be a permanent piece of apparatus. Apply black paint to the inside surfaces.

Two variations are shown: in Fig. 10-1a a slit has been cut in the side of the box; in Fig. 10-1b small flashlight bulbs have been wired to the side of one compartment and to the top of the other. In this way an equal amount of light (and heat) is received by both sets of seedlings. Light

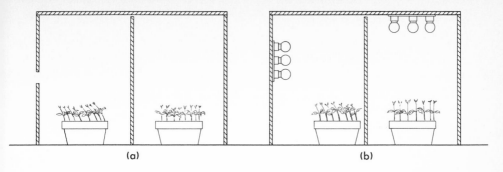

Fig. 10-1 Response of shoots to light (phototropism): two variations.

the bulbs for about 5 minutes every half hour or so.

Light and the growth of shoots. Individual students or small groups may want to repeat some of the classic experiments of Boysen-Jensen and Went on the production of auxin (growth hormone) by the tips of oat coleoptiles. The tips of the coleoptiles, which are the early sheaths which enclose the shoots, are especially sensitive to small amounts of light (when they are only a few centimeters long). Small cups of aluminum foil may be placed over the tips (working in the dark or in red light), or students may cut off the tips. In such cases there is no bending toward light (Fig. 10-2), since sufficient auxin is no longer produced. Thus the tip of the coleoptile is the region which produces auxin and it is the section which is light sensitive. Light (*one* factor among many) seems to deflect the flow of auxin to one side, the shaded side of the shoot (see Fig. 8-10). Therefore the cells of the shaded side,

←—light

Fig. 10-2 Light-sensitive area in oat coleoptiles: A, normal coleoptiles bend toward light source; B, coleoptiles with tips cut off do not.

with the greater concentration of growth hormone, elongate faster and the stems bend toward the light. A physiological regeneration usually takes place within 24 hours, so that tips may have to be cut off again. Some students may want to try some of the techniques using auxin (Chapter 8).

Roots. Roots show a negative response to light. Soak radish or mustard seeds overnight. Spread cheesecloth across several tumblers of water and fasten with a rubber band, allowing some slack so that the cheesecloth remains wet. Then sprinkle seeds on the surface of the cheesecloth.

Enclose some of the tumblers in a darkened box. Cut a small slit into a similar box and cover other preparations with this box. In this way light enters the box from one side (as described above for shoots of seedlings).

You may find it more convenient to make small black paper boxes which fit snugly over individual preparations. Just cut a small slit along one side of some of the paper boxes. After the response of roots (and stems) is apparent, rotate the position of the slit 180 degrees. Notice the change in the growth of stems and roots over the next few days.

Roots show a negative phototropism, i.e., grow away from light, while shoots show a positive phototropism.

Response of roots to water

There are several ways to show responses to the stimulus of water (hydrotropism). You may want groups of students to try several methods.

Pocket garden. Use two squares of glass to fashion a pocket garden. Place two thicknesses of blotting paper between the glass squares so that a clear channel remains in the center (Fig. 10-3). Along the center, arrange small seeds such as radish, mustard, or lettuce, which have been previously soaked. Then plug the ends of the row of seeds with cotton so that they will not fall out. Fasten the glass plates together with rubber bands. Now stand one end of the preparation in water until one blotter becomes soaked. Then attach a strip of filter paper to the edge of this wet blotter to form a wick. Rest the pocket garden on a fingerbowl of water, and immerse the wick as shown. Be sure the other blotter remains dry. Within a few days observe the roots of the germinating seeds growing in the direction of the wet blotter rather than toward the dry blotter. Since the preparation is in a horizontal position, the stimulus of gravity will not interfere with the responses.

Hanging garden. Or shape a ball of sphagnum moss (or use a sponge), soak it in water, and then hold it together with cord. Insert soaked seeds of oats, corn grains, bean, radish, or wheat seeds at different locations: top, sides, and bottom. Hang this ball from a hook somewhere in class. Within a few days (depending on the kind of seed) the seeds will sprout. Students will see that roots grow *into* the sphagnum rather than downwards in response to gravity. That is, the roots show a positive hydrotropism. The stimulus of water is greater than the stimulus of gravity. Should students suggest that the roots grow inward as a negative response to light, have them devise a plan for a control experiment (the same preparation growing in the dark) so they may refute their own suggestions.

Glass panel. You may find this method practical for showing roots growing toward water. Fill a glass tank (or box with a glass panel) containing seedlings with soil, and insert a small flower pot into the box. Then cork the bottom opening of the flower pot and half fill it with water. Water will diffuse out into the soil through the porous pot. As time passes, watch the roots bend and grow in the direction of the supply of water around the flower pot rather than toward drier soil. The same preparation may be made by inserting a small flower pot into a larger one, but the roots and their direction of growth cannot be seen unless the seedlings are lifted out of the soil.

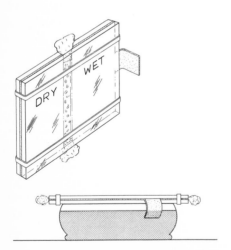

Fig. 10-3 Response of roots to water (hydrotropism): soaked fast-growing seeds are placed in the channel of a glass-blotter-and-rubber-band pocket garden. A piece of blotter serves as a wick to keep one blotter wet when the "garden" is placed over a finger bowl of water.

Response to gravity

Stems

Healthy shoots of *Tradescantia* are excellent materials for demonstrating the negative response of shoots to gravity. Tropic responses can be observed within 1 hour. Clamp to a ringstand three test tubes with stoppers containing shoots of *Tradescantia* in the positions shown in Fig. 10-4a. Be sure to seal the stopper of each test tube with melted paraffin to avoid water leakage. (Germinating seedlings may be used in place of the shoots of *Tradescantia*, but the response will not be as rapid.) Of course, seedlings may be grown in paper cups of sand instead of these test tubes, with some vertical and some horizontal. You may want to place some controls in the dark so that light as a possible factor in this response is eliminated.

Here is another way to use seedlings when fast-growing shoots like *Tradescantia* are not available. Line large test tubes (about 10 inches long) with blotting paper and insert a plug of absorbent cotton into the bottom of each tube. Wet

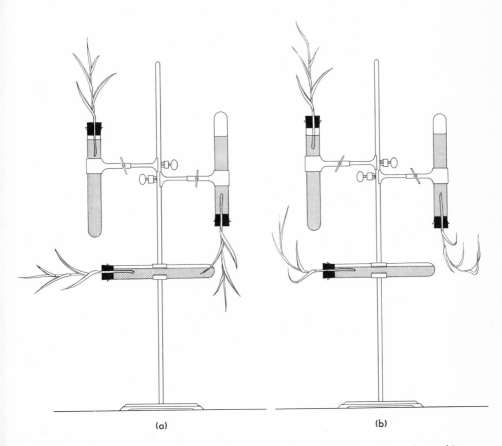

Fig. 10-4 Do shoots respond to gravity (geotropism)? (a) Sprigs of *Tradescantia* are inserted into stoppered tubes of water, clamped in various positions; (b) response.

the blotting paper thoroughly. Between the glass and the blotter arrange soaked seeds of oats, radishes, or wheat. Fill the tubes again with water; pour off the excess. If you attach string or wire to both the top and bottom of each of the test tubes you have a loop through which they can be suspended in different positions from hooks around the classroom. When the test tubes hang at a slant, the growth of stems shows a negative geotropic response. Change the position of the tubes and watch for the change in direction of the growth of stems. In addition, set up replicas covered with carbon paper or hang some in the dark.

Roots

Some of the preparations made to show negative response of stems to gravity are useful here. For example, when using seedlings in place of *Tradescantia,* students will notice that the roots respond positively to the stimulus of gravity. Regardless of their original position roots bend and respond to gravity.

Also have students observe the growth of roots of seedlings planted between the glass tube and blotter and those suspended from hooks in the classroom. The stems show a negative, the roots a positive geotropic response.

If students previously germinated seeds in paper cups of sand to show negative geotropism in stems, they can now demonstrate the direction of root growth. After 3 or 4 days of growth, loosen the seedlings from the moist sand by shaking them gently, and look for the bending of roots toward a vertical position.

Here are some other techniques of dealing with responses of plants; these may be preferable, or give variety to demonstrations.

Using a Petri dish. Select soaked seeds

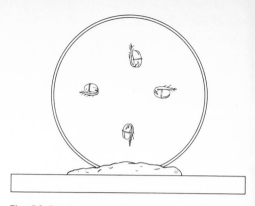

Fig. 10-5 Response of roots to gravity (geotropism): germinating seedlings are attached to moist blotter lining a Petri dish, and the dish is held upright by a ball of clay.

of beans, oats, wheat, or peas which have begun to germinate so that a few centimeters of roots are visible. Then fasten four seeds to a blotter which has been cut to fit the bottom of a Petri dish. Thread fine wire through the cotyledons of the seeds to fasten them to the blotter; arrange the seeds so that the roots face the compass points, wet the blotter and cover the Petri dish. Prepare several of these Petri dishes. Then stand the dishes in various positions by inserting one edge into a bit of modeling clay (Fig. 10-5). When roots show a positive response to gravity, shift the position of the dish and watch the change in the direction of growth of each root. In addition (to show that this is not a response to light) similar dishes may be kept in the dark.

With a glass-marking pencil, trace the path of each growing root on the surface of the Petri dish if the growth pattern of the roots themselves is not apparent.

Using a pocket garden. Students may find a pocket garden easier to handle than Petri dishes. Prepare a "garden" in this way. Soak a sheet of blotting paper and lay it over a glass square. Then scatter soaked radish seeds at random evenly over the surface of the blotter. Cover this with a second glass square and secure with adhesive tape or rubber bands. Now stand one edge of the pocket garden in a fingerbowl containing some water. When the roots of the seedlings have grown sufficiently and demonstrate positive geotropism, invert the pocket garden. Within a few days, note the changed direction of growth of the roots. Students can make several preparations and place some of them inside jars lined with black paper or cover them with a box. If students ask whether light had an effect they may study the controls which were placed in the dark.

Using a battery jar. In a variation of this demonstration, neither pocket gardens nor Petri dishes are required. Pin seedlings to a cork board and place the board in a darkened, covered battery jar, lined with moist blotting paper. You may turn the cork board from time to time and show the persistent tendency of roots to grow downward as a positive response to gravity.

Using a clinostat. Some students can show that when roots are constantly revolving there is no response to gravity. (This may be a project for students especially interested in the "esoteric" responses of plants.) Roots continue to grow in the directions in which they were originally placed. Make a homemade clinostat by attaching the preparation described above, in which seedlings were wired to a blotter in a Petri dish, to the minute-hand shaft of an old alarm clock (in an upright position) so that a continuous revolving motion is produced. A small low-speed electric motor can also be used.

At another time a small committee of students may try to fasten seedlings to a water wheel. A much faster rotation may be effected with a water wheel and stu-dents may show that roots fail to respond to gravity in this condition.

Responses against obstacles. Students may demonstrate how persistent is the response of roots to gravity, even when obstacles exist. For example, roots grow into solidified agar or into mercury.

Line the sides of several finger bowls with sheets of cork. Into the bowls pour a layer of mercury ½-inch deep (or use a layer of agar prepared by boiling together 1 part agar with 4 parts of water). Pin several germinating seedlings, which have a primary root about ½-inch long, around the cork lining so that the roots are in a horizontal position and almost touch the mercury (or agar). Add a film of water to the surface of the mercury to cover the roots. After the finger bowls have been covered and sealed, if necessary, with Vaseline, put some in the dark and others in the light. After a day or so, depending upon the kind of seedlings used, notice how the roots curve and grow into the mercury. Here roots respond to gravity and illustrate an expenditure of energy, for the mercury or agar offers resistance.

Although the use of mercury in this demonstration of the expenditure of energy by seedlings is effective, there are two drawbacks: A large quantity of mercury is needed, and mercury frequently poisons the roots of the seedlings.

Region of sensitivity in roots. Again place seedlings with roots about ½-inch long in the directions of the compass points as described earlier. Then cut off the tips of the roots with a razor. Prepare replicas in which the root tips are left intact. Keep all the preparations in the dark. Students will notice that the roots of the tipless seedlings do not show the normal geotropic response (until a physiological regeneration of the root tips occurs). Thus we demonstrate that it is the tips of roots that receive the stimulus, and an uneven growth of one side of the root results in a bending. Compare this with the effect of auxin on bending in stems (Figs. 8-10, 10-2). Also refer to the region of greatest growth in young roots (Fig. 8-4).

Response to touch and heat

Climbing roses and many vines show a positive thigmotropism, a response to touch that enables them to encircle a trellis. However, there are other cases of sensitivity in plants which probably are not tropisms.

We may show sudden responses in plants such as the sensitive plant *Mimosa* (Fig. 10-6). The responses are the result of changes in turgidity of certain cells found in a swelling, called a pulvinus, situated at the base of each cluster of leaflets. Bring a lighted match close to the tip of a cluster of leaflets. Watch the sudden folding and drooping of the entire cluster of leaflets.

Students may show how these plants respond to mechanical stimulus, touch. Gently tap the terminal leaflets with a pencil, or with your finger, or pinch the leaflets with a forceps. See how quickly the end leaflets fold over each other.

Fig. 10-6   Responses of *Mimosa pudica: left,* the plant undisturbed; *right,* response to touch. (Photos: General Biological Supply House, Inc., Chicago.)

A summary demonstration of several tropisms

You may want students to prepare the demonstrations which were first described by Coulter[1] some seventy years ago. (These are especially good for a "new" view of the topic.) Students can prepare balls of sphagnum moss with soaked seeds) and devise experiments to test whether light, gravity, water, and so forth, affect the growth of stems and roots. Use fast-growing seedlings such as oats, barley, radishes, or corn grains.

[1] J. M. Coulter, "Influence of gravity, moisture, light, upon the direction of growth in the roots and stems of plants," *Science,* 2:5, 1883.

Moisten masses of sphagnum moss and scatter soaked seeds into the moss. Then shape the moss into balls about 4 to 5 inches in diameter. Tie each mass together with string so each retains its shape. Prepare some seven to ten such balls of moss, so that the following demonstrations can be prepared. Where possible, prepare duplicates.

Suspend one sphagnum ball in the classroom so that it receives light from all sides. Place a second ball on a glass tumbler which has some water in it, about 1 inch above the level of water. Prepare a third in the same way over a tumbler, but cover the glass with black paper. Then cut a thin slit in the paper so that light enters from one side.

Insert a fourth ball part way into another tumbler as though the ball were a stopper. Thus one half of the ball is outside the tumbler and the other half is inside. Then prepare a fifth ball in the same way, but place the tumbler in a horizontal position. With two more balls prepare setups similar to the fourth and the fifth, but cover the tumbler with black paper so that light is excluded as a factor in the response.

Mount the eighth ball on a spindle, such as a knitting needle, which runs through its center. Then attach the spindle to the minute hand of an upright alarm clock so that the spindle forms a continuation of the minute hand of the clock.

Watch the direction of the growth of shoots and roots. Students may be able on the basis of these devices to generalize about the direction of tropic responses in plants.

CAPSULE LESSONS
Ways to get started in class

10-1. Ask students why roots of plants grow downward. Is it a response away from light or a response to gravity (or something else)? Establish how an experiment might be designed so that only one factor is tested at a time. This is a good device for teaching the elements of a controlled experiment.

10-2. Have the class plan a field trip around the school grounds to look for examples of tropisms among plants. Students may search for examples of plants responding to environmental conditions. Give one or two examples; then set them free for 10 minutes to find more. Bring the class together again; all of them will be working together to check the examples they have found.

10-3. Ask students to bring in some *Tradescantia* sprigs and supply equipment to set up the demonstration in Fig. 10-4. Get the students to plan the demonstration themselves. Ask what might happen if the plant were reversed (upside down). Why do stems grow up and roots grow into the soil?

10-4. You may want to bring to class an example of some tropism described in the chapter, then elicit explanations from the students as to the cause of this response.

10-5. As independent research, or a group project, students may want to learn more about auxins (see p. 115) and plant growth. They may want to go further into the whole field of polarity. Is it possible for roots to grow at the growing tip of a shoot? Try using cuttings of fast-growing plants—willows, coleus, and similar plants.

10-6. You may want to show a film as an introduction or as a review of behavior in plants. Have you seen *Reactions in Plants and Animals* (Encyclopaedia Britannica)? Or show *Sensitivity of Plants* (Almanac).

PEOPLE, PLACES, AND THINGS

It may be possible to visit a nursery or an experimental station where work is in progress on the effects of hormones on plant growth.

Visit a nearby woods if possible, or plan a field trip near school. Solicit the aid of nurserymen and of parents in landscaping a small area of the school grounds so that you can take classes to this spot to teach many aspects of interrelationships of plants and animals, and aspects of conservation (see pp. 264–65).

Students might prepare several terraria in the classroom. These may be made from leaking aquarium tanks, large mayonnaise jars, or other similar jars. Plan to have terraria which illustrate different environmental relations: plants of a swampy scene, a desert environment, a wooded area (see p. 394 for making terraria).

BOOKS AND PAMPHLETS

These are only a few of the books which are pertinent to the work discussed in this chapter. These and many other references classified by subject and with complete bibliographical data are given in the Bibliography at the end of the book.

Audus, L., *Plant Growth Substances*, 1953.
Avery, G., and E. Johnson, *Hormones and Horticulture*, 1947.
Gibbs, R., *Botany: An Evolutionary Approach*, 1950.
Machlis, L., and J. Torrey, *Plants in Action* (lab manual), 1956.
Meyer, B., and D. Anderson, *Plant Physiology*, 1952.
Miller, E., *Within the Living Plant*, 1953.
Mitchell, J., and P. Marth, *Growth Regulators for Garden, Field, and Orchard*, 1947.

FILMS AND FILMSTRIPS

This partial list is intended only as a guide toward film and filmstrip selection. Refer to the more complete listing at the end of the book where films are classified by subject and where a key to abbreviations and the addresses of distributors are given. The cost of film rental, of course, may be subject to change. Films are sound and black and white unless otherwise specified.

Movements of Some Common Plants (f, si), Iowa State U., $2.00.
Plant Traps (f), EBF, $4.00.
Plant Growth (f), EBF, $2.50.
Power of Plants (f), Almanac, $2.00.
Reactions in Plants and Animals (f), EBF, $2.50.
Roots of Plants (f), EBF, $2.50.
Sensitivity of Plants (f), Almanac, $2.00.
Time Lapse Studies of Growing Trees (f, c), State U. of New York, $3.00.

FREE AND INEXPENSIVE MATERIALS

This is only a partial listing of free and inexpensive materials available to the teacher at this time. A more complete listing, including addresses, is given at the end of the book. Many of these materials are distributed to teachers without charge. Where there is a small fee, the cost is indicated, although the prices are subject to change. While we recommend the material for use in the classroom, we do not necessarily sponsor the products advertised.

Carolina Tips, Carolina Biological Supply Co.
Natural Science Bulletin, Ward's Natural Science Establishment.
Publications on Wildlife, Conservation, Agriculture (catalog), U.S. Govt. Printing Office.
Thousands of Science Projects; Free and Low Cost Materials for Science Clubs of America, Science Clubs of America.
Turtox Leaflets (set of 50), General Biological Supply House.

CHAPTER 11

Reproduction

Classic experiments disproving spontaneous generation

Nowadays we accept the fact that organisms arise from previously existing living things. This idea, however, was not held in ancient times. Redi, among others, suspected that the familiar stories of spontaneous generation of living things were false.

Redi's experiment. Redi set up, as you remember, three jars to discover whether or not maggots and flies came from decaying meat. In season, this may be duplicated (Fig. 11-1). Leave one jar open, another covered with cheesecloth (close mesh), and a third sealed with a

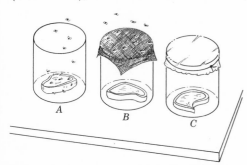

Fig. 11-1 Simulating Redi's experiment: flies have direct access to meat in jar A; jar B is covered with cheesecloth; jar C is covered with clear plastic or glass.

sheet of plastic, as a substitute for Redi's parchment. Place a piece of fresh meat in each jar and set the jars out of doors overnight. You will find eggs of blow flies on the meat in the open jar and on the cheesecloth of the second jar, and no trace of flies on the jar from which the odor could not escape. In fact, any time throughout the year you may use fruit flies and a medium of ripe banana (Chapter 12) in place of decaying meat. If fruit flies are used to repeat this classic experiment, cover sets of half-pint bottles containing the banana medium (some covered with cheesecloth, others with cellophane or plastic, still others open) with an open-top bell jar (Fig. 11-2). Then select a thriving stock bottle of fruit flies and invert the mouth of the bottle into the opening in the bell jar. Quickly place a stopper to close the bell jar. The flies within have the opportunity to select among the bottles. Within a week students should see evidence that eggs have been laid and larvae are burrowing in the bottles which have been kept open.

Spallanzani's experiment. For a time Redi's work seemed at least to have dis-

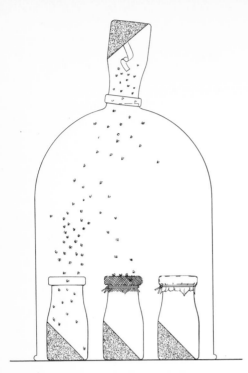

Fig. 11-2 Duplicating Redi's experiment with fruit flies: flies are introduced into bell jar containing bottles of banana medium; some are open, some covered with cheesecloth, some sealed with plastic.

pelled the idea that spontaneous generation occurred in large forms. Then with the invention of the microscope and the discovery of the world of microorganisms doubts again arose. Could such minute organisms have arisen from previously existing organisms also so tiny? You may want to develop some of the case histories involving Needham and Spallanzani, Schwann, Pouchet, and Pasteur (to mention only a few who took sides in this controversy which lasted for some three centuries). Pasteur finally gave evidence of the propagation of microscopic forms from previously existing forms.[1]

[1] J. Conant, ed., *Pasteur's and Tyndall's Study of Spontaneous Generation,* Harvard Case Hist., Harvard U. Press, Cambridge, Mass., 1953. Also see *Pasteur's Study of Fermentation,* another case study in the series.

Spallanzani's experiments disproving spontaneous generation of microorganisms can be repeated in class. You may recall that he boiled broth and quickly sealed the flasks. To prepare similar containers use nine test tubes pulled out in the center (see Fig. 6-4a). Make the constriction about ¾ inch in length. As the tubes cool, prepare beef broth (p. 380) and fill the lower part of each tube with broth. Then arrange the tubes this way (Fig. 11-3):

Boil the broth in three tubes (*A*) in a water bath or double boiler and leave them unsealed.

Boil the broth in another three tubes (*B*). Quickly plug the tubes with cotton. When the test tubes are cool enough to handle, hold them at an angle of 45 degrees over the Bunsen burner and heat the constricted area. Pull out the top and seal each tube (see Fig. 6-4b).

Seal three tubes of broth (*C*) without any preliminary heating.

In a few days students should find that tubes *A* and *C* contain turbid broth while the broth in tubes *B* remains clear. The tops of the sealed tubes may be broken and sample drops of the broth examined

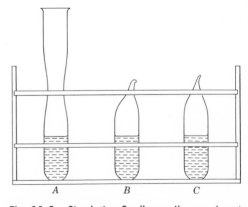

Fig. 11-3 Simulating Spallanzani's experiment: the broth in tube A was boiled and left open to air; in tube B, boiled and sealed; in tube C, sealed, but not boiled.

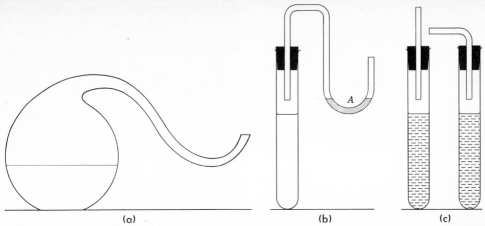

Fig. 11-4 "Flasks" for Pasteur's experiment: (a) one of Pasteur's flasks; (b) simple apparatus which works like Pasteur's flasks, forming at A a water trap for dust particles when the broth is heated; (c) control tubes to be used with the one in (b).

under the microscope under high power. Use a sterile wire loop to transfer a drop of the broth onto a clean glass slide (see Fig. 20-10) and mount with a coverslip. Flame the loop after each dip into the broth. You may want to stain dry smears with methylene blue (p. 309).

Modification of Pasteur's experiment. Pasteur devised many experiments on spontaneous generation. He designed a series of flasks like the one shown in Fig. 11-4a. To simulate his experiments you may want to prepare tubes of broth with an S-shaped delivery tube (Fig. 11-4b). As the test tubes of broth are heated, water vapor will collect in the trap in the delivery tube. In this way Pasteur permitted dust-free (bacteria-free) air to enter the tubes. The heated broth should remain clear, but the controls set up as in Fig. 11-4c should become turbid. Examinations of the bacteria in the broth may be made by students to confirm their observations.

Asexual reproduction in animals and plants

Fission

Many one-celled plants and animals divide into two halves. In well-fed, healthy cultures of protozoa, bacteria, and many algae, organisms undergoing fission can be found (Fig. 11-5). Techniques for preparing such cultures are described in Chapters 18 and 20. In these cultures, transverse and lengthwise fission may be discovered.

On occasion, you may want students to study the rate of fission in some protozoans. They may isolate individual protozoans under a binocular microscope with a micropipette, that is glass tubing

Fig. 11-5 Fission in *Paramecium*: note stages from left to right, in stained preparation. (Photo: General Biological Supply House, Inc., Chicago.)

which has been pulled out to a fine bore (in a Bunsen flame). The students should count the number of protozoans they put into a small quantity of medium in a Syracuse dish. In 24 hours they may find twice as many or possibly four times the original number. Then isolate each of these in fresh medium in other Syracuse dishes.

If a stereoscopic microscope is not available, place a row of small drops of the protozoans on a slide and examine each drop. In a random sampling you should find a drop with only a few animals. This drop may be transferred to a Syracuse dish containing culture medium. After a week or so the number of animals will have increased greatly.

You may want to have students study the rate of division among several protozoans. They may compare the effects of varying temperatures or pH values, or adding vitamins, hormones, or antibiotics to the medium.

Use a solution of methyl cellulose or gum tragacanth (p. 314) for slowing down the protozoans. Vital stains (for temporary mounts) and staining techniques (for permanent mounts) are described in Chapter 17.

Budding

Prepare yeast cultures as described on page 391. You should find many examples of small buds protruding from the parent plants (Fig. 11-6).

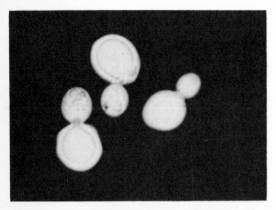

Fig. 11-6 Budding in yeast. (Photo: Dr. Carl Lindegren, Southern Illinois U.)

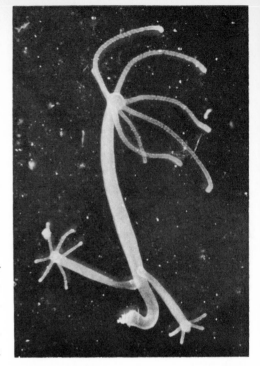

Fig. 11-7 Budding in *Hydra*. (Photo: A. M. Winchester.)

Use a vital stain (such as neutral red) to make the cells easily visible. Add a drop of a 1 per cent solution of neutral red to one side of the coverslip of a mounted specimen. Remove the fluid in which the yeast cells were cultured by applying a piece of filter paper to the opposite side of the coverslip. Note how the volutin vacuoles and the granules of the living cells take up the neutral red stain. Dead cells, on the other hand, stain a uniform red color.

Examine also a culture of *Hydra* and look for budding: small replicas of *Hydra* may be found growing out of the stalk (Fig. 11-7). Culture methods are described in Chapter 18.

Spore formation

Spore formation may be demonstrated readily, using molds such as bread mold (*Rhizopus*) (Fig. 20-13b), *Penicillium* (Fig.

11-8), or *Aspergillus.* Under unfavorable conditions yeasts also may form spores, but these are difficult to show. While sporulation is found to some extent among Protozoa (especially the malarial *Plasmodium*), examples are difficult to demonstrate unless prepared slides are used.

Prepare cultures of molds as described in Chapter 20. Mount the fruiting bodies (sporangia) of the molds in a drop of glycerin or alcohol to prevent the formation of air bubbles in the mounted specimens.

You may also want to study spore formation in forms such as the mildews or even in yeasts and mushrooms (p. 390), or alternation of generation in mosses or ferns (Figs. 11-44, 11-45).

You may want to simulate the mechanical dissemination of spores from a mold spore case. Almost fill a round black balloon with balls of cotton no larger than ¼ inch in diameter.[2] Then put the neck of the balloon over one end of a 3-foot length of ½-inch glass tubing with fire-polished ends. Inflate the balloon by blowing through the open end of the glass tubing. Plug the open end with modeling clay so that the air will not escape. Sink this end into a mass of modeling clay so that the upright "sporangium and sporangiophore" of a bread mold are simulated. The mass of clay may be considered the substrate. A network of glass tubes may be partially imbedded in the clay to represent mycelia.

Burst the "sporangium" by dropping one or two drops of xylol on the balloon, or casually stroke the balloon after wetting your fingers in xylol. Students can watch the bursting and the release of the cotton "spores," and notice that the cotton balls are expelled to fairly great distances around the room.

[2] P. Brandwein, M. Rabinowitz, G. Schwartz, and E. Steiner, *Laboratory Techniques in Biology,* mimeographed, 1940.

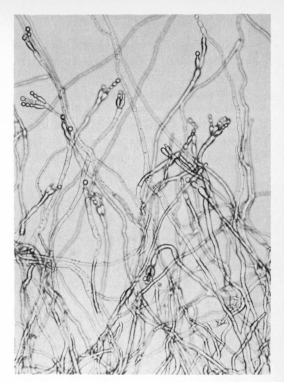

Fig. 11-8 Spore formation in *Penicillium notatum.* (Photo: General Biological Supply House, Inc., Chicago.)

Regeneration

Some animals and many plants have the ability to regenerate parts of the body. In this process new cells are formed as a result of differentiation and growth. When regeneration leads to the formation of new individuals, as it can with planarians and hydras, it may be considered a means of reproduction. The same process in plants is usually called vegetative propagation.

Regeneration in Hydra. Place a well-fed *Hydra* in a Syracuse dish containing aquarium or pond water. Cut the animal transversely with a sharp razor or with a coverslip. Then cover the dish to prevent evaporation. Prepare several specimens in this way. Within 10 days at room temperature (or slightly cooler) you should find that both ends of the animal regenerate the missing halves. Of course, in asexual reproduction in hydras (Fig. 11-7) a small bud regenerates a complete organism.

Regeneration in *Planaria*. Culture the planarians as described in Chapter 18. This small flatworm may be cut in various regions. The rate of regeneration in relation to the metabolic gradient (or degree of cephalization) may be studied as a project activity.

Stretch one of the animals out on a glass slide in a drop of water. With a sharp razor or coverslip carefully cut the planarian. Then isolate the cut pieces into Syracuse dishes containing pond water. (Keep in a covered container in the dark.) Change the water frequently to encourage rapid healing.

Regeneration in *Tubifex* worms. This is an annelid worm which you may purchase in aquarium or pet shops. In these forms posterior regeneration is most successful. Put the specimens in clean Syracuse dishes and make a transverse cut with a clean scalpel or razor blade. Then separate the sections into individual dishes and keep them at room temperature (50 to 60° F). It takes 2 to 3 weeks for successful regeneration. A new anal opening is formed within 48 hours when the cut end heals.

In other demonstrations of regeneration use *Dero,* a microscopic annelid, or try using the earthworm. In the latter, anterior-end regeneration seems to be more successful.

Vegetative propagation

In essence, vegetative propagation involves the "planting" of some vegetative part of the plant, such as a stem, leaves, or roots, to grow another plant. The new plants are essentially similar to the parent plants.

Vegetative propagation may occur naturally; this is true asexual reproduction.

At times we use vegetative propagation to get more plants of the same genetic makeup (barring mutations) as the parent.

Natural methods of vegetative propagation

Root stocks and rhizomes. Many species of plants spread themselves by means of vigorous underground stems which grow out in all directions from the parent plant. Rootlets develop at intervals and stems shoot up at these nodes (Fig. 11-9). Two hardy forms which may be grown in the classroom and used to demonstrate this are varieties of snake plant (*Sansevieria*) and *Aspidistra*. Other common forms which reproduce similarly are Solomon's-seal, Calla lilies, a large number of ferns (especially New York, Boston, holly, hay-scented, and Polypody), Johnson grass, and Bermuda grass.

Runners (stolons). Some plants produce trailing or reclining stems which take root at their ends or at nodes; erect stems grow from these nodes. Specimens of the hardy strawberry geranium (*Saxifraga*) and the spider plant (*Anthericum liliago*) are available for classroom use throughout the year. Other useful plants are the strawberry (*Fragaria*) (Fig. 11-10), cinquefoil (*Potentilla*), and *Cotyledon secunda*. Several aquarium plants, such as eel grass (*Vallisneria*), also produce long runners.

Bulbs and corms. A bulb is a compact group of fleshy scales or leaves surrounding a small, sometimes vestigial stem. In

Fig. 11-9 Rhizomes of Solomon's-seal. (From W. G. Whaley, O. P. Breland, et al., *Principles of Biology*, Harper, 1954.)

Fig. 11-10 Stolon of strawberry. (From W. G. Whaley, O. P. Breland, et al., *Principles of Biology,* Harper, 1954; after Robbins & Weier, *Botany,* Wiley.)

some forms like the lily the scales are narrow and loose, while in the onion, narcissus, amaryllis, daffodil, and hyacinth the scales are continuous and fit closely. Small bulbs, or bulblets, may develop around the parent bulb. These small bulbs are borne above the ground, for example, in the axils of the leaves of the tiger lily, or at the top of the flower stalk in the leek. Other bulbs often divide into two or more parts.

On the other hand, a corm is solid throughout. Cormels are developed in the same way bulblets are formed. Good examples of corms are those of Indian turnip or Jack-in-the-pulpit (*Arisaema*), *Caladium,* crocus (Fig. 11-11), and gladiolus.

Students may grow many of these in class. For example, when onions are partially submerged in water (with the root end just below the water surface), a good root system develops in a week. The onion may be supported by the rim of the container. When bulbs are not placed in water they first send forth shoots, not roots. Similarly, narcissus and hyacinth bulbs may be grown in water or gravel. Narcissus bulbs grow quickly and flower in a warm room in a month's time, while hyacinth bulbs require a preliminary cooling treatment in a dark place for about four weeks. Then flowers appear 2 to 3 months later. Tulip and spring crocus bulbs require a cool temperature

(about 40° F) for a preliminary "forcing." Cover the bulbs lightly with sandy loam, water them well and keep them in a cool, dark place for about 9 to 10 weeks. The bulbs of Easter lilies, which are rather slow to flower, should be covered with some 2 inches of sandy loam, watered well, and kept in the dark until the shoots are a few inches long. After this, transfer them to a warm location, where it takes from 3 to 4 months for the lilies to flower.

Tubers. These are thickened underground stems, in which starch is stored. The new plants arise from rather inconspicuous buds in the tubers, such as the "eyes" in the white potato. Cover tubers of the white potato, dahlias, *Anthericum,* or *Caladium* with ½ inch of wet sand, or set them in a tumbler of water so that about half of the tuber is covered.

Fleshy roots. If sweet potatoes, carrots, or radishes (supported by toothpicks) are placed in containers of water, new shoots will appear.

Artificial methods of vegetative propagation

Cuttings. A cutting is a part of the plant, either a stem or a leaf, which has been separated from the parent plant

Fig. 11-11 Corm of a crocus. (From W. G. Whaley, O. P. Breland, et al., *Principles of Biology,* Harper, 1954; after Holman & Robbins, *Botany,* Wiley.)

and which, under suitable conditions, will produce a complete plant.

(a) *Stem cuttings:* Select the tip of a healthy, vigorous young stem of geranium, begonia, or *Tradescantia* to use for a cutting. Have several nodes in the cutting, usually a piece 1 to 4 inches long, depending on the plant and the length of the internodes. On the other hand, when vines are used, such as bittersweet (*Celastrus*), the older parts will root better.

In preparing a stem cutting, cut squarely below a node with a sharp, clean knife. Pinch off the flower bud if there is one. Then cut off most of the leaves to reduce the rate of transpiration so that the cutting does not wilt. Plant the cutting 1 inch deep in medium-grained wet sand or sphagnum moss.

For good results with fleshy-stemmed plants such as geranium and *Dieffenbachia* (which should see use more often where stem cuttings are desired), the tip of a plant is not used. Instead, cut the stem into 2- or 3-inch pieces and plant them horizontally in moist sand. Allow a cover of about ½ inch of sand.

Other plants suitable for stem cuttings are: coleus, ivy (either *Hedera* or *Parthenocissus*), privet (*Ligustrum*), willow (*Salix*), golden-bell (*Forsythia*), pineapple (*Ananas*), cactus (*Opuntia*); other similar cacti will also do. Succulent forms usually take root within 2 to 3 weeks, while woody types often require months.

There are a few precautions to observe in making cuttings. Use healthy stocks and work in a place that is neither excessively hot or dry so that plants do not wilt rapidly. Keep the plant cuttings in moist newspaper until they are ready for planting.

The planting medium must be moist to keep the plants from wilting, and well drained so they do not rot. Pack the cuttings to keep them upright. Use coarse-grained sand for good drainage. (You will find that round-grained sand such as sea sand does not pack well.)

After the cuttings have been planted in sand, water them well and cover with moist newspaper (or invert a glass tumbler over each plant to retain moisture). These may be removed after a few days. Keep the young cuttings sheltered from strong sunlight.

A callus forms around the cut end and adventitious roots develop in some 2 to 3 weeks. Then set the small plants into 2-inch pots. The pots should first be washed and soaked in water for several hours so that they will not absorb water at once from the potting soil. Prepare this soil by mixing 3 parts loam (garden soil), 1 part sand, and 1 part humus. Crush the lumps so that the soil is smooth and fine textured. Then water this thoroughly about an hour before potting. Finally, fill the pots with the soil.

Slip a broad knife or spatula under the cutting to lift it. Lift the sand along with the cutting; otherwise you may injure the roots. Make a hole in the soil with your finger and set the cutting in place. Avoid packing the soil too tightly. If the roots are long, hold the plant in place in the empty pot and gradually add the soil. When the plants show good growth, transfer them, with the same technique, into 4-inch pots.

In general, most cuttings, fleshy roots, and stems of herbaceous plants are less subject to bacterial or fungus attack when started in moist sand rather than plain water. Storage parts of plants containing sugar or starch are most susceptible to decay.

(A special note about geranium plants. In the fall they should be cut back, repotted, and allowed a period of rest. Cut the plants back about ⅔ of their length and divide the plants so that each cutting

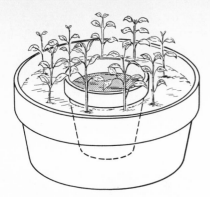

Fig. 11-12 Growing cuttings with equal drainage: the smaller, inset flower pot is kept full of water.

has about three main stems. These cuttings should be repotted in a mixture of equal parts of loam, sand and leaf mold. You may plant cuttings of smaller size in a large flower pot in a circular fashion around a partly submerged smaller pot, as in Fig. 11-12. Water the center pot so that equal drainage takes place with less chance for leaching of the minerals from the soil.)

(b) *Leaf cuttings:* A new plant may be grown from part of a leaf. Use the leaves of *Bryophyllum* (Fig. 11-13), *Kalanchoë*, *Sedum,* begonias (especially *Begonia rex*), or *Sansevieria*. Lay the leaves of the first three plants on wet sand and hold them flat with a small stone or flat piece of

Fig. 11-13 A leaf cutting: small plants arise from the notches along the edges of a leaf of *Bryophyllum pinnatum*. (From W. H. Brown, *The Plant Kingdom*, Ginn, 1935.)

glass placed on the leaf blade. For *Begonia rex* and *Sansevieria* a section some 2 inches long should be planted upright, about 1 inch deep in sand. Look for rooting and the appearance of shoots.

Layering. While layering occurs naturally, especially among wild roses, raspberries, and blackberries, it may be done with purpose. A branch is placed in contact with the moist soil and held fast so that roots and shoots are produced at the point of contact with the soil (Fig. 11-14). These can be separated from the parent plant. This method is used when plants cannot be successfully grown from cuttings because they do not root readily. Layering is the commercial method for propagating such plants as magnolia, grapevines, and raspberries.

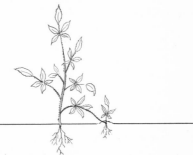

Fig. 11-14 Layering: where the tip of a branch is covered with soil, a new shoot grows.

In class you may want to use such plants as *Vinca*, English ivy, and *Philodendron*. The small climbing rose and the small blackberry, *Rubus villosus,* are especially suitable for classwork.

Sometime you may want to try the Chinese or pot method of layering. This is generally successful with rubber plants (*Ficus*) and castor-oil plant (*Croton*). Cut into the bark of a branch about 1 foot away from the tip, where the wood is slightly hardened, and pack it around with sphagnum moss tied with raffia or cord. Keep this moist. Then cut a flower pot in half lengthwise and shape each half around the wounded section of the stem. Hold it together with cord. Paper may be used instead of the flower pot, but it is less effective. In 2 to 3 weeks, when the stem becomes rooted, cut off the branch from the tree.

Grafting. In this method of vegetative propagation the cut surfaces of two woody plants are placed together; their cambium layers must make contact if they are to grow together. In our experience, useful plants for classroom work in grafting are the potato (*Solanum*) and the tomato (*Lycopersicum*). Thriving tomato plants furnish suitable scions to graft onto the potato stock.

There are some precautions. Try only the simplest kinds of grafts, that is, stem grafts. Bud and saddle and other types are not generally successful in the classroom. The work is fast enough to hold interest and students may practice these grafts with success too. The scion and the stock should be similar in width. Remove all the leaves of both the stock and the scion when you graft. Make clean cuts with a sharp, clean knife (Fig. 11-15).

Fit the cut ends snugly and tie them together with raffia or similar material. Then impregnate this with beeswax or grafting wax (p. 406). When possible the stock should be cut about 1 or 2 inches from the soil line in order to eliminate many buds and still be visible. On the scion there should be as many buds as possible, including the terminal bud.

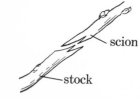

Fig. 11-15 A stem graft: the cut scion (which has its terminal bud, not shown) is fitted to the rooted stock.

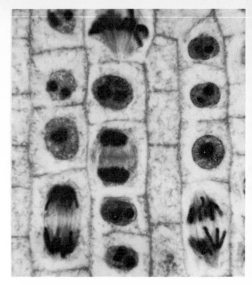

Fig. 11-16 Photomicrograph of onion root tip, showing mitotic stages. (Photo: General Biological Supply House, Inc., Chicago.)

Students may try bud grafts and tongue grafts with apple and with privet where these are available. Select a stem ½ inch in diameter.

Mitosis in cells

Growth of new cells occurs in regeneration of animal parts and in vegetative propagation. New cells are formed as a result of fission, budding, or sporulation. In all cases the nuclear content of the cells is distributed equally to each new cell; chromosomes and genes are divided equally between the new cells. This nuclear division is mitotic in nature.

You may want to have students study mitosis in actively growing tissues; for example, root tips or fertilized eggs are the classic materials for study. These tissues need special staining to make chromosomes visible. Incidentally, chromosomes are not visible unless they are going through mitosis or reduction division (Fig. 11-20).

Prepared slides of onion root tip (Fig. 11-16) or of cleavage stages in the eggs of fish (Fig. 11-17), starfish (Fig. 11-23), or

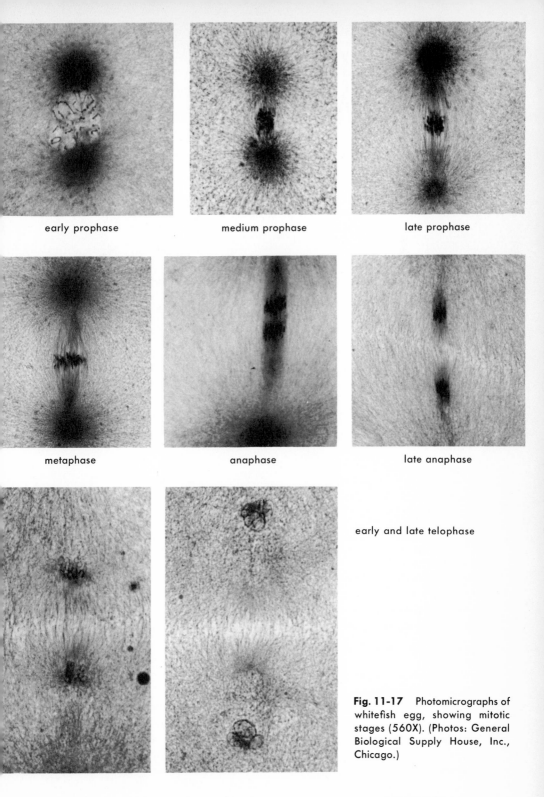

early prophase

medium prophase

late prophase

metaphase

anaphase

late anaphase

early and late telophase

Fig. 11-17 Photomicrographs of whitefish egg, showing mitotic stages (560X). (Photos: General Biological Supply House, Inc., Chicago.)

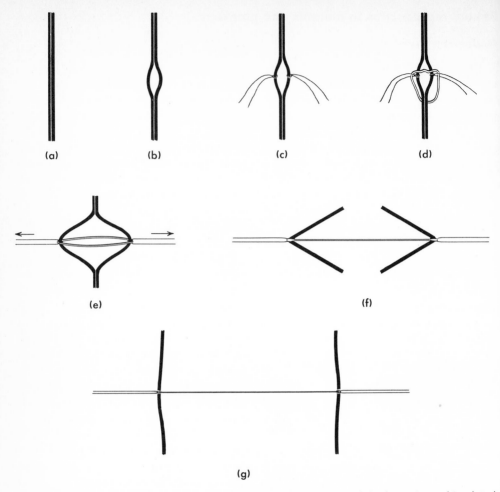

Fig. 11-18 Model of chromosomes and spindle fibers during mitosis: (a) take a piece of insulated electrical cord; (b) separate the middle portion of it; (c) tie a piece of string to each piece; (d) slip a rubber band around the cord, through the strings; (e), (f) pull the strings apart slowly until (g) the wire splits in two, much as chromosomes are drawn out along spindle fibers.

worms may be studied under the high power of the microscope. There are some techniques for staining cells (described in Chapter 17) which you may want to try in class or as a club activity. This may be a group or an individual project.

Wire "chromosomes." The actual mechanics of mitosis (and of reduction division, or meiosis, Fig. 11-20) as a continuous series of chromosome changes is a difficult concept for students.

When they observe mitotic division under the microscope or when they study a chart, they see only a series of "still" shots. Try using insulated electric wire to show the dynamics of the splitting of chromosomes. (Actually the chromosomes duplicate themselves rather than split, but the picture looks the same as the two parts of the chromosome move away from each other.) The technique is described in the legend of Fig. 11-18.

Sexual reproduction in animals and plants

Reduction division

Prepared slides may be used to study reduction of the number of chromosomes prior to sexual fusion of the gametes of plants and animals. This reduction division (meiosis) is part of the maturation process which occurs in the ovaries and testes of animals, in the pollen mother cells in the anther, and in the ovules of flowers. There is a reduction division among many algae (e.g., *Spirogyra*) and in the higher forms of plants as well.

A prepared section through a testis of an insect looks like Fig. 11-19, complicated for a youngster to follow. Diagrams such as Fig. 11-20 may clarify what takes place.

The story begins with a primary sex cell which undergoes a division. Usually, but not necessarily in all species, the first division is a reduction division wherein the pairs of chromosomes line up in the center field of the cell. One member of every pair moves toward one pole, or end, of the cell; the other member moves toward the opposite pole. It is as if the partners in a dance separated and went to opposite sides of a ballroom. But now a new cell wall forms down the center, in plant cells; or the center furrow appears and divides the cell contents, in animal cells. Thus each member of a chromosome pair is in a different cell from its "partner." Each cell has now half the original number of chromosomes; the number is reduced, or haploid.

These cells are not yet capable of fertilization. Chemically or physiologically they are not "ripe." There is still another division to come, but this time the chromosome number is not reduced. This time the cell division is mitotic; each chromosome duplicates itself. As a result of these divisions, there are more sperm cells or pollen grain nuclei than there were primary sex cells. Now these cells are ready for fertilization.

Modeling clay chromosomes. While bright students do not need to manipulate models of chromosomes to under-

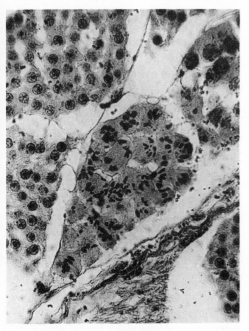

Fig. 11-19 Prepared section through testis of *Anasa* (grasshopper), showing spermatogenesis. (Photo: General Biological Supply House, Inc., Chicago.)

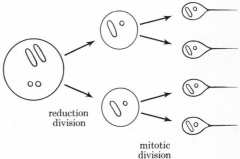

Fig. 11-20 Schematic diagram of maturation of sperm cells.

stand the difference between mitosis and reduction division, certain students, who lack a facility with abstract concepts, will find it helpful. Give each student some clay of various colors, with enough of each color to make pairs of "chromosomes." Then on a sheet of paper have students draw circles to represent cells. Ask them to place the right number and kind of chromosomes in each kind of cell as it undergoes mitosis, and as it undergoes reduction division. This will help clarify the difference between the two processes.

Sexual reproduction in animals

We shall first look into reproduction among Protozoa, and then go on to other invertebrate forms and the vertebrates.

Conjugation in Protozoa. The sexual fusion of two cells or two organisms which superficially are structurally alike is called conjugation. Fertilization, on the other hand, is thought of as the union of two cells which are structurally different, i.e., an egg and a sperm cell. (However, in strict accuracy, fertilization is the union of sperm and egg nuclei.)

The fact that there are complicated chemical differences among *Paramecium,* for example, has been described by Sonneborn and many other workers. You

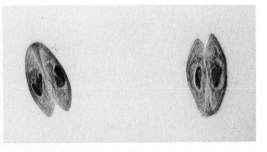

Fig. 11-21 Stained slide showing conjugation in *Paramecium:* two organisms fuse at the oral groove region and exchange parts of their nuclear content. (Photo: General Biological Supply House, Inc., Chicago.)

may want to purchase the different mating types to show conjugation.[3] Or in a well-fed, old, overcrowded culture you may find cases of this union of two protozoans (Fig. 11-21). Selected references for reading more about the heredity of mating types are listed at the end of this chapter (see recent books on heredity).

Eggs and sperms of snails. If the aquatic snail *Physa* is kept in an aquarium tank, material will be available for the study of eggs and sperms. Dissect out the multiple-lobed ovotestis located in the uppermost portion of the spiral of a fair-sized snail and macerate it a bit in a drop of aquarium water on a clean glass slide.

Sperms as well as the spheroid eggs are visible under the high-power objective if the material is at the right stage. Also segregate fertilized eggs found on leaves of aquarium plants or the aquarium glass into finger bowls and watch the early stages of cleavage under a microscope or with a hand lens.

Fertilization in echinoderms. When sea urchins or starfish are available, students may have the opportunity to study fertilization under the microscope. Clean glassware and dissecting needles are needed. Collect unfertilized eggs by stripping the females and placing the eggs in a finger bowl of sea water. Dissect out testes from males and store them in another finger bowl with a small amount of sea water (see anatomy, p. 276). Put a few eggs on a slide with sea water. Mount pieces of straw or broken coverslips with them so that they are not crushed by the coverslip. Locate some eggs under low power. Then with a clean dissecting needle or a micropipette, pick up some sperm suspension (from the finger bowl containing testes) and place this at the edge of the coverslip. As the

[3] The different mating types are available from biological supply houses or from college laboratories.

sperms swim under the coverslip, move the slide around to locate a sperm drawn into the fertilization cone formed by the egg. Watch how the other sperms are pushed aside by the fertilization membrane which arises from the egg's surface after one sperm has entered (Fig. 11-22). Vaseline the coverslip to the slide to prevent drying, and watch early cleavage stages (Fig. 11-23).

Films which show an egg fertilized by a sperm cell are also available (see film listing at the end of this chapter).

Eggs of *Daphnia*. The summer parthe-

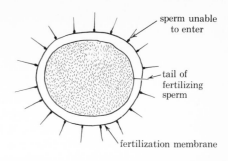

Fig. 11-22 Schematic diagram of sperm entry. A fertilization membrane is raised around the egg immediately after one sperm comes in contact with the surface; other sperm are thereby prevented from entering.

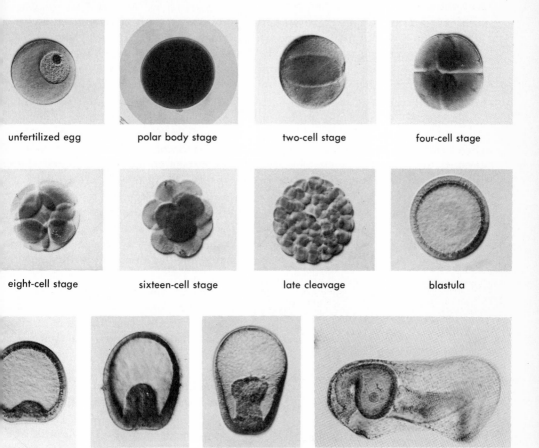

unfertilized egg   polar body stage   two-cell stage   four-cell stage

eight-cell stage   sixteen-cell stage   late cleavage   blastula

arly gastrula   gastrula   late gastrula   bipinnaria

Fig. 11-23 Prepared slides of early cleavage stages of starfish egg (165X). (Photos: General Biological Supply House, Inc., Chicago.)

nogenetic eggs or the winter fertilized eggs may be found in the brood pouch of *Daphnia* examined under the microscope as wet mounts (culturing, Chapter 18).

Eggs of Artemia, the brine shrimp. These eggs remain viable for long periods in the dry state. Students may get them at aquarium shops. The eggs may be developed as follows. To a wide flat pan add 4 tablespoons of rock salt to a gallon of tap water. Introduce ½ teaspoon of dried brine shrimp eggs. If the eggs are put in a fish feeding ring they will not scatter. Keep the pan covered, but leave an opening large enough for light to enter at one end. Larvae are attracted to light, and as they hatch they accumulate at this end of the pan. Then you can transfer them to a fresh salt solution.

The developing forms may be observed in depression slides under the microscope (Fig. 11-24). If the mounts are Vaseline-rimmed, the slides may be used for hours; placing them in a moist chamber will preserve them even longer. You may want to arrange a simple chamber by placing slides across Syracuse dishes containing water; then cover all these with a bell jar.

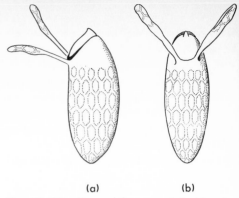

(a)   (b)

Fig. 11-25 *Drosophila* eggs: (a) side view, (b) dorsal view. (After M. Demerec & B. P. Kaufmann, *Drosophila Guide*, Carnegie Institution of Washington, 1945.)

Metamorphosis of Drosophila. Culture fruit flies as described in Chapter 12. When flies are cultured in many small vials of medium they will lay eggs which students may examine closely with a hand lens or microscope. In fact, the students may streak banana mash (or other medium) in depression slides and insert them into bottles of fruit flies. Then some flies will lay eggs on the surface of these slides. Observe that the eggs are white, with two filaments attached to one end (Fig. 11-25). After examination, return the slides to the breeding bottles. In time, pupa formation may be observed on these slides and on the walls of the culture bottles.

Egg masses of tent caterpillar. In winter, you may find egg masses in shiny, almost metallic black clusters circling small branches of trees, especially wild cherry. Enclose some of these small branches in a glass jar with a fine screen or mesh cover. The eggs will hatch into larvae; these caterpillars build a tent (Fig. 11-26).

Egg masses of praying mantis. Students may find the tan, foamy egg masses of the praying mantis. Or you may purchase them, especially from botanical gardens. When these masses are put into a

Fig. 11-24 Larva of the brine shrimp (*Artemia*). (Photo: General Biological Supply House, Inc., Chicago.)

terrarium they will hatch out in early spring. Study the nymph stage of these insects which undergo an incomplete metamorphosis, that is, egg, nymph, and adult. Students may compare this with complete metamorphosis in such insects as fruit flies, tent caterpillars (see above), beetles, and butterflies and moths.

Cocoons and chrysalises. Examine pupal stages of moths and butterflies by cutting open the protective coverings. Commonly found forms include the bagworm (the small spindle-shaped form covered with twig fragments and which dangles on a stalk, Fig. 11-27). Other common forms are pupae of *Cecropia, Polyphemus, Vanessa,* and *Promethea.* Let other pupae remain at room temperature in a terrarium with a bit of moisture. Watch them hatch into adults. Students can study or make models of the life cycles of the silkworm. Or if you lack pupae of butterflies or moths, students may want to study

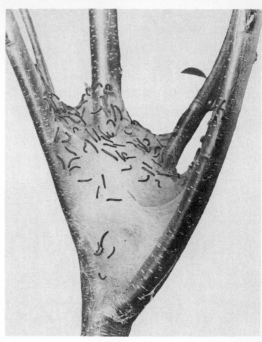

Fig. 11-26   Nest with larvae of the eastern tent caterpillar. (Photo: U.S.D.A.)

Fig. 11-27 Bags, adult, and pupa of *Thyrodopteryx efemoriformis;* the pupal stage is known as the bagworm. (Photo: U.S.D.A.)

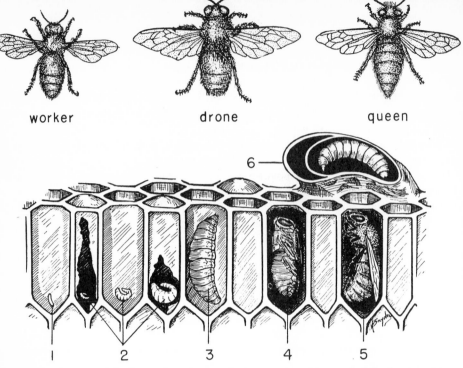

worker   drone   queen

Fig. 11-28   Life cycle of the honey bee: 1, egg; 2, three stages of larva; 3, fully developed larva; 4, pupa; 5, adult queen ready to emerge; 6, queen larva in queen cell. (General Biological Supply House, Inc., Chicago.)

the honey bee (Fig. 11-28).

Ovaries and testes of fish. During the spring, smelts or perch will provide good specimens for dissection in the classroom. Dissect the fish from the anal region toward the head (dissection, Fig. 16-8). Remove the body flap to reveal the ovaries or the testes. Trace the tubes (oviducts or sperm ducts) which carry the eggs or sperms to the cloacal region. Use a hand lens to examine the eggs in the roe or ovaries. Caviar illustrates variations in the size of fish eggs. Also examine the eggs of some tropical fish.

Development of fresh-water medaka (Oryzias latipes). These interesting fish (when given the right amount of food and light) lay eggs daily, shortly before dawn. Then the eggs are fertilized externally and remain attached to the female

for several hours. Students may isolate the eggs into small Syracuse dishes with aquarium water and trace their development through early cleavage stages. They hatch in 6 days. The first cleavage stage occurs 1 hour after fertilization, the second 1½ hours later, and the third 2 hours later.

Keep several fish in a large tank. Feed them such worms as *Tubifex, Enchytraeus,* or mixed dry food on alternate days.

Ovaries and testes of frogs. Dissect freshly killed or preserved frogs (dissection, Fig. 16-9). In season, the two many-lobed ovaries (covered by a membrane) contain large black and cream-colored eggs and occupy the greater part of the female's abdominal cavity. Remove the ovaries, locate the many-coiled oviducts, one on each side of the abdomen, and trace them forward to their origin, under the heart region, high in the chest cavity. Also follow the oviducts along to the cloacal region. Each egg breaks out of the ovaries, is pushed along the abdominal cavity by cilia and brought to the opening of the oviducts. In passage along the oviducts, each egg receives three layers of jelly; the jelly swells when it comes in contact with water.

In the male frog, locate two yellow testes lying ventrally on the kidneys (Fig. 16-10a). The threadlike sperm ducts, finely coiled, may be traced to the cloaca as well as back to their connection with the kidneys. Notice the fingerlike, yellow fat bodies found in the vicinity of the ovaries and testes. Their function is thought to be food storage during hibernation as well as during the active reproductive period.

When fresh material is dissected, the testes may be removed and crushed in water on a slide, to show living sperm cells.

Sperm cells of frogs. Place the testes of a freshly killed frog into a clean Syracuse dish containing some 10 cc of Ringer's solution (p. 409) or spring water. Tease the organs apart with clean forceps. Mount a drop of this suspension on a clean glass slide and apply a coverslip.

At first the sperm cells do not move, for there is a high concentration and accumulation of carbon dioxide. In a few minutes, however, the oscillating heads of sperms may be observed under high power. A drop of methylene blue (p. 309) added to the slide will stain the flagellum of each sperm cell, but the cells will be killed by the stain.

Egg cells of frogs. Dissect freshly killed frogs to show the large masses of eggs. Examine the black and cream-colored eggs with a hand lens. Or collect egg masses in the spring from lakes and ponds.

When live eggs have been fertilized, they rotate within the layers of jelly so that all show the black area uppermost. When the cream-colored part is still uppermost, the eggs are dead or have not been fertilized.

If possible, follow the cleavage stages of living cells with a hand lens or binocular microscope. Compare with the normal stages in the development of a frog's egg (Fig. 11-29).

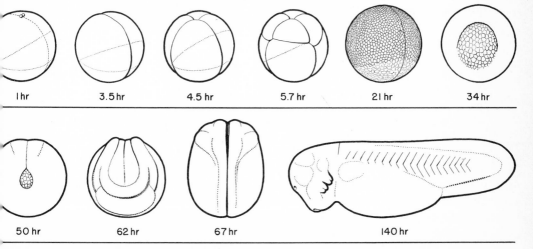

| I hr | 3.5 hr | 4.5 hr | 5.7 hr | 21 hr | 34 hr |

| 50 hr | 62 hr | 67 hr | 140 hr |

Fig. 11-29 Development of a frog egg (*Rana pipiens*); time in hours at 18°C. (Drawings by Dr. J. F. Mueller, from Ward's Natural Science Establishment, Inc.)

If you have collected frogs you can stimulate ovulation. This and artificial fertilization are described later in this chapter.

Effect of temperature on the development of frog eggs. Before students study the rate of cell division or cleavage, and the rate of differentiation in frogs' eggs at different temperatures, the rate of cleavage at some constant temperature should be established. Keep one finger bowl of fertilized eggs in Ringer's solution at 15° C as a control. Set up similar finger bowls and keep at 10° C, 20° C, and 30° C. Then examine the eggs at intervals. Students are likely to find that gastrulation begins in approximately 27 hours at 15° C, in about 72 hours at 10° C (compare with Fig. 11-29).

Induced ovulation in _Rana pipiens_. With most animals the eggs and cleavage stages can be studied only at a specific time of the year. However, certain amphibians can be stimulated to ovulate out of season when injected with the material from the anterior lobe of the pituitary glands.

In the late summer and fall, large doses of pituitary glands are needed, but from October into spring the dose decreases from eight glands down to just one. There is no qualitative difference between the glands in the two sexes, but the female's is larger and probably contains more of the follicle-stimulating hormone. Many teachers prefer to buy pituitary extract, which is readily available in drugstores (it need not come from a frog).

First, dissect out the total required number of pituitary glands; then crush them in Ringer's solution (p. 409) and inject this material under the skin of a female frog with a hypodermic needle; description of the technique follows.

The pituitary gland is located just posterior to the level of the eyes of the frog (Fig. 11-30). It is necessary to cut off the upper head and jaw region of a living frog to reach the pituitary gland. Insert sharp scissors into the mouth at right angles to the jaw, and quickly sever the cranium at its junction with the vertebral column. Then cut the base of the skull (the upper palate) on either side by inserting the point of the scissors through the foramen magnum (the opening into the cranium); turn the point toward the underside of the orbit. Turn back the base of the skull and hold it in position with the left thumb. A small, ovoid, pink pituitary gland adhering to the turned base of the back of the skull should be apparent. Frequently the gland is surrounded by flocculent tissue. Remove the gland, and store it in 70 per cent alcohol if it is not to be used immediately.

Mash the necessary number of whole glands in 2 cc of 0.1 per cent Ringer's solution. Use a needle of rather wide bore to pick up this material and inject it into the abdominal cavity lymph spaces lying directly under the loose skin. Inject along the side of the animal and be careful to avoid injury to other organs.

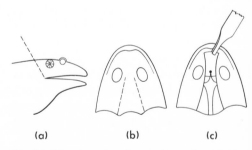

(a)   (b)   (c)

Fig. 11-30 Locating the pituitary gland in the frog: (a) cut off the upper jaw and the head; (b) view of upper palati: insert scissors into back of cranial cavity as far to the right as possible, and cut through bone; repeat on left side; (c) pull up flap with forceps, exposing pituitary (black ball). (Redrawn from _Carolina Tips_, Carolina Biological Supply Co.)

Rub the finger over the injected area after you remove the needle to keep the injected material from running out. Keep the injected female in a battery jar at 15° C in about 1 inch of water. If the frogs are kept at a higher temperature, say 23° C, you will find that the eggs are often abnormal (in addition, the reserve food materials are too rapidly consumed).

If enough frogs are available, you may want to have students dissect one of the ovulating females to study eggs in all stages of development. Cilia which line the coelom propel the eggs to the ostium. And there are also cilia on the edges of the liver, on the pericardium and mesovarium. No cilia are found in males or immature females. Possibly the presence or absence of cilia may be considered a secondary sex characteristic.

Artificial fertilization of frog eggs. After 36 hours at 15° C the eggs of the pituitary-injected female may be stripped from her body. It is certain, however, that after 72 hours most of the eggs will be in the uterus. (At 15° C the eggs can be left in the body for 5 days after injection.) Gently hold a female and apply pressure to both sides of the abdomen and press in the direction of the cloaca. Strip the eggs into large, dry dishes so that the eggs are well separated. Be sure that all glassware is biologically clean. Then with a *clean* pipette, wash the eggs with 0.1 per cent Ringer's solution for a few minutes. Finally draw off the Ringer's solution and pipette previously prepared sperm suspension over the eggs. Now the eggs have been artificially fertilized.

Make the sperm suspension earlier so that it can stand for about 15 minutes, to give the sperms time to become activated. To get the suspension, kill two males (save their pituitary glands in 70 per cent alcohol) and then dissect out the testes. Roll the testes on toweling to remove blood and body fluids; wash them in 0.1 per cent Ringer's solution.

Then macerate the four testes in some 50 cc of 0.1 per cent Ringer's solution and let this stand. This amount of sperm suspension may be used to fertilize about 1000 eggs. If it is necessary to save the testes you can keep them for a few days in wet cotton at a temperature of from 4° to 8° C.

Pipette the sperm suspension over the eggs and shake the dish occasionally. Let this stand for about 20 minutes. Finally, wash the eggs with more 0.1 per cent Ringer's and flood the dish so that the eggs float freely. After half an hour students will be able to see which eggs have been fertilized, because the fertilized eggs rotate within the jelly layers so that the black surfaces are uppermost. When the jelly is completely swollen (after about an hour), cut the clusters of eggs apart with a scissors and separate them into smaller finger bowls. Put about 50 eggs in each finger bowl in the same Ringer's solution and keep at 15° C. Discard the unfertilized eggs before they begin to decay. Transfer the eggs into fresh Ringer's solution twice a week.

Artificial parthenogenesis in frog eggs. Certain eggs can be made to begin cleavage without the entrance of a sperm cell. Rugh[4] describes a technique for causing unfertilized frogs' eggs to develop. Segregate the female to be used in this experiment from males for several days prior to the work. Boil the instruments and glassware or wash them in alcohol to be sure that they are clean and free of sperm cells. If the work is to be done at a time other than the breeding season, you will first need to induce ovulation.

When the eggs are available, parthenogenesis can be induced in this way.

[4] Roberts Rugh, *Experimental Embryology,* Burgess, Minneapolis, Minn., 1948.

Strip the eggs in single file along the length of clean glass slides. Prepare several slides with rows of eggs. The slides may be kept in a moist chamber for about an hour, if necessary, until ready for use. A suitable moist chamber may be made by setting the slides over Syracuse dishes of water and covering with a bell jar. Now pith a nonovulating female frog (Fig. 9-3). Dissect it to expose the heart. Cut off the tip of the ventricle and let the blood flow into the coelomic fluid. Next, dissect out a strip of abdominal muscle and dip it into the mixture of blood and coelomic fluid. Now streak each egg so that a film of blood–coelomic fluid remains on each egg. Then prick each egg with a glass or platinum needle within the animal hemisphere (i.e., the black area), just off center. Finally, immerse the slides with the eggs on them into spring water or distilled water. Keep the eggs in Petri dishes with just enough fluid to cover the eggs. Keep them in a cool place and examine the eggs hourly under a binocular microscope, dissecting microscope, or hand lens for signs of cleavage stages.

Effect of thyroxin-feeding on frog tadpoles. The hormone thyroxin stimulates the metamorphosis of the tadpole into an adult frog. Bullfrog tadpoles with the hind limbs appearing give the best results in this work. Set up finger bowls containing different concentrations of thyroxin. Use a concentration of 1 part of thyroxin to 5 million parts of water in one series. In another set, use 1 part of thyroxin to 10 million parts of water. (The hormone is absorbed directly through the skin of the tadpoles.)

Put individual large bullfrog tadpoles, or some 5 to 10 small frog tadpoles in separate finger bowls. Set aside one series as controls (use spring or pond water without thyroxin); establish two series using different concentrations of thyroxin.

Rugh suggests preparing stock solutions of thyroxin by dissolving 10 mg of thyroxin (crystalline) in 5 cc of 1 per cent sodium hydroxide. Add distilled water to bring it up to a 1 liter volume. This 1:100,000 concentration should be refrigerated until ready for use. Dilute this stock solution to prepare the solutions needed for the series of finger bowls.

Feed the tadpoles on alternate days with small amounts of hard-boiled egg yolk, and change the water each week to prevent fouling of the medium.

Rugh also recommends another method which makes use of thyroxin tablets. When these are available, crush and dissolve 5 two-grain tablets in some 5 cc of distilled water in a mortar. Weigh out an equal amount of whole-wheat flour and grind this up with the thyroxin tablets. Then spread this paste in a thin layer on glass squares and leave to dry. Finally, powder the dry mixture and store it in closed bottles in a refrigerator. Use 50 mg of this wheat-thyroxin powder per tadpole daily for 1 week. Feed the tadpoles, both controls and the experimental animals, with parboiled spinach or lettuce. Change the medium daily to prevent fouling.

Effect of iodine-feeding on frog tadpoles. Since the main fraction in thyroxin is iodine, students may devise a project investigating the effects of iodine on the metamorphosis of amphibian tadpoles.

Here again work with bullfrog tadpoles is most successful, but any species of frog or the salamander, *Necturus*, may be used. No injections are necessary, since iodine is absorbed directly through the skin. Select tadpoles in which the hind limbs are just becoming visible. Set up several finger bowls with a maximum of twenty tadpoles of small frogs such as leopard frogs, or one tadpole of a bullfrog, in about 30 cc of prepared medium. Prepare several finger bowls of animals in spring water or pond water (as controls).

In the experimental dishes use the following medium. First, prepare a stock solution: Dissolve 0.1 gm of iodine (crystalline) in 5 cc of a 95 per cent solution of alcohol; then dilute to 1 liter with distilled water. This is a stock solution of a concentration of 1:10,000.

Dilutions as weak as 1:500,000 and 1:1,000,000 have been successful in stimulating metamorphosis. Each week change the medium to prevent fouling due to decay of food material. However, avoid more frequent changes, for too much iodine will result in such accelerated growth that tadpoles may die. Feed the controls as well as the experimental animals on alternate days with small amounts of hard-boiled egg yolk or partially cooked lettuce. Rugh recommends 1 square inch of parboiled spinach leaf per tadpole. Remove uneaten food.

Keep a record of the changes in the length of tail and hind limbs and the time of appearance of forelimbs in both the experimental and the control animals. Also note the changes in the shape of the head and body.

If students plan a project in the field of experimental embryology, or for club work in this area, they can learn many techniques from a study of Rugh's fine text-manual on *Experimental Embryology* (see Bibliography). Rugh also gives excellent directions for preparing glass operating needles and for making transplants of tissue from donor to host tadpole. The way a transplant of a future eye or gill or limb can be made is also described. Students should be forewarned that the techniques are difficult and require much practice before any de-gree of success can be expected.

Ovaries and testes in the pigeon or chicken. Students may be able to bring to class the ovary of a chicken in order to show the different sized egg cells or "yolks," which look like a bunch of grapes. Or a freshly killed pigeon may be dissected according to the instructions given in Chapter 16.

Look for the ovary, oviduct, and enlarged shell gland near the cloacal region. In the male find the testes and trace the sperm ducts to the cloaca. Study the relationship between the testes and the kidneys.

Living chick embryos. It is a fascinating study to watch a chick come to be out of the apparently amorphous egg. When fertilized eggs are obtainable, students may incubate them in the laboratory and examine them while they develop over a 3-week period. (Students can build an incubator if you cannot afford to buy one for school.) Some companies guarantee eggs up to 90 per cent fertility, but seasonal variations lower this figure. You cannot store fertilized chicken eggs in the laboratory before incubation unless you can get temperatures as low as 10° to 15° C.

Keep the incubator at 37° C and insert the bulb of the thermometer at the level of the eggs, not high up in the incubator, for there may be a difference as great as 10° between the two places. Include a pan of water in the incubator to keep a uniform humidity. A relative humidity of 60 per cent is optimum. Do not wash the egg surface; washing will remove a protective film which reduces bacterial infection. Turn the eggs daily to prevent adhesion of membranes. Students might mark the eggs with a pencil so that they know which surfaces to turn.

There seem to be two periods when mortality is high, the third day and just before hatching time. Some mortality must be expected, for some hens produce fewer viable eggs than do others. And you will want to allow for variations in handling.

After eggs have been incubated for about 36 hours they are relatively easy to handle for examination. The number of hours of incubation is not a true index of the age of the embryo, for cleavage started in the oviduct before the egg was laid. As you remove an egg from the incubator hold it in the same position so that the blastoderm will be floating on top and the heavier yolk underneath.

Crack the egg on the edge of a finger bowl which contains slightly warmed saline solution (or Locke's solution, p. 408). If you place finger bowls of solution in the incubator beforehand, they will be at the proper temperature (the embryo will not run the danger of being chilled). Let the egg contents flow into the saline solution so that the embryo is submerged in solution. Notice how the chick blastoderm rotates to the top position. When the embryos are larger they do not rotate so easily but must be moved with a forceps by pulling on the chalazae, the thickened albumen "ropes" on each side of the egg yolk mass (Fig. 11-31).

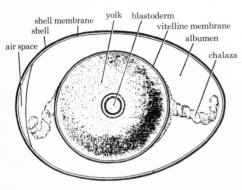

Fig. 11-31 Cross section of fertilized chicken egg. (From J. W. Mavor, *General Biology*, 3d ed., Macmillan, 1947.)

Use a hand lens or a binocular microscope to examine this early embryo. You should find the head beginning to curve to the left side (Fig. 11-32). Three vesicles of the brain should be visible and the neural tube should be closed at this time. In a 40-hour embryo you should begin to see the heart beat and a complete blood circulation should be discernible in a 45-hour embryo. If you begin incubation of the eggs on a stagger system the incubator will have eggs at different stages of development, which can all be studied in one day.

Students in a microscopy club or a biology research club may want to make permanent stained slides (technique, Chapter 17) of 24-hour, 36-hour, 48-hour, and 72-hour chick embryos. Older embryos become too opaque for examination under the microscope.

Ovaries and testes of a mammal. Dissect a freshly killed rat or other small mammal which has been etherized by placing it in a closed container with some ether-soaked absorbent cotton. Check the reflexes to make certain that the animal is dead before you begin to dissect it. Make an incision in the ventral body wall at the posterior end and cut forward along one side of the median line. Cut through the sternum to the shoulder or pectoral girdle. Then cut back the abdominal wall flaps and pin them back to the dissection pan (dissections, Chapter 16).

In the female, identify the ovaries, oviducts, and uterus. Cut into the uterus to look for developing embryos or fetuses if the female is pregnant. Then with a blunt probe examine the uterine lining, and trace the oviducts forward and posteriorly to the vagina. You may want to show a microscope slide of a section of the ovary (Fig. 11-33). In the male, dissect the scrotal sac to expose the testis.

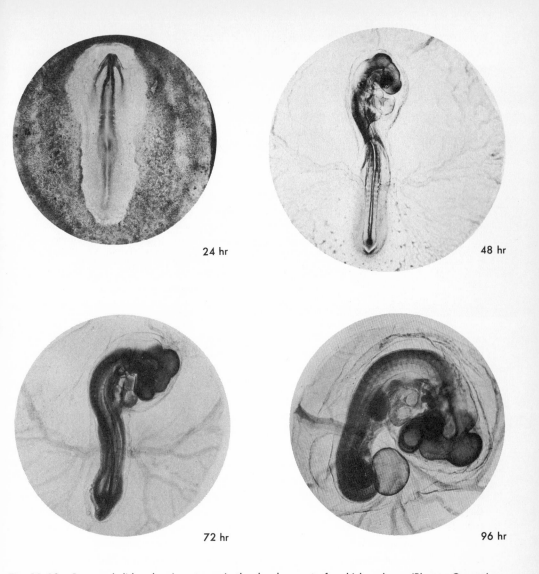

24 hr

48 hr

72 hr

96 hr

Fig. 11-32 Prepared slides showing stages in the development of a chick embryo. (Photos: General Biological Supply House, Inc., Chicago.)

Fig. 11-33 Prepared slide showing section through a cat ovary, with Graafian follicles. (Photo: General Biological Supply House, Inc., Chicago.)

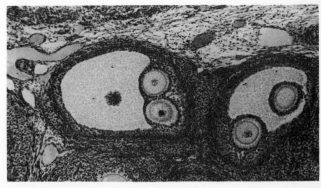

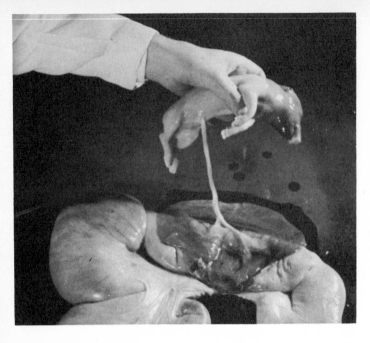

Fig. 11-34 Bifurcated uterus of pig, showing one fetus dissected out. (Photo from "Reproduction Among Mammals," Encyclopaedia Britannica Films, Inc.)

Examine a cross section of the testis; trace the epididymis, vas deferens, vesicles, urethra in the penis.

If there is time, students may identify other organs (dissections, Chapter 16).

Dissecting a pig uterus. If you purchase the uterus of a pig from a supply house you will receive a bifurcated uterus with several fetuses. You may want to demonstrate this to your class before they dissect the uterus. Carefully cut through the uterine wall to reveal the chorion and amnion. Also cut through the amnion, since it contains amniotic fluid. Students will easily identify the placenta and umbilical cord as you gently lift out the fetus (Fig. 11-34). If a sufficient supply is purchased, every student may dissect a portion of the uterus. The fetuses can be cut out and preserved in alcohol or formalin in a museum jar, or saved for future dissection.

Sexual reproduction in plants

First we shall examine reproduction in seed plants, ferns, and mosses, and then discuss the beginnings of sexuality among the algae and fungi.

Fertilization in higher plants is similar to that in animals, but the mode of transfer of the gametes, sperm and eggs, is different. A reduction division, similar to the division in animals, occurs in the maturation divisions in the spore mother cells in the anthers, and within the ovules. Each gamete, then, is haploid, so that when a pollen-grain nucleus unites with the nucleus of an ovule the original diploid number is restored.

A desirable procedure, we believe, is to take students out of doors in season to study flowers of shrubs and trees as they come to blossom (see Chapter 15). *Forsythia,* maple, cherry, magnolia, dogwood, oak, elm, and others blossoming at about the same time may be studied on walks around the school grounds. Students may bring to class tulips, daffodils, crocuses, and pussy willows. Around the lawns you should find dandelions and other flowers. Where the school is in a suburban or rural community, the problem of finding living material is much easier.

Students will learn that not all flowers have petals, and some flowers contain only stamens, while others have only the female organs, the pistils.

Parts of a flower. Tulips, daffodils, and gladioli are excellent forms to show an almost diagrammatic flower; the pistil and stamens are clear. Students should also see a variety of flower shapes and realize that these shapes help to identify families of plants. They might learn to recognize a few, such as composite flowers, members of the Compositae (dandelions, asters, daisies, and so forth, Fig. 11-35); members of the pea family, the Leguminosae (sweet pea, wistaria, locust trees, clover, Fig. 11-36); and the rose family, the Rosaceae (apple, pear, and cherry trees, as well as roses, Fig. 11-37). These families each have a different flower shape or arrangement. Some students who show interest in classifying plants may want to learn how to use a flower key (study the pattern, p. 218). Figure 11-38 shows the main kinds of inflorescence. Some flower keys are listed in the Bibliography at the end of the book.

When students bring flowers to class (as a result of field trips on the school grounds or of individual work), provide them with hand lenses or dissection microscopes, and razor blades or scalpels. They can then dissect out the stamens after the exterior whorls of sepals and petals have been studied. Anthers may be examined under a hand lens, and then dissected to show the pollen chambers. A prepared slide of an anther may

Fig. 11-35   Composite flower *Aster novae-angliae:* composite head, ray flower, and tubular flower. (From G. F. Atkinson, *Botany*, 2d ed., Holt, 1905.)

Fig. 11-36   Typical flower shape of pea family: *Erythrina fusca.* (From W. H. Brown, *The Plant Kingdom*, Ginn, 1935.)

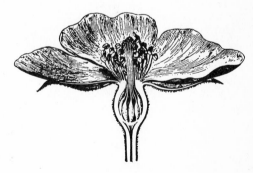

Fig. 11-37   Typical flower shape of rose family: rose flower. (From W. H. Brown, *The Plant Kingdom*, Ginn, 1935.)

Fig. 11-38   Types of inflorescence. (From J. W. Mavor, *General Biology*, 3d ed., Macmillan, 1947.)

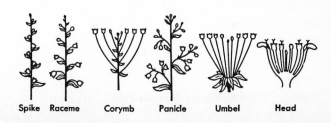

Spike   Raceme   Corymb   Panicle   Umbel   Head

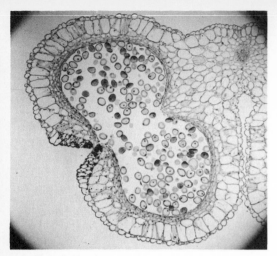

Fig. 11-39 Prepared slide of cross section of anther of lily, showing pollen grains in the pollen chamber. (Photo: General Biological Supply House, Inc., Chicago.)

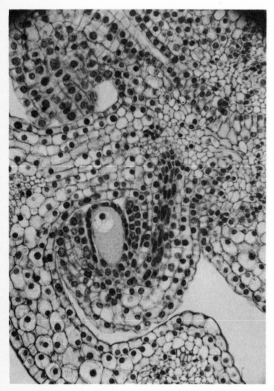

Fig. 11-40 Prepared slide of cross section of ovary of *Fritillaria*, showing megaspore mother cell. (Photo: General Biological Supply House, Inc., Chicago.)

be examined, or pollen grains may be mounted on a slide and examined under high power of the microscope (Fig. 11-39). The sculpturing and the different shapes of pollen grains from different plants will be noted. In fact, flowers may be identified by means of their pollen grains. On occasion, students may want to germinate pollen grains (p. 184).

Similarly, cross sections and lengthwise sections of the ovary may be studied (Fig. 11-40). Students will locate the ovules and note that the number of chambers in the ovary equals (or is a multiple of) the number of petals and stamens. Floral parts are mainly in "fives" or "threes" (especially among the monocots).

During the year short field trips may be taken to show fruits and seeds on trees and shrubs around the school. Students may bring to class the fruits they collect. They may want to prepare a display of some of the special adaptations which facilitate seed dispersal (Fig. 11-41).

Furthermore, seeds themselves may be studied. Students can soak some large seeds such as beans, peas, or the corn grain (the latter is really a fruit containing a seed) and dissect them to learn their structure. They may also try to germinate some seeds (p. 108) and study how the embryo plant grows. In this way, monocotyledonous and dicotyledonous seeds can be distinguished in their pattern of growth.

Some students may also want to study pine cones and the relation of seeds to the scalelike bracts in the cones. The life history of pollination and fertilization in gymnosperms (Fig. 11-43) may also be studied and compared with the life cycle of angiosperms (Fig. 11-42).

Artificial pollination. You may want to demonstrate how a breeder would pollinate flowers which he selects for mating. Hybridization techniques of

Fig. 11-41 Adaptations for seed dispersal: *left,* cocklebur; *right,* milkweed. (Photos: Hugh Spencer.)

this kind are commonly used to get new varieties of flowers through recombinations in the offspring of different genes. The flower to be pollinated should be selected in the bud stage, that is, before its own pollen becomes ripe. Open the flower bud carefully and remove the unripened stamens by cutting them out with a scissors. Wash with alcohol all the equipment you use, to prevent any foreign pollen from entering the plant blossom you have selected. Then cover the flower bud with a small bag (or square of plastic) until you are ready to pollinate that flower. When other plants show ripened stamens, select the special pollen (from the same kind of plant or one closely related) by removing the stamens from those flowers; then touch them to the stigma of the selected flowers. Again cover the flowers you have now pollinated to prevent other pollen grains from fertilizing the ovules. Plan to pollinate several flowers in one operation.

Students can plant the seeds that form, and study the inheritance of flower color.

Examining pollen grains. Prepare slides of many kinds of pollen grains. Students can discover the variety of shapes and patterns of pollen grains by mounting some in a drop of water or in xylol. (The motion of the pollen grains in water is Brownian movement.) Or mount the pollen grains in melted glycerine jelly.

Students may want to study the kinds of pollen grains in the air, at a particular season. Lightly coat slides with Vaseline and suspend the slides out of doors. They will catch pollen grains, and dust as well.

Staining pollen grains. To a small amount of aniline oil add a bit of crystal violet so that a light purple tint results. Mount pollen grains in a few drops of the tinted aniline oil on a slide. Then hold the slide over a Bunsen flame until the pollen grains stain deeply, but do not let the slide become warm to the touch.

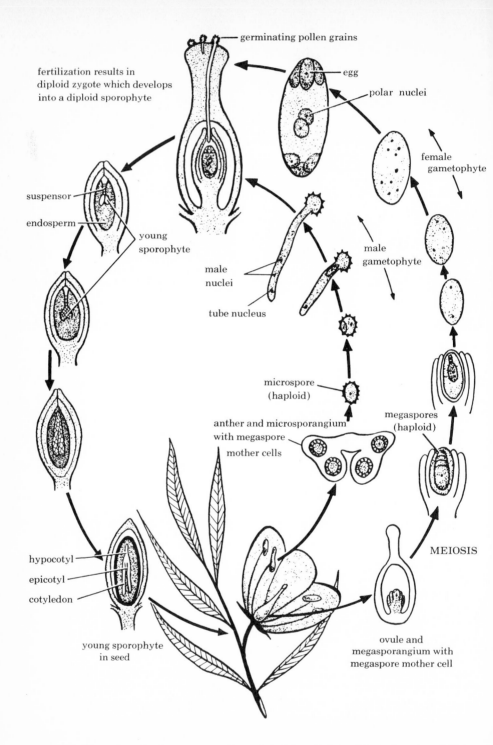

Fig. 11-42 Life cycle of angiosperm. (From C. A. Villee, *Biology*, 2d ed., Saunders, 1954.)

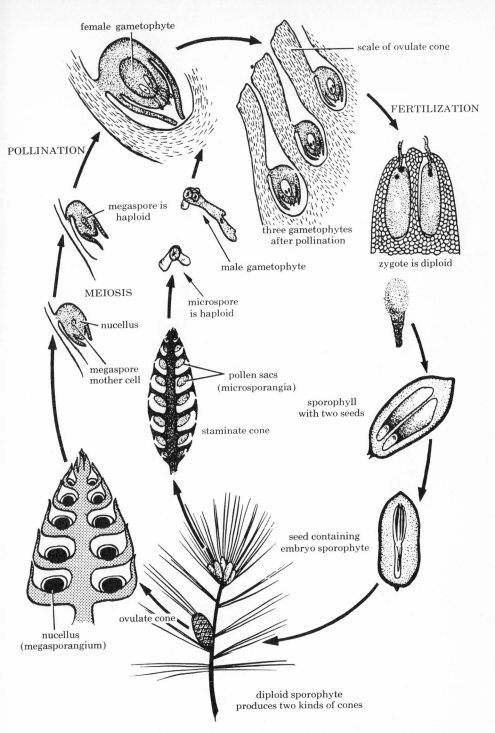

female gametophyte

scale of ovulate cone

FERTILIZATION

POLLINATION

megaspore is haploid

three gametophytes after pollination

male gametophyte

zygote is diploid

MEIOSIS

nucellus

microspore is haploid

megaspore mother cell

pollen sacs (microsporangia)

sporophyll with two seeds

staminate cone

seed containing embryo sporophyte

nucellus (megasporangium)

ovulate cone

diploid sporophyte produces two kinds of cones

Fig. 11-43 Life cycle of gymnosperm. (From C. A. Villee, *Biology*, 2d ed., Saunders, 1954.)

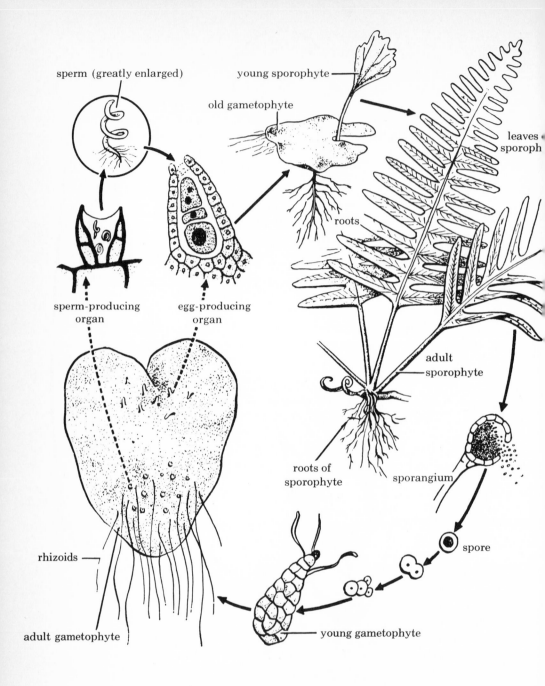

sperm (greatly enlarged)

young sporophyte

old gametophyte

leaves
sporoph

roots

sperm-producing
organ

egg-producing
organ

adult
sporophyte

roots of
sporophyte

sporangium

rhizoids

spore

adult gametophyte

young gametophyte

Fig. 11-44 Life cycle of fern. (From C. A. Villee, *Biology*, 2d ed., Saunders, 1954.)

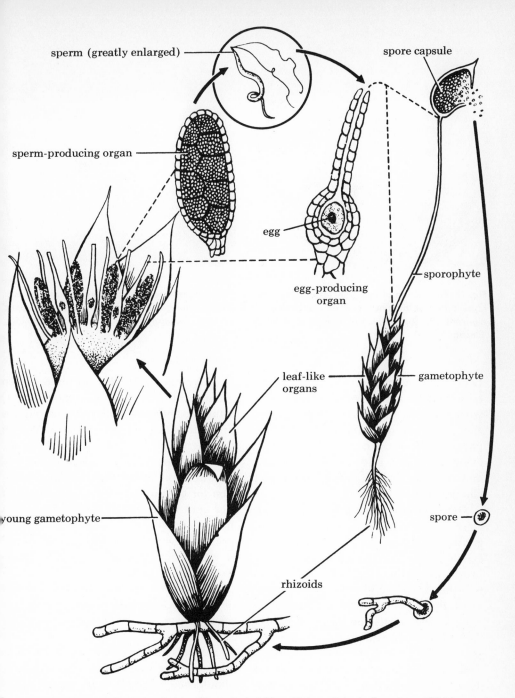

sperm (greatly enlarged)

spore capsule

sperm-producing organ

egg

egg-producing organ

sporophyte

leaf-like organs

gametophyte

young gametophyte

rhizoids

spore

Fig. 11-45 Life cycle of moss. (From C. A. Villee, *Biology*, 2d ed., Saunders, 1954.)

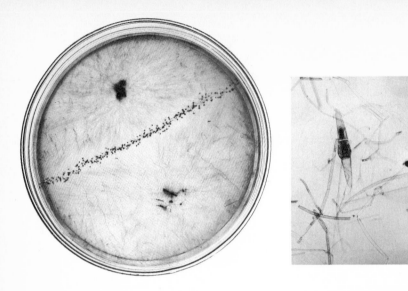

Fig. 11-46 Fusion of two gametes of mold plants to form zygospores: *left, Phycomyces blakesleeanus* mycelia fuse at the juncture of plus and minus strains; *right,* enlarged view of zygospore of *Rhizopus nigricans.* (Photos: *left,* Carolina Biological Supply Co.; *right,* General Biological Supply House, Inc., Chicago.)

Let the slide cool and remove the excess oil with filter paper. Wash several times with xylol, by adding drops of xylol to the slide, then drawing it off with filter paper until the excess stain has been removed. Then add a drop of balsam and a coverslip (staining techniques, Chapter 17).

Germinating pollen grains. There are several ways to grow pollen grains. These grains germinate in the sticky, sugary exudate of the stigma. Students can brush ripe anthers against a ripe stigma (of the same kind of flower), then crush the stigma in water on a slide. Include a few bristles or pieces of broken coverslip before adding the coverslip, to prevent the grains from being crushed; or make a hanging drop preparation (Fig. 17-7). The slides can be kept in a moist chamber between each examination. Students can study pollen grains of narcissus, lily, daffodil, tulip, or sweet pea

in this way, and also sprinkle pollen grains into a sucrose (cane sugar) solution. Different pollen grains require different kinds of sugar content. Where the stigma of the flower is quite sticky, pollen grains from this species of flower require a higher per cent of sugar solution for germination. At times, up to 45 per cent cane sugar solutions may be needed. In general, a majority of pollen grains grow in solutions varying from 2 to 20 per cent; most at 10 per cent. However, many composites require 30 to 45 per cent sugar solution. The pollen grains of many cycads grow tubes in 2 to 3 days when grown in a 10 per cent cane sugar solution.

Students may use more precise methods (described by Johansen[5]). To do this they should boil 1 gm of sugar and 0.5 gm of agar in 25 cc of water. This medium is

[5] D. Johansen, *Plant Microtechnique,* McGraw-Hill, New York, 1940.

cooled to about 35° C; then 0.5 gm of powdered gelatin is added and stirred until it melts.

Keep the solution at 25° C in a water bath or on a hot plate. Put a thin film of this solution on clean slides. Dust the slides with pollen grains and keep them in a moist chamber without applying coverslips. Examine the slides under the microscope for growth of pollen tubes. (Try crushing anthers of *Tradescantia* in a film of this sugar solution.)

Alternation of generation in ferns. You may want to collect spores of ferns and grow them according to the method described on page 395. Use Fig. 11-44 to trace the life history of a fern (the gametophyte generation alternates with the sporophyte generation).

Alternation of generation in mosses. Compare the life history of the moss (Fig. 11-45) with that of the fern. The same pattern exists, although the gametophyte stage in the moss is conspicuous and the sporophyte grows from the gametophyte (some botanists consider this "parasitic").

Try to grow the spores of mosses following steps similar to those for growing fern spores (p. 393).

Sexual reproduction in bread mold. Among *Rhizopus* hyphae there are no visible differences between the two mating types, but a physiological difference exists. This type of sexual union is sometimes called conjugation. Hyphae of opposite mating types (plus and minus) grow toward each other, and the tips of the hyphae fuse. The plus and minus strains of *Rhizopus* and of certain other molds can be obtained from supply houses or college laboratories. Then "seed" opposite sides of moistened bread (culturing, p. 388) with the plus and minus strains. Examine under the microscope the dark zygospores which eventually

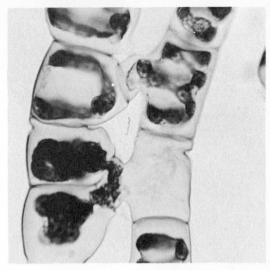

Fig. 11-47 Details of conjugation in *Spirogyra*. Notice the conjugation tubes along which one cell moves into another, forming a zygospore. (Photo: Ward's Natural Science Establishment, Inc.)

form along the middle of the bread (Fig. 11-46).

Sexual reproduction in *Spirogyra*. In a form such as *Spirogyra* the gametes which unite look alike (as in *Rhizopus*, fusion is called conjugation). Trace the process and note that the active cell moves across the "bridge" to fuse with the contents of the passive (female) cell or gamete (Fig. 11-47). A zygospore is formed as the result of each union. Examine prepared slides of conjugation; techniques for culturing *Spirogyra* are described in Chapter 20.

Sexual reproduction in *Oedogonium*. This is a common unbranched green filamentous alga which reproduces by unlike gametes (Fig. 11-48). These are produced in special cells called gametangia which are developed from vegetative cells of the filaments. The female gametangia are oval cells within which an egg develops. Motile ciliated sperms are liberated from the male gametangia

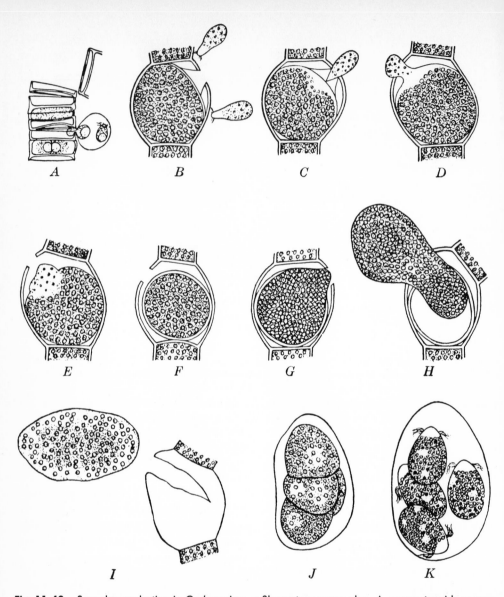

Fig. 11-48 Sexual reproduction in *Oedogonium*, a filamentous green alga: A, spermatozoids escape; B-E, fertilization; F, oospore; G-I, escape of contents of oospore; J, K, formation of zoospores. (From W. H. Brown, *The Plant Kingdom*, Ginn, 1935.)

(antheridia); they swim to the egg through an opening, or pore, formed by the breakdown of a small area of the wall of the oogonium.

Oedogonium also reproduces asexually (Fig. 11-49), by forming ciliated zoospores, which are transformed vegetative cells. These cells with a collar of cilia break away from the filament and swim off to take hold at another location, become elongated, and carry on cell division. Thus they form a new filament. Stain a wet mount with Lugol's solution (pp. 307, 409) to show the cilia.

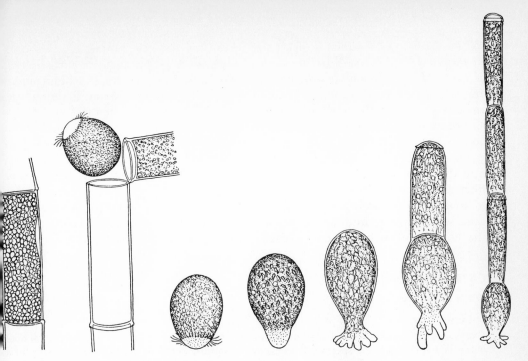

Fig. 11-49 Asexual reproduction of *Oedogonium:* formation and escape of zoospore, and germination of zoospore resulting in a young plant. (From W. H. Brown, *The Plant Kingdom,* Ginn, 1935.)

Hereditary material: chromosomes

In this chapter we have touched upon many modes of reproduction among animals and plants. The end result, no matter what the kind of reproduction, remains the same: a passing on of the hereditary material—chromosomes— from parents to offspring.

In the next chapter we shall develop the principles upon which the transfer of traits are based. What is the underlying conceptual scheme? In describing the laws of heredity, we shall study the organism as product of a given heredity and a specific environment.

Preparation of yeast nucleoproteins

What are chromosomes made of? An individual student or a group may want to try to extract the nucleoproteins from yeast cells as a term project. So much has been written about the chemistry of

the nucleoproteins that some students may want to begin to study some of these techniques as an introduction to the chemistry of cells.

The gist of the procedure described by Hawk, Oser, and Summerson is related here to give an idea of the kind of procedure involved; students may find complete details in this reference.[6]

Crumble two cakes of commercial yeast (or their equivalent in dry form) with a small amount of clean sand in a mortar; add 5 cc of ether (which kills yeast cells) and 10 cc of water; mix thoroughly in grinding. Add about 2 cc of water until the mixture is almost fluid. Macerate for about 5 minutes.

This liquid is then poured into a bottle and enough of a 0.4 per cent solution of

[6] P. Hawk, B. Oser, and W. Summerson, *Practical Physiological Chemistry,* Blakiston (McGraw-Hill), New York, 1954.

sodium hydroxide is added to bring the final volume to 125 cc. Nucleoproteins, as well as the water-soluble proteins, are extracted by sodium hydroxide. A small amount of toluene (inflammable) is added, and this liquid is allowed to stand for 24 hours.

Finally the proteins are precipitated and the fluid is filtered through a wet filter in this way. Add a 10 per cent solution of hydrochloric acid, a drop at a time, while stirring, until the milkiness of the liquid can no longer be increased.

Continue until the protein has all separated out and the liquid is almost clear. Now the solution is acid, and adding more acid will cause re-solution. Filter on wet, fluted filter paper. Then test the precipitate on the filter paper for nucleoproteins. Hawk, Oser, and Summerson describe tests for proteins (xanthoproteic and Millon tests are described on our pp. 61, 62, Chapter 4), then a test for organically combined phosphorus, and a test for the purine base. The latter two tests are beyond the scope of this text.

CAPSULE LESSONS

Ways to get started in class

11-1. Begin by showing the short film *Fertilization* (silent film; Encyclopaedia Britannica). Watch how a living sperm cell seems to be drawn into an egg. Notice that only one sperm enters while the others are rejected after a fertilization membrane lifts off the surface of the egg. Elicit from the students that a sperm carries the "chemicals of heredity," the genes; so does an egg. From this fusion the next generation arises. The class is now into a study of where eggs and sperms "originate." What is the structure of sperms and eggs? How does a fertilized egg develop?

11-2. Plan a field trip in season to collect eggs of animals. Also study flowers as trees and shrubs begin to blossom. Establish the similarity between sexual reproduction in plants and animals; that is, fertilization consists of the union of an egg nucleus and a sperm nucleus.

11-3. Ask students how to grow plants without using seeds. Develop the methods of asexual reproduction. Have students in committee bring in specimens and watch them grow in the classroom. Start sweet potatoes, white potatoes, bulbs, cuttings, and so forth. Develop the notion that cells divide and an equal distribution of chromosome material is effected in mitosis.

11-4. Ask the class how an apple tree could produce 5 different kinds of apples. When possible have students demonstrate how a graft is made. Have students establish the value of vegetative propagation.

11-5. Have students prepare a bulletin board on methods of asexual and sexual reproduction in plants. Where possible, exhibit actual specimens.

11-6. On a field trip around the school grounds, examine the parts of a flower on a tree or shrub. Notice that some flowers lack petals; some are staminate only. Students may notice that flower parts come in multiples of three or five. Key out a specimen; students seem to be very interested in keying out an unknown plant.

11-7. Since reproduction is a means for passing on inherited traits to the next generation, students (in committee) may want to report to the class on the development of eggs of different animals and plants. One committee could describe the reproductive habits of salmon, or of tropical fish. Have students bring in living fish for examination. Fish may be purchased for dissection (if class time is available). In season collect frog eggs and watch them develop. Other students may raise pigeons or chickens; they can bring in eggs. Incubate fertilized eggs if possible, and examine different stages in development. Compare the similarities and differences in reproduction among many groups of animals: How many eggs are laid? Are the eggs fertilized internally or externally? How long does it take for the embryo to develop? How large is the egg? What factors determine the size of the egg? How can a mammal's egg be microscopic?

11-8. Plan several lessons with a microscope to show fission in protozoa, or budding in yeast cells, or sporulation in some fungi. Develop the notion that, in general, asexual reproduction results in offspring whose heredity is identical to that of its parent. How does this compare with reproduction by seeds, or reproduction in higher animals?

11-9. Examine prepared slides of cleavage stages in whitefish eggs or mitotic figures in dividing cells in the tip of the onion root. Trace the stages in the reduplication of chromosomes in mitosis, where each new cell formed receives an equal amount of chromosome material. Have students explain how all the body cells are replicas of the fertilized egg.

11-10. Where possible dissect a pig uterus[7] and study the way a fetus is nourished through the placenta. Discuss the role of the amnion in cushioning the embryo. Compare the role of the amnion in birds or reptiles with that in mammals. Develop the reasons mammals can perpetuate themselves when they produce so few eggs; compare with fish or amphibia.

11-11. In season, crush stigmas of flowers on a slide and under the microscope look for the growth of pollen tubes. (Perhaps a student may try to work out concentrations of sugar solutions which could serve as an artificial medium for germination of pollen grains of a given flower.) From here, have students describe how a sperm nucleus in the pollen grain reaches the nucleus of an egg cell in the ovule so that the egg cell is fertilized. Compare fertilization in plants with that of animals.

11-12. Encourage students to bring in specimens to keep in the aquaria and terraria in the classroom and at home. Some may want to undertake the fascinating study of germinating seeds. Also they may study the devices for dispersing seeds. In the study of reproduction, there are rich opportunities for laboratory work of individual plants or animals. At the end of the period have students bring together the work they did and share their experiences with the

[7] See the directory of suppliers at the end of the book for sources of a pig uterus and similar materials.

rest of the group. Reference books can be made available in the classroom.

11-13. Have students examine prepared slides showing reduction division in testes of insects or other forms.

Examine living sperm cells if frogs are available. Or a club may want to study chromosomes; they may make smears of salivary glands of fruit flies or of onion root tips (pp. 317, 318).

11-14. As a research project, a student might want to study polarity in the regeneration of some worms or *Hydra*. Will the anterior parts of cut pieces always regenerate a "head" part or can they grow a "tail" or posterior portion?

If a shoot of a plant is turned upside down, will a new shoot regenerate at the anterior part, or may roots grow on the portion which was originally in the most anterior (terminal) part?

11-15. As a summary, show the film *Flower to Fruit* (silent; Encyclopaedia Britannica), or *Reproduction among Mammals* (filmstrip; Encyclopaedia Britannica), or *Asexual Reproduction* (University of Indiana); or *Flowers at Work* (Encyclopaedia Britannica). Students might summarize the facts developed in the film or films.

11-16. Use clay of different colors to illustrate chromosomes and show them going through maturation. With clay, have students demonstrate reduction division and compare this division with mitotic division. Also thread a few wooden beads of different colors on wires to represent genes on pairs of chromosomes. Use the wire "chromosome" device (Fig. 11-18) to show mitosis. At some time, show the film *Mitosis and Meiosis* (University of Indiana).

11-17. You may want to refer to conservation of living things and indicate the conditions needed for reproduction; what conditions make for success in survival?

PEOPLE, PLACES, AND THINGS

Students who have a hobby of keeping tropical fish or pigeons, an aquarium shop, a botanical garden, a farmer, a biological supply house, a college laboratory in the vicinity, a librarian—these are the major sources of materials and aid in the vast area of plant and animal reproduction.

Perhaps you may be able to share equipment such as glassware, tanks, films, or living materials with teachers in other schools or colleges. It may be possible to set up a nature center in one school in which student curators (p. 442) learn to cultivate many living things all year round for schools in the community.

You may get living frogs or frog eggs, fruit flies, and living plants the year around from a college biology department. Locate the fruitful areas for field trips to collect materials for the classroom. Students often know many of these areas.

Are there experts you could invite as guest speakers? Could you plan a visit to study some interesting work going on with plants and animals: an experimental farm, an agricultural station, a government conservation project, a fish hatchery?

BOOKS AND PAMPHLETS

These are only a few of the books which are pertinent to the work discussed in this chapter. These and many other references classified by subject and with complete bibliographical data are given in the Bibliography at the end of the book.

Adamstone, F., and Shumway, W., *A Laboratory Manual of Vertebrate Embryology,* 1954.

Arey, L., *Developmental Anatomy,* 1954.

Barth, L., *Embryology,* 1953.

Buchsbaum, R., *Animals Without Backbones,* 1948.

Gibbs, R., *Botany: An Evolutionary Approach,* 1950.

Goldsmith, R., *Understanding Heredity,* 1952.

Graves, A., *Winter Key to Woody Plants,* Author, Wallingford, Conn., 1955.

Guyer, M., *Animal Micrology,* 1953.

Hegner, R., *Parade of the Animal Kingdom,* 1955.

Hunter, G., and Hunter, F., *College Zoology,* 1949.

Johansen, D., *Plant Microtechnique,* 1940.

Marsland, D., *Principles of Modern Biology,* 1957.

Mavor, J., *General Biology,* 1952.

Patten, B., *Human Embryology,* 1946.

———, *The Early Embryo of the Chick,* 1951.

Romer, A., *The Vertebrate Body,* 1955.

Rugh, R., *The Frog: Its Reproduction and Development,* 1951.

———, *A Laboratory Manual of Vertebrate Embryology,* 1949.

———, *Experimental Embryology,* 1948.

Shumway, W., and F. Adamstone, *Introduction to Vertebrate Embryology,* 1954.

Wodehouse, R., *Pollen Grains,* 1935.

FILMS AND FILMSTRIPS

This partial list is intended only as a guide toward film and filmstrip selection. Refer to the more complete listing at the end of the book where films are classified by subject and a key to abbreviations and the addresses of distributors are given. The cost of film rental, of course, may be subject to change. Films are sound and black and white unless otherwise specified.

Alaska's Silver Millions (salmon run) (f), American Can Co., free.

Asexual Reproduction (f), U. of Indiana, $2.00.

Cell Division: The Basis of Growth in All Living Things (f), U. of California, Visual Instruction Dept., $2.50.

Development of the Chick (f), Almanac, $2.00.

Development of the Frog (f), UWF, $3.50.

Ferns (alternation of generation) (f), Almanac, $2.00.

Fertilization (f, si), EBF, inquire rental.

Flowers at Work (f), EBF, $2.00.

From Flower to Fruit (f, si), EBF, inquire rental.

Green Vagabonds (seed dispersal) (f), Almanac, $2.00.

Growth of Bacteria, Yeasts, Molds (f, si), Soc. Amer. Bacteriologists, $2.00.

In the Beginning (rabbit egg) (f), UWF, $1.50.

Life Cycle of Mosquito (f), Almanac, $2.00.

Life Cycle of Trout (f), UWF, $3.00.

Life History of Fern (f), UWF, $3.00.

Life of a Plant (f, c), EBF, $4.00.

Miracle of Life (cell division, fertilization) (f), Almanac, $2.00.

Mitosis and Meiosis (f), Indiana U., $2.00.

Parade of Invertebrates (4f, si, c), Iowa State U., $3.00 ea.

Reproduction in Lower Forms of Life (f, si), Bray, $1.50.

Reproduction in Animals (f), Coronet, inquire rental.

Salamanders and Their Young (f, si, c), Iowa State U., $3.00.

Seed Dispersal (f), EBF, $2.00.

Story of Human Reproduction (f), McGraw-Hill, $3.00.

FREE AND INEXPENSIVE MATERIALS

Many of the biological supply houses publish monthly bulletins of suggestions for using plants and animals in the classroom. These offer excellent sources of ideas for the teacher and resourceful students. See, for example, those listed at the end of Chapter 10. Also refer to the directory of distributors of free and inexpensive materials at the end of the book.

CHAPTER 12

Heredity

Since most youngsters are interested in their own heredity, it is a good idea to begin with a study of heredity in human beings.

Heredity in man

Youngsters enjoy looking into the inheritance of maleness and femaleness, colorblindness, freckles, musical ability, hair color, shape of ears, attached or free ear lobes, curly hair, ability to taste specific chemicals, and blood types. Students can learn the laws of heredity by using examples from human traits as well as those from traditional plant material (garden peas, corn) and other animal material (*Drosophila*). They will want to study Mendel's work, and demonstration crosses using rats, peas, maize, sorghum, and fruit flies.

Tasters vs. nontasters

About seven out of every ten human beings taste P.T.C. (phenylthiocarbamide) as a salt, sweet, sour, or bitter substance. To others, P.T.C. is tasteless. Paper soaked in this harmless chemical may be purchased from the American Genetic Association.[1] Or you may want to prepare

[1] Located at 1507 M Street, N. W., Washington 5, D. C.

it yourself as described below.

Cut the paper into ½-inch squares. (Do not explain what kinds of tastes will be obtained; otherwise some students will imagine a taste.) Distribute the paper and have all the students taste it at the same time. Then notice their reaction. Tally the results; tasters and nontasters. Ability to taste P.T.C. paper seems to be a dominant trait.

Students might use symbols to illustrate the possible crosses, as in Fig. 12-1. Is it possible for one child to be a taster and his sibling a nontaster? Have students calculate these possibilities beginning with the known facts which are given:

nontasters must have genetic make-up tt
tasters must have at least one gene T

Work back to find the parents' genetic make-up. For example, both parents might be hybrid for the trait (Fig. 12-1b); then 75 per cent of the offspring would be tasters, 25 per cent nontasters. Or one parent might be hybrid and the other a

Key: T = taster, t = nontaster

(a) *Parents:*   TT   ×   tt

     Gametes: T   t

     Offspring: Tt

              (hybrid taster)

(b) *Parents:*   Tt   ×   Tt

     Gametes: T t   T t

     Offspring: TT Tt Tt tt

              (75% tasters,

              25% nontasters)

(c) *Parents:*   Tt   ×   tt

     Gametes: T t   t

     Offspring: Tt   tt

              (50% tasters,

              50% nontasters)

Fig. 12-1 Inheritance of the trait of tasting P.T.C. paper: the three possible crosses.

nontaster (Fig. 12-1c); then 50 per cent of the offspring would be tasters and 50 per cent nontasters.

Elicit from students that there are six possible crosses whenever *one* pair of genes is under study:

1. pure dominant × pure dominant
   (TT × TT = 100% TT)
2. pure recessive × pure recessive
   (tt × tt = 100% tt)
3. pure dominant × pure recessive
   (TT × tt = 100% Tt)
4. hybrid × pure dominant
   (Tt × TT = 50% Tt; 50% TT)
5. hybrid × pure recessive
   (Tt × tt = 50% Tt; 50% tt)
6. hybrid × hybrid
   (Tt × Tt = 50% Tt; 25% TT; 25% tt)

Perhaps you may be able to provide enough paper for students to take home to test their parents' reactions as well. Then students might compile all the data.

The American Genetic Association also supplies tablets of mannose, a sugar which is tasted differently by different people. But the genetic basis for these differences is not as well known as in the case of P.T.C. tasting.

PREPARING P.T.C. PAPER.[2] Gradually dissolve 500 mg of phenylthiocarbamide in 1 liter of water. At room temperature this will take about 24 hours. Then soak sheets of filter paper in this solution and hang them up to dry. Cut small pieces, about ½-inch squares, and store them in envelopes for distribution to students. (At higher concentrations, nontasters will also react.)

Rh factor

Although there are many complexities involved in the inheritance of the Rh factor, we shall assume that the trait is inherited as a simple dominant. This assumption is based on the finding of a certain substance in the red corpuscles of 85 per cent of the sample white population tested. This type of blood is called Rh positive. Fifteen per cent of the population lack this substance and are designated as Rh negative. (There are several Rh antigens, however, and people who are Rh negative have another antigen called Hr. This blood condition now seems to be inherited as a set of multiple alleles.)

You may want to have students work out several possible crosses to show the pattern of inheritance. These questions may serve as samples. A woman with Rh-negative blood marries a man who has Rh-positive blood. Will her children all have the Rh-positive factor since this trait is dominant? Explain. What are the chances of her having an Rh-positive child? An Rh-negative child? Explain. If both parents were Rh negative, what would be the chances for getting an Rh-positive child?

At some time in this work students

[2] W. Curtis and M. Guthrie, *Laboratory Directions in General Zoology,* 4th ed., Wiley, New York, 1948.

TABLE 12-1
Inheritance of blood type

blood type of parents		possible genetic combinations of offspring	blood type of offspring
O	O	OO	O
O	A	OA, OO	A, O
O	B	OB, OO	B, O
O	AB	OA, OB	A, B
A	A	AA, OA, OO	A, O
A	B	OA, OB, AB, OO	A, B, AB, O
A	AB	AA, OA, OB, AB	A, B, AB
B	B	BB, OB, OO	B, O
B	AB	OA, BB, OB, AB	A, B, AB
AB	AB	AA, BB, AB	A, B, AB

might report to the class on the role of the Rh factor in pregnancy and in cases of blood transfusions. Have them explain how Landsteiner and Wiener came to identify an "Rh" factor. (Refer to texts on heredity listed at the end of this chapter.)

Blood groups

There are four basic blood types in man, depending on the distribution of the two antigens found in human red corpuscles. See Table 5-1, Fig. 5-10, and the surrounding discussion for the facts underlying blood types and blood typing.

Law of probability

It is important to illustrate the fact that a 3:1 ratio among the offspring of hybrids is the result of random combinations of eggs and sperms. There are several ways to show this symbolically. Among these are the following.

(a) Have students toss two similar coins simultaneously on the desk and keep tallies of the number of combinations of two heads, two tails, and a head-and-tail toss. Have students toss coins 10 times, then 50 times, and finally 100 times. Compile all the results and show

The inheritance of blood types is explained on the basis of multiple genes. However, it is not necessary to involve students with these complex details. The following method has proved successful in the classroom.

Type A person may have genetic make-up AA or OA
  (A is dominant over O)
Type B person may have genetic make-up BB or OB
  (B is dominant over O)
Type AB person can have genetic make-up AB only
  (neither A nor B is dominant over the other)
Type O person can have genetic make-up OO only
  (neither A nor B can be present)

In crossing blood types: Note that group A (or B) never appears in the offspring unless it was present in at least one parent. What are the possible mating combinations (Table 12-1)?

Students readily contribute this information and can foresee what blood group a parent could not have if the child had a known type. You may want to develop several hypothetical cases to have students apply this information to solve the cases. If you have not already typed blood in class, you may want to have students do this now (p. 79).

that only when large numbers are used will the 1:2:1 ratio come out with some accuracy. The two sides of a coin represent two possibilities similar to the segregation of a pair of genes in a hybrid, such as TD × TD. Each pair TD separates into T and D. Thus in recombination at fertilization this ratio appears: 25 per cent TT, 50 per cent TD, and 25 per cent DD.

(b) Mix together in a large bowl 100 green and 100 yellow dried peas. Or use black and white marbles, or beads. Have a student pick out two at a time, without looking. His partner may keep a tally of the number of times each of the three possible combinations appears. Each marble or pea represents an egg or sperm (carrying one gene of a pair). Two together are symbolic of a union, a fertilization. For instance, approximately 25 per cent of the times a student will pick up two green peas, 25 per cent of the times, two yellow ones, and in 50 per cent of the chances he will select a combination of green and yellow peas. Of course, a large number of drawings is needed to approximate this 1:2:1 ratio.

Heredity in rats and mice

You may be able to purchase pedigreed hooded rats from an experimental station or college. Cross hooded with albino rats. Hoodedness seems to be dominant (with a few white, or albino, offspring appearing in the F_2, or second generation, after inbreeding the hybrid hooded F_1 generation). This assumes the original cross was pure hooded $\times$ albino.

Pedigreed mice may be purchased from several supply houses (directions for possible crossings will be supplied by the biological supply house).[3] Make crosses between pure black mice and albino mice (Fig. 12-2); the F_1 offspring will be all black. These are hybrid black, each animal carrying a recessive gene for albinism.

When these F_1 offspring are inbred (Fig. 12-3), the second filial generation, F_2, should show the ratio of three black to one white.

Students may make test crosses (backcrosses) by mating the black offspring in the second generation with an albino parent in order to determine whether the black animal is pure black or hybrid black (Fig. 12-4).

Any of these ratios, of course, can be expected to hold only when large numbers of offspring are produced. In practice, a male would be mated to a large number of genetically identical females in order to get many offspring.

[3] Supply houses are listed in the directory at the end of the book. How to keep mice or rats in the laboratory is described in Chapter 19.

Key: B = black, b = albino

Parents:	BB	$\times$	bb
Gametes:	B		b
Offspring:		Bb	

Fig. 12-2 Crossing pure black and albino mice: offspring are hybrid black.

Parents:	Bb		$\times$	Bb
Gametes:	B	b		B b
Offspring:	BB	Bb Bb bb		

	B	b
B	BB	Bb
b	Bb	bb

Fig. 12-3 Crossing two hybrid black mice: offspring show ratio of 3 black to 1 white (25% pure black, 50% hybrid black, 25% white).

Parents:	B?	$\times$	bb
Gametes:	B ?		b
Offspring:	Bb		?b

	b				b
B	Bb			B	Bb
B	Bb	or		b	bb

Fig. 12-4 Test cross: a black mouse of unknown genetic make-up is mated to an albino; if the mouse was pure black, there can be no white mice in the litter; if the mouse was hybrid, the offspring will show a 1:1 ratio.

Demonstration Punnett square

Students may want to construct this do-it-yourself device by screwing cup hooks into a large square of plywood as in Fig. 12-5. Two small hooks close together represent the diploid condition of the parent organisms; single hooks represent the gametes, or the haploid possibilities. Below this, show a Punnett square with four boxes. In each box show two hooks, representing a diploid organism. Along the top and left side of the square, insert single hooks, representing the gametes.

Then students might make models of flowers out of plywood or cardboard and color them with crayon. Also model small animals such as guinea pigs or rats, black and white ones. Use small circles of color to indicate the genes in the gametes. Make holes in these models and hang them on the hooks. Youngsters may try to make a variety of crosses in front of the class. Errors are easily detected as they occur.

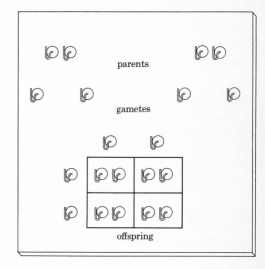

Fig. 12-5 Demonstration board for simple genetic crosses, made of plywood and cup hooks.

Heredity in plants

Corn (maize). Purchase hybrid seeds of corn containing recessive genes for albinism from the Texas Agricultural Experiment Station, College Station, Texas; Meyers Hybrid Seed Corn Company at Hillsboro, Ohio; biological supply houses; Genetics Laboratory Supplies at Clinton, Connecticut (among others). When germinated, these seeds should show 75 per cent green shoots and 25 per cent albino shoots, or a 3:1 ratio (Fig. 12-6). These seedlings show variations in the rate of chlorophyll formation. They should be grown in sunlight for the 75 per cent to show chlorophyll development.

Peas. You may also obtain F_1 seeds from a cross between pure tall and dwarf peas. They will develop into hybrid tall pea plants. At the same time also purchase the seeds which are a result of a cross between two hybrid tall pea plants. Germinate the seeds in paper cups containing moist sand. As the seedlings grow, students will see the difference in height; a ratio of three tall to one short or dwarf will result.

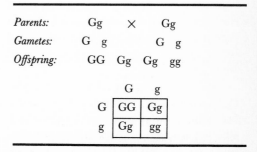

Parents: Gg   ×   Gg
Gametes: G   g   G   g
Offspring: GG   Gg   Gg   gg

	G	g
G	GG	Gg
g	Gg	gg

Fig. 12-6 Law of segregation in maize: hybrid green shoots when inbred produce offspring in the ratio of 3 green to 1 albino (25% pure green, 50% hybrid green, 25% albino).

Sorghum. Red-stemmed sorghum is dominant over green-stemmed (when grown in the presence of sunlight). Seeds produced from inbred hybrid plants may be obtained from supply houses as well as the Brooklyn Botanic Garden (New York). These seedlings will germinate in about 5 days, but the differences in stem color are most obvious in about 7 to 10 days. When large numbers of seeds have been germinated, the 3:1 ratio of red-stemmed to green-stemmed plants results.

Heredity in fruit flies

Pure stocks of *Drosophila* may be obtained from a supply house or college laboratory. Some suggested stocks for work in heredity are these (see map, Fig. 12-7):

1. *Wild:* These are the typical forms found in nature, with red eyes, gray body, and normal wings.
2. *Vestigial wings:* This trait is recessive to normal wings. Mate winged males to virgin vestigial-winged females (since the vestigial forms are unable to fly).
3. *Curly wings:* This is dominant over wild-type normal wings. The wings curl up at the tips so that it is difficult for the insects to fly.
4. *White eyes:* This is a sex-linked trait found in the X-chromosome. Make reciprocal crosses, i.e., cross red-eyed males with white-eyed females; also red-eyed females with white-eyed males. Flies must be pure for these traits. (Figs. 12-13, 12-14.)
5. *Yellow body:* This is a sex-linked trait, found in the X-chromosome.
6. *Black body:* Animals with this characteristic illustrate complete linkage, since the black (or the wild-type) body gene is located in the same chromosome as vestigial (and/or long, normal wild-type) wings. Cross black-bodied vestigial-winged flies with normal gray-bodied wild-type flies having normal long wings. Also cross black, long-winged flies with gray-bodied, vestigial-winged flies (see pp. 201, 203).

Mating fruit flies

Students should refer to the map of the chromosomes of *Drosophila* for an indication of the position of the genes on the chromosomes of the animal (Fig. 12-7). In this way students will discover which genes are linked on the same chromosome.

Virgin female flies are needed when mating flies of two different types, e.g., red eyes × white eyes. Since females retain sperms for a considerable time, females must be isolated as they emerge from pupae. Usually females do not mate for some 12 hours after hatching. A more casual method is to remove the original parents as pupae begin to form in the culture bottles. Then the emerging flies will be virgin for the first 12 hours.

Parent flies should be removed in any case, as they may create errors in determining the results (when counting offspring). When the flies are kept at 20° C, counts of offspring may be continued up to the twentieth day. Thereafter, the second generation will emerge and errors in count will occur.

Examining and crossing fruit flies

Students will quickly learn to identify male and female flies (Fig. 12-8). The abdomen of the male is bluntly rounded with a wide band of dark pigment; the female's abdomen is elongated with

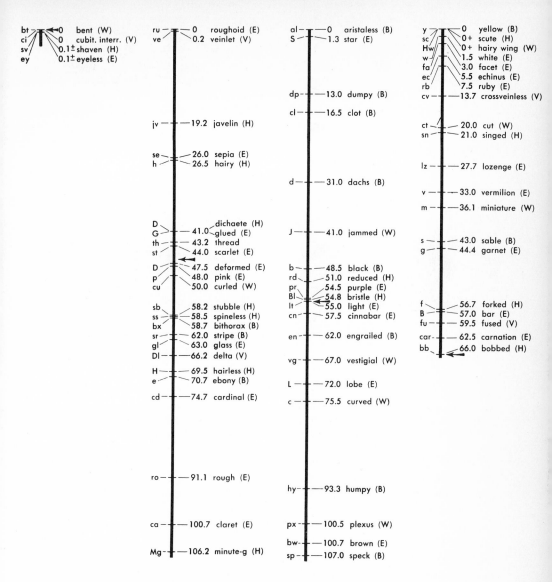

Fig. 12-7 Map of the 4 chromosomes of the fruit fly (*Drosophila*), showing loci of genes.

thinner pigment bands. Females distended with eggs are easily recognized. With a hand lens it is possible to distinguish seven abdominal segments in the female and five in the male. The females have an ovipositor; the males possess sex combs (black bristles) on the end of the tarsal joint of the first pair of legs.

The flies must be etherized so that students may examine them with ease. To make an etherizing container, prepare a bottle or vial having the same circumference as the mouth of the stock bottles. Insert a nail 1-inch long into the cork stopper of the vial. Then cover the nail with layers of cotton and tie the cotton

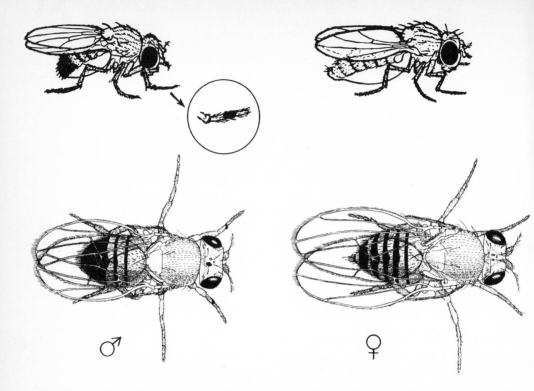

♂   ♀

Fig. 12-8 Male and female fruit flies: *left,* male, side and dorsal view; *right,* female, side and dorsal view. (Dorsal views from A. M. Srb & R. D. Owen, *General Genetics,* Freeman, 1952, after Sturtevant & Beadle; side views from W. G. Whaley, O. P. Breland, et al., *Principles of Biology,* Harper, 1954.)

to the nail with cord (Fig. 12-9b). Put a few drops of ether on the cotton when you plan to etherize the flies.

To transfer the flies, first tap the culture bottle on the table. When the flies fall to the bottom (this will be but for a moment), quickly remove the cover and hold the mouth of the etherizer closely against the mouth of the stock bottle (Fig. 12-9a). Invert the stock bottle and tap it slightly, so that the flies move into the etherizing vial. Since the flies are phototropic, an electric light may be placed near the etherizer to encourage the flies to move into the empty vial. Then quickly separate the bottles and stopper both (Fig. 12-9b). The flies will be anesthetized within a few seconds.

Avoid excess or too rapid etherization or the flies will die. (When the wings stand out at an angle, the flies are dead.)

Spill the anesthetized flies out onto white paper for examination. Should the flies recover before the examination is completed, they must be re-etherized. Have on hand a Petri dish cover in which a strip of filter paper is held fast with adhesive tape. Add a drop of ether to the filter paper and place the dish over the flies for a few seconds.

Since the flies are fragile, use a camel's-hair brush or a copper strip to handle them during examinations and to transfer them from place to place. When you plan to cross two different genetic types, select several pairs of flies of the stock with

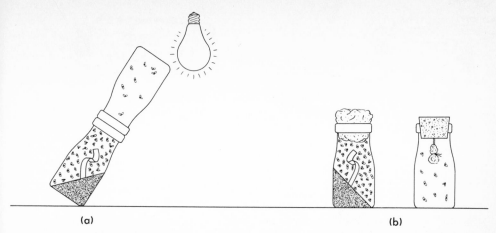

Fig. 12-9 Technique for transferring and etherizing fruit flies: (a) phototropic flies leave culture bottle for new one; (b) old bottle stoppered with cotton plug, new one with etherizing stopper.

which you are dealing and place them in a small cone of paper. Then introduce them into new culture medium for stock. Otherwise, anesthetized flies dropped into the medium will adhere to the medium and drown.

The stock cultures should be kept at a temperature range of 20° to 25° C. At 25° C the life cycle takes 10 days; at 20° C the cycle is lengthened to 15 days. Lower temperatures prolong the life cycle. High temperatures increase sterility and reduce viability. The temperature within the bottles will be a bit higher than the room temperature because of fermentation of the medium.

Subculture or transfer flies to new stock bottles with fresh medium each month, or more frequently, depending upon the temperature and the amount of evaporation of fluid from the medium. Prepare several duplicate stock cultures. Label the bottles and record the date of transfer.

Establishing stock cultures

Fruit flies are attracted to soft grapes, plums, bananas, in fact, any fermenting fruits. Larvae feed freely on yeast and other microorganisms in the fermenting fruit juices; clearly, a fermenting medium must be prepared. For rapid, temporary cultures, where little handling will occur, the simplest medium is prepared by dipping a piece of ripe banana into a suspension of yeast (made from a quarter of a package of yeast dissolved in 100 cc of water). Insert this piece of banana along with a strip of paper toweling into a clean glass vial or bottle. In season, this may be left open to attract fruit flies, or you may introduce flies into the bottles. Then plug with cotton wrapped in cheesecloth, or with milk-bottle caps. However, this medium is not recommended for careful work. In the two-week life span of fruit flies the medium described above will become a mash with the flies imbedded in the soft material. Also, molds will grow in profusion.

Demerec and Kaufmann[4] describe several media which use agar to solidify the medium so that bottles may be inverted; they may then be used with ease

[4] M. Demerec and B. P. Kaufmann, *Drosophila Guide,* Carnegie Institution, Washington, D. C., 1945.

in making transfers. You may want to prepare one or more of these media.

BANANA MEDIUM. Dissolve 1.5 gm of agar in 47.8 cc of water by bringing it to a boil; stir well. To this add 50 gm of banana pulp made by mashing a banana with a fork or putting it through a strainer. You may want to add a trace of a mold inhibitor. (A minute quantity of Methyl Parasepts[5] in 0.15 per cent solution can be added; in excess any inhibitor will reduce the growth of yeast and slow down the development of the flies.)

Heat the medium again so that it comes close to boiling. Then quickly pour the medium into half-pint milk bottles or glass vials to a depth of ½ inch. It is safer to sterilize the bottles before introducing the medium. Then insert a strip of paper toweling into the medium while it is soft; this will provide additional space for egg laying and pupation. Cover the bottles with cotton wrapped in cheesecloth or with milk-bottle caps. Tilt the bottles against a ledge to increase the surface, and allow them to cool; a completed bottle looks like the one in Fig. 12-10. You may want to pour medium from the cooking pot through a funnel into the bottles so that the medium does not spill along the sides of the bottles. Store the bottles in a refrigerator until the flies are to be introduced. Just before using the bottles to accept the flies, add 2 to 3 drops of a rich yeast suspension to the surface of the solid medium. Or add a pinch of dried yeast; this will dissolve in the fluid on the surface.

CREAM OF WHEAT MEDIUM. This preparation eliminates the agar. Measure out 77.5 cc of water, 11.5 cc of molasses or Karo, and 10.3 gm of Cream of Wheat. Add the molasses to two thirds of the water; bring to a boil. Mix the Cream of Wheat with the remaining third of cold water and add this to the boiling mixture. Continue to stir, and cook for 5 minutes after boiling begins. Pour the medium into sterilized bottles, add strips of toweling, stopper the bottles, and tilt them, as before.

CORNMEAL MEDIUM. This medium uses agar. Dissolve 15 gm of agar in 750 cc of water and heat. Then add 100 gm of cornmeal and stir

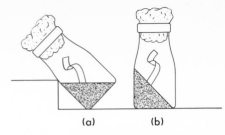

Fig. 12-10 Culture bottles for fruit flies: (a) bottle containing soft medium and strip of paper toweling, left slanted to cool; (b) bottle with hardened medium, ready for flies.

constantly. After this comes to a boil, add 135 cc of corn syrup (Karo) or molasses. Boil this *slowly* for about 5 minutes. Then pour this medium into sterilized bottles or vials, insert toweling as before, and plug the bottles with cotton or cover with caps. This quantity will fill twenty-five culture bottles.

You may want to sterilize these prepared bottles for 20 minutes at 15 pounds pressure, or add a mold inhibitor instead (see footnote 5).

CORNMEAL–MOLASSES–ROLLED-OATS MEDIUM. This recipe requires no agar. Measure out 72.7 cc of water, 11 cc of molasses or Karo, 15 gm of cornmeal, and 1.6 gm of rolled oats (not quick-cooking). To the molasses add two thirds of the water and bring this to a boil. Mix the cornmeal with the remaining cold water and introduce this into the boiling mixture. Cook for a few minutes until it thickens but still can be poured. Then add the rolled oats. You may want to add agar to the medium to prevent it from softening with a rise in temperature.

In fact, for work during the summer months, agar should be included in any medium you use. Cover the bottles of medium after you insert toweling strips and tilt the bottles to increase the surface area, as before.

Should molds appear in the cultures of *Drosophila*, paint the surface of the culture medium with alcohol or with a solution made from 1 part carbolic acid and 8 parts of water. (*Caution:* Remove the flies from the bottle before this treatment.)

[5] One preservative, Methyl Parasepts (p-hydroxybenzoic acid esters), may be purchased from Heyden Newport Chemical Corp., 342 Madison Ave., New York 17, N. Y.

Some demonstration crosses

Law of dominance. Cross a wild-type fruit fly (i.e., gray-bodied, long-winged) with a black-bodied, long-winged fly. The first generation should be 100 per cent hybrid gray-bodied flies if both parents were pure for these traits.

Cross pure long-winged with vestigial-winged flies to get all long-winged offspring (hybrid).

Or cross pure long-winged flies with curly-winged ones to get 100 per cent curly-winged flies. In all these crosses students may observe the appearance in the offspring of one of the pair of contrasting traits. The trait which appears is the dominant trait; the hidden trait is the recessive one.

Law of segregation. Cross the offspring, that is, inbreed the offspring of each of the crosses made above to illustrate dominance. When these hybrids are crossed, students should find that the second generation reveals a 3:1 ratio. Seventy-five per cent will show the dominant trait and 25 per cent will show the recessive trait. Students should see that the recessive trait which was not apparent in the F_1 hybrids has reappeared in the second generation due to the recombination of genes at fertilization.

Test cross or backcross. In order to determine whether an organism showing the dominant gene is pure or hybrid, the "unknown" should be crossed with the recessive type. The answer lies among the offspring of this cross, provided there are enough of them. Let us take a specific example. If we want to find out whether some long-winged flies are hybrid and carry a recessive gene for vestigial, we would cross them with vestigial-winged flies. For if they were pure long-winged, with two genes for long wings, then there could be no vestigial-winged flies among

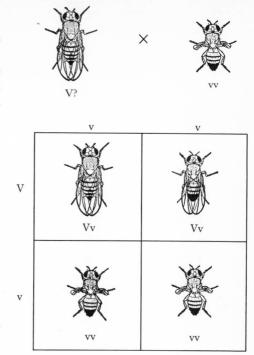

Fig. 12-11 Test cross in fruit flies: long-winged flies of unknown genetic composition are mated with vestigial-winged flies; if some vestigial-winged offspring appear (as shown) the unknown was hybrid for long wings.

the offspring. However, if the long-winged flies were hybrid for the trait and they were crossed with vestigial, 50 per cent of the offspring should show the recessive trait, vestigial wings (Fig. 12-11). In a two-factor backcross, the unknown type would be crossed with the double recessive.

Law of independent assortment of factors. When two genes are located in different chromosomes, they are inherited independently of each other (see chromosome map in Fig. 12-7). Each gene behaves as a unit since the chromosomes segregate in maturation of eggs and sperms (meiosis), and are recombined in fertilization.

Students may undertake to examine

Key: B = gray body; b = black body; P = red eyes, p = pink eyes

(a)   *Parents:*   (BBpp)   ×   (bbPP)

      Gametes: Bp   bP

      Offspring: (BbPp)

(b)   *Parents:*   (BbPp)   ×   (BbPp)

      Gametes: BP Bp bP bp   BP Bp bP bp

	BP	Bp	bP	bp
BP	BBPP gray body, red eyes	BBPp gray body red eyes	BbPP gray body red eyes	BbPp gray body red eyes
Bp	BBPp gray body red eyes	BBpp gray body pink eyes	BbPp gray body red eyes	Bbpp gray body pink eyes
bP	BbPP gray body red eyes	BbPp gray body red eyes	bbPP black body red eyes	bbPp black body red eyes
bp	BbPp gray body red eyes	Bbpp gray body pink eyes	bbPp black body red eyes	bbpp black body pink eyes

Fig. 12-12   Independent assortment in fruit flies: (a) pure gray-bodied, pink-eyed flies are mated with pure black-bodied, red-eyed flies; the offspring are all dihybrid, with gray bodies and red eyes; (b) if these dihybrids are inbred, independent assortment occurs; the genetic and physical make-up of the offspring are shown in the Punnett square.

this type of cross firsthand (in club or project work). At least two factors must be studied. For example, cross fruit flies pure for gray body and pink eyes with flies pure for black body and red eyes (Fig. 12-12). (Note in Fig. 12-7 that these genes are on different chromosomes, not within the same chromosome.) Let B stand for a gene for gray body; b represents a gene for black body; P represents a gene for red eyes; p represents a gene for pink eyes.

Upon inspection of the Punnett square, students should be able to locate the $\frac{9}{16}$ of the flies which have gray body with red eyes; $\frac{3}{16}$, gray body with pink eyes; $\frac{3}{16}$, black body with red eyes; $\frac{1}{16}$, black body with pink eyes. Upon actual counts of fruit flies, students should find similar results if large numbers of flies are counted. A dihybrid cross such as this one yields a 9:3:3:1 ratio. (In a trihybrid cross, multiply the 9:3:3:1 ratio by a 3:1 ratio which represents the added hybrid, so that the offspring would yield a ratio of 27:9:9:9:3:3:3:1. In this case, $\frac{27}{64}$ of the offspring should show the combination of three dominant traits and $\frac{1}{64}$ should show the three recessive traits.)

Sex linkage. After students have learned how maleness or femaleness is inherited on the basis of XX- or XY-

Key: B = gray body; b = black body
      V = long wings; v = vestigial wings
      ♂ = male; ♀ = female

(a)

Parents: (bV)(bV) × (Bv)(Bv)

Gametes: bV   Bv

Offspring: (bV)(Bv)

(b)

Parents: F₁ ♂ (bV)(Bv) × (bv)(bv) ♀

Gametes: bV Bv   bv

Offspring: (bV)(bv)   (Bv)(bv)

(c)

Parents: F₁ ♀ (bV)(Bv) × (bv)(bv) ♂

Gametes: bV Bv BV bv   bv

Off-
spring: (bv)(bV) (bv)(Bv) (bv)(BV) (bv)(bv)

Fig. 12-13 Linkage in fruit flies: (a) pure black-bodied, long-winged × pure gray-bodied, vestigial-winged; (b) F₁ male (gray-bodied, long-winged) × double recessive female (black-bodied, vestigial-winged); (c) reciprocal cross to (b): F₁ female × double recessive male. Note that, while the usual way of symbolizing the parents would be (bbVV), since the genes are linked we use the symbols (bV)(bV) instead.

---

chromosome pairs, some students may want to cross red-eyed female fruit flies with white-eyed males (Fig. 12-14). The gene for red or white eye color is located on the X-chromosome (see Fig. 12-7). In this cross the offspring will all be red-eyed. But in the reciprocal cross (Fig. 12-15), white-eyed females crossed with red-eyed males, the females in the first generation are all red-eyed and the males are white-eyed. Trace the results as shown in both cases in the second generation. This is similar to the inheritance of color-

blindness and hemophilia among human beings.

Linkage. Since there are thousands of genes in *Drosophila* and only four linkage groups or chromosomes, many genes are found together or linked on the same chromosome.

To show the linkage of two genes found on the same chromosome students might try this cross. Cross a pure black-bodied, normal long-winged fly with a gray-bodied, vestigial-winged fly. (See chromosome map, Fig. 12-7, to find on which chromosomes the genes are located.) The offspring of pure parents should all be gray-bodied and long-winged (Fig. 12-13a).

Students who are interested may want to go further. They may show that there usually is not a complete linkage in the female since there is a crossing over of chromosomes. In the male fruit fly however, there is no crossover of chromosomes. As a result, different ratios will be produced, depending upon whether a male or a female of the above F₁ generation is used. If the male F₁ is used (Fig. 12-13b), the offspring are 50 per cent gray-bodied, vestigial-winged, and 50 per cent black-bodied, long-winged. The expected types of crossover, gray-long and black-vestigial, do not appear. However, when the reciprocal cross is made (F₁ female with black, vestigial males, Fig. 12-13c), the four expected types appear.

In 1919 Morgan showed that the percentages from such a cross (as in c) were as follows:

	noncrossovers
gray, vestigial	41.5%
black, long	41.5%
total	83 %

	crossovers
black, vestigial	8.5%
gray, long	8.5%
total	17 %

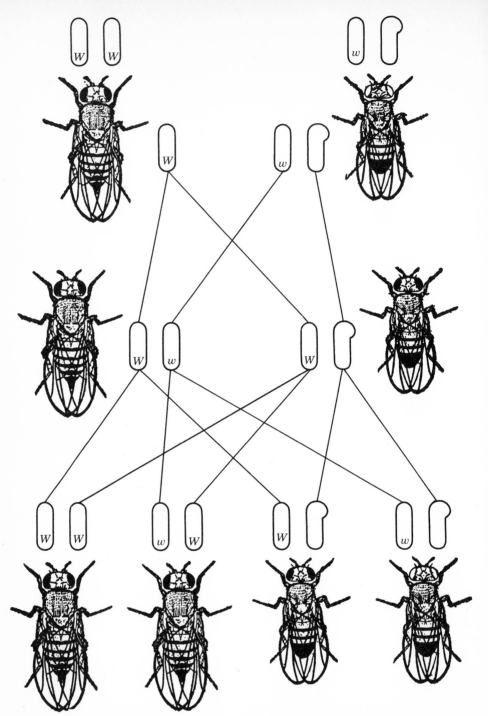

Fig. 12-14 Sex linkage in fruit flies: red-eyed female × white-eyed male. (From E. W. Sinnott & L. C. Dunn, *Principles of Genetics*, 2d ed., McGraw-Hill, 1932; after Morgan, Sturtevant, et al., courtesy Henry Holt.)

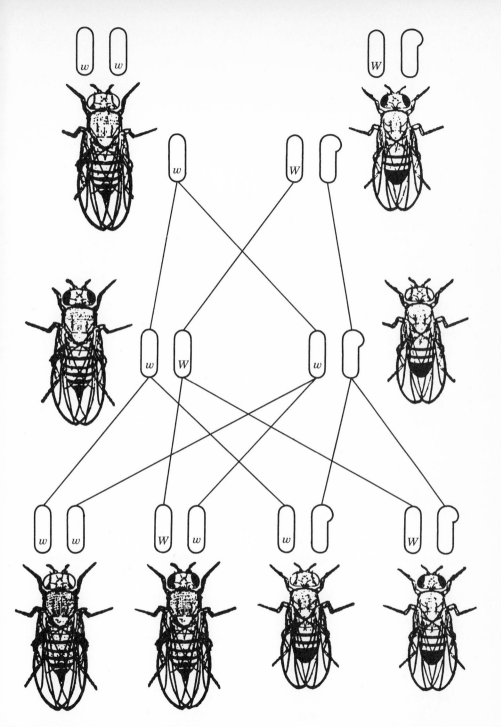

Fig. 12-15 Sex linkage in fruit flies: white-eyed female × red-eyed male. (From E. W. Sinnott & L. C. Dunn, *Principles of Genetics*, 2d ed., McGraw-Hill, 1932; after Morgan, Sturtevant, et al., courtesy Henry Holt.)

Additional facets of heredity

Genes and the effect of environment

Genes have their effect within a given environment. In our desire to make the study of heredity simple we sometimes put stress on genes for a specific trait. We speak of the gene for vestigial wings in fruit flies. Yet if the eggs and the hatching larvae develop at a higher temperature, longer wings result, not the vestigial condition. Recall the Himalayan rabbit: When white fur is plucked from the body and that area is subjected to very low temperatures, the hair which grows back is not white but black in color. We minimize the effect of the environment in which the genes are acting.

In another example, we know there are genes for the development of chlorophyll. But sunlight must be present, or the genes do not "reveal" themselves. As a result, chlorophyll does not appear. Students may show this condition in this way. Grow bean seeds in the dark. Note that the chlorophyll does not develop in the dark. Then remove some of the containers of seedlings to a well-lighted location and watch the development of chlorophyll within a few days. The plastids are always present, but light is needed for the expression of the green color of chlorophyll.

(*Note:* In the high school classroom it is difficult to demonstrate that a trait is the result of the expression of many genes all acting together. Usually a trait is not the expression or the effect of a single gene.)

Artificial pollination and breeding

This method was described in Chapter 11.

When a new type of plant has been developed as a result of careful breeding, or of a mutation, more plants of the same genetic make-up may be produced by using some method of vegetative propagation (Chapter 11). You may want students to recall the methods commonly practiced by the breeder.

A family pedigree

Students may be interested in tracing the inheritance of a trait in their own family. They may study the inheritance of eye color, hair color, freckles, P.T.C. tasting or nontasting, and many other traits. They may want to model their "pedigree" after the one diagramed in Fig. 12-16.

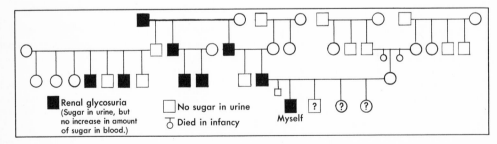

■ Renal glycosuria
(Sugar in urine, but no increase in amount of sugar in blood.)

□ No sugar in urine

⚲ Died in infancy

Myself

Fig. 12-16 Family pedigree of a student who suffered from renal glycosuria, excess sugar in the urine. (From E. Morholt & E. T. Smith, *Experiences in Biology*, Harcourt, Brace, 1954.)

A reading from Mendel's work

There may be times when a reading from an original source is appropriate. Such a translation as the one given below (of Mendel's paper) might be mimeographed and developed in class as part of a case history in heredity. This example shows several methods used by scientists. Or you may want to add questions based on the reading and test the ability of students to interpret what they read.

The Generation Bred from the Hybrids[6]

In this generation there reappear, together with the dominant characters, also the recessive ones with their peculiarities fully developed, and this occurs in the definitely expressed average proportion of three to one, so that among each four plants of this generation three display the dominant character and one the recessive. This relates without exception to all the characters which were investigated in the experiments. The angular wrinkled form of the seed, the green colour of the albumen, the white colour of the seed-coats and the flowers, the constrictions of the pods, the yellow colour of the unripe pod, of the stalk, of the calyx, and of the leaf venation, the umbel-like form of the inflorescence, and the dwarfed stem, all reappear in the numerical proportion given, without any essential alteration. *Transitional forms were not observed in any experiment.*

Expt. 1. Form of seed—From 253 hybrids 7,324 seeds were obtained in the second trial year. Among them were 5,474 round or roundish ones and 1,850 angular wrinkled ones. Therefrom the ratio 2.96 to 1 is deduced.

Expt. 2. Colour of albumen—258 plants yielded 8,023 seeds, 6,022 yellow, and 2,001 green; their ratio, therefore, is as 3.01 to 1.

Expt. 3. Colour of the seed-coats—Among 929 plants 705 bore violet-red flowers and grey-brown seed-coats; 224 had white flowers and white seed-coats, giving the proportion 3.15 to 1.

The entire translation is a splendid example of reporting the results of experiments and the presenting of a working hypothesis to explain inheritance in garden peas.

CAPSULE LESSONS
Ways to get started in class

12-1. Distribute squares of P.T.C. paper and tally the number of students who taste the chemical and those who don't. Have some students test their parents too. How is the trait inherited? Develop the concept of the pairing of factors and their segregation. You may want to follow this lesson with a committee report on Mendel's work. Since the need for reduction division of chromosomes has been developed, students may develop the proof for the Law of Dominance and the Law of Segregation. (A student may read from Mendel's paper.)

12-2. Show culture bottles of fruit flies. Ask the students to predict the approximate number of males and females in the culture. Develop the concept of XX- and XY-chromosomes and how males and females are produced.

12-3. When students know the pattern of inheritance of X- and Y-chromosomes, develop how colorblindness is inherited in humans. Do students understand that the gene is on the X-chromosome? That a colorblind female is thought to have two genes for colorblindness? What is the proof that the gene is not on the Y-chromosome? Have students also diagram the way hemophilia is inherited.

12-4. Have students type their own blood (as a laboratory lesson, p. 79). Before you begin, be certain to get notes of permission from parents. Develop the basic laws of heredity from the data secured. For example, if a student has type *A* blood what possible blood types could his parents have? What blood types could the parents not have? How might a child of *B* type parents have *O* type blood?

12-5. You may want to show a film such as *Heredity* (Encyclopaedia Britannica). This com-

[6] Gregor Mendel, *Experiments in Plant-hybridisation*, Trans. Royal Horticultural Society of London, Harvard U. Press, Cambridge, Mass., 1933, p. 321.

pares reduction division (meiosis) with mitosis and illustrates several cases of dominance.

12-6. Students might make a "flip book" to show how the two processes, mitosis and reduction division, differ. What effect might irregularities in movement of chromosomes have on the heredity of the offspring? Also have students report on radiation damage to chromosomes.

12-7. Committees of students might breed hooded and white rats, or fruit flies. Or they might grow seeds resulting from a cross of two hybrid sorghum plants or corn plants. Students can gain skill in reasoning on the basis of the evidence.

12-8. Students may want to report to the class about improvements which have been made in beef and dairy cattle, in horses, in sheep, in food crops, in fruits, in dogs, bees, and so forth. How does a breeder select points for breeding? What are desirable traits for the consumer? They may consult the Yearbooks of the Department of Agriculture (Washington, D. C.) for 1936 and 1937 on improvements in plants and animals through breeding. Also use the Yearbook for 1943–47 *Science in Farming*. These books give actual case histories of new types of plants and animals. Snyder's book *The Principles of Heredity* (see Bibliography) provides chapters on the genetics of domestic plants and animals. (Human family histories also are analyzed.) Develop the values of inbreeding, hybridization, and selective breeding.

12-9. You may want to pose this problem for solution. A group of science students have purchased a black male guinea pig for a study of heredity. How may the students (limited to one generation of guinea pigs) discover whether this animal is pure black or hybrid black? Elicit from students that the male might be mated to several white females (recessive). Should a white-furred offspring appear, the unknown must have been a hybrid. For if the unknown were pure black, then all the offspring should be black-furred (hybrid black).

12-10. A student might report to the class on exceptions to the "law" of dominance—blended inheritance. For example, when red and white four o'clock flowers are crossed, the hybrid offspring have pink flowers. Many examples may be found in reference books in heredity.

12-11. Show a new plant or animal. You may easily obtain pink grapefruits, double-petaled flowers, and so forth. Elicit the idea of a mutation as a change in a gene. What might

be some causes of a change in the chemistry of a gene? What kinds of irregularities might occur among chromosomes which could result in a different, a "new" organism? Students might report on their reading of a text in genetics (see Bibliography).

12-12. Have students keep seedlings in the dark. Do they notice that chlorophyll is lacking? What is the proof that these genes need specific environmental conditions before an effect is produced in the body of the plant? How long does it take, when the seedlings are put in light, for the shoots to turn green? Develop the interaction of genes in a given environment.

12-13. Or you may want to develop the notion this way. Use several coleus plants of the same genetic make-up (obtained from cuttings from the same plant). Place some in moderate light, others in bright light. How does the environment affect the development of color in coleus plants? Students may find many examples of similar conditions around the school grounds.

12-14. At some time in the work a committee of students might report on the inheritance of the Rh factor in human beings. While there are many genes involved in the inheritance of this blood factor, simple examples of dominance may be used. If 85 per cent of the population tested in the United States have a factor in their red corpuscles called an Rh factor, and about 15 per cent of the people lack this factor and are called Rh minus, the Rh-plus factor is considered dominant. What percentage of the offspring might be Rh negative, if both the parents are hybrid for Rh positive?

12-15. You may want to arrange to have a panel of student "experts" discuss the effects of radiation of genes and chromosomes. Students might get their information from books listed in the Bibliography.

12-16. When possible, have students visit (or report on a previous visit to) a county or state fair. How have new kinds of plants and animals been developed?

12-17. If possible show color slides on variations in cattle (beef and dairy) and in dogs; these may be purchased from supply houses. How do these forms differ from the ancestral wild type? How have these new types been developed? [*Time* Magazine (May 7, 1956) presented a report with fine color photos of variations in beef cattle.]

12-18. What is the difference between identical and fraternal twins? When students know that identical twins develop from one fertilized egg and thereby have the same genetic composition, they should be able to describe in what ways these twins resemble each other. What kinds of traits may be different in a set of identical twins? Students should recognize that learned behavior patterns result in differences between identical twins.

PEOPLE, PLACES, AND THINGS

Perhaps you have a student in class who breeds dogs, or pigeons. Or there may be an experimental station or farm in your vicinity. These students as well as the scientists may be resource people in developing the work in heredity. Zoology laboratories in colleges (or supply houses) may have stocks of fruit flies, white rats and hooded ones, which you can purchase.

On a field trip around the school you may find many examples of variations among plants of the same species. Perhaps you will want to explore the differences in environmental factors which might affect the differences in growth, time of flowering, color variations, and so forth.

Books and pamphlets

These are only a few of the books which are pertinent to the work discussed in this chapter. These and many other references classified by subject and with complete bibliographical data are given in the Bibliography at the end of the book.

Boyd, W., *Genetics and the Races of Man,* 1950.
Colin, E., *Elements of Genetics,* 1949.
Crane, M., and W. Lawrence, *The Genetics of Garden Plants,* 1952.
Curtis, W., and M. Guthrie, *Laboratory Directions in General Zoology,* 1948.
Dunn, L., ed., *Genetics in the Twentieth Century,* 1951.
Dunn, L., and T. Dobzhansky, *Heredity, Race and Society,* 1946.
Glass, B., *Genes and the Man,* 1943.
Goldschmidt, R., *Understanding Heredity,* 1952.
Goldstein, P., *Genetics Is Easy,* Lantern Press, 1955.
Hayes, H., F. Immer, and D. Smith, *Methods of Plant Breeding,* 1955.
Hutt, F., *Genetics of the Fowl,* 1949.
Snyder, L., and P. David, *The Principles of Heredity,* 1957.
Stern, C., *Principles of Human Genetics,* 1949.
U.S. Dept. of Agriculture, Yearbooks: *Breeding*

12-19. There may be a student in class who has been breeding tropical fish. Perhaps he can be encouraged to become an expert in one phase of the genetics of fish. The journal *Heredity,* 1:65–83, 1947, has a fine paper by O. Winze and E. Detlevsen, "Color Inheritance and Sex Determination in *Lebistes.*" The magazine *Your Aquarium* carries many articles on genetics of fish.

in Plants and Animals (1936, 1937), *Science in Farming* (1943–1947), Supt. Documents, U.S. Govt. Printing Office.
Winchester, A., *Genetics,* 1951.
Winge, O., *Inheritance in Dogs,* 1950.

Films and filmstrips

This partial list is intended only as a guide toward film and filmstrip selection. Refer to the more complete listing at the end of the book where films are classified by subject and where a key to abbreviations and the addresses of distributors are given. The cost of film rental, of course, may be subject to change. Films are sound and black and white unless otherwise specified.

Acres of Chix; Acres of Gold (f, c), De Kalb Agricultural Assoc., free.
Animal Breeding (f), EBF, $3.00.
Better Seed (breeding potatoes) (f, c), Farm Film Foundation, free.
Breeding Better Food Crops (f, c), National Garden Bur., free.
Cow Business (f, c), Amer. Nat. Cattlemen's Assoc., free.
Genetics (fs, c), De Kalb Agricultural Assoc., free.
Golden Heritage (cattle breeding) (f, c), Amer. Guernsey Cattle Club, free.
Heredity (f), EBF, $2.00.
Heredity and Environment (f), Coronet, $2.00.
Hybrids (f, c), Allis-Chalmers, free.
New Chicken (fs, c), De Kalb Agricultural Assoc., free.
Twins Are Individuals (f, si), EBF, $2.50.

Free and inexpensive materials

This is only a partial listing of free and inexpensive materials available to the teacher at this time. A more complete listing, including addresses, is given at the end of the book. Many of these materials are distributed to teachers without charge. Where there is a small fee, the cost is indicated, although the prices are subject to change. While we recommend the material for use in the classroom, we do not necessarily sponsor the products advertised.

Drosophila Guide, M. Demerec and B. Kaufmann, Carnegie Institution, 1945, $0.25.

Your Heredity, Science Research Associates, $0.60.

Pedigree charts, lists of articles on heredity of domesticated animals, upon request from the Amer. Genetic Assoc.

The Story of Plants; The Story of Meat Animals, Swift & Co., Education Division.

Human Conservation (The Story of Our Wasted Resources), U.S. Govt. Printing Office. $0.20.

Holstein-Friesian Cow and Bull (charts), Holstein-Friesian Assoc. of Amer.

Story of Cereal Grains, General Mills Inc., Education Section.

The Biological Effects of Atomic Radiation, Nat. Acad. Sciences.

CHAPTER 13

Evolution: changes in living things

How fossils were made

Have students start a collection of fossil specimens. Some students may already have the beginnings of a collection. Plan field trips to fruitful areas—limestone, coal, shale, or sandstone deposits. Some small fossils may be purchased.

Make some imprints of leaves or shells in class to show how some fossils were formed. Students may embed leaves or shells in plaster of Paris. The plaster can be compared to the sediments deposited by a slow-moving stream or to a muddy embankment or swamp.

"Fossils" in plaster. Prepare a mixture of plaster of Paris and water, the consistency of pancake dough; stir until smooth, and pour a layer one inch deep into a cake pan. Then coat a variety of leaves or shells with Vaseline and lay them on the plaster. Cover these with another layer of plaster of Paris. Let it all harden. Later students may remove the plaster from the pan and crack it open. They will find the casts or imprints made by the shells or leaves. The actual molds, especially of the shells, can be compared to what might be found when cracking open a fragment of sedimentary rock.

Students might make an imprint of the human hand, too. Vaseline the hand lightly and make an impression in soft plaster. Let this harden without adding another layer of plaster.

Sedimentary rock. Also show how layers of sedimentary rock are formed. Students might partially fill large jars (pickle or mayonnaise jars) with fine sand, coarse gravel, small rocks, humus, and clay. If possible, try to include several different textures and colors. Include some shells in this muddy mixture to simulate fossil remnants. Fill the container with water so that all this material represents a muddy stream. Shake the jar and then let it stand; note the size and kinds of materials which settle to the bottom first (Fig. 13-1). (Have students explain how shells might be found in sedimentary rock.)

Fig. 13-1 Sedimentation in a jar, showing the layers of different-sized particles which settle out of still water.

"Fossils" in ice. Students will know of the small figures of animals that are sold as toys or charms. Place these in water in the compartments of an ice tray in a refrigerator and let the water freeze. Each ice cube shows the "animal fossil" imbedded in ice. Or use fresh pieces of fruit in the same way to show that no decay takes place when bacteria of decay do not have access to the material or when conditions are unfavorable for their growth.

"Fossils" in amber. Melt several pieces of rosin (used to coat a violin bow) over a low flame; avoid boiling. Then make small paper boxes of the type used to imbed tissue in paraffin (see Fig. 17-19). They may be about 1 inch square, stapled or clipped together. Now pour the molten rosin into several paper boxes. Completely submerge an insect, preferably a hard-bodied one, such as a beetle, in the rosin. Should air bubbles appear in the rosin heat a dissecting needle and insert it into each air bubble.

Let the rosin harden at room temperature; rapid cooling causes cracking. After it has cooled, slough off the paper covering by soaking the box in water. Here is an insect "fossil" which simulates the manner in which ancient insects, mainly ants and small flies, became imbedded in drops of rosin which trickled down the bark of evergreens.

In fact, students may imbed small insects in a drop of clear Karo syrup on a glass slide to represent the way insects were imbedded.

"Fossils" in gelatin. You may want students to use gelatin as an imbedding material instead of rosin. Add ¼ cup of cold water to a teaspoon of gelatin. When the water has been absorbed, dissolve the mass in ¾ cup of hot water. Then pour this into paper boxes or Syracuse dishes. Imbed small objects, such as fruits, in the gelatin.

Animals in plastic. Organisms imbedded in plastic may be purchased from supply houses (Fig. 21-3). As an individual or club project students may learn the technique (p. 414) for making these fine preparations mounted in clear plastic.

You may also want to "demonstrate" many of the points developed by Darwin and others to explain the "how" of evolution, either out of doors or in the classroom.

Overproduction among living things

Collect the cones of pine trees, the pods of milkweeds, or the heads of sunflowers. On a trip around the school grounds have students count the number of seeds produced by several other plants. Count the number of seeds in each pine cone and estimate the number of cones on one tree. What would be the total number of seeds from one tree? What are the chances of survival for each seed? If students have estimated the number of seeds on a maple tree, have them return later to count the number of seedlings nearby. Why are there so few?

Similarly, students might count the number of seeds in one pod of a milkweed and calculate the total number of seeds one plant could produce. Also, how many seeds might one sunflower produce?

Examine the roe of one fish, the eggs of one frog; look up the number of eggs laid by one shrimp, one oyster, one insect, and so forth. What are the chances for each egg to be fertilized? To grow into an embryo? To reach adulthood?

What are the conditions which operate against the development of a seedling or spore? The fertilization of an egg and its development into an embryo?

Overcrowding in seedlings. Students

may study how space can be a limiting factor in the growth of seedlings. Soak overnight a large number of seeds, such as mustard, radish, oats, beans, or corn grains. Plant half the number of seeds (of one kind) in a small flower pot and the other half in a pot twice the size.

Keep the seeds in a dark place and water them regularly. Over the next 3 weeks, count the number of seedlings which grow and survive in each flower pot.

Or you may want to try this variation. Plant soaked seeds in several flower pots of the same size, but vary the number of seeds. For example, in one box plant 10 seeds, in another plant 20 seeds, in a third plant 30, then plant 50 in another, and finally in another box plant 100 seeds. Keep other conditions constant (the same kind of soil, temperature, and water conditions), and compare the percentage of seeds which grow in each pot. Compare this with conditions of growth under a parent tree outdoors.

Overcrowding among fruit flies. Does overcrowding of organisms in one area affect their survival? Examine how the food supply can be a limiting factor in the survival of organisms.

Prepare fruit fly medium and pour into culture bottles (p. 200). This time pour the medium into several quart milk bottles and also into several small vials. Then introduce four pairs of fruit flies into each container. (Students should be reminded to sprinkle the surface with yeast before introducing the flies.) During a 3- to 4-week period, students may count the number of offspring surviving in each quart bottle and in each small vial.

A student may want to try this variation as an individual project. Prepare several half-pint bottles, each containing food and four pairs of flies. In this way there is an increase in the total number of flies within a uniform environment. In about 2 months when the population is at an ebb, counts should be made of the total number of flies in all these bottles, distinguishing the dead ones from the living. The student should total the number of dead and living flies from all the bottles. Now he should transfer the total number of living flies in each bottle into bottles of fresh culture medium. The total population expands each time a new food supply is added at the end of every reproductive cycle. Then counts might be made of the initial increase in population in each bottle with an increase in food. Again after 2 months, when the food supply has reached a low point, count the number of living flies. Is there a point at which the food supply is not large enough to sustain a further increase in population?

Overcrowding among praying mantis. If egg masses of the praying mantis are available, they may be kept in a small terrarium. Provide a source of water (or sugar water), such as a small sponge inserted half way into a vial of water. Students may examine and estimate the tremendous number of nymphs which hatch out of each egg mass. Each day watch the decrease in population as cannibalism increases. You may later provide fruit flies as food for the nymphs or release them in a garden or park since they are beneficial insects.

Similarity and variation

Similarity in related plants

Monocots. Soak the seeds of monocotyledonous plants such as oats, rye, barley, bluegrass, and corn grains. Plant them in flats of moist sand or light soil and label the types of seeds. As the seedlings begin to grow observe the first leaves. Since there is a similar genetic pattern based on common ancestry these first leaves resemble each other closely.

Dicots. At the same time, show the similarity among the first leaves of dicotyledonous seedlings. For example, soak seeds of mustard, lettuce, pumpkin, marigold, melon, radish, pepper, tomato, pansy, and sweet peas. As before, plant these seeds in flats of moistened sand and compare their first leaves. (Be sure to label the seeds or students will not be able to recognize the plants.)

Gymnosperms. Soak the seeds of a number of gymnosperms such as pine, hemlock, spruce, arbor vitae, and fir. Then plant them in moist sand or light soil. They germinate slowly, but the results are rewarding. Compare the first leaves of the seedlings. Note their similarity. Students may watch the specific differences among the seedlings which develop later, showing that the seeds also contain different genes as well as the early similar patterns which first are expressed.

Mustard family. Students may also want to do this. Select seeds of members of the same *family* of plants, for example, the mustard family. Plant soaked seeds of cabbage, brussels sprouts, kale, cauliflower, kohl-rabi, and collards. Label the seeds as they are planted. All of these forms are members of one family, descendants of the wild cabbage.

Variations in plants

Measuring seeds and leaves. In class, students might examine variations among seeds of one kind. For example, get several pounds of dried lima beans or other seeds; have each student measure the length in millimeters of five seeds. Arrange eight to ten large jars or test tubes of uniform size. Label the jars in millimeter intervals to correspond with the range of distribution you might find among the seeds. If students measure the lengths of

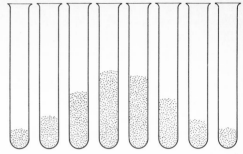

Fig. 13-2 Seeds sorted, according to length, into tubes: note normal distribution curve.

the seeds and then place them in the appropriately labeled jar or test tube (Fig. 13-2), a continuous normal curve of distribution results; a visualized histogram is produced. When these seeds are kept dry, they can be saved from year to year for this activity.

Other times you may want to distribute a few pounds of fresh green pea pods. Students might measure the length of each pod. (In addition they could compare the weight of each pod.) Find the average length of the pea pods and compare this average with the length of individual pods. Students might plot their data.

You may find sunflower seeds useful for studying other variations. Students might find the differences in variations in stripings on the seeds. Seed clusters of linden (*Tilia*), the Chinese Tree of Heaven, *Ailanthus,* the tulip tree (*Liriodendron*), maples, or evergreen cones may be measured. Or measure the size of acorns for one species of oak.

Students might examine variations in the length of needles from one evergreen, or the diameter of leaves of broad-leaved plants. Collect a large number of needles from one kind of pine, or the leaves from a single maple, oak, elm, or sassafras tree. With a centimeter ruler measure the width of the leaves from the one tree. Plot the frequency distribution in a graph.

Percentage of germination of seeds. You may want to show some qualitative differences among seeds of the same species in this way. Soak seeds overnight, and place them between pieces of wet blotting paper which have first been ruled off in squares. Students might place an equal number of seeds in each square, the number depending upon the size of the seeds. Or they may use flats for germinating seeds. Prepare several dishes or flats containing different kinds of seeds. Then students might keep a daily record of the rate of germination. They may estimate the percentage of seeds which germinated in a period of 24 hours, in 36 hours, 48 hours, and so on. Also count the number of nonviable seeds (those which do not germinate).

Variations due to differences in the environment. Members of the same species of plant may show variations due to the environmental factors under which the organisms grow. Students may recall that development of chlorophyll in seedlings is dependent on light (p. 206). Seedlings grown in the dark are yellow and spindly (etiolated). Variegated coleus plants develop patterns of brilliant color in sunlight. What is the effect of sunlight on red corn?

On field trips students may find many of these examples: (a) variations in color of leaves on barberry shrubs, dependent on differences in the amount of light which reaches the leaves; (b) differences in the shape of leaves of many plants growing along a stream or lake. Many plants show variations depending on whether the leaves are growing in water or in air. Students may collect specimens of crowfoot (*Ranunculus*) several of which have filamentous leaves when growing in water. Also find some specimens which grow farther back from the water's edge and examine their broad leaves. In beggar's ticks (*Bidens Beckii*) the lower sub-merged leaves are deeply cleft, while farther up on the stem, well above the water level, the leaves are almost entire; whereas in the water parsnip the sub-merged leaves are feathery while the aerial leaves are almost entire (Fig. 13-3). The submerged leaves of arrowhead (*Sagittaria*) are thin and linear, while the leaves above water are arrow-shaped. And many transitional stages can be found.

Effect of a moisture-laden atmosphere on the form of growth of herbaceous plants. Dandelion plants and *Sempervivum*, and the like, may be grown in a moist terrarium or under a bell jar in which the air has been saturated with moisture by placing a wet sponge inside. In controls, develop dry conditions by placing the plants under a

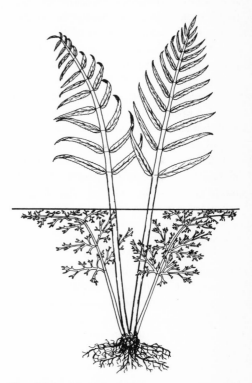

Fig. 13-3 Variations due to environment of water parsnip (*Sium suave*): note submerged and aerial leaves. (From C. L. Wilson & W. E. Loomis, *Botany*, rev. ed., Dryden, 1957.)

bell jar with an open glass container of calcium chloride (or some concentrated sulfuric acid). Other plants may be maintained under conditions of usual humidity. The long internodes and broad leaf blades which develop under conditions of high moisture content should be apparent. In dry conditions students should find that the plants have short internodes and small leaf blades.

Among dandelion plants grown under normal conditions, leaves usually grow some 15 cm in length; in a moist atmosphere they may grow to 60 cm. Under moist conditions, *Sempervivum* loses its low growth form and becomes spindly with smaller leaves and a thinner cuticle.

Effect of darkness on potato plants. A group of students may try to reproduce this classic experiment, performed by Vochting in 1887, which Palladin[1] describes. Terminal buds of potato plants were enclosed in a darkened box supported by a ring stand; aerial tubers developed. Other plants were placed in darkened boxes with the upper branches exposed to light; here, potato tubers formed above the soil on the darkened stem portions.

You may also want to demonstrate the effect of darkness on the growth of potato plants (Fig. 13-4).

Effect of mineral deficiencies on plant growth. Students may grow the young shoots of one kind of plant in different solutions of chemicals, then study the effect of mineral deficiencies on the growth and the form of the plants (nutrient solutions, p. 113).

From these demonstrations students may come to recognize that changes in the environment affect the expression of the genetic pattern, thereby causing the appearance of plants to be altered. In other words, the appearance of an organism depends upon the combined effect of

[1] Vladimir Palladin, *Plant Physiology*, Blakiston (McGraw-Hill), New York, 1926.

Fig. 13-4 Effect of darkness on potato plants: etiolated plant at *left* was grown in dark; normal plant of same age is shown at *right*. (Photo: Dr. Carl L. Wilson, Dartmouth.)

a specific heredity acting in a specific environment.

In effect, an organism does not "become adapted" to an environment. Instead, it already *has* the special adaptation or genetic variation. When the organism is in an environment where this variation is not a hindrance, the organism survives and reproduces more of its own kind. Thus the organism is said to be adapted to its environment. In fact, the variation may be beneficial and thereby have special survival value. Students might "explain" these examples of adaptations (among many): cactus, sun-loving plants, shade-loving plants, dandelions (see specialization of leaves, p. 294).

Similarity in animals

Students may examine the early stages of related animals to see how similar they are in their early development. Differences appear at later stages. Collect egg masses of several species of frogs, and of toads and salamanders. Have students compare the early stages of cleavage and the growth of the tadpoles. These similarities are due to a common pattern of genes which are inherited through a common ancestor back in time.

While there is a fundamental similarity among the members of a given family of plants or animals, or among a whole order of plants or animals, there are also variations within species and genera. In addition, there are differences among the offspring of the same parents, as we well know.

Variations in animals

Comparing internal structures. You may want to have students compare the internal anatomy—for example, the digestive system or circulatory system—of several invertebrate or vertebrate forms (dissections, Chapter 16).

Variations within a species. It may be possible for students to collect, on a field trip, large numbers of mollusk shells of some one species, for example, scallop shells (*Pecten*), or oyster shells (*Ostrea vulgaris*), or fresh-water mussels (*Anodonta mutabilis*). In class, students might measure the width in centimeters of the shells of one species. Then plot a graph of the frequency distribution, using the measurement as the abscissa and the frequency as the ordinate. Notice that while the basic pattern of genes is similar within the same species, there are still some variations due to different recombinations of genes.

Variations among human beings. In class, students may want to study some differences among themselves. For instance, all the boys who are 15 years old might stand. The rest of the class could record the height and the weight of these boys. Then plot the data on a graph. Perhaps a small committee of students might gather the same facts, height and weight, for large numbers of 15-year-old boys in school. Then add these to the graph. Does the law of normal distribution hold for human beings as well as for beans and shells? If we could plot a graph of the I.Q., or the grades in school, would they fall into a similar pattern when the assortment was as random as in the study of the height of 15-year-old boys?

Classification of plants and animals

You may decide to bring to class a sampling of animals or plants. Better still, take your class out of doors to examine a biome, such as a pond, beach, desert, or wooded area. How do you help develop in your students the idea of order among the many kinds of plants and animals so that the students can identify them or classify them for reference? Some students may suggest grouping according to habitats or habits of getting food. Certainly organisms differing as sharply as the animal inhabitants of a pond (fish, frogs, water striders, *Daphnia,* protozoans, snails, planarians, water snakes, perhaps a beaver) cannot be placed or classified together. Students can readily name one outstanding trait that makes a fish different from a frog, a snake, a planarian, or other inhabitants of the pond.

Your students may compare the categories (kingdom, phylum, order, family, genus, species) with the categories used by a librarian to classify books. This is familiar ground. Here is a book entitled *The Fight to Live* by Raymond Ditmars. In what area of the library should it be placed? This book might be classified:

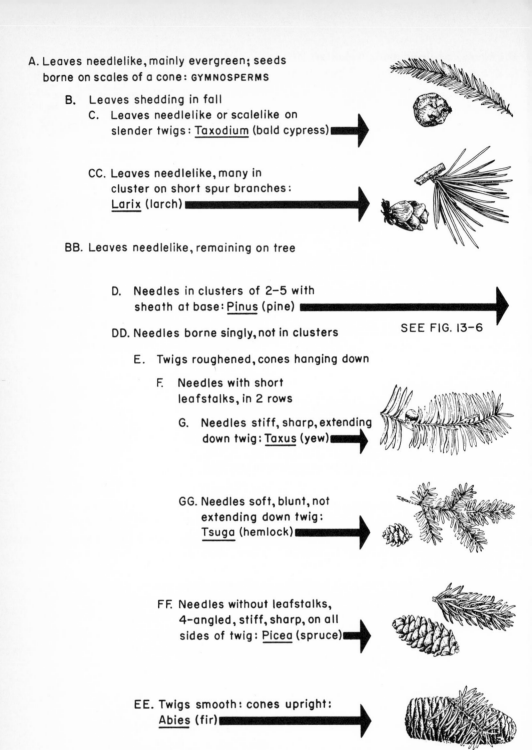

A. Leaves needlelike, mainly evergreen; seeds
borne on scales of a cone: GYMNOSPERMS

 B. Leaves shedding in fall
 C. Leaves needlelike or scalelike on
 slender twigs: <u>Taxodium</u> (bald cypress)

 CC. Leaves needlelike, many in
 cluster on short spur branches:
 <u>Larix</u> (larch)

 BB. Leaves needlelike, remaining on tree

 D. Needles in clusters of 2–5 with
 sheath at base: <u>Pinus</u> (pine)
 DD. Needles borne singly, not in clusters   SEE FIG. 13–6

 E. Twigs roughened, cones hanging down
 F. Needles with short
 leafstalks, in 2 rows
 G. Needles stiff, sharp, extending
 down twig: <u>Taxus</u> (yew)

 GG. Needles soft, blunt, not
 extending down twig:
 <u>Tsuga</u> (hemlock)

 FF. Needles without leafstalks,
 4-angled, stiff, sharp, on all
 sides of twig: <u>Picea</u> (spruce)

 EE. Twigs smooth: cones upright:
 <u>Abies</u> (fir)

Fig. 13-5 Beginning classification of gymnosperms. (Drawings from *Trees, The Yearbook of Agriculture*, U.S.D.A., 1949.)

D. Leaves needle shaped, in clusters of
   2-5 with sheath at base: <u>Pinus</u> (pine)

   a. 5 needles in cluster:
       <u>Pinus strobus</u> L. (eastern white pine)

       <u>Pinus monticola</u> Dougl. (western white pine)

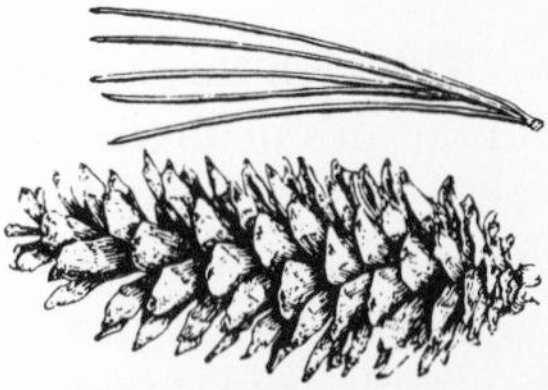

   aa. 2-3 needles in cluster (yellow, hard or pitch pines)

       b. 3 needles in cluster;
           cone scales armed with spine

           c. Needles greater than 8" long
               <u>Pinus palustris</u>
               (long leaf or southern pine)

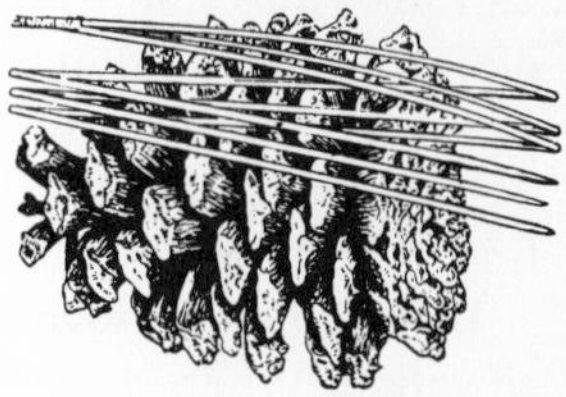

           cc. Needles less than 8" long:
               <u>Pinus rigida</u> (pitch pine)

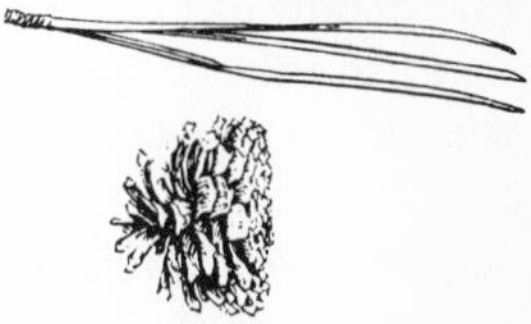

       bb. 2 needles in cluster; cone scales unarmed

           d. Needles greater than 3" long:
               <u>Pinus resinosa</u>
               (red pine)

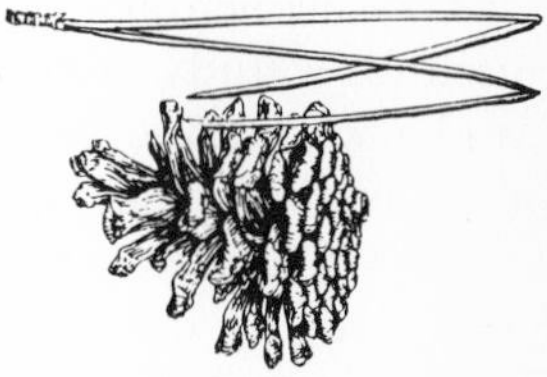

           dd. Needles less than 3" long:
               <u>Pinus banksiana</u>
               (northern scrub pine, or jack pine)

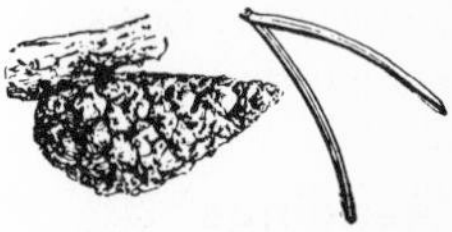

       bbb. 3 or 2 and 3 needles in cluster,
            4 to 7" long, cone scales armed:
            <u>Pinus ponderosa</u> Laws (ponderosa pine)

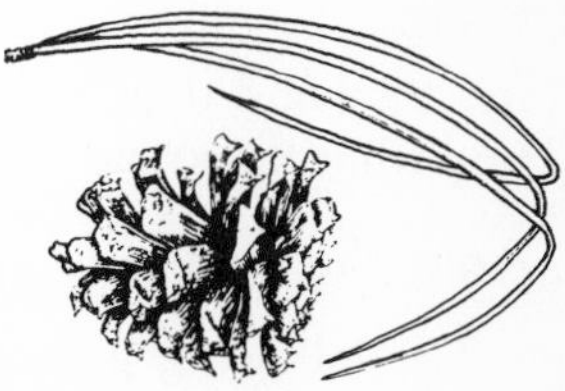

Fig. 13-6 Beginning classification of pines. (Drawings from *Trees, The Yearbook of Agriculture*, U.S.D.A., 1949.)

Area of library—Nonfiction
Section of Nonfiction Area—Science
Case in Science Section—Biology
Shelves in Biology Case—Zoology
Group on Zoology Shelves—Books
about Animals

Although this is a simplification of the librarian's method, it illustrates the principle of sorting and classifying—putting together the things that are closely related.

Students may practice putting similar animals or plants into broad categories and then into smaller groups. For example, are all the frogs in the pond the same? What are the identifying characteristics of a leopard frog, a green frog, a wood frog, a bullfrog?

Using a key for identification and classification. When students' observation of fine details has been sharpened, you may want to take them out of doors to learn the nature of a key as a means for identifying or classifying a plant or an animal. Suppose we begin with plants, since they are available the year around.

This elementary approach might be used for a study of trees in winter. Have students examine trees and shrubs and select one *single*, obvious difference among them. Obviously, some trees have leaves and some do not. Begin to build a key by pairing off these evident single characteristics. Look more closely at the trees which do have leaves in the winter. Find one single characteristic that sets one tree or shrub apart from another. Perhaps one tree has clusters of needles, another has needles growing out in all directions from the stem, some have needles growing in one plane so they look 2-ranked, another kind has especially small, fine needles (Fig. 13-5).

Then have students concentrate upon examining one group more carefully, perhaps those with needles in clusters (the pines); what differences can be observed? Do you find that some clusters have two needles? Others three or five needles in a bundle, or fascicle? Students can readily distinguish these differences within the genus: species differences (Fig. 13-6).

Figures 13-5 and 13-6 are highly simplified keys used here to indicate one way that students may approach the problem of variations among living things and glean a basis for classification of organisms. Should you want to have students practice using a standard key, they may use such references as Graves' guide to trees and shrubs or an insect key such as Swain's. These and other guides for all kinds of plants and animals are listed in the Bibliography at the end of the book.

A simplified key to Protozoa is given in Fig. 18-6 and to insects in Fig. 15-4; from these, students may recognize basic differences and begin to build their own simplified keys, which may then be compared with standardized keys in textbooks.

Readings

Students often enjoy this type of activity; they find they gain skill in interpreting what they read.

From *The Origin of Species*

The following passage from Darwin's writings might be used at some time in developing his theory of natural selection.

The giraffe, by its lofty stature, much elong-ated neck, forelegs, head and tongue, has its whole frame beautifully adapted for browsing on the higher branches of trees. It can thus obtain food beyond the reach of the other *Ungulata* or hoofed animals inhabiting the same country; and this must be a great advantage to it during dearths. The Niata cattle in South America show us how a small difference in structure may make, during such periods, a great difference in preserving an animal's life. These cattle can browse as well as others on grass, but from the projection of the lower jaw they cannot, during the often recurrent droughts, browse on the twigs of trees, reeds, etc., to which food the common cattle and horses are then driven; so that at these times the Niatas perish if not fed by their owners . . . . Man has modified some of his animals, without necessarily having attended to special points of structure, by simply preserving and breeding from the fleetest individuals, as with the race horse and greyhound, or as with the gamecock, by breeding from the victorious birds. So under nature with the nascent [beginning] giraffe, the individuals which were the highest browsers and were able during dearths to reach even an inch or two above the others, will often have been preserved; for they will have roamed over the whole country in search of food. That the individuals of the same species often differ slightly in the relative lengths of all their parts may be seen in many works of natural history, in which careful measurements are given. These slight proportional differences, due to the laws of growth and variation, are not of the slightest use or importance to most species. But it will have been otherwise with the nascent giraffe, considering its probable habits of life; for those individuals which had some one part or several parts of their bodies rather more elongated than usual, would generally have survived. These will have intercrossed and left offspring, either inheriting the same bodily peculiarities, or with a tendency to vary again in the same manner; while the individuals less favored in the same respects will have been the most liable to perish.

Elicit from students a discussion of the main points developed by Darwin in his theory. You may want students to answer questions of the kind which follow, or compose others. (If the material is mimeographed, students have time to study the passage and the questions which follow.)

A. Select the best answer.
1. According to Darwin, an advantage the giraffe has over other grazing animals is that
(a) it can eat more food.
(b) it can get along with less water.
(c) it can reach food on the higher branches of trees.
(d) it migrates from place to place.

2. According to Darwin, when food is plentiful the possession of a long neck is
(a) an advantage.
(b) a hazard.
(c) a nuisance.
(d) of no special advantage.

3. Darwin used the example of Niata cattle to show that
(a) changes in the environment have little effect on the welfare of animals.
(b) Niata cattle are better fitted than giraffes for survival.
(c) some animals have adaptations which fit them for survival.
(d) the environment stimulates animals to develop variations.

B. Indicate whether the following are true or false statements.
1. According to the passage, Darwin
(a) recognized that living things differ among themselves.
(b) thought that variations arose by mutation.
(c) thought that breeders usually selected the fastest or the strongest animals for breeding purposes.
(d) said that a small variation might spell the difference between survival or death for an animal.
(e) stated that long-necked giraffes survived because they left more descendants than the short-necked giraffes did.

Concerning chemical evolution

You may want to introduce students to the kind of speculation and experimentation under way in learning about the primordial chemicals which became organized into "living" systems.

A passage has been selected from a longer paper by Dr. Melvin Calvin in the

American Scientist.[2] This might be used as a focus for discussion in class, or a committee of students may report on the original paper (much of it they will understand). Or you may want to reproduce it and compose a series of questions related to the reading (as shown in the previous reading based on Darwin's work).

The time element that is involved is a very long one. By extrapolating the idea of evolution to include nonliving systems as well as living ones, we can go clear back to a time when the universe and the stars were evolved and eventually an earth was formed. This time period starts roughly about 5 to 10 billion years ago, as far as the astrophysicists can tell us. Roughly ten billion years ago the universe was formed by an explosion of matter and the elements were formed in an evolutionary pattern, a discussion of which would be beyond our present scope, and which may more properly be called "nuclear evolution." The next period that we can characterize after the earth's formation is the time for the formation of chemicals of various degrees of complexity upon the surface of the earth, but before the appearance of systems that we could call living—"chemical evolution." . . .

In order to begin the discussion of chemical evolution, we have to decide what sort of an earth we had to work on. What sort of a chemical system did we have about 2½ billion years ago, when the earth first began to take its present form? I might point out that these various periods that I have tried to delineate are, of course, simply regions in time, and there is no sharp dividing line between them—they grade one into the other. One can say only that the earth gradually took shape, by some process—perhaps by aggregation, which is one of the modern cosmological theories. Regardless of what path its formation followed, we can say that at some period of time the earth had acquired very nearly its present form, and by this time chemical evolution was well under way—it had already begun. We should try to decide what sort of an earth, i.e., what sort of chemicals, we had to deal with, and what the earth was like at that time. Unfortunately, the geochemists can't agree on whether the atmosphere of the earth was an oxidized one or a reduced one, or some intermediate stage between.

[2] M. Calvin, "Chemical Evolution and the Origin of Life," *Am. Sci.,* 44:3, July 1956, pp. 248–51.

For the present purpose it isn't necessary to know exactly what form the atmosphere of the earth had during that period. The reason is that there exist at least four different ways in which more or less complicated chemical compounds could have been formed in either condition—oxidized or reduced—although the reduced starting point seems the easier one to develop. These ways have been described as follows, and in this order. The first method by which larger molecules containing more than one carbon atom could have been formed from simple ones was suggested by J. B. S. Haldane about 1926, and has been experimentally checked. (We, among others, have checked it.) Under the influence of ultraviolet light from the sun, it is possible to make more or less complex substances, like the amino acids and heterocyclic compounds that are now found in biological materials, by simply illuminating aqueous solutions containing simple carbon compounds such as formic acid or formaldehyde (one-carbon compounds) and a nitrogen-containing material such as ammonia, nitric acid, or nitrates; and one can get fairly complex organic materials. A second possible method is the one that was suggested by the Russian biochemist Oparin. He had the idea that the earth cooled down from a hot miasma and that carbon was mostly in the form of metallic carbide which, upon being put in contact with water, formed acetylene; the acetylene under suitable catalytic influences such as rocks and minerals could polymerize and form large chains which could give rise to molecules of the type we now see in biological materials. The third way in which simple organic substances could have been formed in a world without life is by means of the action of very high-energy radiation, such as is produced by radioactive materials or comes to us from the stars in the form of cosmic rays. This we have also checked in an experimental way. We have taken solutions of carbon dioxide and water and irradiated them in the cyclotron and have gotten formic acid, and irradiation of formic acid produced oxalic acid (a two-carbon compound). My colleagues have irradiated a variety of other substances since then. They have irradiated two-carbon substances and obtained four-carbon compounds such as succinic acid, which are even now important metabolites in modern living organisms. . . . These three methods have permitted the building up of complex chains of atoms from simple ones, and this is essentially what we are trying to do: to devise ways and means of getting more complex substances from simple ones, without the intervention of living organisms, which today is the only way it occurs in nature, outside the laboratory.

The last method that has been suggested, and tested experimentally, is the one involving an electric discharge in the upper atmosphere, like a lightning discharge, when there are present methane, hydrogen, ammonia, and water, i.e., a reduced atmosphere. If an electric discharge is passed through such a mixture, a variety of compounds can be produced in which there are carbon atoms tied to each other, particularly compounds of the type of amino acids, which are the essential building blocks of proteins.

Certain students, especially those with a high level of ability and an interest in science, may find a passage such as this one the springboard for an interest in learning more about the chemistry of living things. They may try to read with profit *New Biology No. 16: The Origin of Life* (Penguin Books, 1954); Julian Huxley, *Evolution in Action* (Harper, 1953); and H. Blum, *Time's Arrow and Evolution* (Princeton U. Press, 1955).

Many of the methods used by scientists are included in this report. There is a value, we believe, in bringing the reports of scientists, actively engaged in some research, into the science classroom.

CAPSULE LESSONS
Ways to get started in class

13-1. Plan a field trip to a museum to study fossil remains of ancient plants and animals. Or take your class through time by means of a series of Kodachrome slides, such as *Digging Up Dinosaurs, Changes in the Horse,* or *Ancient Man* (available from the American Museum of Natural History, New York City).

The horse has changed through time. How? What were dinosaurs like? How did Neanderthal man differ from Cro-Magnon?

13-2. Some students may be able to model dinosaurs (of clay) (model-making, p. 411). Or develop a diorama. Use such devices to explore the question: How much of the reconstruction of prehistoric animals or plants is fact and how much is the imagination of the artist? Plan an exhibit of "Life One Million Years Ago." Or have students prepare a phylogenetic collection of plants and animals.

13-3. You may want to have students demonstrate the way some fossils were formed. Use the techniques described in this chapter. Also make a sedimentation jar. Students may use plaster of Paris or ice as imbedding materials. Establish the need for a quick burial, that is, removal from bacteria of decay, to inhibit the decay of the plant or animal. Discuss the other materials in which fossils have been found: ice, amber, tar pits, coal, etc. Plan a trip to a museum if possible.

13-4. In a laboratory lesson you may want to have students study variations found in a few pounds of lima beans. Measure the length of seeds and graph the findings. Or give each student an envelope containing a pine cone full of seeds. If possible have the cones from a single tree. Again, have students measure the length of the seeds. Elicit the possible causes of the variations. Estimate the total number of seeds produced by a single tree. What are the chances for all the seeds from one tree to develop into new pine trees? Explain.

13-5. How might Darwin have modified his theory if he had known of Mendel's work? This might be an approach to a review of the steps in Darwin's theory. You may want to discuss a reading from Darwin's book to show that he was not certain as to how variations occurred. Compare this with the concept that inheritable changes in plants and animals are based on changes in genes.

13-6. Give a committee of students a variety of seeds of one family of plants, such as the mustard family; to another committee give seeds of cereal plants; to a third committee seeds of different members of the legume family. Do this at least a week in advance. Then students may compare the shape, size, and time of appearance of the first leaves of the plants within each family. Have students notice the similarity. Develop the notion that these plants share a pool of genes from a common ancestor in that family group. Students may notice that variations exist in the rate of germination of seeds of the same kind. What is an advantage of rapidly germinating seeds?

13-7. Possibly you would like to use a film

as an introduction to the theories of evolution. Do you know the series on *Camouflage in Nature* (2 reels, Coronet)? Develop a discussion around the questions: How did the different kinds of mimicry originate? How is it that an animal matches its environment in pattern, form, and color? What are some adaptations in plants?

13-8. Or you might want to begin a discussion of theories relating to evolution in this manner. Although each female frog lays several hundreds of eggs each spring, the population of frogs in a certain pond remains relatively constant. Establish the facts about overproduction, the role of enemies, unfavorable environment, and so forth. What is meant by the "fittest" organisms?

13-9. At some time you may want to show the film *Heredity and Environment* (Coronet) as one way of reviewing the role of heredity in a new context, i.e., in relation to changes in living things.

13-10. A committee of students might report to the class on evidences indicating relationships among plants or animals, for example, comparative embryology, vestigial remains in plants and animals, and so forth. How have different species of oaks, maples, azaleas, etc., developed?

13-11. You may want to have students plan short debates or a panel discussion on some of these topics: (a) the role of mutations and recombinations in evolution; (b) the role of barriers in the formation of new species; (c) genetic drift and its effect on populations of organisms; (d) the differences between natural selection and artificial selection (i.e., man's use of selective breeding); (e) the role of lethal mutations.

13-12. After a study of the classic theories of Lamarck, Darwin, and De Vries, you may want to have students apply these theories to an explanation of this adaptation: Assume that all bears were originally brown; how might the origin of white polar bears have been explained by Lamarck? By Darwin? By De Vries?

How might each of these men have accounted for the long neck of giraffes? How might they have explained camouflage in animals (walking-stick insect, moths the color of tree bark, green grasshoppers, and brown ones, too, among many other examples)?

13-13. Students may want to trace human migration over the world. They may report on the evidences of relationship among groups of people based on their possession of certain blood types. Students will find material in Boyd's text (see Bibliography).

13-14. You may want to use reprints of the series of articles which appeared in *Life* Magazine, under the heading *The World We Live In.*[3] The first in the series is *The Earth Is Born* (Dec. 8, 1952); the subsequent issues are these: *Miracle of the Sea* (Feb. 9, 1953); *The Face of the Land* (April 13, 1953); *The Canopy of Air* (June 8, 1953); *Two Billion Years of Evolution* (Sept. 7, 1953); *Age of Mammals* (Oct. 19, 1953); *Creatures of the Sea* (Nov. 30, 1953); *The Coral Reef* (Feb. 8, 1954); *The Land of the Sun* (deserts) (April 5, 1954); *The Arctic Barrens* (June 7, 1954); *The Rain Forest* (Sept. 20, 1954); *The Woods of Home* (Nov. 8, 1954); *The Starry Universe* (Dec. 20, 1954). Filmstrips are also available.

13-15. You may have skeletons of several vertebrates (or study these in a visit to a museum) which students may use to compare the similarities and differences among the skeletons. How do we explain the similar pattern among the vertebrates? the differences?

13-16. It may be possible to plan a trip to a zoo to study primitive mammals like the duck-billed platypus and the spiny anteater. And at a botanical garden students can examine an ancient gymnosperm, the last species of *Gingko*.

[3] Reprints may be purchased for $0.20 each from *Life* Magazine, Dept. W., 9 Rockefeller Plaza, New York 20.

PEOPLE, PLACES, AND THINGS

Is there a museum of natural history near you? (Or is there one near enough to supply your school with traveling exhibits?) You may want to take your classes on a field trip through a section of the museum. In fact, you may be able to make arrangements to have your classes go behind the scenes; there scientists will explain how fossil bone preparations and other displays are made.

A member of a science department in another school or the teachers in a college biology department may help you by lending fresh or preserved materials for a study of interrelationships among groups of organisms. Perhaps you may be able to share films, color slides, and projection equipment.

Students may take frequent short field trips around the school grounds in search of the number of seedlings growing under a parent tree. An extension of a lesson might guide students to look, on their own, for variations due to environmental factors. (See p. 265, for ways to use a school lawn.) Students may collect some seeds and fruits; others may be purchased as you need them from a grocery or seed distributor.

BOOKS AND PAMPHLETS

These are only a few of the books which are pertinent to the work discussed in this chapter. These and many other references classified by subject and with complete bibliographical data are given in the Bibliography at the end of the book.

Andrews, H., *Ancient Plants,* 1947.
Blum, H., *Time's Arrow and Evolution,* 1955.
Boyd, W., *Genetics and the Races of Man,* 1950.
Buchsbaum, R., *Animals Without Backbones,* 1948.
Colbert, E., *Evolution of the Vertebrates,* 1955.
Florkin, M., *Biochemical Evolution,* 1949.
Gibbs, R., *Botany: An Evolutionary Approach,* 1950.
Hegner, R., *Parade of the Animal Kingdom,* 1955.
Huxley, J., *Evolution in Action,* 1953.
Kuhn, H., *On the Track of Prehistoric Man,* 1955.
Moody, R., *Introduction to Evolution,* 1953.
Moore, R., *Man, Time, and Fossils,* 1953.
Oparin, A., *The Origin of Life,* 1938.
Raymond, P., *Prehistoric Life,* 1950.
Simpson, G. G., *Life of the Past: An Introduction to Paleontology,* 1953.
Simpson, G. G., C. Pittendrigh, and L. Tiffany, *Life,* 1957.
Smart, W., *The Origin of the Earth,* 1953.
Spector, W., *Handbook of Biological Data,* 1957.

FILMS AND FILMSTRIPS

This partial list is intended only as a guide toward film and filmstrip selection. Refer to the more complete listing at the end of the book where films are classified by subject and a key to abbreviations and addresses of distributors are given. The cost of film rental, of course, may be subject to change. Films are sound and black and white unless otherwise specified.

Camouflage in Nature Through Form and Color (f, c), Coronet (inquire local film library), $4.00.
Development of the Aortic Arch (f. c), Squibb, free.
Digging Up Dinosaurs; History of the Horse; The Story of Ancient Man (sets of Kodachrome slides, 2" x 2"), Amer. Museum of Natural History, inquire rental or purchase.
Dinosaurs (fs), Bowmar, $3.00.
Evolution (f, 3 rls), Almanac, $4.50.
The Fossil Story (f, c), Shell Oil Co., free.
In the Beginning (story of the Grand Canyon) (f, c), Modern Talking Picture Service, free.
Lascaux, Cradle of Man's Art (f, c, 2 rls), New York U. film library, $7.00.
Men of the Old Stone Age; Men of the New Stone Age (fs), Society for Visual Education, $3.50.
Prehistoric Life (6 fs, c), EBF, $6.00 ea.
This Vital Earth (interrelationships) (f, c), EBF, $4.00, free through Soil Conservation Service.
The World We Live In (fs), Life Magazine, $6.00 ea.

FREE AND INEXPENSIVE MATERIALS

This is only a partial listing of free and inexpensive materials available to the teacher at this time. A more complete listing, including addresses, is given at the end of the book. Many of these materials are distributed to teachers without charge. Where there is a small fee, the cost is indicated, although the prices are subject to change. While we recommend the material for use in the classroom, we do not necessarily sponsor the products advertised.

Animals of Yesterday, Row, Peterson, $0.27.
Classification of Animals (chart), Denoyer-Geppert Co., $0.35.
The First Land Animals, A. Romer, Amer. Museum of Natural History, $0.35.
The Meaning of Evolution, G. G. Simpson, Mentor, $0.35.
Prehistoric Men, Chicago Natural History Museum, $1.50.
Races of Mankind, Chicago Natural History Museum, $0.50.
World We Live In (series of reprints: *Dinosaurs, Mammals*), *Life* Magazine, $0.20 ea.

CHAPTER 14

Conservation: web of life

The term *conservation* refers to the wise use and intelligent development of our resources, not to preservation per se. Before wise methods of conservation may be practiced it is useful to understand the relationships between animal and animal, plant and plant, and animal and plant, and between living things and their environment. It is useful to realize that human beings are, like other living things, a part of a balanced landscape.

This chapter is divided into two sections:[1]

A. Interrelationships among living things

B. Relations of living things to their environment

Interrelationships among living things

Study of a biome

Take field trips around the school lawns, along a stretch of beach at ebb tide, in an open meadow, in the woods, in a burned-over region; students are certain to find some kinds of plants and animals living together, dependent upon each other. The animals are clearly dependent upon the green plants. Such a community of living things is known as a biome. Students may be able to follow the succession of living things over a period of several years, as one kind of plant gives way to another in a forest, as plants begin to invade a lake and turn it into a swamp and finally into dry land. As this happens, the kinds of animals and plants in the region change too.

Several biotic relations are described here which may be useful for group investigations either in the classroom or out of doors. (You may want to refer now to Chapter 15, Field Work: Study of Living Things.)

Study of a quiet pond. Many students find a study of the plant and animal relationships in a biome, such as a pond, a rewarding experience. Begin by listing

[1] The individual teacher will want to select those activities which are best for his students and community. Perhaps you will want to see how other teachers develop these concepts. Look into *Conservation Handbook for Idaho Teachers,* State Dept. of Education, Boise, Idaho, 1954; *Conservation Projects for the High School,* H. Dittmer, ed., Bull. 19, New Mexico State Board of Educ., 1955; *Nevada Conservation Adventure Lesson Plan,* Conservation Educ. Workshop, U. of Nevada and Nevada State Fish and Game Commission, 1956.

the kinds of animals that are present in the pond. Are there forms which skim the surface, like water striders? Are there free-swimming forms? Any attached to vegetation? Bottom dwellers and tube dwellers? Are they vertebrate or invertebrate?

With a dip net students might gather living specimens. If they spread the contents of the net out on a white cloth or white pan they will find it easier to identify the specimens. Some pictorial guides, such as Needham and Needham, *A Guide to the Study of Fresh Water Biology,* or Morgan, *Fieldbook of Ponds and Streams,* or Pennak, *Fresh Water Invertebrates of the United States,* may be of help (see Bibliography).

Similarly, examine the vegetation. Are there floating forms—algae or duckweed or water lilies? Submerged forms? What kinds? Seed plants or algae? Try to identify them.

A diagram such as Fig. 14-1 might be made of a cross-sectional view of the pond, with the plants and animals at the proper level—floating, submerged, free-swimming, attached, and so forth.

What are some of the forces which may alter the dynamic interactions among the organisms? How may changes in physical conditions affect life in the pond? Of course, the green plants make their food supply. What is the food source for microscopic animals, for the insects, larvae, small fish, snails, or other inhabitants? Try to trace food chains. What might result if one kind of organism were killed off, or in some other way removed from the pond? Would there be an effect on the other organisms in the web of life in that pond? Which forms hold others in check so that they do not overreproduce?

You may want students to draw contour maps of the pond, showing its depth, its elevation in relation to land, and its area and shape. Students might record their observations of other features as well. For example, what is the source of the water? The possibility of contamination? What is the temperature of the water? Which kind of water would hold more oxygen and support active life—cold or warm water? Is it clear water or turbid? What kind of bed—gravel, flat rock, mud, hard clay?

Photographs might be taken of the pond each year. Over a period of years a comparison of photographs might show a succession of different plant and animal migrants. It may be possible to study an area where plants invade the pond; as their roots bind soil, a swamp may gradually result. What kinds of plants and animals survive in this new biome?

You will find directions for transporting water plants and animals to classroom aquaria in Chapter 15.

Study of fast-moving streams. It may also be possible to have students examine the inhabitants of a fast-moving stream. Then a comparative study can be made of the two biomes.

Students may identify the plant and

Fig. 14-1 Schematic cross section of a pond, showing typical forms of life. (After Buchsbaum, *Basic Ecology,* Boxwood Press, Pittsburgh 13, Pa., 1957.)

animal inhabitants and record these in their proper location in a cross-sectional view, as shown in Fig. 14-1 for a pond.

Study the life in the stream. Which organisms live under submerged rocks? Which are free-swimming, which attached? Are there living things found on the banks and shallow part of the stream? Which are found in the deeper water? Do organisms move with the current or face into it?

Finally, develop the food chains which exist between plants and animals, animals and animals. What factors might upset the balance in this web of life?

In a contour map students might show the nature of the bed and banks. Also keep a record of the temperature, clarity, and velocity of the water in the stream, as well as the nature of the slope. Are the organisms active or slow moving? A fast-moving stream often has increased oxygen content which supports active organisms.

If students plan to transport living materials from a stream to the classroom, they may have more success in keeping the forms alive if they select organisms from a quiet stream rather than a fast-moving one.

In your vicinity, it may be more appropriate to study a floodplain marsh, a bog, a desert, woods, a beach at ebb tide, or an open meadow. Students may make similar records of the kinds of organisms and the physical features of each area. In these places they may want to test the acidity of the soil (p. 236). Also examine the organisms living in a section of soil (p. 235). What natural enemies hold the existing organisms in check?

Food chains

One form of life feeds upon another, and ultimately the food source upon which all other forms are dependent is the green plant. Students may have gained this broad concept in a study of the biomes previously described or in a study of photosynthesis (Chapter 1). This is basic to an understanding of conservation of living things.

Study of plankton. With a dip net collect samples (directions, p. 248) of the free-floating surface organisms from a lake or slow-moving stream. Many small crustaceans, algae, small fresh-water mollusks, and microorganisms (protozoa, desmids, rotifers, and so forth) may be present. Turn the samples from a dip net into a white-bottomed tray for close examination. With a hand lens students may identify some forms; examine other specimens in class with a microscope.

When it is not feasible to go out of doors for this kind of study, an aquarium in class can be used to develop the idea of the balance in nature.

Students may prepare an aquarium (fresh water, p. 362; marine, p. 356) or a microaquarium (p. 86). Trace the food chains and the interdependence of the living things in an aquarium. Then compare this with a lake or an ocean which contains many food chains, all of which relate back to a green plant source.

Students may examine the specialized ways in which organisms, such as parasites (dodder, p. 229; frog parasites, p. 230), get their food. Try to collect specimens of fungus parasites such as corn smut or wheat rust (Fig. 20-14). Look for nematode worms, which infest plant crops.

Saprophytes, such as molds (p. 231), yeasts (p. 231), mushrooms, and shelf fungi, may be examined in class. Examples of symbionts (p. 231) are not difficult for students to find.

As part of their study of interdependence of living things students have learned some facts about the use of foods in the body, that is, digestion, circulation, respiration, and assimilation of new tissues. They have learned the ways living things reproduce themselves, which traits have survival value, and how variations adapt certain organisms for their way of living. Students need to know that intelligent development of resources presupposes an understanding of basic life functions of both plants and animals.

Web of life in a microaquarium

If a small snail were sealed in a test tube, how long would it live? Students already are aware of the conceptual scheme: Living plants and animals are dependent upon each other. They know that a snail cannot exist long without green plants. Sealing a snail and a water plant in a test tube is effective as a demonstration or a laboratory exercise. For the technique see Fig. 6-4. You may save time, but the effect is less dramatic, if you merely close several test tubes with rubber stoppers in place of sealing them in a flame.

If students are familiar with the indicator brom thymol blue, you may want to add to the tubes some which has been turned to a yellow color (by exhaling into it through a straw). Students may then be asked to explain why the brom thymol yellow in the tubes containing the green plants turns blue in the presence of light. Why does the blue color turn yellow during the night? They will recall that green plants absorb carbon dioxide from the water during sunlight. Therefore the yellow color (yellow in the presence of excess carbon dioxide) of the indicator is changed back to blue since the reduction in carbon dioxide content of the water decreases the acidity of the water. Thus the indicator is in a less acid condition; the more alkaline medium turns blue. During the night, the green plants

give off carbon dioxide (in respiration) and since there is no light, photosynthesis is stopped. Therefore the yellow color results, since the plants release carbon dioxide into the aquarium water. But as soon as light appears, the carbon dioxide is absorbed and the indicator becomes blue again.

Some specialized ways of getting food

Parasite and host

Dodder. On a field trip look for dodder, an orange-colored seed plant which grows like a vine around a host plant such as goldenrod (Fig. 14-2; see also p. 400).

Dodder produces small clusters of white flowers and large number of seeds. When students try to separate the parasite from

Fig. 14-2 Dodder (*Cuscuta Gronovui*) on host plant. (From C. L. Wilson & W. E. Loomis, *Botany*, rev. ed., Dryden, 1957.)

its host plant, they'll notice that dodder has projections (haustoria) growing into the phloem tubes of the host. What would happen if dodder seeds germinated in a region where independent green plants were absent? Why is dodder considered a parasite while Indian pipe (Fig. 14-5), another seed plant lacking chlorophyll, is a saprophyte?

Frogs and their parasites. When freshly killed frogs are dissected in class, students are likely to find examples of parasitic worms whirling around in the region of the lungs and liver or inside these organs. These worms may be mounted in a drop of Ringer's solution (p. 409) and viewed under the microscope.

Look for protozoans living as parasites within the digestive system of frogs. Begin below the stomach, and remove a bit of upper intestine. Mount the contents of the intestine in a drop of Ringer's solution. From this transfer a bit onto a clean slide as a dilute wet mount. Students may find the large protozoan *Opalina* (Fig. 14-3a) (note the lack of an oral groove) along with *Balantidium,* a smaller form (Fig. 14-3b).

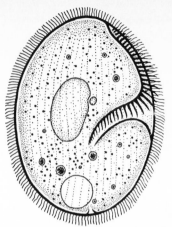

Fig. 14-4 *Nyctotherus,* a protozoan found in rectum of frogs or intestine of centipedes and cockroaches. (From W. S. Bullough, *Practical Invertebrate Anatomy,* Macmillan, 1954.)

In the rectum of the frog another protozoan, *Nyctotherus* (Fig. 14-4), may be found. It is not definitely known whether this form is parasitic in the frog or whether it is free-living. It is often present in the intestine of cockroaches, centipedes, and millipedes as well.

Parasites and several hosts. Unraveling the complete food chain of some parasites and their hosts has taken years of intensive study. Often one stage of a parasitic worm might be found in a bird, another in a fish, and a third in a snail. In each host the parasitic worm was in a different stage of its life cycle, and these were not recognized as developmental stages of one organism. Students may find many examples of parasites which have two or three hosts. You may want them to report on several examples, such as the malarial plasmodium, the broad tapeworm of man (*Diphyllobothrium*), the pork tapeworm (*Taenia solium*), and the Oriental liver fluke (*Clonorchis*).

What effect on the food chain would result if a parasite destroyed its host? Explain why parasitic forms produce such large numbers of eggs.

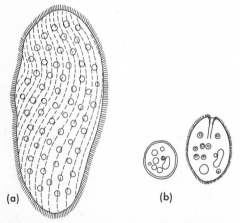

Fig. 14-3 Protozoa often found in frog's intestine: (a) *Opalina;* (b) encysted and nonencysted forms of *Balantidium.* (From D. F. Miller & J. G. Haub, *General Zoology,* Holt, 1956.)

Part-time parasites. Several living forms are partially parasitic in the sense that they are not permanently attached to or do not live continuously within a host. Mistletoe carries on photosynthesis and absorbs water and minerals from the host plant. Forms such as mosquitoes or leeches are also temporary parasites.

In a web of life there are many methods for obtaining a food or water supply.

Saprophytes. Molds growing on bread or lemons probably have been studied previously in class (pp. 388, 390). Or students may grow mold cultures on bread (p. 387).

At this time you may want students to expand upon the role of saprophytes in a food chain. Students may collect puffballs, mushrooms, shelf fungi, mildews, fungi, and bacteria of decay in soil, among many saprophytes which affect the storage of food crops.

You may want students to examine several specimens under a microscope (see field trips, p. 246; culturing, p. 389).

What is the role of saprophytes? List some saprophytes beneficial to man in that they return minerals to soil. For example, what would happen to the fertility of soil and the balance of life if bacteria of decay disappeared from the earth? What use has man made of bacteria of decay? Of yeast plants (p. 391)? Name several saprophytes which are harmful to man since they interfere with man's use of resources such as lumber or food crops. How does man attempt to hold these saprophytes in check?

Indian pipe. Students may find examples of the white seed plant Indian pipe (Fig. 14-5) growing in shaded regions, sometimes pushing up under masses of fallen leaves. Here is a higher plant without chlorophyll, unable to manufacture carbohydrates. It exists as a saprophyte, breaking down decaying vegetation and

Fig. 14-5 Indian pipe, a seed plant lacking chlorophyll, which lives as a saprophyte. (Photo: Harold V. Green.)

absorbing nutrient materials as mushrooms do.

A whole cluster may be transferred carefully to a terrarium, with the soil in which they are growing. When bruised the plants turn blackish in color.

Symbiosis

Lichens. Students may collect lichens from rocks or tree barks (Fig. 14-6). When a bit of the lichen is teased apart in a drop of water on a glass slide (wet mounts, p. 307) and examined under the microscope, the green algal cells enmeshed in filaments of fungi can be distinguished. In this mutual partnership of two plants the algae carry on food-making and the fungi absorb and hold water and minerals. Together these two plants can thrive on rocks, tree bark, and fence posts. Alone, each plant would have a limited range of existence.

Fig. 14-6 Lichen (*Physcia*): *left,* growing on tree trunk; *right,* microscopic view. (Photo: General Biological Supply House, Inc., Chicago.)

Termites and their protozoa. Termites consume wood, yet they lack an enzyme to break down this "food." Living symbiotically in their intestine are flagellated protozoa (see Fig. 17-10) which have the ability to digest woody materials.

On a field trip students may locate a termite colony in a tree stump. (This can be kept in the laboratory, p. 358.)

Prepare a wet mount of the flagellates, using the method described on page 311 in which the intestine of a termite is teased apart in a drop of Ringer's solution. (At some other time students may want to examine the flagellates found in the intestines of sow bugs.)

What would happen to termites if they didn't become infected with flagellates immediately upon hatching?

Nitrogen-fixing bacteria and legumes. In season, on a field trip, students may uproot leguminous plants such as clover, peanuts, alfalfa, or beans. Look for swellings or nodules on the roots. Each contains thousands of nitrogen-fixing bacteria which have invaded the root tissues but do little harm. Bring some back to class.

In class, wash off the roots. Crush a nodule between two glass slides. Add a drop of water to each slide and examine each as a wet mount. These slides may be stained for more careful study in the following way. Place in advance a drop of methylene blue stain (p. 309) on each of several slides. Let the stain dry; store the slides in a box so that they are ready for use. Add a drop of water containing nitrogen-fixing bacteria to the slide, apply a coverslip, and examine under high power. Notice how the stain gradually diffuses into the water and stains the bacteria.

Or you may prefer to make a smear of the bacteria and stain the smear to prepare a permanent slide, as follows. Make a thin film of the bacteria by spreading the fluid of a wet mount along the slide with a dissecting needle or with another slide. Fix the bacteria to the slide by waving the slide through a Bunsen flame two or three times. Lay the slide across a Syracuse dish and flood it with methylene blue for a minute. Then rinse off the stain with water, let it dry, and examine under high power.

Why do farmers rotate their crops with

leguminous plants? How do these nitrogen-fixing bacteria aid in replenishing the nitrate content of soil? Is there a difference between the growth of plants in poor soil and soil rich in nitrates?

Effect of nitrogen-fixing bacteria on plant growth. Students may demonstrate the difference in growth of plants grown in soil deficient in nitrates and soil rich in nitrates.

Sterilize four small flower pots of soil in an autoclave or an oven. Then add nitrogen-fixing bacteria (purchased from a seed company) to the soil in two of the flower pots. Add an equal amount of soaked clover seeds to each of the four flower pots. In which pots do students notice a more luxuriant growth of clover plants? What is the advantage of rotating nonleguminous crops with leguminous plants?

Other examples. Students may come upon many cases of symbiosis and commensalism on field trips near school.

If there is a beach or bay in the vicinity, students may find hermit crabs (Fig. 14-7). These inhabit deserted mollusk shells—whelk, periwinkle, moonsnail. To the shells are attached sea anemones (as shown), sea lettuce, or other forms. This is a type of camouflage. When the crabs are extricated from the shells, students can see the degenerated abdomen of each crab. Notice how the abdomen is

Fig. 14-7 A hermit crab and its "home": an empty whelk shell. Note the sea anemone attached to the shell. (Photo: © Douglas P. Wilson.)

twisted to fit into the spirals of the mollusk shell. The usually sessile anemones are now carried about to sources of food, and possibly the hermit crab has better chances of survival with these devices for camouflage.

In collecting from ponds you may come upon green hydras or green paramecia (or they may be purchased from supply houses). In these animals live green algae in a symbiotic relationship.

Students may find ants and their "cows," plant lice. These aphids or lice are tended by some species of ants which "milk" the aphids of a sugar solution they excrete. This is considered a symbiotic relationship.

Insectivorous plants. Several insectivorous plants may be found in bogs (or purchased). Students may find sundew, pitcher plant, or Venus fly-trap (Fig. 14-8).

Fig. 14-8   Insectivorous plants: *left,* sundew; *center,* Venus fly-trap; *right,* pitcher plant. (Photos: *left, center,* Carolina Biological Supply Co.; *right,* General Biological Supply House, Inc., Chicago.)

In fresh water they may find *Utricularia,* a floating plant which has small traps into which microorganisms swim and become captive (Fig. 14-9).

In all these cases the plants are green and carry on photosynthesis. Yet there may be a deficiency in nitrates; the plants secrete enzymes which act upon the insects, and possibly this protein material supplies the sources of nitrogen for plant growth.

Fig. 14-9 *Utricularia.* (General Biological Supply House, Inc., Chicago.)

Students may try to establish these bog plants in a terrarium which duplicates the environment from which they were transferred. Add some bits of charcoal to the tank to absorb odors. Introduce fruit flies into the tank (p. 400).

When the plants are not available, students may report to the class on these unusual plants and their kind of nutrition, or you may choose to show a film (see listings at the end of the chapter).

Upsetting the balance in nature

How have certain plants and animals become "pests" in this country when they are part of a natural food niche in another location?

Students may report on the history of the invasion and spread of the European corn borer, Tussock moth, Japanese beetle, English sparrow, thistle, Mediterranean fruit fly, and starling, among many others. What conditions enabled these immigrant insects, plants, or birds to overproduce? What is a natural enemy? What is the role of natural enemies in the web or balance of life?

This may be the time to elaborate upon the facts of overproduction in animals and plants (pp. 212, 213, 264) and to clarify the concept of natural enemies. What other factors prevent the survival of each egg, seed, or spore produced by an animal or plant? Students may recall the unfavorable conditions, such as shade or crowding, under which seedlings germinate, or the lack of food and water and overcrowding among the young of a given species of animals which are all looking for the same conditions for survival.

Students can list the ways man has upset the web of interrelationships in nature. Aside from introducing organisms into a new territory, man has upset the balance in nature in these ways: (1) forest fires due to carelessness; (2) reckless cutting down of trees; (3) overgrazing of land by sheep and cattle; (4) overcultivation of land; (5) contamination of waterways; (6) paying bounties for destruction of certain animals; (7) breeding new plants and animals.

Students may, in committee, report on several of these practices. They should come to realize the need to know the life cycles of insects (pp. 166, 357) so that they may be destroyed, or reared with care, depending upon their role in relation to a balance in nature and the needs of man. Why is it more advantageous to control insect pests by introducing their natural enemies than by chemical controls, such as insecticides like D.D.T.?

What is the value in knowing the facts about reproduction and development of frogs, birds, plants of all kinds, fish, snails, and so forth?

How are the seeds of plant pests disseminated? How does man through his actions encourage the spread of seeds of plant pests?

Are there living things which have become extinct as a result of man's careless use of resources? Students may describe many examples, such as the story of the passing of the passenger pigeon. What is the value of sanctuaries? Of closed seasons?

Going further; projects

Making a film. Members of a photography club or individual students interested in this hobby may develop a fine documentary. They might select areas around the community which are in need of repair, barren slopes, effects of raindrop erosion, and the like, and then show the effects of correcting the barren regions by planting cover, terracing, or contour plowing. Or they might show in film all the intricacies of a few selected examples of plant and animal relations in a biome —a woods, an open field, a fence post, a pond.

Another committee of students might write the script for this film. Perhaps it might be shown as an assembly program in school. Might it be useful to show at a P.T.A. meeting?

A broad view. Students may find it interesting to trace the changes in geographical distribution of plants and animals over a period of time as the land masses changed, the climate changed, or rivers were diverted. These changes are going on today. And the "meddling" of man is a part of this picture.

Review Darwin's writings on the effects of barriers upon the migration of plants and animals and the rise of new species. Students may go further into reading in population genetics and the importance of genetic drift in accounting for the kinds of plants and animals which exist anywhere. The work of Sewall Wright and G. G. Simpson, as well as the writings of Richard Goldschmidt, offer a broader view of the origin of new species.

Relations of living things to their environment

Soil

Living organisms in soil. What kind of plant and animal communities exist in soil? Have students collect samples, 1-foot blocks of rich garden soil, or soil from a woods or a meadow.

Describe the texture and color of the top and the undersurface. Examine the soil for earthworms, sow bugs, slugs, insect larvae and pupae, millipedes, and other living things. Are there small snakes, or buried eggs of small reptiles? Transfer small samples of soil into dishes containing a little water. Mount a bit of soil in a drop of water on a glass slide. Under the high power of the microscope, look for fungi, small worms, possibly some large bacteria. You may want students to stain some slides with methylene blue dye (p. 309) in an attempt to locate some of the larger bacteria.

List all the kinds of organisms found together in soil. What is their role in increasing the fertility of soil?

Effect of nitrates on growing plants. Students probably know that plants need certain minerals for proper growth. Or you may want to show the effect of mineral deficiencies on growing plants at this time. Have students place seedlings in jars of nutrient solutions (pp. 113, 398) which have been made up so that each solution in individual jars is lacking in some one mineral—nitrate, phosphate, or sulfate. Compare the growth of the seedlings with seedlings growing in "complete" nutrient solutions.

An outdoor field experiment may be devised wherever a patch of sandy soil is available. Locate an area where the grass seems pale (due perhaps to a deficiency of nitrates in the soil). Mark off a section several square feet in area and evenly scatter about 10 to 30 gm of sodium nitrate over this region. (Emerson and Shields[2] recommend about 30 gm for a 10-square-foot area of land.) Then water this area immediately so that the nitrates will be absorbed into the soil. During the next few weeks look for differences in color of the grass in the treated area and the surrounding, untreated area. Students should find that plants grow faster and grass is greener than in the untreated control area.

You may want to relate this activity to crop rotation and the role of nitrogen-fixing bacteria in the soil and in the nodules of leguminous plants (p. 232).

Binding force of roots. That roots hold soil and thereby reduce erosion can be shown in class. Germinate some rapidly growing seeds such as radish, oats, or mustard seeds in paper cups of moistened sand. Soak the seeds first to speed their germination. Let the seedlings grow for 2 weeks but water them sparingly. Root systems will be more extensive when the plants have not been well watered. With a firm tug on the shoots try to remove from the paper cups the entire sand mass bound by the roots. Students will find the sand particles held together by the root system so that the sand takes the shape of the container. Each student can germinate seeds to show this binding force. There may be time to study root hairs with a hand lens (p. 108).

Why are cover plants grown on a slope? Why is soil eroded quickly on a denuded hillside?

Water-holding ability of soils. Students may prepare three funnels or glass chimneys, with gauze taped or tied to the bottom of the mouth. Then pack one with

[2] F. Emerson and L. Shields, *Laboratory and Field Exercises in Botany,* Blakiston (McGraw-Hill), New York, 1949.

sand, another with clay, and the third with soil rich in humus. Now pour equal amounts of water into each funnel and watch the water run through the soil. If graduated cylinders are placed beneath the funnels, students can readily measure the amount of "runoff" water. Which soil permits water to run through most quickly? Which soil retains the water?

Capillarity of soils. The texture of the soil is a factor in determining how much water clings to particles of soil and is readily accessible to the roots of plants.

Use the same materials as above but instead of pouring water into the funnels, put an equal amount of water into each of the graduated cylinders. Be sure that the stem of the funnel reaches the water level in each case.

Watch the rate of water absorption in each preparation. Through which kind of soil does water rise readily?

Soil for plants. Students may prepare several flowerpots in this way. In some place sand, in others a clay soil, and in a third group a rich loam (clay, sand, and humus). Sow soaked seeds of fast-growing plants, such as mustard, oats, or radish, in each flowerpot. Compare the growth of seedlings in each kind of soil. In what ways do the texture and composition of soils affect plant growth? Which type of soil holds water best? In which soil does water move readily by capillarity?

Testing the acidity of soils. You may want to have students collect small samples of soil from different places, such as a weedy region, swamp area, beach, woods, burned-over area, well-tended garden, along a fence row, and also along a whitewashed wall. Cut a section of soil with a spade so that a slice about 5 inches deep is transported to class. These sections of soil might be wrapped carefully in newspaper or transported in a pan.

Use litmus paper as an indicator. Acid

turns litmus from blue to red; alkaline turns red litmus blue. Each student can test several samples of soil. Lay moistened strips of litmus paper, red and blue, side by side in several Syracuse dishes or on glass slides. Then put ½ teaspoon or less of a sample of soil on the strips of litmus paper. Perhaps a bit more water may be needed to moisten the soil. Then turn the glass dish or slide over and inspect the litmus paper. Use samples of soil from different levels of the section of soil and repeat the procedure. Are the top and bottom layers of the same pH? (See p. 406 for discussion of pH.)

One student might demonstrate the effect of adding a bit of lime to a sample of acid soil. Repeat the litmus test. (In fact, soil may be prepared for demonstration. Add a bit of vinegar or other acid to a sample of soil when you want to show the test for an acid soil. Add lime, CaO, when you want alkaline soil samples.)

Committees of students might use different indicators (p. 407) as a check on their observations with litmus paper. When a liquid indicator such as brom thymol blue is used, a bit of soil to be tested is placed in a small evaporating dish or against a white background of some sort. Then the indicator is added and the dish tilted to examine the color of the indicator as it flows from the moistened soil.

Students may recognize that the pH of the soil, one factor among many, affects the type of plant community existing in different soil. In fact, an experienced observer can estimate approximately the pH of the soil from the kinds of plants growing in a given region. Table 14-1 shows some of the plants which thrive in soil of three different pH ranges.

What change in the kinds of plant communities results when the minerals

Table 14-1
Acidity of soil in which certain plants thrive

pH 6–8 (neutral)	pH 5–7 (slightly acid)	pH 4–5 (very acid)
ailanthus	bayberry	azalea
ash	begonia	sweet pepper
barberry	bittersweet	bush
cherry	candytuft	maple-leaved
elm	chokeberry	viburnum
honeysuckle	chrysanthemum	stagger bush
locust	coleus	hydrangea
pear	goldenrod	lady slipper
sugar maple	mountain laurel	sheep laurel
	privet	many ferns
	wintergreen	

are constantly leached out of the soil? A student, looking for an interesting project, may want to read further in a text on soil-less growth of plants to learn how the ability of plants to absorb minerals is affected by the pH of the soil.

Profile of soil. How does the top layer of soil differ from subsoil and bedrock? When possible, have students examine an excavation under way, or a hillside cut through so that more than 5 feet of soil in profile is exposed. If you live in a desert area, compare the difference between the top layer of sand and the more granular, rocky layers several feet below the surface. What factors contribute to the formation of fine-textured sand?

In a study of so-called average soil, students may recognize the comparatively thin layer of dark topsoil. Under this layer, about 1½ to 2 feet down, is a layer of subsoil. This rests on a deep (below 5 feet) layer of bedrock. An examination of the content of the soil will reveal that living organisms are found only in topsoil (p. 235).

How does the texture of the usual topsoil differ from subsoil? Which kind of soil holds water best? (See above.) You might want a committee of students to report on the way that bedrock, like granite and basalt, was formed. What factors change rock into soil? For example, what effect do each of these conditions have on the breaking down of rock into soil— weathering such as alternate heat and cold, winds, water in motion, plant roots, ground water?

When they study fragmentation and exfoliation of rock, students can demonstrate some factors responsible for the breaking up of rock masses. Pour a dilute acid, such as vinegar, on limestone. This reaction might simulate the action of carbonic acid (carbon dioxide) dissolved in ground water. Have students bring to class bits of rock on which mosses or lichens are growing. Notice how readily the rock crumbles? Can students find examples to show how the outer layers of rock "peel" off after they have been subjected to alternating contraction and expansion due to cold and heat? If a rock were cracked, what effect would freezing water trapped in the cracks have on the rock?

Conversely, how does soil form sedimentary rock (see Fig. 13-1)?

How leaves add to the soil. Have students ever tested the sponginess of soil, particularly in a wooded region? Perhaps such a region is near enough for a short field trip. Examine the layers of leaves which form a cushion. Notice that the top layers of these leaves can be identified. Lift up layers of leaves. Notice how only veins of the underlying leaves are apparent. In layers below this, only fragments of leaves can be found. Now squeeze a mass of this material in your hands. Feel the moisture? Students may have had similar experiences in observing the changes in a compost heap made of grass cuttings and leaves around their own homes.

Which organisms in the soil aid in the rapid change of dead leaves into humus, giving this absorbent quality to the top-soil? How would the nitrogen cycle (as well as cycles of other minerals) be affected if bacteria of decay and soil fungi disappeared?

Erosion and the slope of the land. Does erosion of soil go on faster when land is sloped or flat? Do cover crops protect the soil on a hillside and prevent the transportation of soil distances away? Where it has been possible to plan a section of the school grounds for outdoor demonstrations and field trips (see pp. 264– 65), a committee of students may undertake this demonstration in a natural setting using flat and sloped land, land covered with vegetation, and bare soil.

Or it may be necessary to construct boxes, at least three, about 1 foot deep and 3 feet square and filled to the top with a loam soil. It would be best to set this demonstration out of doors. Students on the committee will need to plan this work well in advance, for one box needs a thick growth of a cover crop such as grass, oats, barley, rye, or some other fast-growing crop.

In the demonstration students should let one box of loam lie flat, and tilt the other box of loam and the third box containing a cover crop. In short, one box represents flat land, and two boxes show sloped land (one with vegetation). What will happen to the soil in each box in a rainstorm?

Have students direct a gentle spray of water from a garden hose on the three boxes of loam. Are there differences in amounts of soil carried away from the flat box as the water overflows the box and the transport of soil from the bare soil in the tilted box? What is the effect of cover crops? Where these conditions occur naturally around school, students may visit these areas after a heavy rainstorm. In fact, they may want to put into practice some corrective measures like planting cover crops, or terracing. Students might

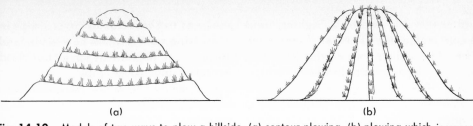

(a)   (b)

Fig. 14-10 Models of two ways to plow a hillside: (a) contour plowing; (b) plowing which increases erosion of the soil.

also record their observations of the follow-up of the corrective measures. Do they reduce soil erosion?

Contour plowing. Another committee of students may show the effect of poor farming methods on promoting erosion of soil. For instance, they may build several mounds of topsoil and pack these firmly. In some mounds furrows are indented so that they run vertically from the top of the mounds like spokes of a wheel. Indent other mounds with furrows which circle around the mounds (Fig. 14-10). Students might plant "crops" in the furrows and then pour equal quantities of water over each mound. How does the amount of runoff water (with soil) compare in the two "plowing" techniques?

Using the blackboard to show terracing. A slate blackboard often could be used more effectively as a visual device. Try this simple way to show how soil absorbs water and helps to prevent floods. This

may be terracing or strip cropping or the effect of a dam, whatever you wish. Dash some water on the board and as the small rivulets of water flow downstream along the board, dam these streams by pasting strips of wet toweling across them. Notice how the flow of water is stopped or slowed down (Fig. 14-11).

Staking out a contour line. There may be the occasion, if your school is in a farming community, when a group of students want to learn simple ways to lay out a contour line for contour plowing or strip cropping. An easy method is described in a Cornell Rural School Leaflet called *Conservation: A Handbook For Teachers* (Vol. 45:1, Sept. 1951).[3] In this method a car-

[3] This booklet is available from the New York State College of Agriculture, Cornell U., Ithaca, N. Y. In this booklet you will find reference to many other useful Cornell Rural School Leaflets. The devices used in the demonstrations described in these leaflets are simple and effective: water penetration using tin cans, making a wind card and a rainfall gauge, measuring moisture in the air with old photographic film which curls when dry, etc.

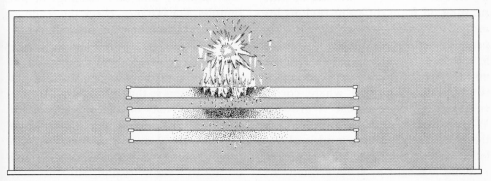

Fig. 14-11 Using the blackboard to demonstrate terracing: water splashed on the board runs down quickly until it meets the paper toweling; each strip absorbs some water, breaks its stream, and slows it down.

penter's level is used by a "sighter," and a companion, the "lineman," marks the line. The sighter locates the level line along a slope or hillside where both he and the lineman are in position.

Raindrop erosion. What kind of soil is eroded easily by the force of raindrops? Students may set out discs of metal or wood on bare soil. After a heavy rainstorm they will probably find that the soil under the discs is at a slightly higher level than in the region of exposed soil (where some soil was carried away).

You may want to use a method described in *Conservation: A Handbook for Teachers* (mentioned above) where the amount of soil splashed up on stakes covered with white paper can be measured. In soil covered with vegetation there should be less splashed or transported soil than on uncovered soil. At what seasons in the year is it likely that more soil is transported from cultivated regions?

How muddy is the runoff water? Another way to gain an understanding of how much soil is transported or eroded from any one place is to measure the amount of sediment in the water. Water carries many minerals which have been leached from the soil in solution, but much of the soil is transported as a suspension.

After a rainstorm it may be possible for students to collect samples of water running off from different regions into individual large bottles. After the suspended particles have settled, what difference is there in the amount of sediment and the size of the particles carried by runoff water from soil where corn is cultivated? Where wheat is growing? Where there is no cover crop? Where there is a gully? Where land is plowed following its contour? Along a roadbank?

What is meant by sheet erosion? Explain how silt is deposited at the foot of a slope. What comparison can students make as to the value of cover crops in conserving soil? Explain how wells (and springs) are dependent for a continued existence upon cover crops.

Studying the trees in your community. Students have learned that trees and cover crops help prevent floods and soil erosion. Does your community plant trees—or conserve them in other ways?

On individual field trips, as well as a group trip, students can make a count of trees, a tree census. What kinds of trees are there and how tall are they? Have youngsters identify the kinds of trees and shrubs in the neighborhood. Which kinds of trees are used for special purposes, for example, for attracting birds to the gardens or fields, as windbreaks for cultivated land, as pioneers in moving into a new area?

Students might list many ways in which trees aid in conserving the resources of the region in which they live.

Is the temperature of soil uniform? Certain plants and animals exist in sunny areas and others seem to grow only in a shaded region. Is there a difference in temperature of soils in the shaded and the sunny regions which might affect the kind of community of living things which exist there?

Students may devise ways to use a thermometer and take readings of soil samples. For instance, check the readings of several thermometers beforehand by placing them in ice water and in boiling water. Keep a record of any degree of error in the readings among the different thermometers so that fractions of a degree (or degrees) may be added or subtracted from the readings students take. Now lay one thermometer so that the bulb touches soil in a shaded area, a second on soil in a sunny region. Students may want to take a reading of soil which is light in color and compare this with dark-colored soil. Which surface warms up faster? Similarly, is there a difference between the temperature of soil on the surface layer and the soil several feet down? Tie a string on a thermometer and lower it into a hole which students have made so that a reading is taken of the soil several feet down. How does this compare with the temperature at the surface?

As a matter of fact, this demonstration may be done at any time in the year. Students might take readings of soil temperatures under a blanket of snow and on the surface of the soil.

Water

Well water. In a community where wells are common, students can trace the origin of well water back to precipitation, then to ground water and types of rock formation in relation to drilling a well. What cautions should be observed in deciding on the location of a well? How can water spoilage be avoided?

What causes water to rise in a well? Insert a straw into a glass of water. Let the water level represent the water table in the soil. When air is sucked out of the straw, what causes water to rise in the straw? How deep can wells be drilled? What is the difference between a simple well and an artesian well? What is the community doing to prevent water waste and spoilage or pollution of water in streams, wells, and reservoirs?

Study of watersheds. From where does your water supply come? Maps of the watersheds which supply your community may be available from your state departments of agriculture (or geology). Students may bring maps of this area to class. Then trace the path of water from the watershed to the individual home. For instance, how is water treated to make it fit to drink? What are the requirements

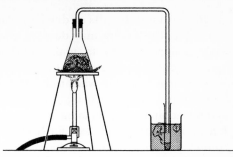

Fig. 14-12 Demonstrating the water cycle: evaporation and condensation.

of a good watershed region? What precautions are in practice to control forest fires in this region, to control insect pests which damage forests, to prevent stream pollution?

Besides reading the excellent booklets published by state departments, students should learn to find information in the Yearbooks of the U.S. Department of Agriculture. The 1955 Yearbook called *Water* is a mine of valuable information for students in all sections of the country. (Many agencies which supply reference materials are listed at the end of the chapter.)

Tracing the water cycle. You may want to have students demonstrate principles involved in evaporation and condensation; then their observations may be extended to an interpretation of the water cycle over the earth.

A student might streak the blackboard with cotton soaked in water. Where does the water go when the board becomes dry? Set up a simple demonstration as in Fig. 14-12. Begin with muddy water (or water colored with a dye); boil this and collect water vapor in a cold container so that students can see drops of clear water condensing in the container.

Students can relate this work to changes in water in a water cycle: evaporation, condensation of water on dust particles, and cloud formation followed by precipitation. (A student might report on seeding clouds with iodide salts or dry ice). An extension of this work may develop into a discussion of ways to make muddy water, from streams in a watershed, fit for drinking. You may want to have students demonstrate settling (Fig. 13-1) and the addition of alum to muddy water. Filtration, aeration, the need for bacterial counts, and the addition of chemicals to purify water may develop from this demonstration.

Action of ground water. After precipitation, some water may run off into streams, but much of it soaks into the ground; the quantity depends upon the kind of soil (p. 237). What is the action of this ground water? Students may demonstrate how ground water in which carbon dioxide is dissolved (carbonic acid) helps to break down rock into soils. Have them add dilute hydrochloric or even acetic acid to limestone or marble chips (calcium carbonate). Notice the destructive action of the acid on the bits of "rock." This destructive action goes on in limestone beds where ground water percolates between layers of rock, forming caverns and sinkholes. Students will also recognize that the formation of stalactites and stalagmites in limestone caves illustrates the constructive action of ground water.

Interested students may be referred to texts in metallurgy and geology for explanations of the ways ores and precious stones are formed in rocks. A student may demonstrate tests for different ores. How are copper ores or iron ores identified? How does ground water supply artesian wells; under what conditions does ground water form springs? What relation have these studies to conservation?

CAPSULE LESSONS

Ways to get started in class

14-1. Take a field trip around the school grounds and list places which show erosion of soil by wind, water, or ice. Decide the kind of conservation practices which could be used effectively in each area. Have students explain the value of each of their suggestions.

In some cases a class or a club might put some of these ideas into practice. They might terrace the lawn or a piece of land nearby to reduce a sharp angle of an existing slope. Or plant saplings or cover crops on a hillside or a burned-over area. If a photographic record were kept year by year, students in subsequent classes might continue the practices when they see how effective they have been.

14-2. Have students bring in samples of soil from different regions and examine under a microscope the living organisms found in the soil. Develop the notion of the interdependence of these plants and animals. What would happen if one kind of organism disappeared?

14-3. You may plan to have a committee of students make a survey of good land practices in use in your community. They might also recommend conservation measures which could effectively be introduced. Perhaps they may be permitted to write an article for a newspaper—either school or community—to report their findings and their suggestions.

Students should learn to explain in simple language the usefulness of these farming techniques: crop rotation, strip cropping, ways to spread ground water, terracing, use of green manure, irrigation, contour plowing, and the use of fertilizers and the proportion of sulfates, phosphates, and nitrates these should contain for specific crops.

14-4. There are soil-testing kits available for purchase. Demonstrate as described in this chapter the acidity or alkalinity of some soils around the school area. How would living things be affected if the acid soil of swamps or bogs became more alkaline? Use compost formed from decaying leaves for tests of acid soil.

Develop the idea that plants require certain conditions for growth, such as the proper pH. In fact, the degree of acidity of the soil determines, in some measure, the availability of minerals to the plants.

14-5. That minute bacteria have an essential role in the balance of nature may be developed by asking students to explain what would happen if all bacteria of decay disappeared from the earth. This is the time to develop the idea that not all bacteria are disease-producing; a good number are helpful.

14-6. Begin a study of the relationship between water and soil by demonstrating the ability of different soils to hold water. Use funnels of different soils as described in this chapter. Have students explain how cover plants and forests prevent floods and the erosion of soil.

14-7. Perhaps a debate may be planned in this area: Thoughtful people consider that conservation needs constitute the most pressing problem in the world today.

14-8. Have students report on the destruction of soil by overgrazing. Also plan to have reports on the use of radioactive isotopes as tracers added to fertilizers to learn the amounts and the kinds of minerals that different crop plants take from the soil. Many reference materials are available from the Atomic Energy Commission and from current magazine articles.

14-9. Perhaps your school is located in a vicinity where you may solicit the help of a forester (or a county agent). He may, on a field trip, demonstrate how forests are handled as crops; the succession of trees in woods and climax forests; what kinds of seedlings are pioneers in a new region; whether the prevailing winds carry light seeds or heavy seeds greater distances into new regions. Students might prepare questions in advance to ask the expert. What are the new practices in forest management?

You may ask a county agricultural agent to explain how to test crops and soil for mineral deficiencies.

14-10. There are excellent bulletins available from experimental stations and state and federal departments of agriculture. You may want to plan a class period of free reading at which time large numbers of publications are available. Students will profit from a perusal of these publications which show scientists at work. Be certain to include the fine Yearbooks of the U.S. Department of Agriculture, Washington, D. C.: *Insects* (1952); *Plant Diseases* (1953); *Marketing* (1954) (students may practice reading the many different kinds of graphs in the back of this yearbook); *Water* (1955);

Trees (1949); *Science in Farming* (1943–47); *Food and Life* (1939); *Soils and Men* (1938); *Soil* (1957).

14-11. As a student or club project, the value of attracting birds to a garden (school grounds) may be investigated. For example, a survey of the kinds of birds attracted to a given area could be made. Then build birdhouses to attract birds to the area. Although many may consume seeds, how effective in general are birds in holding down the insect population? Perhaps students can explain the practice of planting berry shrubs and trees along rows of cultivated crops.

While chicken hawks may consume some chickens, why is it a poor practice for a community to offer a bounty for dead hawks?

(Many colleges of forestry and departments of agriculture in colleges offer splendid publications. For example, you may send for a list of publications of the New York State College of Agriculture, Cornell University, Ithaca, New York, to learn the kinds of materials available for student work.)

14-12. In a broad view of human conservation, you may want to relate conservation of resources to constructive measures at work in the community to improve human health, plans for hospitalization, possibilities for scholarships and education, playgrounds, and similar civic measures. What effect has the increased use of electrical power had on man's standard of living and his life span? What will the life span probably be in the year 2000? the population of the United States? the population of the world? Will there be land area to feed this population?

14-13. Begin with a snail sealed in a test tube (Fig. 6-4) and ask how long it will live. Elicit from students the dependence of living things on green plants. Then develop different kinds of nutrition among plants and animals (saprophytes, parasites, symbiotic relations, other special types as described in this chapter).

14-14. If possible, begin with a field trip to examine a specific plant-animal community or habitat: pond, desert area, beach, woods, meadow, or bog. Have students describe the food chains in the habitat. You will find Ralph and Mildred Buchsbaum's *Basic Ecology*[4] a useful guide.

PEOPLE, PLACES, AND THINGS

The work of this chapter is as broad as life. Many people can offer help to the classroom teacher. You may be in a vicinity where a for-

ester can help you, or where a county agent can demonstrate useful practices.

A visit may be planned to a sanctuary, a

[4] Boxwood Press, Pittsburgh 13, 1957.

fish hatchery, an experimental farm using radioactive isotope techniques, a commercial or a college laboratory which contributes to some aspect of the wise development of resources.

Your local conservation, wildlife, and agricultural agencies will be eager to help. Perhaps you may borrow a film or some equipment for a demonstration, or get pamphlets suggesting many demonstrations that students might undertake in class or as individual or club projects.

If your school grounds are limited, it may be possible that someone in the community has fields, or a lot, or a bit of woodland you may use for field trips. Many schools have made successful arrangements of this sort.

BOOKS AND PAMPHLETS

These are only a few of the books which are pertinent to the work discussed in this chapter. These and many other references classified by subject and with complete bibliographical data are given in the Bibliography at the end of the book. You will find nature books a help in the identification of all sorts of plants and animals. A tremendous amount of literature is available in many specialized areas in conservation. The suggestions here are only a sample of the many agencies which you may contact for literature.

American Association of School Administrators, *Conservation Education in American Schools,* yearbook, Washington, D. C., 1951.

Beard, W., *Teaching Conservation,* American Forestry Assoc., Washington, D. C., 1948.

Bennett, H. H., *Elements of Soil Conservation,* 1947.

Borror, D., and D. DeLong, *An Introduction to the Study of Insects,* 1954.

Buchsbaum, R., and M. Buchsbaum, *Basic Ecology,* 1957.

Carson, R., *The Sea Around Us,* 1951.

Cope, J., and W. Winch, *Woodlot Management,* Cornell 4-H Club, Bull. 43, Roberts Hall, Cornell U., Ithaca, N. Y., 1955.

Dale, T., and V. G. Carter, *Topsoil and Civilization,* 1955.

Fitzpatrick, H., and W. Ray, *Some Common Edible and Poisonous Mushrooms,* Cornell Extension Bull. 386, Cornell U., Ithaca, N. Y., 1955.

Gabrielson, I., *Wildlife Conservation,* 1952.

Graves, A., *Illustrated Guide to Trees and Shrubs,* Published by author, Wallingford, Conn., 1952.

Gustafson, G., C. Guise, et al., *Conservation in the United States,* 1949.

Jaeger, E., *Tracks and Trailcraft,* 1948.

Kellogg, C., *The Soils That Support Us,* 1955.

Lapage, G., *Animals Parasitic in Man,* 1957.

Metcalf, C., W. Flint, and R. Metcalf, *Destructive and Useful Insects,* 1951.

Mills, W., and A. La Plante, *Diseases and Insects in the Orchard,* Cornell Extension Bull. 711, Cornell U., Ithaca, N. Y., 1954.

Morgan, A., *Fieldbook of Ponds and Streams,* 1927.

Muenscher, W., and W. Winne, *Common Poisonous Plants,* Cornell Extension Bull. 538, Cornell U., Ithaca, N. Y., 1955.

Needham, J., and P. Needham, *A Guide to the Study of Fresh-Water Biology,* 1955.

Oosting, H., *The Study of Plant Communities,* 1948.

Palmer, E., *Cornell Rural School Leaflets* (on many specified areas related to conservation); also *Conservation: a Handbook for Teachers,* Roberts Hall, Cornell U., Ithaca, N. Y.

Palmer, E., *Fieldbook of Natural History,* 1949.

Pennak, R., *Fresh Water Invertebrates of the United States,* 1953.

Schwartz, C., *Conservation Sketch Book,* Missouri Conservation Commission, Jefferson City, Missouri, 1950.

U.S. Dept. of Agriculture, ask for publications on conservation practices.

———, Forest Service, ask for available films on conservation.

———, Soil Conservation Service, ask for list of pamphlets and films on water and soil conservation.

U.S. Dept. of Interior, Fish and Wildlife Service, ask for publications.

Walford, L., *Marine Resources,* 1957.

Winch, F., *Future Forests,* Cornell 4-H Club Bull. 90, Cornell U., Ithaca, N. Y., 1950.

Woodbury, A., *Principles of General Ecology,* 1954.

FILMS AND FILMSTRIPS

This partial list is intended only as a guide toward film and filmstrip selection. Refer to the more complete listing at the end of the book where films are classified by subject, and where a key to abbreviations and the addresses of distributors are given. The cost of film rental, of course, may be subject to change. Films are sound and black and white unless otherwise specified.

The Atom and Agriculture (f), EBF, free loan from field offices of U.S. Atomic Energy Commission.

Atomic Greenhouse (f), Handel Film Corp; free loan from U.S. Atomic Energy Commission.

Battle of the Beetles (f, c), U.S. Dept. of Agriculture, Forest Service, free.

Blades of Grass, (f, c), Union Pacific R. R., free.

Chemical Weed Control (f, c), Dow Chemical, free.

County Agricultural Agent (f, c), Venard Organization, free.

Erosion (f), U.S. Dept. of Agriculture, Soil Conservation Service, free.

Grassland Report (f, c), New Holland Machine Co., free.

Life of the Soil (f, c), Nat. Fertilizer Assoc., free.

The Master Element (water) (f, c), Amer. Waterways Operators, free.

More Food from Fewer Acres (irrigation), (f, c), Case, free.

Muddy Waters (f), U.S. Dept. of Agriculture, Soil Conservation Service, free.

Pipeline to the Clouds (f, c), General Electric, free.

Plant Speaks Through Deficiency Symptoms (f, c), American Potash, free.

Plant Traps (f), EBF, $1.50.

Rain on the Plains (f), U.S. Dept. Agriculture, $1.00.

Raindrops and Soil Erosion (f, c), U.S. Dept. of Agriculture, Soil Conservation Service, free.

Rivers and the Soil, (f, c), Minneapolis-Moline, free.

Story of West Coast Lumber (fs), West Coast Lumbermen's Assoc., free.

Upstream Where the Floods Begin (f), U.S. Dept. of Agriculture, Soil Conservation Service, free.

FREE AND INEXPENSIVE MATERIALS

This is only a partial listing of free and inexpensive materials available to the teacher at this time. A more complete listing, including addresses, is given at the end of the book. Many of these materials are distributed to teachers without charge. Where there is a small fee, the cost is indicated, although the prices are subject to change. While we recommend the material for use in the classroom, we do not necessarily sponsor the products advertised.

Concepts of Conservation, Conservation Foundation, 1956, $0.25.

Conservation of Natural Resources, Merrill Books, 1954, $0.40.

Home Canning Booklets, Kerr Glass Manufacturing Co.

Home Freezing Materials, National Electrical Manufacturers' Assoc.

Life and Death of the Soil, Science Research Associates, 1955, $0.50.

Man and the Soil, International Harvester Co.

Materials to Help Teach Forest Conservation, U.S. Dept. Agriculture, Forest Service.

More Food from Fewer, J. I. Case Co., 1947.

Outline for Teaching Conservation in the High Schools, U.S. Dept. Agriculture, Soil Conservation Service, 1952.

Outline for Teaching Conservation in the Elementary Schools, U.S. Dept. Agriculture, Soil Conservation Service, 1955.

Protecting our Living Waters, National Wildlife Federation, 1954, $0.10.

Story of Farm Chemicals, DuPont de Nemours & Co.

Ten Lessons in Forestry, Southern Pine Assoc.

To Know the Trees: Important Forest Trees of U.S., Supt. Documents, U.S. Govt. Printing Office, $0.20.

Tree Farming; Suggestions for Teachers, International Paper Co., Southern Kraft Division.

West Coast Tree Farms, West Coast Lumbermen's Assoc.

Forest Conservation, College of Forestry, Syracuse, New York.

CHAPTER 15

Field work: living things

in their environment

Field work—getting out of doors, when possible, to observe living things—is an essential part of biology. These trips may be brief—part of a period, one period— or a day's planned excursion, or a week end at a nature camp. From these activities young people may develop a deeper understanding and appreciation of the way living things carry on their functions, their interdependence, the effect of the environment on their survival, and the selective forces which affect heredity and evolution.

This chapter describes methods of collecting living things for a more or less immediate study in class, and ways to preserve some living things for a school museum. Subsequent chapters describe many ways to keep alive, in class and laboratory, the plants and animals which have been collected in field work.

Field trips

Many varieties of field trips (Fig. 15-1) are possible, depending on the purposes of the teacher and the location of the school.[1] Whatever the nature of the trip, it should be carefully planned. Are students going to gather water forms or land forms? Are they going to the seashore or to a wooded area? Proper clothes and equipment are necessary. The size of specimen bottles and the kind of nets students take along will differ with your purpose. Bring along hand lenses for a preliminary examination in the field. (Several types may be purchased from a supply house or an optical firm.) Students should remember to bring along field-book guides to help identify plants and

[1] Many teachers plan field trips with their classes. You may examine the concepts they develop by reading publications of different cities: *Guide to School Camping for Wisconsin,* Curriculum Bull., G. Watson, Dept. Public Instruction, Madison, Sept. 1956; *Teachers' Guide For Conservation and Nature Study,* S. Mulaik, Biology Div., U. of Utah, 1955; *Teaching Guide for Science,* B. Willis, Chicago Public Schools, 1955; *Challenging the Gifted Student Through Projects in Biology,* Houston Independent School District, Houston, 1956; *A Sourcebook of Science Experiences,* Curriculum Bull. 11:2, Louisville Public Schools, 1954.

Fig. 15-1 Field trips can be taken to many places: a forest pool, a section of the school grounds, a slow-moving stream. (Photos: Hays from Monkmeyer, Board of Education of Baltimore County, Howard H. Michand of Purdue U.)

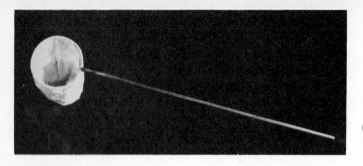

Fig. 15-2 One type of dip net for collecting aquatic forms. (Photo: General Biological Supply House, Inc., Chicago.)

animals. (See Bibliography at the end of the book.)

Collecting and examining water forms

There are several kinds of dip nets used to collect small water forms such as insect larvae, crustaceans, and plankton. One type of net, used to brush through pond weeds and mud or sand at low tide (Fig. 15-2), should have a strong wire frame, a diameter of about 6 to 8 inches, and strong netting, either bobbinet or nylon. It is well to have two kinds of nets which may be fastened to the same handle: a fine-weave net to catch the smaller specimens and a coarser net to catch larger forms (crayfish, fiddler crabs, mussels) and for brushing through weeds. For ease in handling, the handle should not be more than 3 feet long.

Sand or mud which accumulates on the net may be rinsed out by swishing the net through the water. Transfer the collected specimens into shallow white pans or place them on large sheets of paper and spread them out in the sun for inspection.

When pond water is collected, large clean jars should be filled with the water and some of the mud from the region added. When plants are collected, packing too many plants in one container should be avoided. Some submerged branches and aquatic plants should also be collected. These may be transported to the laboratory in wet newspaper. Within 5 hours transfer the pond water, twigs, and plants to large battery jars or small aquaria.

After the mud settles, identify the swimming specimens with a hand lens or binocular microscope. In the spring you are likely to find *Daphnia* (Fig. 18-16) and mosquito, dragonfly, damsel fly, and mayfly larvae. In samples of mud you may find caddice-fly cases and *Tubifex* worms (Fig. 18-12).

Microorganisms congregate at different levels in the battery jars—some are surface forms, others bottom dwellers. For a rapid inventory of the microscopic forms which have been collected, place some clean coverslips on the bottom of the containers and float others on the surface of the water. If these coverslips are left in these positions for several hours (or overnight), many microorganisms become attached to them. Carefully remove the coverslips with forceps, place them on a drop of water on clean slides, and examine under the microscope. If you scrape the surfaces of submerged leaves, and examine the scrapings under the microscope, you may find protozoa such as *Amoeba* (Fig. 18-1) and *Vorticella* (Fig. 9-2), and some flatworms such as planarians (Fig. 18-9), as well as insect eggs, rotifers, and some snails. Break apart swollen rotting twigs which have been submerged. Look for snails, planarians, hydras (Fig. 18-8), and in clean water, specimens of the fresh-water sponge, *Spongilla* (Fig. 18-7).

Keep all these containers in moderate light. Maintain a temperature below 75° F and keep the containers covered to prevent evaporation. Plan to subculture certain organisms important to your work by isolating them in containers of aquarium water in which plants and animals have been growing.

Plant specimens may include diatoms, blue-green and green algae, elodea, duckweed, *Cabomba,* and other types of water plants. Spores, eggs, and encysted forms develop quickly in the laboratory. Other forms become dormant for a time and reappear within a period of a month or so. This is excellent material for studies of food cycles and ecological patterns in different biomes.

The cultivation of animals in the laboratory is given in Chapters 18 and 19; cultivation of plants is described in Chapter 20.

In some cases the collection of living material is not feasible, and the materials, such as soft-bodied specimens, might better be preserved in the field. Methods for preserving specific animal forms are given in brief, easy reference form in Table 15-1 (pp. 256–59).

Collecting land animals

Collecting insects. Collecting nets to be used for capturing insects differ in size from the water nets previously described. One type, a light-weight collecting net, is used primarily for the collection of fragile insects such as butterflies, moths, and dragonflies. The material of the net is fine mesh, possibly nylon, sewed to a rim about 1 foot in diameter. The net should be at least 2 times deeper than the diameter of the rim, since a twist of the net is made when a specimen is caught in the bottom of the net. This confines the specimen and makes it possible to transfer it to a collecting bottle. The

handle should be lightweight and about 3 feet long.

Another type of net, a sweeping net, is used to brush or sweep through tall vegetation; different kinds of insects may be captured in this way, including many beetles. This net should have a stout wire rim and a stout handle. The length of the handle depends somewhat upon the individual, since increased length will need additional strength. In fact, some nets on the market have handles only about 6 inches long. The sweep net may be made of white muslin, nylon, or duck; the diameter of the wire rim should be about 1 foot. (Again, this depends upon the strength of the individual.) The depth of the net should be at least 1½ to 2 times the diameter of the net.

When hunting insect specimens with a net, twist the net to enclose the insects in the bottom. Then transfer them into a killing jar (described below). When flying specimens or delicate-winged lepidoptera have been captured, their wings may be damaged as they struggle within the net; this can be avoided by placing a drop of ether or chloroform on the net. Then they may be transferred to a killing jar and later to an insect case.

The culturing of certain insects useful in classroom demonstrations is described in Chapter 18.

Experience gained in field work will result in the development of some ingenious devices for carrying the variety of bottles and jars which should be on hand. A sturdy knapsack is desirable; it is usually expandable so that it may hold jars of many sizes. Both hands then are free for work. Vials and bottles may be made of plastic rather than glass; the "pack" is then lighter in weight and there is less danger from broken glass. If a section of the plastic containers is rubbed with sandpaper or emery cloth to roughen it a bit, it is possible to write on the bottles with pencil. This may be washed off later in the laboratory or classroom. (Some plastic bottles, available from supply houses, have been coated inside with a special lining so that strong chemicals may be stored in them.)

Small vials will be useful in collecting arachnids, larvae, and other soft-bodied forms which must be preserved immediately in alcohol. Two or three uniformly sized vials should be prepared as killing jars, others should contain alcohol (70 per cent), and the remainder might be left as transfers, to carry specimens from the net to a large jar.

Out in the field you will also need medicine droppers (carry them in one envelope), as well as forceps, hand lenses, and prepared envelopes to pack lepidopterans in, as described below.

To repeat, larval stages and soft-bodied insects should be dropped, in the field, into vials of 70 per cent alcohol. Methods for preserving these forms permanently are described later in this chapter. However, lepidoptera, green insects, most beetles, flies, and bees (and other Hymenoptera) should not generally be put into alcohol.

Killing jars. Prepare large killing jars for lepidoptera and dragonflies, as well as some smaller ones. The standard killing jar contains potassium cyanide. You may purchase these already prepared or make them yourself. Since the crystals and fumes are deadly, and poisonous to handle, it may be more advisable to buy the jars already made. But for those who want to prepare their own jars, here is one method. Sprinkle (without touching) pea-sized bits of potassium cyanide in the bottom of several different-sized bottles and cover the bottom of each with a layer of plaster of Paris.

As the bottles are used, moisture accumulates in the bottom from the secretions of captured insects. To avoid this, the cyanide may be packed in dry plaster of Paris and then covered with a wet layer of plaster of Paris. Another way you may avoid the accumulation of moisture is to cover the hardened plaster with a thin sheet of blotting paper or cork sheeting.

A safer type of killing jar is made by packing rubber bands into the bottoms of jars of different sizes, then soaking the rubber with carbon tetrachloride (or Carbona). Cover this with absorbent cotton and pack tightly. Finally, cover this with a circle of cardboard or a thin disk of cork to hold the materials in place. Since the fumes are not as lingering as cyanide, lift the cork disk and add carbon tetrachloride from time to time.

When large, fragile-winged specimens are placed in killing jars, they may struggle furiously, since the fumes act slowly. Wet a bit of cotton with ether or chloroform (also carried in the knapsack) and put this into the killing jar, or dab it on the insect net before you transfer the captured animal to the killing jar, so that the wings will not be damaged.

Paper envelopes for large-winged insects. Dragonflies, damsel flies, butterflies, and Dobson flies should be put into special envelopes (Fig. 15-3) to prevent wing damage. In fact, these insects may be stored in the laboratory in these envelopes until you are ready to mount them. At that time they may be put into a relaxing jar, then placed on a wing spreader, and finally mounted (all three techniques are described later in this chapter). You can purchase these envelopes, made of cellophane, from supply houses; or take slips of paper of various sizes, the largest about the size of a postcard, and fold them as shown.

Students should have a good supply of them before starting out on a field trip.

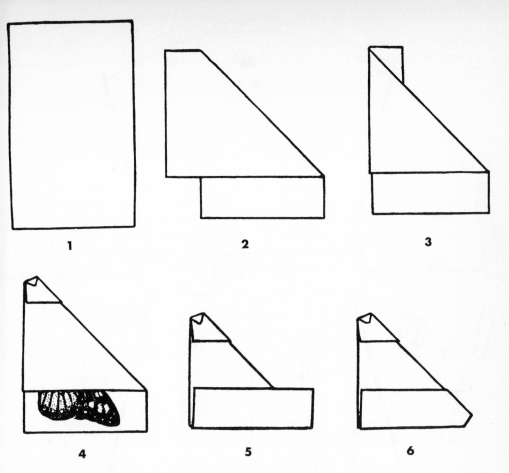

Fig. 15-3 Folding paper envelopes for transporting moths and butterflies. (From F. E. Lutz, *Fieldbook of Insects,* 2d ed., Putnam's, 1921; copyright renewed 1945.)

As they are filled, label all collected materials giving location, date, time of day, and ecology of the collecting area.

Collecting other land animals. While we have thus far confined the discussion of collection of land forms to the insects, spiders and other arachnids may also be collected by net. Earthworms, slugs, land snails, and insect eggs (as well as vertebrates such as salamanders), should be collected in cigar boxes or jars containing soil. Decaying tree stumps may be transported to the laboratory (in moist newspaper), and placed in covered containers (since termites may be in the decaying wood). The flagellates in the intestine of termites, sow bugs, and related forms are excellent for microscopic study. See page 311 for methods of preparing wet mounts of symbiotic flagellates.

Using an insect key. Prior to a field trip, the main orders of insects may be distinguished by studying illustrations in textbooks. On field trips many students like to be able to distinguish a beetle from a wasp or a cicada. An introduction to the notion of classifying animals and plants was given in Chapter 13, where the categorization of living things was compared with a library system of classifying books.

Students may devise their own sim-

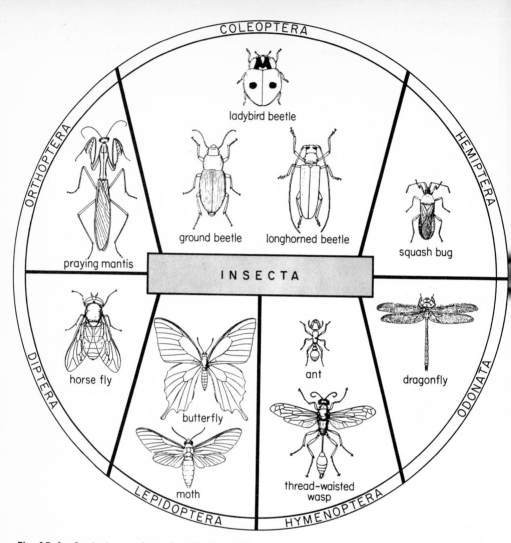

Fig. 15-4 Beginning guide to classification of insects. (Drawings from *Insects, The Yearbook of Agriculture*, U.S.D.A., 1952.)

plified classification system to "key" out insect unknowns when they know the basic patterns of differences among the orders. Broadly speaking, what kinds of variations distinguish the orders of insects? Students might collect many samples of insects, then sort them into probable similar groups. How does a beetle differ from a dragonfly, a bee, a fly, or a grasshopper? What are the distinguishing features that set apart one order from others? While students will recognize that insects, in general, have 3 body parts, 2 pairs of wings, and 3 pairs of jointed legs, there are some large differences that are evident to students. One order has front wings that are scalelike (beetles), another order has one pair of wings (flies), another has leathery front wings and color-patterned hind wings which pleat below the upper ones (grasshopper group), another has colored wings of overlapping scales (butterflies and moths), another has membranous wings and a constricted "waist" (wasp and bee group). Figure 15-4 shows representatives of these groups and a few others. There are many, many orders of insects that have not been included in this much abbreviated introduction.

Now *within* an order of insects, such as the Coleoptera, students should be able to choose the traits which differentiate ground beetles from cucumber beetles, weevils, longhorned beetles, or ladybird beetles. Similarly, they should be able to distinguish families within the order Hymenoptera. Why are wasps in a different family from ants or bees?

When students have learned the traits of each order and have a nodding acquaintance with the notion of families, they may look again with sharpened observation for the distinguishing differences *within a family.* Students may turn to a professional key such as those found in books on insects (see Bibliography at the end of the book) and learn the genera which make up specific families of insects. Furthermore, *within one genus,* for example, among ladybird beetles or potato bugs, what variations may be counted?

At the same time also you may want to use the studies of variations described among protozoans (Chapter 18) or evergreens (Chapter 13); or refer to other examples of variations and their causes as developed in Chapter 13.

Collecting plants

Collecting algae. While some algae may be collected on land, especially in damp or boggy places, most fresh-water algae are found in ponds and lakes. Marine algae may be studied immediately or kept for a short time in marine aquaria (pp. 355–56),[2] but they cannot

[2] If students search for *Fucus* in the fall, they will find that fertilization is going on; antheridia are orange-red in color and the branches containing eggs are a dull green. Dry and preserve *Fucus* and other marine forms, such as *Ulva* and the delicate red algae, on cardboard or bristol board.

be maintained in class as readily as fresh-water forms.

When collecting fresh-water algae (Fig. 15-5), it is best to get specimens which thrive in slow-moving bodies of water; these forms have a better chance of surviving in the school aquarium. Avoid

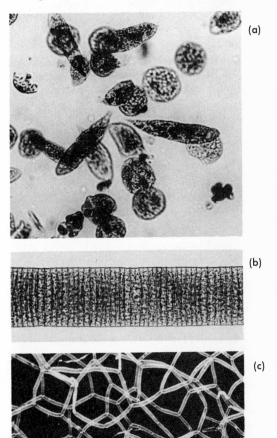

Fig. 15-5 Some fresh-water algae: (a) *Euglena;* (b) *Oscillatoria* (portion of single filament); (c) *Hydrodictyon,* showing two sizes of net. (Photos: a, General Biological Supply House, Inc., Chicago; b, c, Carolina Biological Supply Co.)

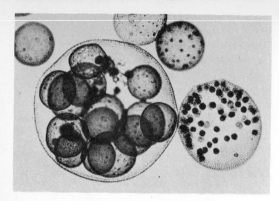

Fig. 15-6 *Volvox globator*, a colonial green alga, with sexual stages and several daughter colonies. (Photo: Carolina Biological Supply Co.)

overcrowding the specimens; transfer them as soon as feasible into large containers in the laboratory. If you can refrigerate the specimens, you can add days to their viability.

In shallow water you may find the slow-moving, blue-green filaments of *Oscillatoria* (Fig. 15-5b). This form is also found in damp places (such as the outer black layer on damp flowerpots). The blue-black mats on the surface of damp soil in the pots are also likely to be *Oscillatoria*. *Euglena* (Fig. 15-5a) may be found in shallow pools, and you may well find desmids (Fig. 20-3) of several kinds in the greenish mud of very shallow ponds and at the edge of a lake. The silky threads which float in sunny spots of ponds, lakes, and ditches, and have a slippery feel between the fingers, are likely to be those of *Spirogyra* (Fig. 20-1). And in the same locale you may find the water net *Hydrodictyon* (Fig. 15-5c). The colonial green algae *Volvox* (Fig. 15-6) composed of hundreds to thousands of cells, are also inhabitants of lakes and ponds. *Volvox* are green spheres, about the size of the head of a pin, which can be more easily recognized with a hand lens.

You may also recognize *Vaucheria*, which is found as a green felt covering on rocks in ponds and ditches or on flowerpots.

On the other hand, a green, fuzzy or hairy covering on rocks in ponds and slow-moving rivers may be the simple filamentous alga *Ulothrix*. Note the difference in the illustration (Fig. 15-7). *Vaucheria* has branching filaments which lack cross-cell walls; it is multinucleated, a syncytium.

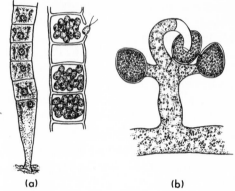

(a)   (b)

Fig. 15-7 Two filamentous green algae: (a) *Ulothrix*; (b) *Vaucheria*. (General Biological Supply House, Inc., Chicago.)

In damp places on land, especially in greenhouses, or on damp bark, fences, and rocks, students will find a green covering made of *Protococcus* (or *Pleurococcus*). This simple form (Fig. 15-8) seems to be more likely a reduced form, rather than a

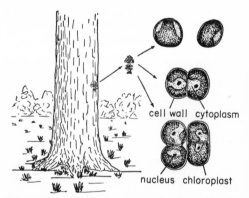

cell wall   cytoplasm

nucleus   chloroplast

Fig. 15-8 *Protococcus (Pleurococcus)*, a simple green alga found on damp bark. (From J. W. Mavor, *General Biology*, 3d ed., Macmillan, 1947.)

primitive alga. Yet it is a useful plant form for class study.

In samples of pond water along with desmids (which can be recognized by their two symmetrical halves) you should find the primitive green alga *Chlamydomonas* (Fig. 15-9). Under high power look for the chloroplast, two contractile vacuoles, and two flagella in the anterior region. Some species also have a red eye spot.

Collecting fungi, mosses, ferns, and seed plants. These may be transported in small boxes along with some of the soil

Fig. 15-9 *Chlamydomonas, a green alga.* (From G. G. Simpson, C. Pittendrigh, & L. Tiffany, *Life,* Harcourt, Brace, 1957.)

in which they were growing. Refer to Chapter 20 for places to locate specific plants and descriptions of ways to grow the plants in school.

Preserving animal specimens (invertebrates and vertebrates)

You may want to refer to Table 15-1 and to the descriptions that follow for some notes on the preservation of animals in the laboratory or in the field. Preserved specimens are useful in lessons on relationships among living things (classification and dissection) and identification of animals, when the weather does not permit field trips out of doors. Also, students may want to learn these techniques for project work.

Preserving soft-bodied specimens

In general, soft-bodied animals should be preserved first in 50 per cent alcohol for a few days, then transferred to 70 per cent, and finally to 90 per cent alcohol. Formaldehyde may also be used as a

preserving fluid, although it tends to make the specimens more brittle. Puncture the body of each animal at several widely separated places with a dissecting needle before you put it in the preserving fluid so that complete penetration of the preservative takes place. (See pp. 325–26 for the preparation of some fixatives, or preserving fluids.)

Later, the preserved specimens can be mounted in jars (Fig. 15-10). Each specimen can be supported against a glass slide and fastened to the glass with thread. Use uniformly sized, wide-mouthed jars and seal the jars with paraffin to prevent evaporation of the preserving fluid. Label the jars and cover the labels with plastic tape so that they will not get smudged in

Fig. 15-10 Professional museum jars containing preserved animal specimens. (Photo: General Biological Supply House, Inc., Chicago.)

TABLE 15-1
Condensed outline of methods of collecting and preserving animals*

animal	where found	special collecting devices	how to kill	fixative	preservative
Fresh-water sponges	Mid-summer in fresh water attached to branches and submerged wood	Flat-bladed knife or scalpel	70% alcohol, changed when it becomes discolored	70% alcohol	70% alcohol
Hydra	Lagoons, ponds, rivers, lakes, attached to vegetation, stones, fallen leaves	Flat-bladed knife or scalpel and pipette	Hot Bouin's solution flooded over specimens from base to peristome; or use menthol	Bouin's solution	70% alcohol
Fresh-water planarians	Fresh spring-fed streams, lakes, rivers	Fresh liver placed in water where *Planaria* are found	Use menthol crystal method; or extend on glass slide and submerge in hot Gilson's or corrosive sublimate†	Gilson's or corrosive sublimate†	Formalin or 70% alcohol
Tapeworms	Intestine of dogs, cats, rabbits, sheep	Scalpel and forceps	Relax in cold water; wrap animals around support to stretch them and immerse in 10% formalin	Bouin's or formalin	Alcohol or formalin
Ascaris	Intestines of pig, horse, cat or dog	Scalpel and forceps	Dip momentarily into 98° C water	5% formalin or saturated corrosive sublimate†	5% formalin or alcohol
Rotifers	Plant material taken from ponds or lagoons	Pipette	Anesthetize with solution magnesium sulfate or menthol crystals	When cilia cease to move add few drops of osmic acid	Wash in water and store in 10% formalin

*From Turtox Service Leaflet, #2, General Biological Supply House, Inc., Chicago.
†*Caution:* poison.

animal	where found	special collecting devices	how to kill	fixative	preservative
Pectinatella and Plumatella (Bryozoa)	Attached to stems, rocks, leaves in streams, especially in late fall	Scalpel	When fully expanded, flood with boiling Bouin's	Bouin's	70% alcohol
Earthworms	In spring on rainy nights on golf courses or bluegrass lawns	Flashlight and pail	Anesthetize by slowly adding alcohol to water in which worms are (or see p. 314)	5% formalin	5% formalin
Leeches	Hand pick from hosts or with dip net among weeds in ponds and streams	Dip net	Anesthetize in warm chloretone or magnesium sulfate; or asphyxiate in closed jar	Inject with 10% formalin and submerge in same extended position	8% formalin
Crayfish	Streams, ponds, lagoons, in water or burrowing in mud	Dip net, seine, or spade	Drop alive into alcohol or 8% formalin	70% alcohol or 8% formalin	70% alcohol or 8% formalin
Ticks and mites	Cattle, dogs, horses, old cheese, decaying organic matter	White paper and brush for taking specimens from parasitized animals	Drop directly into 70% alcohol	70% alcohol	70% alcohol
Centipedes and millipedes	Under logs or stones	Forceps	Carl's solution	Carl's solution, injected into body cavity	Carl's solution

TABLE 15-1 *(continued)*

animal	where found	special collecting devices	how to kill	fixative	preservative
Insects	Woods, fields, water, air— everywhere	Nets, forceps, and other equipment, depending on the kind collected	For drying, in killing jars; for liquid preservation, in alcohol	Alcohol, Carl's solution, chloral hydrate, and special solutions	70% alcohol, Carl's solution, or drying
Slugs	In damp places under leaves, logs, stones		Anesthetize in boiled water which has been cooled, and immerse in formalin or alcohol	Alcohol or formalin	70% alcohol or 8% formalin
Aquatic snails	Streams, ponds, lakes; most abundant among vegetation	Dip net, scraper net	Anesthetize in warm water by adding magnesium sulfate causing them to expand; then drop into 10% formalin	10% formalin	8% formalin
Clams	Streams, lakes, partly buried in the bottom	For large numbers, dredge or crowfoot hooks are used	Place wooden pegs between· the two halves of shell and drop into 10% formalin	10% formalin	8% formalin
Lampreys	Occasionally may be taken from fish but for large numbers must be taken in breeding season in streams	Seine	Remove from water for few minutes and inject 10% formalin into body cavity	10% formalin	8% formalin
Fish	Streams, lakes	Nets, seines, or hook and line, depending on kind	Drop into full strength formalin	10% formalin	8% formalin

animal	where found	special collecting devices	how to kill	fixative	preservative
Grassfrogs	In meadows or borders of marshy lakes	Net	Inject ether into body cavity or drop into 80% alcohol	Inject 5% formalin into body and place in 5% formalin	5% formalin
Grassfrog eggs	Shallow water of ponds in early spring when singing is started	Jars	Place in fixative	8% formalin	8% formalin
Salamanders	Damp places in woods, ponds, rivers, streams	Hook and line or nets	Inject ether into body cavity and drop into 80% alcohol	5% formalin	5% formalin injected into body cavity
Reptiles	Woods, fields, dunes, depending on kind	Snares for handling poisonous snakes; nets for capturing turtles and aquatic forms	Inject ether and drop into 70% alcohol	10% formalin	8% formalin injected into body cavity
Birds and small mammals	Most of world	For taxidermy purposes, a 12-gauge shotgun and shells with fine shot (No. 8 or 12)	Bird skins are most generally used for study or reference; body is removed and skin dusted with arsenic powder;† skin is then stuffed with cotton and dried		
Large mammals			Gas or drown if taken to laboratory alive	Embalm or inject 8% formalin into body and large muscles	8% formalin

†*Caution:* poison.

FIELD WORK: LIVING THINGS IN THEIR ENVIRONMENT   **259**

use. Then you have the beginning of a museum collection.

In time, the specimens will bleach and fragment; that is a signal to get new specimens and fresh fluid.

In summary, *soft-bodied forms* which may be preserved in alcohol or formaldehyde (formalin, p. 330) include the following.

Jellyfish and *hydras* should be anesthetized before preserving so that they will remain in an extended position. Ways to anesthetize small forms are described on pages 256 and 314. The specimens will become opaque in preserving fluid. See further instructions in Table 15-1.

Flatworms, roundworms, and *annelid worms* should be anesthetized before preserving. Flatworms can be flattened between two glass slides which should then be inserted into alcohol. Further notes are given in Table 15-1.

Soft-bodied mollusks, such as squids, become opaque and pinkish in color when preserved.

Crustaceans, such as hermit crabs, fiddler crabs and larger crabs, as well as barnacles and the shipworm (*Teredo*), may be preserved or mounted (see below).

Soft-bodied insects, such as grasshoppers, praying mantes, locusts, some beetles (and larvae and pupae stages), should be preserved. Barker's dehydration method[3] may be used to preserve insects (as well as soft-bodied specimens). In this method a fat solvent such as carbon bisulfide or benzol (*caution:* inflammable) is added to 80 per cent alcohol in the ratio of 1 part solvent to 10 parts alcohol. The specimens are punctured and placed in this fluid for 24 to 72 hours, depending upon their size. Then the specimens are transferred to 95 per cent alcohol for a similar period of time. The next transfer is to absolute

[3] Barker's dehydration method in *How to Prepare Insect Displays,* Ward's Natural Science Bull., Ward's Natural Science Establishment, Rochester 9, N. Y., 1950.

alcohol to which a bit of calcium chloride has been added to absorb any moisture. This dehydrates the specimen. Finally transfer to xylol and dry on a plaster block. Students may want to mount the insect forms on pins and display them in an insect box. Larvae, as well as insects, may be mounted on pins for display. For methods of pinning insects for display, refer to pages 261–62.

Spiders, centipedes, millipedes, scorpions, mites, and *ticks* may be preserved in 70 per cent alcohol.

Small fish, as well as their *eggs* and *fry,* may be preserved individually in 70 per cent alcohol in small vials to make a life-history series.

Among *amphibia,* all the stages in the life history may be preserved (preferably in 70 per cent alcohol).

Young bird embryos and *embryos of mammals* should be preserved in a fixative or transferred through a graded series of alcohol (70, to 80, to 90 per cent) to prevent undue shrinkage.

Preserving hard-bodied specimens

Preserve the following, where possible, in the dry state.

Sponges may be mounted on bristol board after drying in the sun.

Starfish may be dried in the sun and weighted down in a flat position before complete drying, then mounted.

Sea urchins should be dried in the sun after removing the viscera; with a knife cut away the mouth parts (Aristotle's lantern), and pull away the attached internal organs.

Sand dollars are quite flat and may be completely dried in the sun.

Crabs may be preserved whole in alcohol. Or the carapace may be dissected away carefully, and the crab then dried completely and mounted.

Mollusk shells may be dried out com-

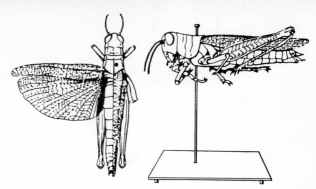

Fig. 15-11 Mounting grasshoppers: note that the wings on one side of the body are extended to show coloration of the underwings. (From *Insects, The Yearbook of Agriculture,* U.S.D.A., 1952.)

pletely, after the shells are boiled. Mount on bristol board or in boxes containing cotton (Riker mounts, perhaps).

Small horseshoe crabs, in various stages of development, may be collected and allowed to dry thoroughly. Then the surfaces can be shellacked (if the forms are not completely dry, the shellac will become opaque). Larger forms of horseshoe crabs must be eviscerated. Then the cleaned shells can be dried.

Young crayfish may be dried in the sun.

Treatment of specimens which have become brittle. When preserved specimens become brittle and fragmented, they should be replaced with new specimens. On occasion, however, you may have a form which is not readily obtainable. A method has been suggested for reclaiming dried specimens, mainly soft-bodied forms such as worms. This method[4] suggests that the specimens be first soaked in 0.5 per cent trisodium phosphate solution, then warmed in this solution for about 1 hour at 35° C. After the forms are removed from the heat they should be kept in a closed container to avoid evaporation. Within 1 hour the specimens should appear normal; within 2 days they should be soft.

Special techniques for mounting and displaying insects

Mounting insects. While it is a better

[4] H. Bennett, ed., *Chemical Formulary,* Chemical Publishing Co., New York, 1951.

practice to mount insects soon after collecting, this step may be postponed. Keep the larger insects in the paper envelopes which you brought from the field. However, as time passes insects become brittle, and antennae, legs, and wings break.

Insects such as lepidoptera, dragonflies, and damsel flies are mounted with their wings fully extended. Grasshoppers are mounted with one wing outspread (Fig. 15-11) to show the color and pattern of the underlying wing, a point often required for identification. Frequently the wings of cicadas, lacewings, and Dobson flies are spread before they are mounted.

If insects have become brittle they may be put into a relaxing jar to soften, then placed on a spreading board if their wings are to be extended.

Relaxing jars. Prepare several jars of different sizes to accommodate insects of varying sizes. Into the bottom of each glass jar insert a wad of wet cotton to which a few drops of carbolic acid have been added (to inhibit the growth of molds). Cover this with a layer of blotting paper. (You may prefer to substitute moist sand at the bottom of the jar. In such a case, add a few drops of carbolic acid to the blotter.)

Students should now place the dried insects on the blotter; cover the jar. After 24 hours the insects are soft enough to handle for mounting or for spreading on a spreading board. Nevertheless, they must be handled with some care, as they

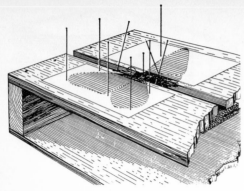

Fig. 15-12 Spreader used for spreading and drying the wings of insects such as butterflies, dragonflies, etc. (From *Insects, The Yearbook of Agriculture*, U.S.D.A., 1952.)

are not as pliable as they were when freshly killed.

Spreading the wings of insects. The kind of spreader shown in Fig. 15-12 may be purchased from biological supply houses, or students may make them. The spreader consists of two side sections made of soft wood with a channel along the center just wide enough to accommodate the body of an insect such as a moth or grasshopper.

Students should learn to pin insects such as dragonflies, damsel flies, caddice flies, butterflies, and moths through the thorax and insert the mounting pin into the cork in the groove of the wing spreader. Use forceps to insert the pin into the cork so that the pin does not bend under the pressure of the fingers.

Arrange the legs of the insects as they are in life and use forceps to spread out the wings. Pin down the outspread wings by inserting pins along the front marginal part of the wings. Use strips of paper as shown to hold the wings in position and fasten them with pins.

Notice that the wings will dry in a slightly tilted position. But the weight of the wings will cause them to droop a bit when the insects are finally mounted. You will find that the length of time needed for the insect to dry out depends

upon the size of the body of the insect. It may vary from 1 day to 2 weeks.

Mounting insects for display. The usual method for mounting insects for observational study or exhibit is to set them on pins which can be inserted into a cork-lined box. Cigar boxes make fine display cases, with a bottom lining of pressed cork, corrugated paper, or balsa wood.

Use special black enamel insect-mounting pins about 1½ inches long. The commonly used grades are numbers 1 and 3. There is a uniform method for pinning insects.

Most insects are pinned through the thorax. Moths and butterflies are pinned squarely in the center of the thorax. On the other hand, grasshoppers, flies, bees, wasps, squash bugs, and the like are pinned to the right of center in the thorax. Beetles are not pinned through the thorax at all, but through the right wing cover about a quarter of the way back.

Very small beetles, such as weevils, are too small to be pinned. First, fasten these small insects to small triangles of light-weight stiff paper, such as library card stock, using thinned white shellac. Then insert the pin through the broad base of the paper triangle. Small fragile insects like mosquitoes may be first pinned to a bit of cork (Fig. 15-13).

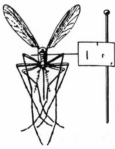

Fig. 15-13 Method of pinning and labeling small insects: a mosquito, pinned with a "minuten nadeln" to a block of cork on a regular insect pin. (From *Insects, The Yearbook of Agriculture*, U.S.D.A., 1952.)

Label insects in this way. Prepare a small strip of paper (about ¼ by ½ inch) carrying the name, location, and date of collection. Place this under the insect by transfixing it with the same pin.

Insects that have a high fat content leave brown stains at the base of the pin. You may avoid this by first immersing the insect (except lepidopterans) in carbon tetrachloride for 2 to 3 hours before pinning the insects in the box.

Care of insect collections. There are some small insects which attack preserved insects. To keep these museum pests under control, heat a number of pins and insert them through small chunks of paradichlorobenzene. Pin the paradichlorobenzene in two corners of each box which houses your collection.

Mounting specimens preserved in alcohol. At times it is desirable to show the complete life history of a specific insect. This may be important in the life history of insect pests or of special beneficial insects. Place each stage (eggs, larvae, and pupae) into separate small vials of 70 per cent alcohol or 5 per cent formalin. Seal the vials with paraffin. Keep the adult stage or nymphs dried.

Mount the small vials and the adult stage in Riker mounts (Fig. 15-14) or in homemade display cases containing cotton. Students may make these by cutting away the paper cover of several boxes of the same size in such a way that a ½-inch margin remains as a frame, and taping a sheet of glass or cellophane to the inside of the cut-away box cover. Now line the box with cotton. Lay the specimens in the cotton and close the box

Fig. 15-14 Riker mount, useful for displaying early stages of an insect's life, in vials, and the adult form. (General Biological Supply House, Inc., Chicago.)

with the glass cover. Insert pins on each of the four sides of the box to fasten the cover to the box.

Going further; projects. Some students may prepare valuable collections of a single species of insect. For example, a study may be made of variations of striping among potato beetles, or the number of spots in one species of ladybird beetles.

Those students and teachers who want more advanced information concerning the handling of insects are fortunate, for there is a tremendous literature on collecting, preserving, exhibiting, and identifying insects. A book such as *An Introduction to the Study of Insects* by D. Borror and D. DeLong is a valuable guide. It provides interesting details of each order of insects. Further, it gives suggestions for projects concerning insects, for collecting and preserving them in greater detail than presented in this short account. For further information on those insects which live in water or lead a partially aquatic existence, look into the chapters dealing with insects in that splendid reference *Fresh-water Invertebrates of the United States* by Robert Pennak. These and other valuable books are listed in the Bibliography at the end of the book.

Indoor field trips

It is useful to have a museum of living organisms in school. This may be a room or a portion of a laboratory, the size dependent upon the space you have available.

Students readily bring living things to

class; some living organisms may be purchased. More often than not there are some students who know how to keep fish in an aquarium. Student curators may be trained to maintain both freshwater and marine aquaria. They may be trained to prepare terraria of various kinds—one duplicating an arid environment with sand, cactus plants, horned "toads," another containing a miniature woodland with humus in which ferns, mosses, lichens, and small wild flowers are kept. If students place a pan of water at one end of a terrarium they may include frog eggs, tadpoles, or adult frogs or salamanders. (Toads mess a tank since they burrow.) A bog can be made when sphagnum moss and insectivorous plants are added to another terrarium. Add charcoal to absorb odors and reduce acidity. (Preparation of aquaria and terraria, pp. 366, 395.)

Turtles, snakes, small lizards such as chameleons, and small mammals like rats and hamsters may be cared for by students trained to handle these animals (student curators and squads, Chapter 22; caring for animals, Chapter 19).

Students can be taught to culture protozoa, fruit flies, many worms, and other organisms useful in the year's work in biology. There is the possibility that a living-material center may grow out of these activities. Then one school might be in a position to supply schools nearby with living materials (also some exhibits of life cycles of plants or insects which may be preserved).

You may have facilities to arrange a small greenhouse or, more simply, a sand box in which seeds or cuttings of plants and other kinds of vegetative propagation may grow. Battery jars or bell jars can be used to cover young plants to increase moisture around them.

Many lessons may be taught in this museum. In fact, you may find it useful to prepare a guide—a mimeographed sheet of questions which guide the observations and thinking of students. In this learning situation, students may study food chains, reproduction, behavior, interdependence of living things, camouflage, heredity, evolutionary relationships, and many aspects of nutrition.

Nature trails around school

It may be possible to develop nature paths as a class or club project. In such a project, some schools plant trees and shrubs which are especially useful in teaching. For example, reproduction in different flowers, variations, and evolutionary sequence may be shown on a field trip around the school grounds if you have these trees and shrubs: magnolia, forsythia, varieties of cherry trees, flowering crabapple, maples of several varieties, dogwood, elm, oak, barberry. If possible, include witch hazel, which blossoms in the fall. On the lawn, dandelions probably flourish. These complex flowers, which

are really clusters of flowers, might be compared with the flowers of the primitive magnolia.

The trees and shrubs may attract insects and birds to the school grounds. Students might build birdhouses in shop classes. They may make attractive markers for a nature trail and erect a bulletin board showing a map of the trail or announcing interesting things to look for each month. Committees of students often prepare a mimeographed guide sheet.

Later, seedlings may be observed and aspects of the struggle for existence and the survival value of some seedlings may be investigated on the school grounds.

You may also find it possible to have students prepare specific associations of plants and animals to exemplify interdependence in a web of life. For example, in a shady area on the school grounds, with moist, slightly acid soil, some ferns, mosses, and spring flowers from other regions might be transplanted. Perhaps a decaying log with its "inhabitants" might also be transported.

A small pond might even be constructed near school and stocked with plants and animals taken from a nearby lake.

Many field trips may be short, possibly 15 minutes of one period, to study flowers, or to measure variations in plants of the same kind, or to get a sample of soil to test its pH, or to look for examples of tropisms, or to study a compost pile of decaying leaves and cut grass in order to study the steps in the breakdown of vegetation through the action of bacteria of decay.

Students might search for examples of erosion and go about using corrective measures to reduce the loss of soil.

Using the school grounds

If nature trails are not feasible, some other useful ways to use the grounds may be practical in your school situation. Here are some practices which have been used with success by many teachers. One or more of these techniques may be found useful in your school.

1. Plant trees and shrubs which show a variety of flowers for students to study.

2. Take a census of insect pests in a measured area of land.

3. Examine and list all the kinds of organisms living in the top 2 inches of 1 square foot of soil (p. 235).

4. Test a weed killer on one part of a lawn and leave the other as a control (p. 116).

5. Add fertilizer (or inoculate the soil with nitrogen-fixing bacteria) to one portion of lawn and leave the other untreated (pp. 233, 235).

6. Practice soil-saving methods on a slope, such as terracing, contour planting, use of cover plants (pp. 236, 238).

7. Study raindrop erosion. Set out discs of wood over a barren region. After a heavy rain, are there higher levels of soil under the discs than in the exposed regions? What happened to the soil in the exposed regions?

8. Plant seeds of flowering plants or use crops, so that the complete life cycle may be studied.

9. Illustrate methods of vegetative propagation; demonstrate the use of cuttings, bulbs, layering, runners. It may be possible to make several grafts.

10. Test the effect of growth hormones in speeding regeneration of roots of cuttings.

11. Try artificial pollination of flowers as a breeder might practice it.

12. Investigate the effect of shortening or lengthening the period of light (or the hours of darkness) that a plant receives (photoperiodism).

13. Are there insect pests around the grounds? Perhaps you may try the effect of specific insecticides. What stage do they attack in the insects' life cycle?

CAPSULE LESSONS
Ways to get started in class

15-1. You may want to introduce the topic "reproduction in plants" by taking students on a short walk around the school grounds. Students can study the floral structure and compare the flowers of many different plants in bloom without picking the flowers from trees or shrubs. Elicit through questions the essential organs needed for reproduction in flowering plants. How do pollen grains get to the stigma of flowers? How is a seed formed?

15-2. Study seed-dispersal mechanisms out of doors. What are the chances for survival of seeds around the parent plants? The rate of migration, and possible effect on other plants and animals?

15-3. Or use the same motivation to elicit the major ideas of overproduction, variations, need for survival and the "fittest," which are needed to understand heredity and evolution.

15-4. It may be possible to collect stages in the life cycle of an insect or in the development of frogs or young seedlings. This might lead into a study of reproduction.

15-5. Field work is a requirement in any study of soil, water, and conservation needs and practices. (See suggestions throughout Chapter 14.)

15-6. Out of doors you may show variations in leaves, in fruits, in shells, in beetles, in the shaded undersurface of leaves compared with the top (barberry), the shape of leaves underwater and their aerial shoots. Why do some trees of the same kind flower earlier than others?

15-7. Plan to study some kind of biome— the plants and animals living together in a given area. What are the needs of living plants? Of animals? Here you may develop the work for the entire year.

15-8. Collect living things for examination under the microscope. What role do microscopic forms of life play in the lives of the other plants and animals in the community?

15-9. Show organisms found in the soil, community life in a fallen log. Develop the concept of interrelations, and the checks and balances among living things. What are natural enemies? Look for examples of parasites, saprophytes, and symbionts.

15-10. Can students recognize poisonous plants such as poison ivy or poison oak which may be found in your community? Do they know the harmful plant and animal pests? Can they recognize poisonous spiders, scorpions, snakes in the community?

15-11. There are many fine films and film-strips which enable you to take your classes on a trip when no other type of trip is possible. Many are listed at the end of the book; they are not listed separately at this time since the subjects overlap.

15-12. Possibly as a club project, a section of the school grounds may be used to build a nature trail; or prepare the section for outdoor demonstrations and field work (see suggestions in this chapter).

PEOPLE, PLACES, AND THINGS

Many teachers are expert in field work; some are not. Over several years, one may become competent in recognizing about a dozen of the trees and shrubs around the community, the orders of insects, and some representative forms of invertebrates and vertebrates in the area. These are the specimens that students bring into class. There are many people in the community who can help. Someone at a botanical garden or zoological park, or another science teacher nearby may give help, or suggest a source of help. It is possible to send specimens of organisms, carefully packed, to an "expert" at a museum or an agricultural station.

At times there may be a student at school who has developed competence in some area of field work. You may want to have such a student lead a field trip. Is there a parent in the community, or a student, who has a hobby of bird watching or insect collecting? Here is a resource person students may turn to for help in suggesting projects for long-range study (see p. 10, Section I).

BOOKS AND PAMPHLETS

In the Bibliography at the end of the book, we have indicated field books and references in specific areas, such as algae, fresh-water biology, birds, mushrooms, snakes, or fish.

Films and filmstrips

Please refer to the listing of films and filmstrips given in Bibliography at the end of the book so that you may find those films which best meet your needs concerning field work with plants and animals, or in the area of conservation or variations in living things. You may want to use a film on bees to show life in the hive or to plan some similar field trip by means of films.

Free and inexpensive materials

You will find many useful hints in the free publications of the biological supply houses. Many low-cost pamphlets are available from state and federal agricultural departments, and from agricultural stations attached to colleges.

When you refer to this section at the end of each chapter you will find other bulletins needed for field work. Have you the *Turtox Leaflets* (General Biological Supply House)? Also refer to Ward's *Natural Science Bulletin* and Welch's *Biology and General Science Digest.* Many tips are given in *Field Trip Guide,* American Gas Association, Education Service Bureau, 420 Lexington Avenue, New York 17. (Addresses are at the end of the book under Free and Inexpensive Materials.)

To Know the Trees (Forest Trees of U.S.), Supt. Documents, U.S. Govt. Printing Office, Washington 25, D. C., 1949, $0.20.

Section Three SPECIAL TECHNIQUES

CHAPTER 16

Anatomy of selected animals and plants

Unless students have some knowledge of the specialized structure of animals and plants, they will find it difficult to understand how these organisms carry on their specialized functions. This chapter brings together information about anatomy, based on the following premise: Function depends upon specialization in structure.

The material presented may serve as a guide for the dissection of some representative animals, invertebrate and vertebrate, and for a study of the anatomy of plants (leaves, stems, and roots; flowers, seeds, and fruits were presented in connection with their function, reproduction, in Chapter 11). The descriptions in this chapter are only *beginning study guides;* you will probably want to consult the many dissection guides available for both plants and animals.

Microscopic examination of tissue cells is described in some cases where it seems relevant to the study of anatomy. However, Chapter 17 is given over completely to a description of the microscopic anatomy of animals and plants—both one-celled organisms and tissue cells of higher animals and plants.

Several of the smaller animals among the Crustacea, such as the water flea (*Daphnia*), the fairy shrimp, or some of the transparent worms, need to be studied under the microscope. The preparation of these organisms for study as wet mounts under the microscope is described with diagrams in Chapter 17.

Earthworm (Lumbricus)

When living earthworms are available, their behavior in response to many stimuli such as light, touch, sound, and moisture may be studied (see Chapter 9). Students will also want to study the external anatomy of the animals. When this has been done and the animal is ready for dissection, gradually add chloroform to the water in a container holding several earthworms. Now stretch out one worm and firmly pin it down, dorsal surface up, through the first segment and the posterior end, in a waxed dissecting pan or on a corkboard.

Then cut through the skin of the back, beginning at the posterior end. Continue forward, cutting to one side of the midline. Cut the partitions, or septa, that hold down the body wall, and pin back the body wall. If pins are inserted through segments 5, 10, 15, and 20, the organs can be readily located. Start at the beginning of the alimentary canal and locate the buccal region, the pharynx leading into the esophagus with its pouches in segments 10 and 13; and look for the glands in 11 and 12. In the vicinity of segment 15, locate the crop, and further along, the muscular gizzard. Then trace the digestive tract as it continues as a yellow-colored intestine to the posterior end. Locate the large blood vessel dorsal to the stomach-intestine.

Carefully move aside the seminal vesicles to trace the aortic arches which branch from the dorsal blood vessel and circle around to connect with the ventral blood vessel found under the digestive tube. In a freshly killed specimen pulsations of these swollen aortic "hearts" may be visible.

In short, blood is carried forward along the dorsal vessel to the five pairs of "hearts" in segments 7 to 11 and then into the ventral blood vessel. Here blood moves the length of the body ventral to the digestive system, branching off to supply organs along the way. Along the ventral nerve cord you may also locate the subneural blood vessel and the two lateral neural vessels. These also carry blood back along the length of the worm.

Now students may want to turn to a study of the reproductive system. Remove the esophagus to get a clear view of the seminal vesicles, consisting of three lobes on each side of the esophagus. Also try to locate the small testes on the septa of segments 10 and 11.

In segment 13 try to find a small ovary, and look for the yellowish seminal receptacles in segments 9 and 10. Crush one in a drop of water on a slide and look for masses of filamentous sperms which have been received from another worm, in copulation.

Also, each segment (except the first three and the last) contains a pair of nephridia.

Finally, locate the two white cerebral ganglia above the buccal region in segment 3. Lift aside or carefully remove the pharynx to reveal the nerve ring, a pair of subpharyngeal ganglia, and the long ventral double nerve cord.

Students may also want to study the parasites found in earthworms; see *Monocystis* (p. 310).

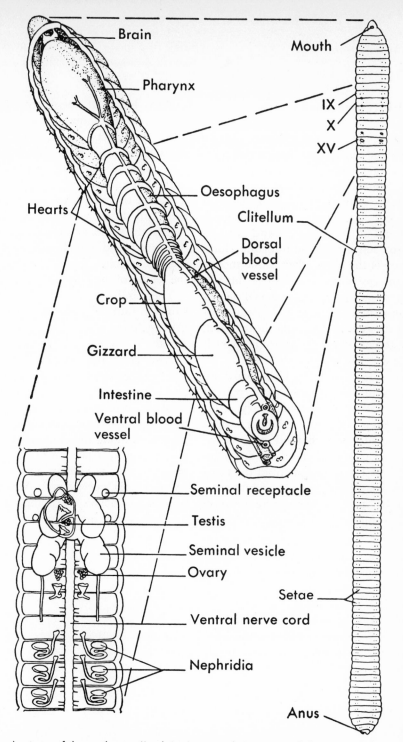

Fig. 16-1 Anatomy of the earthworm (*Lumbricus*): external view, general dissection, and reproductive system. (From D. F. Miller & J. G. Haub, *General Zoology*, Holt, 1956.)

Crayfish (*Cambarus*)

Examine the external anatomy. Notice that the body is divided into two distinct parts, a rigid cephalothorax and a more flexible, segmented abdomen.

In a dissecting pan place a crayfish dorsal side up. Begin at the posterior dorsal end of the carapace and cut forward to each side of the mid-line along each side of the outer edges of the thorax up to the rostrum. Now remove this top part of the carapace. In the dorsal part of the thorax find the pericardial sinus containing the angular, muscular heart. Look for the three pairs of ostia through which blood enters the heart.

Under the heart and a bit forward are the reproductive organs. In a mature female, find the bilobed ovary, containing eggs, in front of the heart and a single fused mass behind the heart. Locate an oviduct extending down on each side to the first segment of the third thoracic leg. In the male, the white testis should be in a corresponding position with two highly coiled vasa deferentia (sperm ducts). If these are filled with sperms, mount some in a drop of water, tease the ducts apart, and examine the unusual shape of the sperm cells. The vasa deferentia open on the first segment of the hindmost thoracic leg.

Under the roof of the head locate the thin-walled sac which is the stomach. Where the stomach joins the intestine lie digestive glands which may be brown or greenish in color. Trace the intestine along the length of the abdomen.

Then, in front of, and a bit below, the stomach find the kidneys, a pair of light green glands sometimes called "green glands."

Next trace the nervous system. Find the large ganglion in back of the gullet and trace two branches which unite into another large ganglion above the gullet forming an esophageal collar. Moving backward along the animal, at intervals, students may trace pairs of segmental ganglia, or enlargements, joined together by a double nerve cord. Also look for branches or nerves extending into muscle on each side of the abdomen.

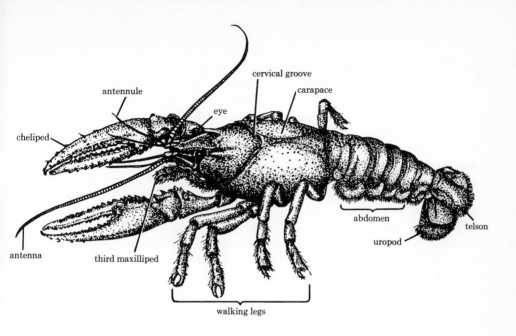

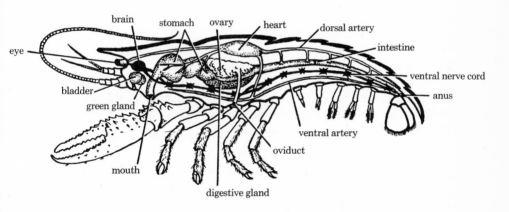

Fig. 16-2 Anatomy of the crayfish: external and internal. (From W. G. Whaley, O. P. Breland, et. al., *Principles of Biology*, Harper, 1954.)

Clam (*Anodonta*)

The directions given for this fresh-water clam or mussel can be applied as well to other mussels, and oysters.

Pry the two valves apart and carefully cut through the large posterior adductor muscle below and behind the hinge. Then cut through the anterior adductor muscle. These two muscles keep the shell closed. Notice the mantle, a white membrane which lines each shell. Examine the posterior end where the edges of the mantle meet to form the pigmented siphons. Notice too the papillae on the ventral siphon through which water and food enter, and the smooth edges of the dorsal, exhalant siphon.

Turn back the mantle lobe. If you have a freshly killed specimen, scrape some cells from the edge of the mantle and from the gills. Examine in a drop of water and look for ciliated cells (see p. 283). Notice that the gills on each side unite, forming a channel above the gills from which the dorsal siphon leads. The lower or inhalant siphon leads to the lower body cavity.

Now firmly grip the mantle lobe and pull the body away from the dorsal margin. Under the hinge locate the heart. Carefully cut into this pericardial cavity and find the yellowish ventricle, which may still be pulsating. A tube, the intestine, runs through the ventricle but has no connection with it. Look for an auricle on each side of the ventricle. Trace the anterior aorta (above the intestine) carrying blood forward, and the posterior aorta (below the intestine).

Posterior to the heart and in front of the posterior adductor muscle are the dark kidneys. Also part of the excretory system are the paired Keber organs.

Next trace the entire digestive system. Pull down the anterior part of the foot and locate the mouth surrounded by ciliated labial palps just back of the anterior adductor muscle, and in front of and above the foot. Behind the anterior adductor muscle find the darkly colored digestive gland which surrounds the stomach. From here trace the intestine through the heart toward the excurrent siphon.

Carefully pare away the muscle of the foot to expose the ovary or testis in the posterior dorsal part. In a mature female small brown glochidia larvae (which soon attach themselves parasitically to the skin of fish) may be found in the lamellae of the gills. Examine under the microscope.

It is difficult to locate the nervous system unless the specimen has been boiled or hardened in alcohol. Directly under the posterior adductor muscle try to find the two yellowish visceral ganglia encased within a thin membrane. From these try to trace the nerves forward to where they join the cerebral ganglia, near the surface at the mouth region close to the base of the labial palps. Continue to follow the nerves into a pair of orange pedal ganglia deeply embedded in the foot (anterior to the gonad).

Microscopic examination of tissues

When living clams are available, you can show ciliated epithelial tissue (p. 283). Peel off thin sections, with a forceps, from the edges of the mantle and gills, and mount in the juice of the clam. Under high power examine the rhythmic beating of the cilia; stain with Janus green, methylene blue, or Lugol's solution (p. 409). Students may also study the effects of different ions on ciliary motion (p. 309).

In a relative of the clam, the aquarium snail *Physa*, ciliated epithelial cells line the intestine. Narcotize a snail in a warm solution of 1 per cent magnesium sulfate. Mount its body in pond water on a glass slide and dissect the intestine. With forceps peel off this lining and mount in a drop of pond water on a fresh slide; stain as above, if desired.

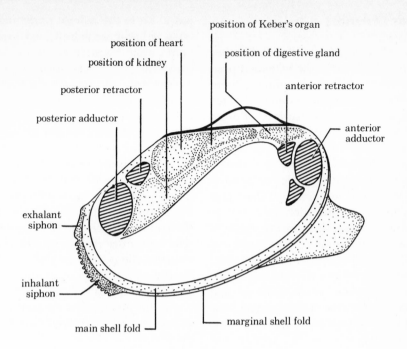

position of Keber's organ

position of heart

position of digestive gland

position of kidney

posterior retractor

anterior retractor

posterior adductor

anterior
adductor

exhalant
siphon

inhalant
siphon

main shell fold

marginal shell fold

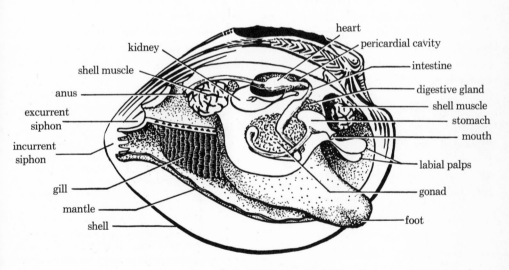

heart

kidney

pericardial cavity

shell muscle

intestine

anus

digestive gland

excurrent
siphon

shell muscle

stomach

incurrent
siphon

mouth

labial palps

gill

gonad

mantle

foot

shell

Fig. 16-3 Anatomy of the fresh-water clam (*Anodonta*): *top,* details of mantle after removal of right shell valve; *bottom,* internal anatomy, with shell, mantle, and gills on one side removed. (*bottom,* W. G. Whaley, O. P. Breland, et al., *Principles of Biology,* Harper, 1954; after Hegner, *Invertebrate Zoology,* Macmillan, 1933.)

Starfish (Asterias)

When living starfish are available they may be narcotized, in the extended position for later dissection by placing them in a small amount of water to which some crystals of magnesium sulfate (Epsom salts) have been added. If the starfish are put upside down when narcotized, the tube feet will probably remain extended. When the animals no longer respond to touch, they may be stored in 70 per cent alcohol for future dissection.

Examine a starfish to locate the ventral mouth, the oral surface, and the ambulacral grooves containing tube feet. Each of these end in suction cups, and this is the means of locomotion and attachment. On the dorsal surface, the aboral side, find the madreporite, which is part of the water vascular system.

First remove the skin from the dorsal region without breaking the madreporite. Carefully separate the skin from the central disc where parts of the digestive system are attached. Note the branched stomach divided into pyloric and cardiac parts. From the pyloric parts ducts lead outward and branch into pyloric caeca containing digestive enzymes. Now remove the pyloric caeca (from one arm) to reveal the two retractor muscles, connected to the cardiac regions of the stomach, which pull in the everted stomach. Cut away these muscles and find the tubes of the water vascular system. Below the madreporite locate the calcareous stone canal. Water enters through the madreporite into the stone canal which leads into the water vascular ring around the mouth. Notice the Tiedemann bodies which produce the amoeboid corpuscles found in the water vascular system. This fluid moves along radial canals to ampullae into the tube feet.

At the junction of the arms are the paired reproductive organs, either testes or ovaries.

The blood system and the nervous system are difficult to trace. Although you may find a nerve ring around the mouth, the radial nerves into the arms are not readily visible.

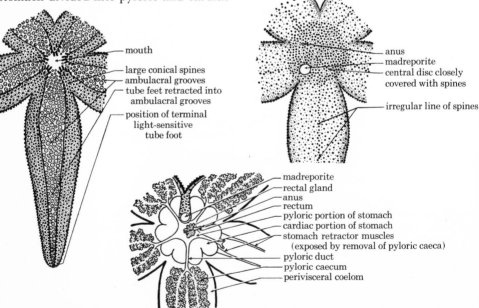

left labels:
mouth
large conical spines
ambulacral grooves
tube feet retracted into ambulacral grooves
position of terminal light-sensitive tube foot

right labels:
anus
madreporite
central disc closely covered with spines
irregular line of spines

center labels:
madreporite
rectal gland
anus
rectum
pyloric portion of stomach
cardiac portion of stomach
stomach retractor muscles (exposed by removal of pyloric caeca)
pyloric duct
pyloric caecum
perivisceral coelom

Fig. 16-4 Anatomy of a starfish (Asterias): *left*, external ventral (oral) view; *right*, external dorsal view; *center*, internal anatomy. (From W. S. Bullough, *Practical Invertebrate Anatomy*, Macmillan, 1954.)

Grasshopper (*Melanoplus*)

Remove the wings from a freshly killed or preserved grasshopper. Lay the specimen dorsal side uppermost in a dissecting pan. Cut through each side of the top of the posterior abdomen, then remove this upper part of the abdomen; the heart, which is a delicate tube, may be attached to it. Notice the white air sacs and air tubes on each side of the abdomen.

If the specimen is a female, look in the anterior end of the abdomen for a mass of yellow eggs. Trace oviducts from the two ovaries to an opening in the ovipositor. Push aside the eggs to find the dark-colored intestine.

When you remove the roof of the thorax, look for the muscles which move the wings. In the prothorax is the crop, which contains hooked teeth. From this region locate the gastric caeca, which are cone-shaped pouches; then find the stomach, which leads into the intestine. Along the ventral region of the abdomen you may find enlargements of the nerve cord, the ganglia, from which many nerves may be seen to branch to tissues.

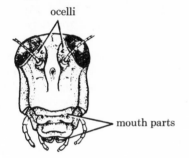

ocelli

mouth parts

Fig. 16-5 Anatomy of grasshopper: external, internal, and detail of head. (From W. G. Whaley, O. P. Breland, et al., *Principles of Biology*, Harper, 1954.)

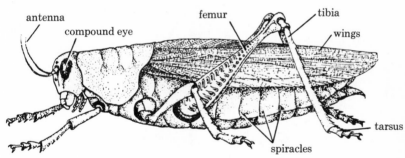

antenna
compound eye
femur
tibia
wings
tarsus
spiracles

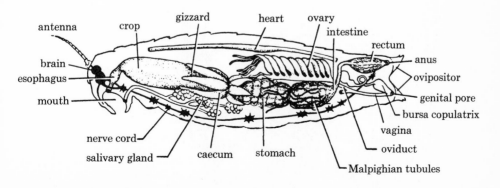

antenna
crop
gizzard
heart
ovary
intestine
rectum
brain
anus
esophagus
ovipositor
mouth
genital pore
bursa copulatrix
nerve cord
vagina
salivary gland
caecum
stomach
oviduct
Malpighian tubules

Cockroach (*Blatta*)

For studying insect anatomy some teachers prefer the oriental cockroach *Blatta* or the larger *Periplaneta*. These as well as grasshoppers are available from biological supply houses.

Examine the external anatomy; if possible, compare with that of the grasshopper. Identify the head and its appendages, the three segments of the thorax, and the eleven segments of the abdomen. The end segments are not distinguished easily for they overlap and are reduced. Locate spiracles.

Pin the roach ventral side down in a waxed pan or on a corkboard. Remove the leathery elytra and wings and cut into the specimen along one side so that the dorsal section may be flapped over to expose the internal organs. Students can identify the dorsal "heart," a chain of nodelike swellings which extend along the length of the roach. In the vicinity of the first leg locate the white salivary glands surrounding the esophagus. Trace the food tube; find the extended crop, thickwalled gizzard, hepatic caeca, colon, and rectum. The threadlike mass is composed of Malpighian tubules. Now remove the fatty tissue and the digestive tract and trace the tracheal tubes which branch throughout the body.

In the fourth and fifth segments of a male try to locate the thin, coiled testes and the large accessory gland. In a female look for the two ovaries with many-branched ovarioles which probably contain clusters of eggs. You may try to trace the location of the spermatheca and the egg capsule in the seventh segment (which comes to a point). Finally, move the organs aside to locate the ventral double nerve cord and chains of ganglia associated with it.

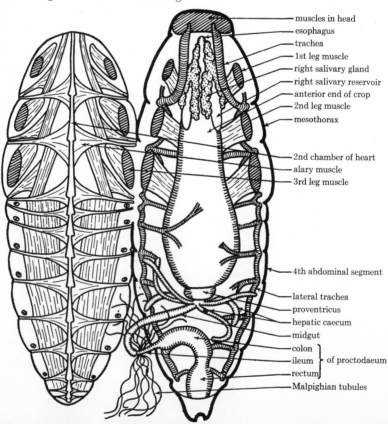

muscles in head
esophagus
trachea
1st leg muscle
right salivary gland
right salivary reservoir
anterior end of crop
2nd leg muscle
mesothorax

2nd chamber of heart
alary muscle
3rd leg muscle

4th abdominal segment

lateral trachea
proventricus
hepatic caecum
midgut
colon ⎫
ileum ⎬ of proctodaeum
rectum ⎭
Malpighian tubules

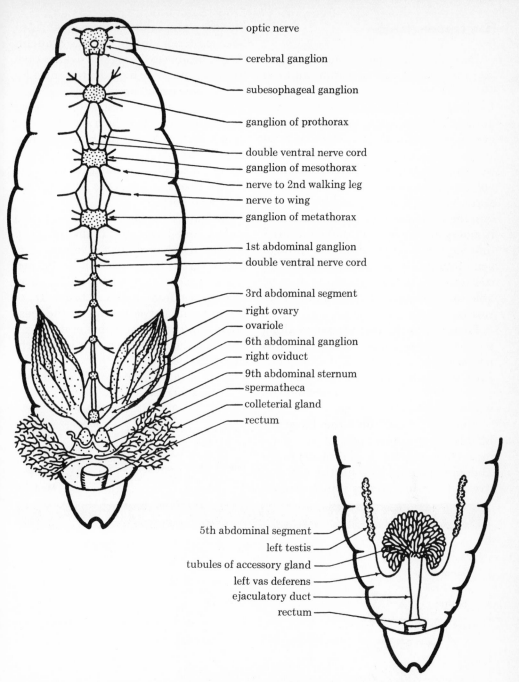

optic nerve

cerebral ganglion

subesophageal ganglion

ganglion of prothorax

double ventral nerve cord
ganglion of mesothorax
nerve to 2nd walking leg
nerve to wing
ganglion of metathorax

1st abdominal ganglion
double ventral nerve cord

3rd abdominal segment
right ovary
ovariole
6th abdominal ganglion
right oviduct
9th abdominal sternum
spermatheca
colleterial gland
rectum

5th abdominal segment
left testis
tubules of accessory gland
left vas deferens
ejaculatory duct
rectum

Fig. 16-6 (*above*) Anatomy of cockroach: *left,* nervous system and female reproductive system; *right,* male reproductive system. (From W. S. Bullough, *Practical Invertebrate Anatomy,* Macmillan, 1954.)

Fig. 16-7 (*opposite*) Anatomy of cockroach (*Blatta*): general dissection. The animal has been split lengthwise and spread open. (From W. S. Bullough, *Practical Invertebrate Anatomy,* Macmillan, 1954.)

Fish (*generalized*)

Hold the fish in one hand, begin the incision near the anal region, and cut forward for an inch or so. Then lay the fish in a waxed pan or on a corkboard and cut forward along the mid-line. Be careful not to injure any organs. Find the heart in a pericardial sac beneath the pharynx. Blood moves from the auricle, into the ventricle, into the ventral aorta, along afferent branchial arteries, into the gills. After the blood is aerated, it moves into efferent branchial arteries into the dorsal aorta. It returns through veins into the sinus venosus, which empties into the auricle. Students may be able to trace some of these main blood vessels.

Food enters the mouth, passes along a short esophagus into a stomach, then past the pyloric valve into the intestine. Look for the liver and the gall bladder. At the anterior end of the intestine you may find a large red spleen.

Students should find the large air bladder in the dorsal part of the abdomen. High up in the dorsal region of the abdominal cavity look for the kidneys. Try to trace the ureters into a urinary bladder opening into a urinogenital orifice, posterior to the anus. Students should be able to distinguish ovaries from testes and trace the reproductive tubes into the urinogenital opening.

Next examine the respiratory system. Find the paired gills, which are supported by gill arches. Notice the branchial filaments (double rows) on each gill and their rich supply of capillaries. Also note the gill rakers, which act as sieves to hold back food particles.

Pare away the bony brain case with a scalpel and locate the brain, which is composed of four distinct divisions: cerebrum, cerebellum, optic lobes, and medulla. Students may be able to find olfactory lobes in front of the cerebrum. Try to trace cranial nerves leading to the sense organs. In the neural arches of the vertebrae find the spinal cord with its branching spinal nerves.

A dissection of the eye of the fish will reveal a spherical lens.

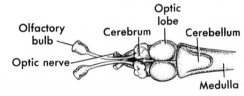

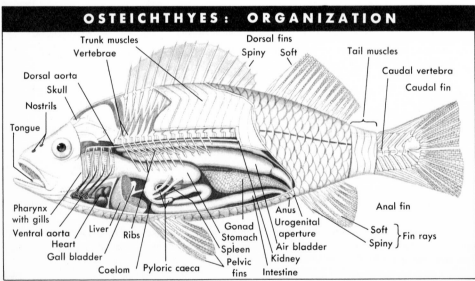

Fig. 16-8 Anatomy of a fish (generalized): lateral view and detail of brain. (From G. G. Simpson, C. Pittendrigh, & L. Tiffany, *Life*, Harcourt, Brace, 1957.)

Frog (Rana)

This description of the anatomy of the frog will hold for a study of frogs generally and for most toads and salamanders.

When you have preserved frogs, there is no chance to see a beating heart or to study the contrast of colors of the organs. Try to have at least one freshly killed, pithed (p. 130), or anesthetized (p. 132) frog so that students can see the deeply colored auricles contract to pass blood to the ventricle, and the ventricle contract, changing from deep red to light pink, as it sends blood into the dorsal aorta.

If you have live frogs, students can observe the breathing movements and eye reflex (p. 127); demonstrate circulation in the webbed foot (p. 72); or study fresh blood cells, ciliated epithelial cells from the roof of the mouth, intestinal protozoa, or sperms, as described below (see also Chapter 17).

For dissection, lay a dead frog on its back in a waxed pan, and pin down the extended limbs. Use forceps to pick up the loose skin of the abdomen between the hind legs, and cut from there up to the lower jaw. Turn back the skin (notice its rich supply of blood vessels) and pin it down. Cut through the white abdominal muscles, being careful not to cut into the ventral abdominal vein or the organs beneath. At the pectoral region you will have to cut through bone. Now use both hands to spread out the pectoral region, carefully. Cut away any connecting mesentery and pin the muscles back to the pan. Make incisions into each of the limbs so that the abdominal wall can be turned back and pinned.

Locate the heart in a pericardial sac, and identify each organ system: respiratory, digestive, circulatory, excretory, and

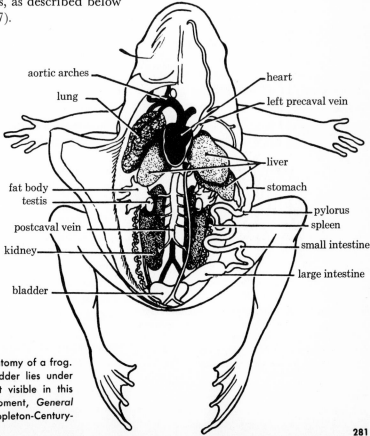

Fig. 16-9 Internal anatomy of a frog. Note that the gall bladder lies under the liver and so is not visible in this view. (From G. B. Moment, *General Biology*, 2d ed., Appleton-Century-Crofts, 1950.)

reproductive. Blow into the glottis with a fire-polished glass tube to inflate the lungs. Use a blunt flexible probe to push back into the mouth so that the gullet

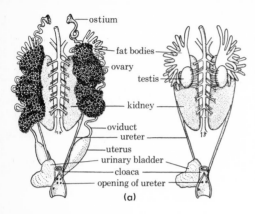

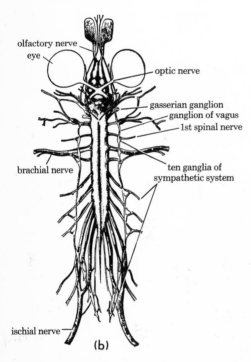

Fig. 16-10 (a) Reproductive and excretory systems of a frog, female and male; (b) nervous system of frog. (a, D. F. Miller & J. G. Haub, *General Zoology*, Holt, 1956; b, R. W. Hegner, *College Zoology*, rev. ed., Macmillan, 1930.)

can be identified. Locate the pancreas, which looks like a yellow cord, in the loop formed by the stomach and intestine.

If your specimen is a female distended with eggs, one ovary and an oviduct should be removed. Trace the other oviduct to locate the funnel (ostium at the base of the lungs) where eggs which break away from the ovary migrate by action of ciliated cells lining the body cavity to enter the oviducts. Locate at the other end of the oviducts the opening to the exterior, via the cloaca.

In the male locate two oval orange or yellow testes. Trace the fine threads of the vasa efferentia connecting each testis to a kidney. Find the vas deferens or ureter leading from the outer edge of the posterior part of each kidney back to the cloaca.

Observe the yellow fat bodies, finger-like masses, connected to both ovaries and testes. Near the cloaca find the red, spherical spleen. Insert a flexible probe through the anus to locate the urinary bladder. Or inflate it by blowing through a fire-polished glass tube.

In a preserved specimen students may be able to study the nervous system in fine detail. Pare away the top of the skull with a scalpel until you find between the eyes the two hemispheres of the cerebrum. In front of these you may be able to locate the two pear-shaped olfactory lobes, which lead out into the nasal region. Posterior to the cerebrum the optic nerves may be found extending from the optic lobes. Then trace the cerebellum and extension of the medulla into the spinal cord. When you lift up the organs within the abdomen locate the ganglia and branching spinal nerves extending from the spinal cord. Study the relation in position of the spinal cord to the spinal column. Follow the sciatic nerves into the muscles of the thighs.

Microscopic examination of frog tissues

Epithelial tissue. A live frog placed in a jar (with about 1 inch of water) will desquamate in about 24 hours. Mount small pieces of the sloughing skin in Lugol's solution or methylene blue (p. 309) on a clean slide with a coverslip. These mounts last for several hours if rimmed with Vaseline (ciliated epithelial, p. 32).

Dissect out small pieces of the stomach, intestine, and lining of the mouth of a freshly pithed frog; place in a macerating solution, 5 per cent chloral hydrate (Caution: poison). After 24 to 48 hours, tease them apart with dissecting needles; mount in a drop of the solution. Students should be able to identify cell membrane, cilia, cylindrical cells, and goblet cells.

Nerve cells. Dissect out small pieces of the spinal cord of a freshly killed frog; transfer to a clean slide. Gently press a second slide against this, mashing the tissue; hold the two slides parallel and pull apart, leaving a smear on each.[1] Nerve cells, nuclei, cell contents, and bits of connective tissue should be seen. You can make permanent slides by drying these smears in air. Then treat and stain them like fixed tissue (p. 324). They may show mitochondria, fat globules, nuclear constituents, and intracellular fibrils.

Blood cells. Study a wet mount of fresh frog blood in a drop of Ringer's solution (p. 409). Prepare blood smears and stain with Wright's blood stain (pp. 76, 319); compare red and white corpuscles.

Muscle cells. Tease apart a bit of muscle tissue from the abdominal region and from the thigh of a freshly killed frog. Stain with methylene blue or Lugol's solution (p. 409). What is the difference between striated and smooth muscle cells?

Sperm cells. Mount crushed testes of freshly killed frogs (p. 169).

Examination of frog parasites

Freshly killed frogs are a rich source of live parasites for microscopic examination. Students may find roundworms in the visceral cavity just as the abdominal wall is cut. Tease apart some lung tissue and look for roundworms and flatworms. The contents of the stomach and intestine may have roundworms and protozoa (*Opalina* and *Balantidium*, Fig. 14-3). Tease apart

[1] R. Bensley and S. Bensley, *Handbook of Histological and Cytological Technique*, U. of Chicago Press, Chicago, 1938.

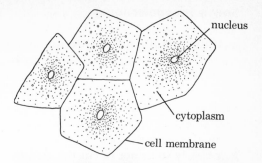

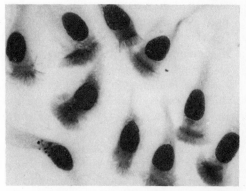

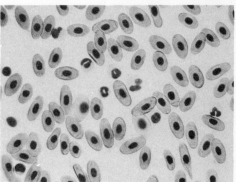

Fig. 16-11 Microscopic views of frog tissues: *top,* epithelial tissue (skin); *center,* ciliated epithelial cells from mouth; *bottom,* blood cells stained with Wright's stain. (Photos: *center,* General Biological Supply House, Inc., Chicago; *bottom,* Carolina Biological Supply Co.)

pieces of the liver in a Syracuse dish; examine for flatworms. Inspect the contents of the urinary bladder for roundworms and flatworms.

Students may undertake an interesting project: a comparative study of the parasites in frogs from different localities (parasites travel with their hosts).

Snake (*nonpoisonous*)

If the spinal cord of a freshly killed snake is not destroyed, the snake must be fastened securely to a board. (It is best of course to destroy the cord.) Lay it on its back and tack down the upper jaw and the tail end. Carefully pick up the skin at the throat, and make an incision (cutting slowly so as not to cut through the distended air sac which fills most of the body) extending to the anus; pin back the skin every few inches. Cut through the membranes across the rib section, avoiding blood vessels.

Use glass tubing to inflate the stomach, then the lungs. Notice the air sac extending from the lung. Look for the undeveloped second lung.

Push aside the organs to find the two auricles and one ventricle of the heart lying within a pericardium. Perhaps students can trace the large aorta leading out of the ventricle between the auricles and bending around the gullet; follow its path posteriorly or find some of the anterior branches.

Find the dark liver near the stomach, the dark gall bladder, and the pale pancreas, near the spleen. Trace the intestine along the length of the abdomen. In the posterior region of the abdomen find the testes or ovaries. Trace the pinkish oviduct or the smaller sperm duct to the cloaca. Posterior to the sex glands, find the dark red, elongated kidneys and their ureters.

In a preserved specimen students might try to dissect the brain, as described for the frog (p. 282).

Fig. 16-12 Internal anatomy of a snake. Note that there is a break in the drawing. Note also the enormous stomach. (After J. T. Saunders & S. M. Manton, *A Manual of Practical Vertebrate Morphology*, 2d ed., Oxford, 1949.)

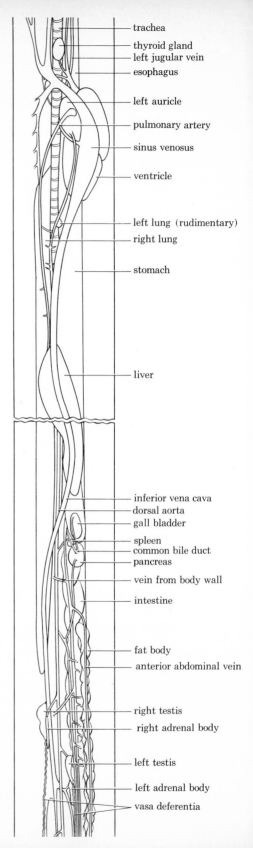

trachea
thyroid gland
left jugular vein
esophagus
left auricle
pulmonary artery
sinus venosus
ventricle
left lung (rudimentary)
right lung
stomach
liver
inferior vena cava
dorsal aorta
gall bladder
spleen
common bile duct
pancreas
vein from body wall
intestine
fat body
anterior abdominal vein
right testis
right adrenal body
left testis
left adrenal body
vasa deferentia

Turtle (generalized)

In preparing a fresh turtle for dissection, use a strong forceps to hold the head extended, and snip through the spinal cord at the back of the neck with strong clippers or shears. Then, with a hacksaw or coping saw, cut through the bridge which connects the carapace (upper shell) and the plastron (lower shell) on each side. Raise the plastron and cut away the connecting membranes, then remove the plastron.

Cut through the membrane to reveal the internal organs and examine the conspicuous heart. Near the heart find the liver and the gall bladder. The stomach is near or under the left lobe of the liver. Lift up the liver to locate the lungs. Try to inflate them by blowing into them with glass tubing.

Follow along the intestine from the stomach to the transverse vent under the tail. Locate the urinary bladder and trace ureters back to the kidneys. Masses of eggs may be found in the ovary of a female specimen. Trace the ducts leading from the gonads (ovaries or testes) to the outside.

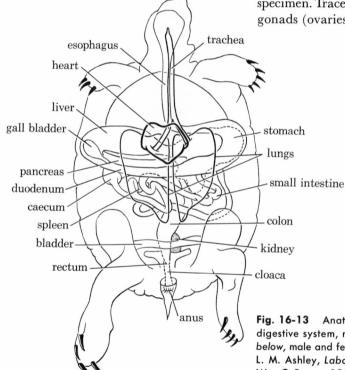

Fig. 16-13 Anatomy of the turtle: *above, left,* digestive system, respiratory system, and heart; *below,* male and female urogenital systems. (After L. M. Ashley, *Laboratory Anatomy of the Turtle,* Wm. C. Brown, 1955.)

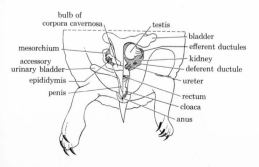

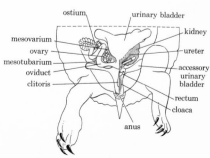

Pigeon

Before any bird is dissected it should be dipped into hot water so that the feathers can be plucked off easily.

Stretch the wings and legs out on a corkboard or dissecting pan and fasten securely. Cut forward from the posterior end of the keel, or breastbone, revealing the crop (where food is macerated). Pull the crop forward to see how it is connected to the stomach, or proventriculus. Then identify the trachea with its cartilage rings. Students may also find the jugular vein on each side of the neck.

Try to insert glass tubing into the glottis and blow into it to inflate the air sacs in front of the breastbone. Students may want to experiment by blowing air into a broken humerus and tracing the path of air through the hollow bones from the windpipe. Air which passes from the glottis into the trachea finally enters nine large thin-walled air sacs which lie mainly along the dorsal sides of the body cavity. When air is exhaled, the muscles of the thorax and the abdomen contract sending air out of the air sacs into the lungs and finally out through the trachea.

A structure peculiar to birds is the syrinx, a vocal organ found at the base of the trachea where the trachea divides to form two bronchi.

Now cut through the skin of the abdomen posterior down to the anus. Abdominal air sacs may be seen if they are inflated. Students should locate the heart in front of the large liver. Since the heart is comparatively large, students may dissect it to locate its four chambers.

Also find the pink lungs attached to the back of the animal. To the left of the body cavity find the hard gizzard extending from the stomach. Trace the intestine from the gizzard. Cut into the gizzard and explain its structure. Find the pink-colored pancreas in a loop of the duodenum of the intestine. Toward the end of the intestine, near the rectum, find two side branches, caeca, and finally trace the intestine to the cloaca.

In the hollow of the pelvis find the lobed kidneys. Below these, students may look for the sciatic nerves which lead from the spinal cord into the hind legs.

Next, students should find the two testes or the single ovary (the left one) in front of the kidneys. Trace the one oviduct or the sperm ducts to the cloaca. There is no urinary bladder in birds.

Dissect the leg to show how a bird remains perched when asleep. Show that in a relaxed position the toes grasp the perch.

The dissection of the brain is a more difficult task. With a sharp knife pare away the bone of the skull to expose the soft brain. Try to identify the parts of the brain.

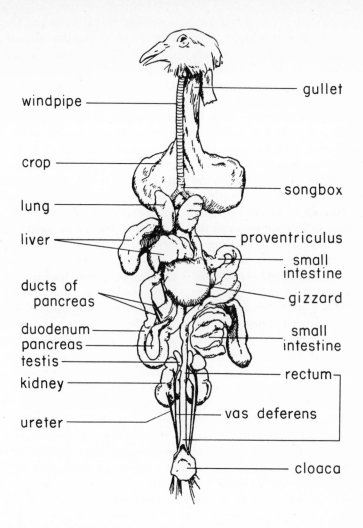

windpipe

crop

lung

liver

ducts of
pancreas

duodenum
pancreas
testis

kidney

ureter

gullet

songbox

proventriculus

small
intestine

gizzard

small
intestine

rectum

vas deferens

cloaca

Fig. 16-14 Internal organs of the pigeon (the heart has been removed). (A. J. Thomson, *The Biology of Birds,* Sidgwick & Jackson Ltd., 1923.)

Fetal pig

In some areas fetal pigs may be more readily available for dissection than rabbits, cats, or white rats. If you purchase a pig's uterus for a study of the relationship of the embryo, placenta, and umbilical cord (p. 176), there will be several fetuses available for dissection.

Place the pig fetus on its back in a waxed pan. Tie a cord around one forelimb and bring it around underneath the pan to fasten back the other forelimb. Spread apart the hind limbs in the same way. Then make an incision between the hind limbs and cut forward, keeping to one side of the umbilical cord. Cut across to each forelimb and hind limb. The umbilical vein must be cut before you can fold over that part of the body wall with the umbilical cord. Fold over the body wall and pin down. In the umbilical cord stump find the allantoic stalk, one umbilical vein, and two umbilical arteries.

Identify the liver, stomach, intestine, and diaphragm. Carefully remove the pericardium and trace the blood vessels leading from the heart, especially the dorsal aorta. Look for the thymus gland found ventral to the heart, extending forward.

Now trace the digestive system, including the gall bladder, bile duct, and the pancreas. You will also find the spleen, a flattened dark-red organ near the stomach.

Examine the lungs and trace their connection to the trachea.

Then begin a careful study of the urinogenital system. In a female first trace the urinary system. Find the kidneys lying in the dorsal part of the abdomen. From these trace the ureters towards the urinary or allantoic bladder. Can students find that one end of the bladder extends as the allantoic stalk into the umbilical cord? Atop the kidneys find the long, narrow adrenal glands. Then locate the small, oval ovaries a little posterior to the kidneys. Study the position of the Fallopian tubes and the uterus. Now cut through the muscle in the pelvic girdle and locate the white line of fusion, the pubic symphysis. At this point, split the girdle with a scalpel to reveal the rest of the reproductive system: the urethra (duct leading from the urinary bladder to the urogenital sinus), vagina, and urinogenital sinus.

In the male trace the position of the penis after separating it from the ventral body wall posterior to the umbilical cord. In older specimens the testes may have already descended into scrotal sacs. Look for the vasa deferentia, the thin sperm ducts from the testes, and find how they loop over the ureters. Locate the crescent-shaped epididymis enclosing the inner side of each testis and see how each is connected with the vas deferens. Also trace the urethra from the bladder to the penis.

Finally, students may try to trace the nervous system and make a study of the structure of the eye. A hemisection of the brain may be more practical.

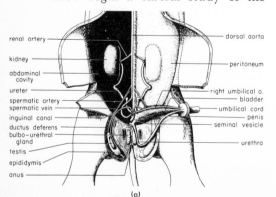

renal artery
kidney
abdominal cavity
ureter
spermatic artery
spermatic vein
inguinal canal
ductus deferens
bulbo–urethral gland
testis
epididymis
anus

dorsal aorta
peritoneum
right umbilical a.
bladder
umbilical cord
penis
seminal vesicle
urethra

(a)

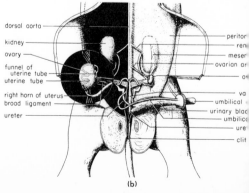

dorsal aorta
kidney
ovary
funnel of uterine tube
uterine tube
right horn of uterus
broad ligament
ureter

perito
ren
meser
ovarian ar
ov
va
umbilical
urinary blad
umbilic
ure
clit

(b)

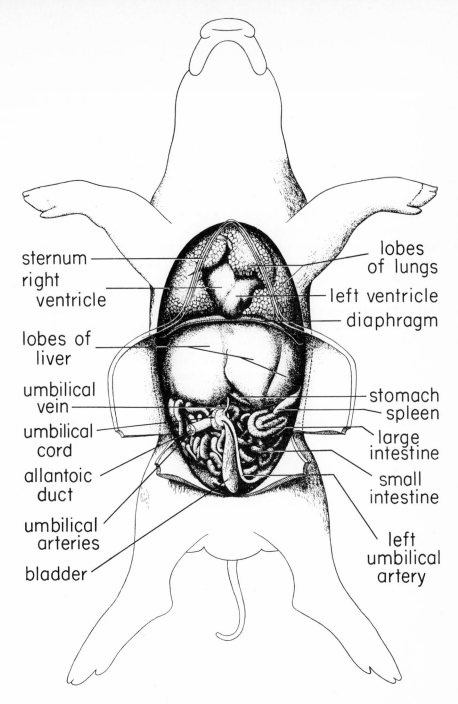

sternum

right
ventricle

lobes of
liver

umbilical
vein

umbilical
cord

allantoic
duct

umbilical
arteries

bladder

lobes
of lungs

left ventricle

diaphragm

stomach

spleen

large
intestine

small
intestine

left
umbilical
artery

Fig. 16-15 (*above*) Anatomy of fetal pig. (From T. Odlaug, *Laboratory Anatomy of the Fetal Pig,* Wm. C. Brown, 1955.)

Fig. 16-16 (*opposite*) Reproductive and excretory systems of fetal pig: (a) male; (b) female. (From T. Odlaug, *Laboratory Anatomy of the Fetal Pig,* Wm. C. Brown, 1955.)

Rat (laboratory)

Lay the animal ventral side up and fasten with cords as described for the fetal pig. Make an incision in the skin along the mid-line from the base of the neck to the pelvis. Fold back the skin and fasten it to a board or dissecting pan with stout pins. Carefully cut through the muscular abdominal wall up to the breastbone. When the chest is opened, the lungs and heart collapse. If possible try to inflate the lungs to their normal size. Then students may see that the lungs fill the chest cavity and nearly encircle the heart. Study the lobes of the lungs; examine the muscles of the diaphragm.

For the most part, the rest of the anatomy can be identified from previous dissections. Students should be able to trace the path of food through the alimentary canal and identify the pancreas and liver.

Locate the main blood vessels leaving the heart; trace the branches of the aorta carrying blood to the head, brachial vessels, and the main stem supplying the body organs. With care, students may try to trace the pulmonary circulation, and notice the large veins, inferior and superior venae cavae, which enter the right auricle.

Now move aside the digestive organs and trace the urinogenital system. Find the kidneys (with adrenal glands on top) and the ureters leading to the bladder; identify the ovaries or testes and their ducts. Prepare a slide of sperm suspension from a testis macerated in Ringer's solution (mammalian, p. 409).

Raise these organs and find the dorsal spinal column with spinal nerves leading out of the spinal cord. Dissect a limb and trace the sciatic nerve into it; examine the relationships of muscles, nerves, and bones in the leg.

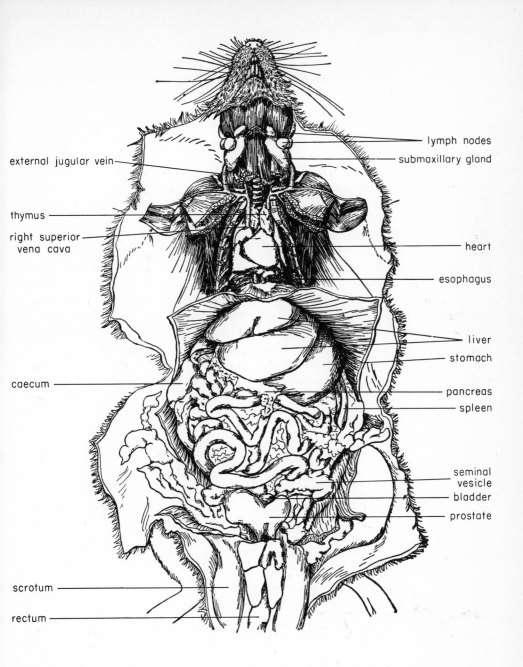

Fig. 16-17 Dissection of a rat (male). (From E. J. Farris & J. O. Griffith, *The Rat in Laboratory Investigation*, 2d ed., Lippincott, 1949.)

Anatomy of plants

Leaves

While leaves may take many shapes, their function is the same, food-making for the plant. Some leaves are only a few cells thick (*elodea,* p. 17), while others are elaborate with adaptations.

You may want students to make some crude, freehand sections of a leaf (or you may prefer to purchase prepared slides). To make a freehand cross section, sandwich a piece of leaf between two halves of elderberry pith or balsa wood (p. 315). With a sharp razor slice thin sections at an angle; mount in a drop of water. Some sections cut in this way will have thin edges; under a microscope the cellular structure of the leaves can be seen.

Students may be able to identify the upper epidermis (which lacks chloroplasts). Under this layer look for the palisade layer (or layers) filled with chloroplasts. This is the layer in which most of the food-making occurs. Below this is the loosely packed spongy layer, cells interspersed with many air spaces. Below this layer students should find the lower epidermis, the layer throughout which the stomata and their guard cells (containing chloroplasts) are usually found. It is through these stomata that air containing carbon dioxide enters. It dissolves in the water within the air spaces around the cells, diffuses through the membranes of cells, and passes from cell to cell, finally reaching the actively photosynthesizing palisade cells.

Students may study the guard cells and stomates in the lower epidermis of some leaves. Peel the lower epidermis from a fleshy leaf such as *Peperomia,* geranium, *Kalanchoë,* or *Tradescantia,* or the shoot of an onion (p. 21). Mount in a drop of water and examine this lower epidermis to find the numerous kidney-shaped pairs of guard cells surrounding the stomates.

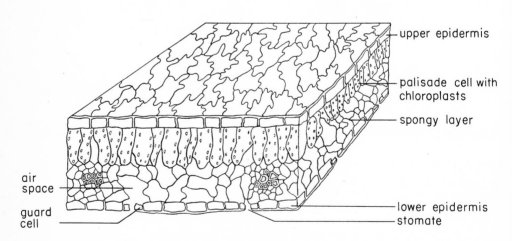

Fig. 16-18   Cross section of a green leaf.

Fig. 16-19 Types of leaves: *top row,* entire margin (mountain laurel), serrate (birch), dentate (chestnut); *bottom row,* lobed (chestnut oak), cut (black oak), compound (black locust). (Photos: A. M. Winchester.)

Specialization of leaves. Some leaves are highly specialized organs. The familiar pink and white "petals" of dogwood are really modified leaves. Students may remember that the leaves of onions and other bulbs are adapted to store food materials. Still other leaves are modified to capture insects, such as Venus fly-trap (Fig. 14-8). Plants such as the water hyacinth have leaves containing large air spaces which keep the plants afloat. The tendrils of smilax, the garden pea, and many other plants are also modified leaves, as are the spines of cactus. And the leaves of *Bryophyllum* are modified so that vegetative propagation occurs easily; the notches of the leaves are primordia of plants (Fig. 11-13).

Fig. 16-20 Colored bracts of dogwood are modified leaves; flower clusters are in the center. (Photo: U.S. Forest Service.)

Fig. 16-21 Specialization for storage: *left,* lily bulb; *right,* onion bulb. (From W. H. Brown, *The Plant Kingdom,* Ginn, 1935.)

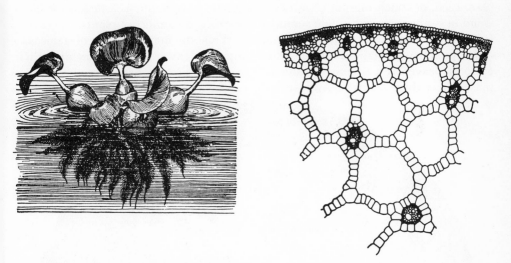

Fig. 16-22 Specialization for floating: *left,* water hyacinth (*Eichhornia crassipes)* showing petioles modified as floats; *right,* cross section of petiole showing large air spaces. (From W. H. Brown, *The Plant Kingdom,* Ginn, 1935.)

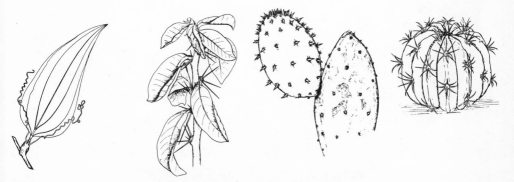

Fig. 16-23 Other modified leaves: tendrils of *Smilax;* three examples of spines on cactus. (*Smilax,* W. H. Brown, *The Plant Kingdom,* Ginn, 1935; cactus, C. L. Wilson & W. E. Loomis, *Botany,* rev. ed., Dryden, 1957.)

Stems

Students can also make freehand sections of stems. Compare cross sections of monocotyledonous and dicotyledonous stems.

The rise of colored liquids through the fibrovascular bundles of celery or carrots or growing seedlings may be demonstrated (p. 43). Still better, fibrovascular bundles can be studied in the orange-flowered jewelweed, or touch-me-not (*Impatiens*), found in swampy regions in late summer. Its stems are practically transparent and show the fibrovascular bundles leading up to the leaves. If it is desired, students may collect these stems in August, cut them into short sections, and preserve them in 70 per cent alcohol until they are needed.

They may also study the stem of a gymnosperm. This is similar to the dicotyledonous stem, except that conifers have no companion cells in the phloem; the xylem of conifers contains only tracheids. Since vessels are lacking, the tracheids carry on conduction of water.

The pattern of stem growth, either alternate or opposite, is a means for identification of families of plants.

While the main function of stems is to support leaves and flowers and their fruits, many stems have specialized adaptations for other work. For instance, some

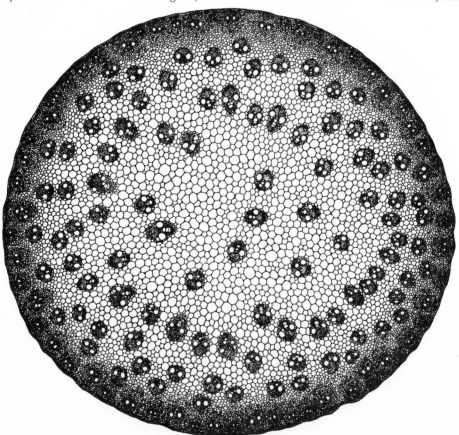

Fig. 16-24 Cross section of monocotyledonous stem (*Zea mays*): fibrovascular bundles are scattered in the pith; the cortex is a layer only one or two cells thick between the epidermis and the outermost series of vascular bundles. (From W. H. Brown, *The Plant Kingdom*, Ginn, 1935.)

stems may be storage regions, such as the fleshy stem of the white potato (tubers), the thickened stem of kohl-rabi, or the rhizome of ginger. In fact, the wide spates of green which make up a cactus plant are not leaves, but stems which have taken over the work of carrying on photosynthesis. Some stems are modified into twiners, such as in the morning glory. Some stems, such as those of dodder and some epiphytes, are specialized to absorb water and minerals, thus taking on the usual function of roots. Runners and rhizomes (p. 156) may also serve a reproductive function in that they produce new plants without using seeds.

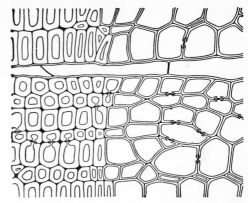

Fig. 16-26 Cross section of small portion of stem of a gymnosperm (redwood tree), showing xylem (tracheids) on both sides of a pith ray. (From W. H. Brown, *The Plant Kingdom*, Ginn, 1935.)

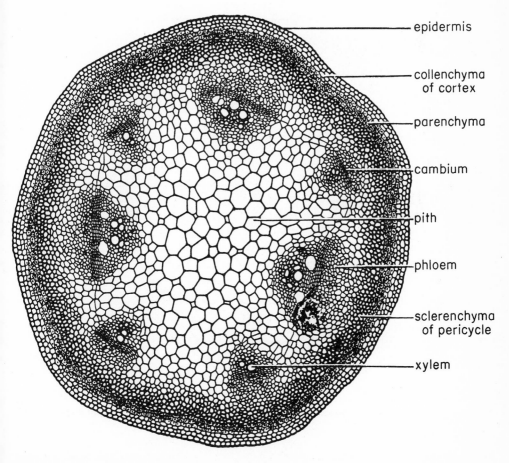

epidermis

collenchyma of cortex

parenchyma

cambium

pith

phloem

sclerenchyma of pericycle

xylem

Fig. 16-25 Cross section of dicotyledonous stem (*Aristolochia elegans*). (From W. H. Brown, *The Plant Kingdom*, Ginn, 1935.)

Roots

Perhaps students have already made a study of root hairs on growing seedlings (p. 44), or measured the elongation of young growing roots (p. 109).

Cross sections of carrots or of the large castor-bean roots will give a fair picture of their structure. Prepared slides of roots may also be purchased (see p. 479 for supply houses). There is a close similarity between the structure of monocotyledonous and dicotyledonous roots, although there is a distinct difference in their stem structure.

While roots serve primarily for anchorage and absorption of soil water, some roots show wide modifications. Compare the fleshy storage root of the carrot, sweet potato, beet, radish and dahlia. Brace roots and prop roots are found among the Indian rubber plant and the strangling fig tree. New plants can be grown from some of the fleshy roots; thus these roots serve a reproductive function too. Climbing plants, such as ivy, cling by means of adventitious roots.

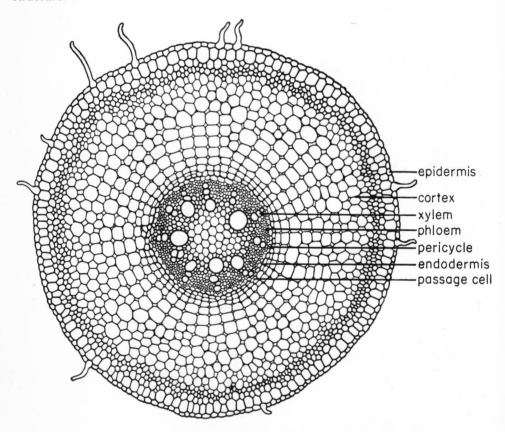

epidermis
cortex
xylem
phloem
pericycle
endodermis
passage cell

Fig. 16-27   Cross section of monocot root (*Commelina*). (From W. H. Brown, *The Plant Kingdom*, Ginn, 1935.)

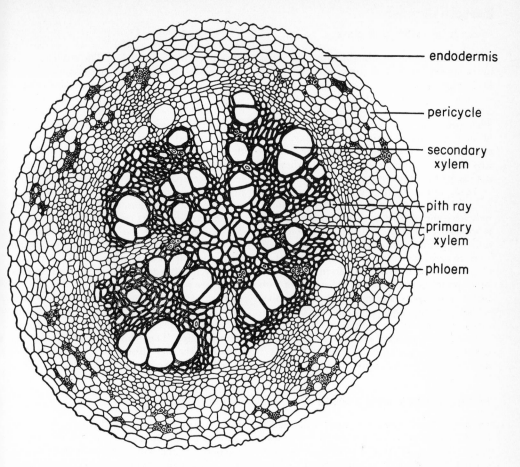

— endodermis

— pericycle

— secondary xylem

— pith ray
— primary xylem

— phloem

Fig. 16-28 Cross section of dicot root (mungo bean). (From W. H. Brown, *The Plant Kingdom,* Ginn, 1935.)

CAPSULE LESSONS

Ways to get started in class

16-1. Some teachers begin with dissections as an introduction to a study of relationships among living things. The class may be divided into smaller groups; each of these will dissect a fish, a frog, or a snake (or other vertebrate). The specimens can be tagged and stored in alcohol or formalin until the next day. Then students may switch places and study similarities and differences in the organisms they did not dissect the previous day.

16-2. Students interested in nature study (or students who plan to be biology majors), may form the nucleus of a club whose purpose is to take field trips to learn the ecology of different locales in the community. They may want to organize a nature center which might supply schools nearby with living materials (from protozoa to mammals). This type of club might also supply student speakers for other schools, young people who have become proficient at some skill or technique.

16-3. In a biology club or a specialized curators club, students may want to dissect and compare the anatomy of many kinds of animals and plants. Perhaps they'll go further to examine tissues under the microscope (as developed in Chapter 17). The students may prepare and mimeograph guide sheets for dissection of several animals. Some teachers have worked with students to prepare a film of a dissection. Have students make an exhibit of adaptations among leaves for different kinds of functions in the plant. Exhibit these for all students to see.

16-4. Many ideas for student projects arise from a comparative study of plants and animals. For instance, students may make a phylogenetic collection of animals, preserved and mounted in jars (see Fig. 15-10, p. 255). This collection may be used in the study of evolution. Or they may plant a plot of ground with examples of the various phyla of plants. Or they may try to culture some kinds of protozoa (see p. 334).

16-5. On occasion you may bring to class an "unknown" plant or animal. Have students decide upon procedures to use to determine relationships. They should think of studying anatomy through dissection and examination of cells under the microscope.

PEOPLE, PLACES, AND THINGS

It may be possible for you to meet with teachers in different schools to plan joint club meetings, science fairs, seminars, and field trips. Students can combine their efforts and publish a science journal. This accomplishes two things: Students come together to exchange views and stimulate each other's learning, and they can afford to publish a more ambitious journal since a large number of students will share in the expenses.

Students in a central school might take responsibility for developing a culture center for all sorts of living materials—plants and animals—to supply other schools. Films and projectors may be shared between schools and with nearby colleges.

In addition, there may be in your community aquarium shops, nurseries, experimental laboratories and farms, or a zoological park. The helpful people in these places will offer both teachers and students their good services.

Books and pamphlets

You will find books on nature study and fieldbook guides for identification listed in the Bibliography at the end of the book. In the sections listing books in botany and zoology are books which will guide students in dissections of animals and plants. You may also want to use some of the texts listed under the heading Cells and Microscope Technique.

Films and filmstrips

This partial list is intended only as a guide toward film and filmstrip selection. Refer to the more complete listing at the end of the book where films are classified by subject and a key to abbreviations and the addresses of distributors are given. The cost of film rental, of course, is subject to change. Films are sound and black and white unless otherwise specified.

Animal Life (f), EBF, $1.50.
Arthropoda (f, si, c), Rutgers U., $2.50.
Bee City (f), Almanac, $2.00.
Cells and Their Functions (f), Athena, $4.50.
Earthworm (f), Almanac, $2.00.
Echinodermata (2f, si, c), Iowa State U., $3.00.
Ferns (f), Almanac, $2.00.

Flowers at Work (f), EBF, $2.50.

Fungus Plants (f), EBF, $2.50.

Insect Catchers of the Bog Jungle (f, c), U. of California, Dept. Visual Instruction, $4.00.

Leaves (f), EBF, $2.50.

Life of Plants (f), UWF, $1.50.

Marine Invertebrates of the Maine Coast (set of 34 Kodachrome slides, 2″ × 2″), Ward's Natural Science Establishment, $25.50.

Nature Activities for Camp, Club, and Classroom (f, si, c), Nat. Audubon Soc., $1.00.

Parade of the Invertebrates (4f, si, c), Iowa State U., $3.00 ea.

Pond Life (f), EBF, $2.00.

Seifritz on Protoplasm (f), Educ. Film Library Assoc., New York U., $6.00.

Spermatophytes and General Biology (fs), Bowmar, $2.50.

FREE AND INEXPENSIVE MATERIALS

You may want to order the set of Turtox leaflets and *Turtox News* from the General Biological Supply House, and *Ward's Natural Science Bulletin*. These materials offer valuable information for both teacher and students.

Other supply houses offer valuable aids; try the Welch Manufacturing Company's *A Living Biological Laboratory,* which gives suggestions for caring for living animals in the laboratory.

A more complete listing, including addresses, is given at the end of the book. Many of these materials are distributed to teachers without charge. Where there is a small fee, the cost is indicated, although the prices are subject to change. While we recommend the material for use in the classroom, we do not necessarily sponsor the products advertised.

CHAPTER 17

Cells and tissues

under the microscope

While most of the individual techniques for preparing microscopic demonstrations are described in context, throughout the chapters, certain special techniques are described here. This chapter is in effect an outline of various kinds of techniques in preparing living material for examination with the microscope.

Use of the microscope

Students enjoy using the microscope (Fig. 17-1) and they should be trained to use it correctly. Many teachers have found these routines useful, and students should be encouraged to practice them.

1. Carry the microscope upright by holding the arm of the microscope with one hand and supporting its weight with the other hand. Set it down gently.

2. Align the low-power objective with the tube until it clicks into place.

3. Move the mirror to find the best light, using the concave side if the microscope has no condenser. It is not good practice to have direct sunlight fall on the microscope or reflect up through the mirror to the eye.

4. Watch the low-power objective (the shorter one, usually) as it is turned down near the slide so that the working distance of the objective from the slide can be noted. Learn to lower the objective so that it is at a working distance about ¼ inch from the slide. Many microscopes are adjusted to lock in this point.

5. While looking through the eye piece, or ocular, slowly raise the barrel or tube by turning the coarse adjustment screw. Practice keeping both eyes open to avoid eye strain. Learn to move the slide with the free hand to locate the material to be examined.

6. Center the specimen found under low power; then slowly turn the fine adjustment screw a few degrees in each direction until the object is focused clearly. (It is important that the specimen be centered before switching to high power, for in high power a smaller part of the field is viewed and enlarged.)

7. Switch to high power (this can be done without changing the working dis-

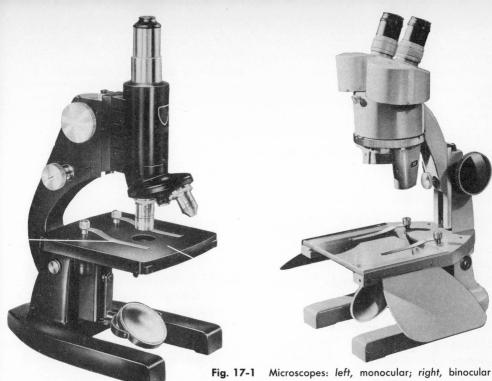

Fig. 17-1 Microscopes: *left*, monocular; *right*, binocular (stereoscopic). (Photos: American Optical Co.)

tance if the microscope is parfocal). Adjust the light again by moving the mirror, and use the fine adjustment screw to focus the object clearly. The fine adjustment screw should be used with care. If the object was in focus under low power, students need make no more than a 10-degree turn in either direction to get a sharp image. Open and close the iris diaphragm until the light is comfortable to the eye.

Much of the beginning student's difficulty results from failure to clean the lenses of the microscope. Cloudiness of the surface of the glass lenses may be removed by breathing on them and then quickly wiping them with lens paper. If this does not remove the film, students should wipe the surface with lens paper moistened with 95 per cent alcohol, then dry the surface. Dried glycerin, blood, or other albuminous materials may be removed by lens paper moistened with water to which a drop of ammonia has been added; then the lenses should be wiped dry. Balsam, paraffin, or oily substances may be wiped away rapidly with lens paper moistened with xylol. Since lens glass is softer than ordinary glass, care should be taken to avoid scratches from dust or other fine particles. If there are black specks which obscure the view, check to see where they are by turning the ocular. If the specks also turn, remove the ocular and brush the inner glass surface with a camel's hair brush or lens paper. Do not use any other cloth, paper, or fingers (which are oily).

Degree of magnification. For a compound microscope, magnification is expressed in diameters. The total magnification may be determined by multiplying the magnification of the ocular lens by the magnification of the objective lens. For low power this is generally $10\times$ (ocular) by $10\times$ (objective), and for high power, $10\times$ (ocular) by $43\times$ (objective). (Check the data on your microscope.)

On the low-power objective there is usually another number, which indicates the actual diameter of the field viewed under the low power, often 1.6 mm. The diameter under high power is usually 0.4 mm.

Ocular micrometer measurements. An ocular micrometer is a ruled section of glass which is fitted into the ocular. Observe the number of divisions on the micrometer covered by the dimensions of the image and calibrate against a micrometer slide (which is placed on the stage) as shown in Table 17-1. (These calibrations are very rough, but useful for high school purposes.)

Oil immersion lens. In general, an oil immersion lens is needed for the examination of bacteria and other minute objects. (The substage diaphragm must be opened whenever the oil immersion lens is used.) Place a drop of cedar oil on the slide (or on the lens), and slowly and carefully lower the oil immersion objective so that it just touches the oil drop. Then focus with the fine adjustment screw. (Stained slides may be examined with or without a coverslip. Wet mounts must be covered with a coverslip.)

If the oil remains on the objective after a study is completed, it will harden; xylol will remove it, but xylol is detrimental to the oiled parts of the microscope. Therefore, students should immediately wipe the oil off the objective and the slide with lens paper.

Binocular (stereoscopic) microscope. The compound monocular (and the double-ocular) microscope provides a two-dimensional image for observation; some appreciation of depth or thickness may be realized by using the fine adjustment screw. Thus one sees sections or slices as if cut from the top, the middle, down to the bottom of a cell.

The binocular stereoscopic microscope

TABLE 17-1
Calibrating an ocular micrometer

	divisions on ocular scale	specimen size (approx.) in mm
16-mm objective	7.75	1.0
	1.0	0.13
	0.1	0.013
4-mm objective	1.0	0.03
	0.1	0.003
1.8-mm objective	1.0	0.013
	0.1	0.0013

(Fig. 17-1, *right*) has two oculars and gives a three-dimensional image. The true stereoscopic microscope is really two microscopes, for it has two oculars and two objectives. The oculars can be adjusted to the user's eyes so that a stereoscopic effect is achieved. In this microscope, the image is not reversed or inverted as in the monocular compound microscope. Of course, these microscopes give less magnification, since they are used to locate objects and provide a wide field for gross examination.

First microscope lesson. Some teachers like to train students in the use of the microscope by beginning with a wet mount or prepared slide of newspaper print. Cut out a single letter, say an "e," from a newspaper and mount it in a drop of water. Apply a coverslip. Students should locate the "e" under low power, then center it. They should notice in which direction the letter is on the slide, then compare its position under the microscope (the image). Is it right side up, reversed, or upside down? Later, students may center the letter and switch to high power. If they move the slide a bit to the left, in which direction does the letter move under the microscope?

Some teachers make a number of permanent, prepared slides containing three crossed threads of different colors.

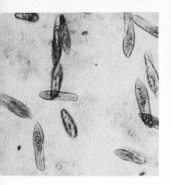

Fig. 17-2 Typical protozoa often used as an introduction to the study of microorganisms: *left, Paramecium; center, Stentor; right, Blepharisma.* (Photos: General Biological Supply House, Inc., Chicago.)

The exercise is one in which the students find the bottom thread, and then find the center and upper ones by proper change of focus. Students enjoy this opportunity to practice the art of focusing.

Other teachers find that students learn quickly that the image of living material on a slide is reversed and inverted and start with a study of living materials immediately. For example, when students move the slide to follow a motile form, they notice in what direction the slide must be moved. In fact, some teachers like to use rich cultures of mixed protozoa—gray *Paramecium,* pink *Blepharisma,* and green *Stentor* (Fig. 17-2). With slides of a mixed culture such as this, all students in class can see a variety of distinctive organisms at the same time. Or you may want to begin with living algae (Figs. 20-1, 20-2) or epithelial cells from the cheek (Fig. 17-5). Other times, students may start with *Daphnia* or *Cyclops* or a microscopic worm like *Dero* or *Tubifex* (culturing, Chapter 18).

This first lesson often may be made exploratory by giving students some freedom in selection of materials for their study. Have several cultures available for study in a first lesson. These lessons can be followed later on with more careful studies of individual types.

Microprojection

At times sufficient numbers of microscopes are not available (due to lack of funds, perhaps). And sometimes it is desirable to demonstrate to the class as a whole just which microorganism, or portion of a slide, should be studied. A microprojector is highly useful in such circumstances; the entire class, or groups of students, may view a fairly large image at the same time.

One commercial microprojector is shown in Fig. 17-3a. Detailed, careful directions for operation come with all commercial projectors. However, an essential requirement for efficient microprojection is a darkened room—the darker the better. If dark shades are not obtainable or do not darken the room sufficiently, you may want to devise a box with a screen, as shown in Fig. 17-3b. In this box is shown a "home-made" microprojector which can also be used in the standard way. Directions for both uses follow.

"Home-made" microprojector. If you have a microscope and a lantern-slide projector you can prepare a microprojector at no cost. Simply remove the eyepiece lens from the microscope and the front lens from the projector. Now focus the

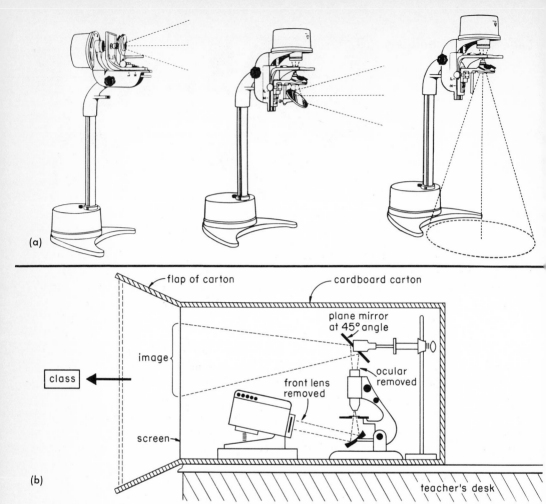

(a)

(b)

Fig. 17-3   Microprojectors: (a) Bausch & Lomb Tri-Simplex Micro-Projector; (b) a home-made micro-projector, shown for use in daylight. Without the cardboard container, the same apparatus can be used to throw an enlarged image on a screen (or, without the plane mirror, on the ceiling) in a darkened room.

light beam from the projector at the mirror of the microscope. Place a slide on the stage and adjust the mirror until a spot of light shows on the ceiling overhead. Then adjust the position of the projector until the cone of light just fills the mirror. (You can check this by tapping chalk dust from an eraser to show the Tyndall cone.) Now focus on the specimen, using the low-power objective. A clear, enlarged image will form on the ceiling. If you wish, you can use a pocket mirror, clamped at a 45° angle as shown, to throw the image forward to a screen.

If dark window shades are not available, set up the whole apparatus, with the mirror, inside a large carton. One side of the carton should be opened, leaving four flaps, and a translucent screen, of tracing paper or tracing cloth, attached across the opening. (The completely assembled apparatus is shown in Fig. 17-3b.) The flaps of the box can be braced open to act as a shadow shield, as shown. The carton can be placed on the teacher's desk, with the screen facing the class; a large, clear image will be seen on it.

Specialized techniques

There may be times when you want a temporary wet mount, or you may want to have students use a stain for a rapid examination of a temporary mount. There are many techniques for preparing slides, depending upon the kind of materials on hand. Only a few of the major techniques are described here. (Full descriptions of techniques can be found in the specialized texts listed at the end of this chapter and in the Bibliography at the end of the book.) Following is an outline of the main techniques in this chapter for handling plant and animal tissue cells and micro-organisms.

I. Temporary wet mounts
  A. Preventing swelling
  B. Slowing down evaporation
  C. Hanging-drop preparation
II. Stained temporary mounts; vital dyes
III. Special studies of cells and micro-organisms
  A. Ion antagonism
  B. Chromatophores
  C. Parasitic protozoa
  D. Rotifers
  E. Flagellates in termites
  F. Nematocysts of hydra
  G. Epithelio-muscle tissue of hydra
  H. Streaming of cytoplasm (cyclosis)
  I. Enzyme activity of mitochondria
IV. Concentrating the number of organisms in a culture
V. Slowing down protozoa
VI. Anesthetization of small forms
VII. Freehand sections
VIII. Maceration of tissue
IX. Mounting small objects
X. Smear slide techniques
  A. Salivary chromosome smears
  B. Smear of onion root tip
  C. Blood smears
  D. Bacterial smears

XI. Temporary stained slides of protozoa
XII. Permanent stained slides of protozoa
  A. Concentrating protozoa
  B. Fixation
  C. Staining
  D. Other stains
XIII. Permanent tissue slides (histological techniques)
  A. Preparation of fixatives
  B. Dehydrating, clearing, and embedding
  C. Sectioning and staining
  D. Preparation of stains
  E. Other solutions needed in histological work
XIV. Permanent slides of chick embryos

Temporary wet mounts

A wet mount is a specimen on a slide in a drop of fluid (water, salt solution, or stain) prepared for examination under low and high power. Since the fluid will evaporate, the mount is temporary.

Temporary wet mounts of protozoa can be made in class. A drop of protozoa culture is placed on a slide; a coverslip is applied to flatten out the drop.

One whole leaf of elodea is thin enough to be mounted in a drop of water (p. 17).

Or the lower epidermis of a leaf may be peeled off a leaf and mounted in water or Lugol's solution (p. 409) to show guard cells and stomates (Fig. 1-11).

Onion cells can be mounted in this way. Cut a section of an onion into ¼-inch pieces. With a forceps lift off the thin membrane from the *inner* surface of each bit of onion. Mount this material on slides in drops of water and add a coverslip. Students may notice that the cells are rectangular, but they cannot see any details of cell structure without a stain. Then they may add 1 drop of Lugol's solution to one side of the coverslip as they remove water from the opposite side with a piece of filter paper. When students examine the stained cells, they should find the parts shown in Fig. 17-4.

In a study of the structure of plant and animal cells you may want to have students examine epithelial cells from their cheek for comparison with the onion cell or elodea cell. Students might gently scrape the lining of the cheek with the flat end of a clean toothpick. Place the scrapings in a drop of Lugol's iodine solution on a clean slide and apply a coverslip. Notice how the nucleus of each cell stains brown, the cytoplasm granules a very light brown. Other materials of sputum, such as free myelin globules and bronchial epithelial cells, may be found along with large scattered masses of stained squamous epithelial cells (Fig. 17-5).

Preventing swelling. Cells which have a fairly high salt concentration may swell when mounted in tap or aquarium water. This swelling can be prevented by putting the cells in a 10 per cent aqueous solution of glycerin. Then add a coverslip. On the other hand, when the mounting fluid has a higher salt or sugar concentration than the cell, the cell loses water, resulting in a shrunken or plasmolyzed state.

Slowing down evaporation. Students may ring a wet mount with Vaseline to slow down evaporation. Dip the mouth of a test tube into Vaseline. Apply this circle of Vaseline around the drop of material on the slide, and place a coverslip so that its edges are sealed to the slide.

Hanging-drop preparation. If a drop of water on a slide were examined under the microscope, light would be reflected in several directions (Fig. 17-6). To avoid this we flatten out the drop with a coverslip. However, in so doing, we reduce the

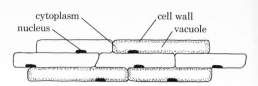

Fig. 17-4 Schematic diagram of onion cells (stained with Lugol's iodine solution so that nuclei are visible).

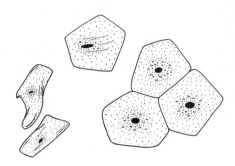

Fig. 17-5 Epithelial cells from the lining of the cheek (stained with Lugol's iodine solution).

Fig. 17-6 Curved surface of a drop of water on a slide reflects light in all directions.

motility (if any) in organisms by the "crush" of the coverslip. A hanging drop preparation enables students to study motility, especially in bacteria, fission in protozoa, germination of pollen grains, and similar subjects. Use a clean slide and coverslip, so that the surface tension of the water is not reduced (or a drop will not form). Place a small drop of the culture medium on a coverslip. Then Vaseline the rim of the depression in a welled, or depression, slide. Place the inverted slide over the coverslip so that the rim of the coverslip and slide are

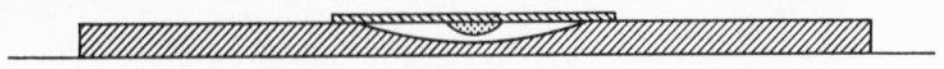

Fig. 17-7 Hanging-drop preparation.

sealed by Vaseline. Quickly invert the whole preparation; it should look like the one in Fig. 17-7.

Stained temporary mounts; vital dyes

Temporary wet mounts of microorganisms and tissue cells, as well as such plant cells as algae or the protenema of mosses, may be studied. Throughout the earlier chapters directions are given in context for making many kinds of temporary mounts. There may be times when you want students to stain living cells with dyes other than Lugol's solution to bring out specific details of cell structure. (The use of Lugol's iodine solution kills the cells rapidly.)

Living cells may be stained to show cilia, flagella, or structures within the cells. Some stains destroy cells immediately, while others, called *vital stains,* kill the organisms slowly. The organisms absorb these stains and continue to carry on their life functions for some time.

Place a drop of the stain (several are listed below) on a clean slide and let it dry as a uniform film on the slide. Prepare several of these dried films of stain on slides and keep them stored in a clean slide box. When they are to be used, just add a drop of protozoa culture, bacteria, yeast culture, or tissue cells to the slide. The stain will dissolve slowly into the drop of material on the slide. Some dilute vital dyes follow.

Methylene blue is used in dilutions of 1 part stain to 10,000 parts or more of distilled water. This stains the nucleus as well as granules of cytoplasm.

Neutral red is dissolved in absolute alcohol, 1 part to 3000–30,000 parts of alcohol. As an indicator, it is yellowish red in alkali, cherry red in weak acid, and blue in strong acid. It stains the nucleus lightly.

Congo red may be used in dilutions of 1 part of stain to 1000 parts of water. In the presence of weak acids the indicator turns from red to blue.

Special studies of cells and microorganisms

Ion antagonism. A clear example may be studied in the ciliary motion of epithelial tissue from the gills of a living clam, mouth of a live frog (p. 32), or intestine of an aquarium snail (Chap. 16, p. 274). Dissect out several pieces of the gill and put these in 10 cc of sea water in small watch glasses. Under low power watch the free ends of the cells, which show vigorously beating cilia. Then transfer the pieces of gill to the following solutions in watch glasses and examine each under the microscope. First, put them into 0.9 per cent potassium chloride solution; then transfer them into a 1 per cent calcium chloride solution; finally return the tissue to Ringer's solution. Compare the movement of cilia in each solution (refer to effect of ions on frog's heart, p. 70).

Chromatophores. Scales of live fish may be mounted in Ringer's solution for the observation of normal pigment-containing cells (chromatophores). Students may watch the contraction and expansion of these cells. First draw off the Ringer's solution on the slide by putting filter paper on one side of the coverslip as a drop of chloretone (p. 314) is put on the opposite side. After students have examined these mounts, use the same procedure to draw off the chloretone and add a drop of adrenalin or potassium chloride to the same mount. Watch the contraction of the chromatophores. In this way, by altering the size of the chromatophores, such animals as fish, amphibians, and several kinds of invertebrates are able to simulate the coloration or the varied intensity of the shadows in their background. Light is usually the original stimulus for the change in chromatophores.

Parasitic protozoa. There are some large, slow-moving ciliates to be found in the intestine and rectum of many frogs and toads. Possibly these were studied previously as examples of parasitic relationships (p. 230). Cut open the rectum of a freshly killed frog and mount bits of fecal material in 0.7 per cent sodium chloride solution. Look for *Opalina* (Fig. 14-3), a slow-moving ciliate which lacks an oral groove and a contractile vacuole. Students may also find *Nyctotherus* and, at times, also *Balantidium* (Fig. 14-3). Both of these are smaller forms; *Nyctotherus* may also be distinguished from *Opalina* in that it has a laterally placed oral groove. This flattened form may be only partially parasitic.

Another parasitic form, *Monocystis* (belonging to the Sporozoa), may be found in the seminal vesicles of sexually mature earthworms. Mount a seminal vesicle of the earthworm in 0.7 per cent sodium chloride solution and crush the contents on a slide. While the adult protozoa lack any form of motility, young forms go through an elongated stage called a trophozoite (Fig. 17-8). However, the resting stages are more commonly found in the seminal vesicles.

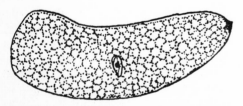

Fig. 17-8 Trophozoite state of *Monocystis*, a parasitic sporozoan often found in the seminal vesicles of earthworms. (From R. R. Kudo, *Protozoology*, 4th ed., Chas. C. Thomas, 1954.)

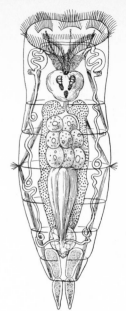

Fig. 17-9 A common rotifer, *Hydatina senta.* (General Biological Supply House, Inc., Chicago.)

Rotifers. These multicellular but microscopic forms (Fig. 17-9) are ubiquitous in any well-established culture of protozoa. In fact, their appearance often signifies the decline of the protozoan culture. When protozoan cultures are not on hand, prepare cultures for rotifers (p. 347).

Notice how rotifers move. The head is provided with cilia which aid in locomotion as well as help direct food into the mouth. The tail foot is bifurcated and has a cement gland. Look for the chitinous "jaws" in constant motion in the stomach. Egg masses may be visible. Parthenogenetic (summer) eggs are of two sizes and thin-shelled. Males are not often found; they are very small and often degenerate. Many forms, if dried slowly, secrete a gelatinous covering which resists further desiccation.

Flagellates in termites. The large, slow-moving flagellates (Fig. 17-10) found in the intestinal tract of termites are symbiotic organisms which digest the cellulose consumed by termites (refer to special kinds of nutrition, p. 232).

Place a termite in a drop of physiological salt solution (0.5 to 0.7 per cent) or Ringer's solution (p. 409) on a clean slide. Use forceps to hold down the abdomen on the slide. With another forceps pull off its head. The intestine (with other viscera) will be found attached to the head part. Then remove the remains of the termite from the slide, keeping only the intestine. Macerate the intestinal contents, and then apply a coverslip. Under high power the long flagella are visible on these specimens. Preparations may be circled with Vaseline, covered, and used for several hours. Students may also want to add a vital dye (p. 309).

Many of the flagellates belong to the Kofoidea (order Hypermastigina) or to the Pyrsonympha (order Polymastigina). They reproduce asexually by longitudinal fission and encystment. These organisms possess a cellulose-splitting enzyme lacking in termites. Cleveland[1] in 1925 showed that when termites were defaunated they died within a few days. However, when dying termites were reinfected with flagellates through oral feeding, digestion again took place.

When the termites molt, the chitinous lining of the gut is lost along with the flagellates. After molting, reinfection occurs. Some wood-eating beetles, woodroaches, and cockroaches have similar flagellates, amoebae, or bacteria serving the same function. *Trichonympha* is common in the woodroach (*Cryptocercus*). En-

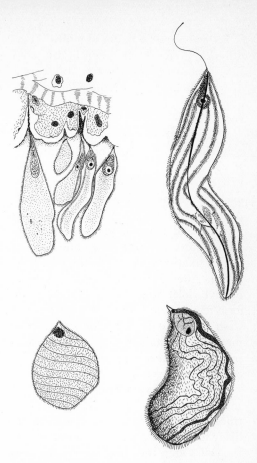

Fig. 17-10 Flagellates found in intestines of termites (*Pyrsonympha vertens*): section of a portion of the intestine of a termite showing young *Pyrsonymphae* attached; and three single forms (contracted and extended), one showing wood fibers inside. (After J. F. Porter, "Trichonympha and Other Parasites," *Bull. Museum Comp. Zoo.*, 1897–1898.)

cystment has been observed once a year when the woodroach molts. Students may collect and keep cultures using the method described on page 354.

Nematocysts of hydra. Mount a hydra in pond water on a slide. Include small bristles to prevent the coverslip from crushing the specimen. If a small drop of the stain safranin or a dilute acid is added to the wet mount, the nematocysts will be released.

[1] L. R. Cleveland, "The Effects of Oxygenation and Starvation on Symbiosis between the Termite Termopsis and Its Intestinal Flagellates," *Biol. Bull.*, 48:455, 1925.

Epithelio-muscle tissue of hydra. Place a hydra, preferably a green hydra, on a slide containing pond water, and tease it apart with dissecting needles. This maceration will release the symbiotic green zoochlorellae.

Under high power examine the large epithelio-muscle cells of the living animal. If you want students to stain the cells, first fix the cells, add stain, and then macerate the stained cells as follows. Prepare a solution by mixing 1 part of glycerin and 1 part of glacial acetic acid with 2 parts of water. Then add 2 drops of this fixative to a clean slide; add the hydra. After 3 minutes add 1 drop of methyl violet stain (p. 329). Leave this for a few minutes; draw off the stain and wash the slide in a bit of water. Now macerate the stained hydra with dissecting needles in a drop of water. Add a coverslip and examine under high power.

Streaming of cytoplasm (cyclosis). In many living cells mounted in salt solutions or aquarium water, students are likely to find cytoplasm streaming around the cell. Often they may see chloroplasts in green plant cells moving around the border of a cell. (In some cases, it is believed that the chloroplasts have motility, aside from floating in streaming cytoplasm. Sauvageau[2] has shown that chloroplasts of the alga *Saccorhiza* when exposed to strong light show contractions and dilations when they move.)

Many aquatic plants illustrate this circulation of cytoplasm called cyclosis. Mount a leaf of elodea (*Anacharis*), *Nitella*, *Chara*, or *Vallisneria* on a clean slide. In *Nitella* and *Chara*, focus especially on the internodal cells. In elodea, use the growing tips and focus on the midrib cells. Keep the uppermost layer of cells facing upward on the slide. Place the leaves in

warmed water or bring a warming light near the container to stimulate cyclosis. There are also some techniques which suggest adding a bit of thiamine hydrochloride (vitamin B_1) to the water. The rate of streaming may be from 3 to 15 cm per hour and as high as 45 cm per hour at a temperature around 30° C. At times it is sufficient to heat the slide in the palm of the hand.

In *Nitella* there are many nuclei in the internodes, and they also move. However, the chloroplasts are fixed within the inner surface of the cell walls and therefore do not move.

Students may find cytoplasmic streaming in other living material. Mount several threads of the mycelium of the bread mold *Mucor* in water or glycerin. Cytoplasm may be seen to be streaming up one side of the thread and down the other side.

Strip the epidermis from one of the inner scales of an onion bulb and look for streaming in unstained cells mounted in water. Slight warming of the water may stimulate streaming.

At other times, examine the unicellular hairs on the roots of *Tradescantia* seedlings, or the staminate hairs in the flower. Mount a filament of the stamen, which has several hairs attached, in warm water on a slide. Granules may be seen moving from the strands around the nucleus along the wall to another strand leading to the nucleus. At times the direction of streaming reverses.

Streaming is studied with ease in one of the large amoebae, *Chaos chaos* (Fig. 2-2). Mount in a drop of culture solution (p. 337). Include a small bristle or broken coverslip in the drop to avoid crushing the specimen when the coverslip is applied. Students should see the many vacuoles and the actively streaming cytoplasm which changes from sol to gel. The clearer

[2] As described in A. Guilliermond, *The Cytoplasm of the Plant Cell,* Chronica Botanica, 1941.

ectoplasm and the denser endoplasm illustrate this change.

Enzyme activity of mitochondria. There may be times when you will want to go further into the functions of cells and have students observe mitochondria as centers of enzyme activity. In the following demonstration[3] Janus Green B is used to dye mitochondria of cells in celery, and then the dye is bleached by enzymes produced by these bodies.

Cut across two "strings" (collenchyma) of a fresh celery stalk, then make a similar transverse cut 1 cm from the first. Transfer this 1-cm length, *inner surface up,* to a drop of 5 per cent sucrose solution on a clean slide. With a razor blade carefully cut away the two strings of the strip, leaving the transparent center section containing two or three layers of cells. For ease in cutting, use two razor blades, as follows. Hold the two blades close to and parallel with the string. Keep the inner blade stationary and draw the outer blade along the edge of the string to make the cut. The stationary blade keeps the section from twisting. Repeat for the string on the other side. Now seal with a coverslip and look for cytoplasmic streaming in the epidermis and the uppermost, subepidermal layer. Also find the green plastids, clear nucleus, and small moving spheres and rods which are the mitochondria. Apply filter paper to one end of the coverslip and at the same time add several drops of 0.001 per cent Janus Green B solution to the opposite side. Watch the mitochondria dye blue; then, within minutes, they will be decolorized by enzymes (dehydrogenases) on the mitochondria. The slides may be used over several days if they are placed in

[3] Paper by H. Du Buy and J. Showacre in *Laboratory Experiments in Biology, Physics, and Chemistry,* mimeographed, Staff of Nat. Institute of Health. U.S. Dept. Health, Education and Welfare, Nat. Institute of Health, Bethesda 14, Md., 1956.

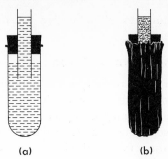

(a)   (b)

Fig. 17-11 A simple way to concentrate a culture of protozoa: (a) culture vial fitted with stopper and short glass tube; (b) vial covered with carbon paper: many protozoa seem to be phototropic and gather in the short tube.

Petri dishes lined with moist toweling and stored in a refrigerator.

Concentrating the number of organisms in a culture

Rich cultures of protozoa (*Paramecium, Blepharisma*) should be available for study with a microscope. Many students will also want to examine flagellates and other motile algae (culturing, pp. 341, 378). At times a culture may be too diluted, that is, few organisms in the culture so that only a small number of specimens is picked up in a drop of fluid for a temporary slide. Students can increase the concentration of organisms in a volume of fluid by centrifuging 10 to 20 cc of the culture. Or pour a portion of the culture into long vials or test tubes, and cover all but the top third of the tubes with carbon paper. Or prepare a short length of glass tubing, insert it into a one-hole stopper in a vial filled with culture as in Fig. 17-11a, and cover the vial with carbon paper. The protozoa concentrate in the uncovered portions (the tops of the test tubes, or the tubing in the stopper, Fig. 17-11b), since most of them are positively phototropic or negatively geotropic, or gather where the concentration of oxygen is greatest (at the top surface). Then prepare temporary mounts containing large numbers of organisms for microscopic study.

Slowing down protozoa

Protozoa, especially the ciliated forms, move too rapidly for high school students, especially beginners, to follow under the microscope. There are several ways to slow down the motion of ciliates for close, careful study.

Most experienced workers simply prepare several slides ahead of time and let the fluid begin to evaporate. As evaporation continues, the weight of the coverslip is enough to slow down the organisms. It is well to mention here that *Paramecium* as well as *Blepharisma, Spirostomum,* and *Stentor* have conspicuous contractile vacuoles which are best observed when the slides begin to dry so that the pressure of the coverslip flattens the organisms. Under a darkened field (reduce light by closing the diaphragm a bit), the rhythmic pulsations of the vacuoles may be seen clearly.

In another method, tease apart lens paper and apply the fibers on the slide containing a drop of rich protozoa culture. However, there is a danger that cilia and the larger cirri will be damaged with this crude method.

The following solutions may also be used to slow down motion.

GUM TRAGACANTH. Get tragacanth at a drug store or supply house and grind some in a mortar to a fine powder. Add cold water to this to make a thick jelly. Dilute the material to the proper viscosity by placing a drop of protozoa culture and a drop of the jelly on a slide. Students may want to try out different dilutions.

METHYL CELLULOSE. Prepare a solution by dissolving 10 gm of methyl cellulose in 90 cc of water. Place 1 drop of this syrupy solution with 1 drop of protozoa culture on a slide.

GELATIN. Prepare a 2 to 3 per cent solution of clear gelatin by dissolving in cold water and then heating gently until dissolved. Allow to cool to room temperature and add 1 drop of

this to a slide along with 1 drop of the culture containing the microorganisms.

You may also want to try a bit of isopropyl alcohol or chloretone, but these alter the structure and physiology of the organisms.

Anesthetization of small forms

There are times when you may want to examine flatworms, a hydra, or some other form which has contractile tissue. Or students may want to anesthetize a large animal in order to dissect out a bit of tissue for examination (for example, ciliated epithelial tissue from the roof of the frog's mouth, p. 32). The following materials and methods of narcotization or anesthetization are referred to throughout the chapters.

1. Spray ether or chloroform or alcohol on water containing the specimen. This method may also be used to kill small crustaceans and earthworms.

2. Add 1 per cent magnesium sulfate (Epsom salts) to the water in which the specimens (mainly protozoa) are moving. Make a more concentrated solution to anesthetize larger forms.

3. Add 0.1 per cent chloretone to water containing goldfish or frogs. One drop of chloretone of this dilution added to a large drop of culture of protozoa, hydras, or rotifers acts as an anesthetic. A frog may be immersed for 15 to 30 minutes in a solution made of 1 part 0.5 per cent chloretone and 4 parts Ringer's solution. Use a 1 per cent solution to kill planarians.

4. Add a 1 per cent solution of urethane to the water or inject it into the specimen (Chapter 9).

5. Add about a teaspoonful of menthol crystals and a medium-sized crystal of chloral hydrate (*caution:* poison) to a small amount of aquarium water. This is a fine anesthetizing agent to relax and extend small contractile animals before they are to be fixed in formalin or Bouin's solution.

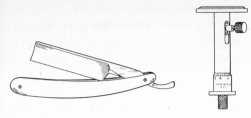

Fig. 17-12 Section razor and hand microtome for making freehand sections of plant tissue.

Freehand sections

Most tissues are not rigid enough to slice into thin sections for examination under the microscope. The usual procedure is to embed tissue in some paraffin mixture. A more rapid method is to freeze the tissue with carbon dioxide from a carbon dioxide cartridge, and then cut sections.

Nevertheless, some plant leaves and some woody stems may be prepared as temporary mounts simply by inserting them between lengths of elderberry pith or fresh carrots and then cutting slices. These are, of course, better when inserted into a hand microtome and sliced with a microtome razor blade (Fig. 17-12); for the microtome, which can be adjusted for thickness, enables students to cut uniformly thin slices. Thin sections may be cut with a razor blade alone if a hand microtome is not available. The preparation is the same.

Slice a length of elderberry (or sunflower) pith, or a raw carrot, in half, and sandwich between the two halves a piece of a leaf, such as privet, or a woody stem. Wrap these halves together tightly and soak in water for a few hours. The pith and the enclosed tissue specimen will expand and become rigid.

Then the material may be sliced with a sharp razor blade, at a slight angle, into thin sections. Keep the blade as well as the tissue wet and float the sections on water so they will not curl. Or insert the carrot-and-leaf preparation into the hand microtome, regulate the thickness of the slice, and cut with a sharp blade.

Staining is optional; methylene blue, eosin, or Lugol's iodine solution may be used.

Maceration of tissue

Using nitric acid. Mix 80 cc of water with 20 cc of concentrated nitric acid. (*Caution:* Pour the *acid* slowly into the *water.*) Place fresh muscle tissue from a frog or mammal in a glass dish containing this dilute nitric acid. This reagent should dissolve the connective tissue, so that the muscle fibers become isolated, in 1 to 3 days at room temperature. It may be found that different sections of muscle require varying periods of time for tissue breakdown. Shake the container to see the rate of maceration. Isolate and tease apart the fibers on a slide with dissecting needles, pour off the nitric acid, and wash the muscle tissue. You may want to have students stain the fibers with such stains as methylene blue and finally mount in glycerin or glycerin jelly.

When it is desired to keep the specimens for several days or indefinitely, pour the water off before staining and add a half-saturated solution of alum, prepared as follows. Add 100 gm of alum to 500 cc of water and heat in an agate dish. All the alum should dissolve; let the solution cool. Some alum will crystallize out; decant off the resulting cold saturated solution. Then from this prepare a 50 per cent saturated solution by adding 100 cc of the saturated solution to 100 cc of water. (This alum preparation is also desirable if the specimens are to be stained and mounted in glycerin.)

Using potassium hydroxide. A weak solution of potassium hydroxide will dissolve cells; a strong solution will separate the cells but will not destroy them. Prepare a solution by warming 35 gm of potassium hydroxide in 100 cc of distilled water until it dissolves. Let the solution cool to room temperature.

Dissect out small pieces of tissue from the leg of a frog (striated muscle), from the stomach or intestinal wall (smooth muscle), and from the heart (cardiac muscle). Place these in separate containers of potassium hydroxide solution for 15 to 30 minutes. Then on separate slides mount in a drop of solution a piece of each kind of tissue. Tease apart the tissue with dissecting needles and apply a coverslip.

Using formalin. Prepare formalin in a normal salt solution by adding 2 cc of formalin (40 per cent solution of formaldehyde, p. 330) to 1000 cc of a normal salt solution (p. 409). This serves as a good dissociating agent for brain tissue and all kinds of epithelial cells. While it acts quickly, it also preserves delicate cilia of epithelial tissue and the ependymal cells of the brain. Place small pieces of tissue in this solution. Two hours to 2 days later, depending on the size of the specimens, isolate nerve cells from the brain tissue. Examine a sample under the microscope to study how fast the process is taking place. Often it is found that epithelial tissue from the intestines and trachea may be isolated within 2 hours; stratified epithelial cells from the mouth and skin may require up to 3 days.

Finally, tease apart cells (in a drop of the solution) with dissecting needles on a clean slide. If you wish to have stained mounts, stain with a 1 per cent aqueous solution of eosin. Draw off the formalin solution with filter paper at one end of the slide, and at the same time apply stain to the opposite side. For a more lasting preparation mount in glycerin.

Using Jeffrey's fluid (for plant tissues). In a Syracuse dish mix together equal parts of 10 per cent solution of nitric acid and a 10 per cent solution of chromic acid. (*Caution:* Do not inhale fumes; work in a well-ventilated room.) Drop thin sections of plant tissue into this fluid. Mount small bits of tissue in water on a slide to examine the rate of maceration. When the cells separate from each other fairly readily, pour off the fluid and wash the tissue in water. Mount the cells in water and press down with the coverslip to separate them. Stain with eosin, methylene blue, or similar dyes. (Avoid putting metal forceps into the macerating fluids.)

Mounting small objects

Whole small forms may be mounted more or less permanently in several media. Forms which contain water need to be dehydrated before they can be embedded in balsam, or the balsam will become cloudy. On the other hand, some whole mounts may be embedded in glycerin jelly or in Karo syrup without dehydration. We shall describe only a few of the simpler techniques which seem practical for the classroom.

In syrup. Small forms like *Drosophila* and other small flies, ants, fleas, mosquito larvae, *Daphnia, Artemia,* and *Gammarus* may be mounted in a large drop of clear syrup, such as Karo. Dehydration is not necessary. After the organism is oriented in the syrup, add a bristle (so that the coverslip will not crush the specimen), and gently lower the coverslip at a 45-degree angle from one side; let it sink slowly into the syrup so that no air bubbles form. Should air bubbles form, they may be broken with a dissecting needle. Then remove the excess embedding fluid with wet lens paper.

In glycerin jelly. Such organisms as

roundworms, insects, small crustaceans, and plant specimens may be transferred into glycerin jelly from alcohol or formalin, as follows. Add glycerin to the alcohol or formalin in which the specimen is contained, until 10 per cent of the storage fluid is glycerin. Cover the container with a bit of gauze and allow evaporation to concentrate the glycerin. After the glycerin has become concentrated (this may take several days), transfer the specimens to a clean slide with a drop of glycerin jelly, prepared in the following way. Soak 10 gm of gelatin in 60 cc of distilled water for about 2 hours. Then add 70 cc of glycerin and 1 gm of phenol. Heat the solution in a water bath, and then let it cool. When ready to embed specimens on a slide, heat the mounting medium to about 40° C in a water bath so that it is soft. The temperature should not be allowed to rise above 40° C, or the colloid will no longer solidify.

Put a coverslip on the slide and ring it with balsam to slow down evaporation. These slides need not be stained. They must be handled with care, for the glycerin jelly melts near room temperature. Examine under the microscope with reduced light intensity.

In balsam. Scales of fish and snakes, insect wings, hair of mammals, feathers, and similar dry specimens may be embedded in balsam. They do contain some water, so that in making permanent slides it is safer to dehydrate the specimens first in xylol for several hours (see p. 326); then mount them in a drop of balsam and seal with a coverslip. Whole small insects must first be dehydrated before mounting in balsam. For a rapid method, they may be put into glacial acetic acid for dehydration, then mounted directly in a drop of balsam.

Or the dead insects may be put in a carbol-xylol solution made by adding 1 part of carbolic acid crystals to 2 parts of xylol. After 1 to 2 hours transfer to pure xylol for 6 to 24 hours; then mount in balsam and apply a coverslip.

In all these cases leave the slides flat for several days until the balsam hardens; later stack the slides in a slide box.

The preparation and staining of whole chick embryos in balsam is described later in this chapter.

Smear slide techniques

Three basic techniques for making smears on slides are described here: smears of dividing cells to show chromosomes, blood films, and smears of bacteria.

Salivary chromosome smears. The salivary glands of fruit flies are excellent for the study of chromosomes; these insects have "giant" chromosomes, about a hundred times as large as ordinary ones.

Demerec and Kaufmann[4] have published detailed instructions on preparing stained smears of salivary glands of the larvae of fruit flies. They advise that larvae be reared at a temperature between 16° and 18° C with extra yeast added to the culture bottles (p. 200, preparation of media). Females laying eggs should be transferred to fresh bottles of medium every 2 days. In this way only a few eggs are laid in each bottle, and the larvae have a chance to grow without overcrowding. Full-grown larvae are collected as they emerge and begin to pupate. (Male larvae can be distinguished because they have larger, more conspicuous gonads which can be seen through the transparent skin in the posterior third of the body.)

Dissect out the salivary glands of the larvae in 0.7 per cent sodium chloride solution. On a clean glass slide add 2

[4] M. Demerec and B. P. Kaufmann, *Drosophila Guide,* Carnegie Institution, Washington, D. C., 1945, $0.25.

drops of acetocarmine (see stains for protozoa, p. 322) to a dissected gland. Crush the glands on the slide by pressing a coverslip against them. Examine under low and high power.

Bensley and Bensley[5] describe a similar technique using *Chironomus* flies (midges). The larvae may be found in tubes in mud or in water. They are soft, worm-like, often red in color, and they may be found in the autumn and early spring. Collect them and culture them on decaying vegetation or in earth.

The recommended technique for handling these larvae is to mount an intact larva on a clean slide and gently press down with the coverslip to smear it. When examined under high power, the nucleolus and nuclear contents are visible. This may be stained with neutral red (p. 406) or acetocarmine.

Smear of onion root tip. As a group activity (in class or in your science club) you may want students to stain the dividing cells in the growing tip of onion roots so that chromosomes are visible. The method described here is modified from one in *Stain Technology.*[6]

Germinate seedlings or place an onion bulb in water so that roots begin to grow. With a razor blade cut off the root tips and place them in a saturated aqueous solution of *p*-dichlorobenzene for 3 hours (at 12° to 16° C). Next, transfer the root tips to a Pyrex test tube containing a mixture of 2 per cent aceto-orcein solution and 1 N hydrochloric acid in the ratio of 9:1. Heat this for a few seconds until it just reaches the boiling point; pour into a Syracuse dish or watch glass and let it cool for 5 minutes. Then transfer the

root tips to a drop of 1 per cent aceto-orcein solution on a clean slide.

Carefully cut off the deeply colored region of the root tip; discard the rest of the material. Now apply a coverslip and press uniformly with a dissecting needle along the coverslip so that the material is squashed. Place filter paper over the coverslip to squeeze out the excess stain. Examine under high power for mitotic figures.

If these smear slides are sealed with a ring of paraffin they will last up to 15 days. The slides can be made permanent if they are placed in 10 per cent acetic acid until the coverslips fall off. Then pass the slides through this series: acetic acid and alcohol (half and half), absolute alcohol, then xylol, 2 to 3 minutes in each solution. Mount in balsam.

Blood smears. Clean the finger with cotton moistened in alcohol. Sterilize a needle or lancet in alcohol and over a Bunsen flame (or liquid fuel can). These practices are similar to those described for making a slide of blood (p. 75) and for typing blood (p. 79). Students may be required to bring parental consent notes; regulations vary in different communities.

Puncture the finger and put a drop of blood on one end of a clean slide. Place a second slide, with one end at a 30-degree angle, on the first slide (Fig. 17-13). Bring the upper slide up to the drop of blood until the blood spreads along the narrow end of the slide, forming a uniform layer. *Push* the top slide rapidly

[5] R. Bensley and S. Bensley, *Handbook of Histological and Cytological Technique,* U. of Chicago Press, Chicago, 1938.

[6] A. Scharma and A. Mookerjea, "Paradichlorobenzene and Other Chemicals in Chromosome Work," *Stain Technol.,* 30:1, Jan. 1955.

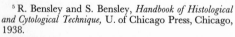

Fig. 17-13 Making a blood smear.

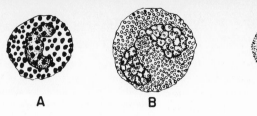

A   B   C

Fig. 17-14 White blood cells stained with Wright's stain: A, basophil; B, eosinophil; C, neutrophil. (From C. A. Villee, *Biology*, 2d ed., Saunders, 1954.)

toward the opposite end of the first slide to form a thin film. The greater the angle of the second slide, the thicker the film that is formed. Let the slide dry in the air. A good film should be smooth and not show wavy surfaces.

Chemically clean glassware is a requirement in preparing good blood smears. Use new slides and coverslips, or place them in a beaker of 95 per cent alcohol, wipe dry, and flame over a Bunsen burner before use.

Staining blood smears: Wright's blood stain. Stand the dried blood smear slide across a Syracuse dish or support it across a wide cork in a Petri dish. Cover the dry blood film completely with Wright's stain for 1 to 3 minutes. This fixes the blood film. Next add distilled water, or in another technique, a buffer solution, with a pipette, drop by drop, until a metallic greenish scum forms on the surface of the slide. (The buffer solution is prepared by adding 1.63 gm of monobasic potassium phosphate and 3.2 gm of dibasic sodium phosphate to 1 liter of distilled water.) Continue to add water or buffer until you have diluted the stain by half. Let this stand for 2 to 3 minutes.

The staining time varies with each batch of slides and should be predetermined by some trial slides, in this way. After the first application of distilled water or buffer to the original stain, place the slides in distilled water for 2 to 3 minutes. Now examine under the microscope; the granules in the basophils

should stain deep blue, in the eosinophils bright red, and in the neutrophils lilac (Fig. 17-14). Wash the slide with water continuously, until it is lavender-pink. Then stand the slides on edge to dry or blot them dry with filter paper. Inspect under the microscope, without a coverslip or balsam, for the desired stain. If it is too dark, decolorize by returning the slides to distilled water.

Students may study these slides under an oil immersion lens. The immersion oil should be added directly to the stained dried blood film.

Staining blood smears: Giemsa stain. This is a fine stain for both blood smears and bacterial smears. A stock solution of Giemsa stain may be purchased, or prepared as follows. Dissolve 0.5 gm of Giemsa powder in 33 cc of glycerin (this will take 1 to 2 hours). Then add 33 cc of acetone-free absolute methyl alcohol. To use the stain, dilute it by adding 10 cc of distilled water to each cc of stock solution of stain.

Let the blood smear dry in the air, and then fix the film by standing the slide in a Coplin jar (Fig. 17-15) with 70 per cent methyl alcohol for 3 to 5 minutes. Dry in the air or blot dry with filter paper. Next transfer the slide to a second Coplin jar containing dilute Giemsa stain for 15 to 30 minutes. Finally wash the slide in distilled water and dry it.

Bacterial smears. Motility and fission in bacteria can be studied by using a hanging drop (Fig. 17-7). To a lesser extent, motility and fission may be seen in a wet mount using high power or an oil immersion lens. A stain such as methylene blue may also be used in a wet mount (p. 309). However, "Brownian motion" will be seen and should not be confused with motility.

On the other hand, when bacteria are to be stained as permanent mounts, they must first be fixed to the slide. This is accomplished by transferring a loopful (see preparation of loop, p. 384) of the bacterial suspension to a clean slide. Then with the wire loop spread this small drop into a thin film and let it dry in the air. (When the bacteria are transferred from a solid agar culture, use a sterile needle and transfer a small sample of a colony into a loopful of sterile water on a slide.)

When the film is dry, pass the bottom of the slide through a flame three times to fix the bacteria to the slide, so that they will not be washed off in the subsequent staining procedure. There are many stains, generally basic aniline dyes, that can be used. These may be prepared and stored as *stock* solutions in saturated alcoholic solution. Prepare one or more of the following stains.[7]

CRYSTAL VIOLET. Add 13.87 gm (or slightly more) of the dye to 100 cc of 95 per cent ethyl alcohol. Let this stand for about 2 days, stirring frequently; filter and store.

BASIC FUCHSIN. Add 8.16 gm (or a bit more) of the dye to 100 cc of 95 per cent ethyl alcohol. Let it stand for 2 days, stirring frequently; then filter and store.

SAFRANIN. Add 3.41 gm to 100 cc of 95 per cent ethyl alcohol and follow the procedure given above.

METHYLENE BLUE. Add 1.48 gm of the dye to 100 cc of 95 per cent ethyl alcohol and follow the same method.

In use, *dilute* the stock solution of the stains. For each 10 cc of the stock solution, add 90 cc of distilled water.

Apply the dilute stain to a bacterial smear on a slide (which has been fixed in a flame) for 2 to 4 minutes, then wash off with water and blot dry. Examine under the microscope. The time for staining varies with the thickness of the film, the concentration of the stain, and the kinds of bacteria under study. With practice, students will learn how many minutes to stain the bacterial film. Coverslips need not be used. For permanent slides, however, add 1 drop of balsam when the slide is thoroughly dry and then apply a coverslip.

Methods for culturing bacteria are described in Chapter 20, along with special techniques for plating and making transfers. Bacterial smears can be made from sauerkraut juice, yoghurt, timothy hay or beans left to decay in water, or the scrapings from one's teeth.

Gram's stain for bacterial smears. Gram's stain is used as one step in distinguishing bacteria; some are "Gram-positive," others "Gram-negative." Gram-positive

Fig. 17-15 Coplin jar: slides are placed in grooves for staining. (Photo: Ward's Natural Science Establishment, Inc.)

[7] Procedures are those suggested in War Dept., *Methods for Laboratory Technicians*, Tech. Man. 8-227, Supt. Documents, Govt. Printing Office, Washington, D. C., 1941.

organisms are stained violet or blue with this differential stain; Gram-negative organisms give a pink to reddish stain. Gram's stain involves the application of a stain, then a decolorizing agent, Gram's iodine, and finally a counterstain. In this technique, Gram-positive organisms do not become decolorized after treatment with a dye and iodine, while Gram-negative organisms lose the stain. In Gram-positive bacteria, either because the cell membrane has different properties, or because it possesses different chemicals, or for a number of other reasons, these organisms remain stained. In general, cocci are Gram-positive (except meningococci, gonococci, and catarrhalis group). Spirilla and spirochetes, as well as most bacilli (except the organisms which cause diphtheria), acid-fast bacteria, and many of the forms which produce spores are Gram-negative (Fig. 17-16).

Following are the stains which need to be purchased or prepared for Gram's stain technique.

CRYSTAL VIOLET, AMMONIUM OXALATE SOLUTION. Mix together 5 cc of crystal violet (stock solution) and 5 cc of 95 per cent ethyl alcohol. To this add 40 cc of a 1 per cent aqueous solution of ammonium oxalate.

GRAM'S IODINE. Mix together 2 gm of potassium iodide and 1 gm of iodine in 300 cc of distilled water. (For careful work, substitute 240 cc of distilled water and 60 cc of a 5 per cent aqueous solution of sodium bicarbonate.)

This is the usual staining technique. Let a thin film of bacterial suspension dry on a slide and then fix it in a Bunsen flame (wave slide three times through the flame). Let it stand in crystal violet stain for 1 minute. Pour off the excess stain. Then add Gram's iodine for 1 minute. This fixes the Gram-positive organisms. Wash off in water, and decolorize with 95 per cent ethyl alcohol. This is the step where the Gram-negative organisms lose the stain. Then wash in several changes of decolorizer until no more stain washes off. This may vary from less than 1 minute to 3 minutes. Then wash in water again.

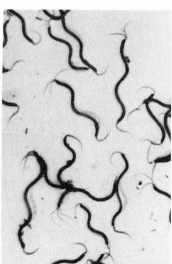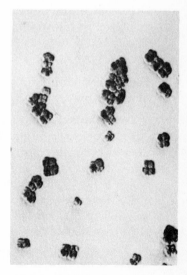

Fig. 17-16 Three kinds of bacteria: *left,* bacillus or rod (*Clostridium tetani;* note that this photograph shows the typical vegetative rods, and developing spores as well); *center,* spirillum or spiral (*Spirillum rubrum*); *right,* cocci or spherical (*Sarcina lutea*). (Photos: General Biological Supply House, Inc., Chicago.)

Now counterstain the slide with safranin (p. 320) for about ½ minute. Wash off in water and blot dry.

Temporary stained slides of protozoa

These may be used for several hours at a time if the coverslips are ringed with Vaseline. For this, protozoa are killed rapidly (or fixed) and then stained to permit an examination of structure or possibly changes in nuclear content during stages in division. The following two methods and many others are described in the literature.

Using methyl green acetic acid. Prepare the fixative-stain by saturating a 1 per cent solution of acetic acid with methyl green (p. 329) and filtering. Add 1 drop of a rich culture of protozoa to 1 drop of the methyl green acetic acid solution. The cytoplasm of the cells should remain clear while the nucleus is stained.

Using acetocarmine. Add carmine powder to a boiling 45 per cent solution of acetic acid until it is saturated. Then filter. Add 1 drop of the protozoa culture to 1 drop of the stain on a clean slide. This stain is used to differentiate the nucleus.

Permanent stained slides of protozoa

Concentrating protozoa. Several methods for concentrating protozoa may be used in preparing protozoa for fixation and staining. Here are three methods which are in common use.

1. Spread a thin film of Mayer's albumen (p. 330) on each of several clean coverslips. Then float some of these on the surface of a rich culture of protozoa, others at the bottom of the culture jars. After 12 to 24 hours remove the coverslips with clean forceps and place them in a fixative.

2. Draw out a pipette in a Bunsen flame to form a capillary pipette (p. 419). Then use it to squirt a drop of a rich culture onto a slide or coverslip which has been spread with a film of Mayer's albumen. Quickly place the slide or coverslip into a jar of fixative.

3. This method permits the fixing of large quantities of protozoa in bulk. Centrifuge a culture slowly for some 30 seconds. (Small hand centrifuges are available from biological supply houses.) Draw off the fluid quickly and pipette the concentrated culture of protozoa at the bottom into a small container of fixative. When they are to be transferred out of the fixative into alcohol, concentrate them again by centrifuging.

Fixation. While Schaudinn's fixative is recommended especially for fixing protozoa, others, such as Bouin's and Zenker's fixative solutions (pp. 325, 326), are also useful. Prepare Schaudinn's fixative so that it is on hand, as follows. Prepare a saturated aqueous solution of mercuric chloride. Then to 2 parts of this solution add 1 part of absolute alcohol. Just before it is to be used, add 1 cc of glacial acetic acid.

Protozoa should stand in this fixative for 10 to 30 minutes (the average time is somewhere about 15 minutes). The time requirements are different for other fixatives. Then centrifuge the protozoa and transfer them into a small amount of 50 per cent alcohol. After 10 minutes, transfer into 70 per cent alcohol to which a few drops of a concentrated solution of iodine in alcohol has been added, so that the alcohol is slightly brown in color. After a few minutes, transfer to 90 per cent alcohol, and finally into absolute alcohol, always keeping the quantity of alcohol as small as possible.

Staining. Spread a film of albumen on slides or coverslips (see Mayer's albumen,

p. 330); squirt a drop of previously fixed protozoa onto a slide or coverslip with some force so that the protozoa adhere to the albumen, and return the slides to absolute alcohol. Now the protozoa are on the slides, ready for staining. There are several suitable stains. Hematoxylin is a chromosome stain, and so is the Feulgen nuclear reagent. Borax carmine may be used for whole mounts (Chap. 17); or try Borrel's stain, which stains nuclei red and cytoplasm green. Many of these stains for protozoa may be found in textbooks of protozoology (some are included here under stains, p. 328). Delafield's or Ehrlich's hematoxylin may be used in place of Heidenhain's (p. 329).

The procedure for staining with hematoxylin is as follows. Remove the albumen-coated slides of protozoa from absolute alcohol and transfer down the series of alcohols to water. For instance, leave the slides (or coverslips) for about 2 minutes in each of these: from absolute alcohol to 90 per cent, then to 70 per cent, to 50 per cent, to 30 per cent, and finally to water. Then place the slides in hematoxylin for 5 to 15 minutes so that the nuclei become stained (inspect under the microscope during the process); wash off the stain in water. Transfer the slides to ammonia water (about 1 drop of concentrated ammonium hydroxide added to 250 cc of tap water).

Next, counterstain with a cytoplasmic dye such as eosin (1 per cent alcoholic solution). After some 5 to 10 minutes transfer to water, then to 30 per cent alcohol. Now follow with transfers at 2-minute intervals into an upward series of alcohols: to 60 per cent, 70, 90, and finally absolute alcohol. Next, transfer the stained slides into xylol.

It is well to inspect the slides under the microscope before adding balsam for final mounting. Should the nuclei be stained too deeply with hematoxylin, decolorize by placing the slides into 70 per cent alcohol to which a small amount of 1 per cent hydrochloric acid has been added. Then place the slides into alkaline 70 per cent alcohol again to regain the blue color. (Prepare alkaline alcohol by adding 1 drop of 1 per cent ammonium hydroxide to a Coplin jar of the alcohol.) Continue into 90 per cent alcohol and the steps which lead to final mounting of the slides.

Complete the slide by adding a drop of Canada balsam to each slide; then apply coverslips. (Or add the balsam to the slide and cover with stained coverslip, if that has been the procedure.)

Other stains. Kudo[8] recommends some special techniques, such as using Delafield's hematoxylin of a stock solution diluted to 1 to 5 or 10 in order to get a slow progressive staining of protozoa. Should slides become overstained, they can be decolorized in a 0.5 per cent solution of hydrochloric acid in water or in alcohol. Then mount the protozoa in neutral mounting medium.

Mayer's paracarmine is recommended as a useful stain. It is prepared in slightly acidified 70 per cent alcohol solution. As before, should protozoa become overstained, they may be decolorized in a 0.5 per cent solution of hydrochloric acid in alcohol.

If students for a project need to show the silver line system of ciliated protozoa (Fig. 17-17), they may impregnate ciliates with silver nitrate solution, as follows. Add 2 per cent silver nitrate solution to a rich culture of a ciliate such as *Paramecium* on a slide, and let the slide dry in the air. This should take from 5 to 10 minutes. Then wash the slide thoroughly and expose it to sunlight. Keep the slide

[8] Richard Kudo, *Protozoology,* Thomas, Springfield, Ill., 1954.

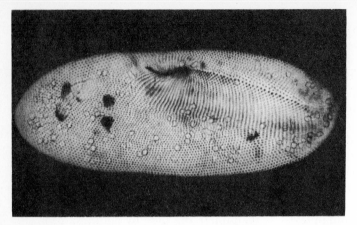

Fig. 17-17 *Paramecium* stained with silver nitrate solution to show silver line system. (Photo: General Biological Supply House, Inc., Chicago.)

in a porcelain dish of distilled water for 3 to 8 hours. On occasion, examine the slide under low power to watch the progress. Finally wash thoroughly again, dry, and then mount in Canada balsam.

Permanent tissue slides (histological techniques)

Single-celled organisms or bits of tissues are placed in a fixative for two reasons. First, the cells must be killed rapidly so that cell contents are preserved and the cells closely resemble living cells. In addition, fixative hardens tissue cells so that they can be cut into thin, transparent sections for examination under the microscope.

The fixative must be washed out of the cells before the cells can be processed for staining. The type of fixative used determines how they should be washed. When tissues have been killed in a fixative containing mercuric chloride (corrosive sublimate, poisonous) or picric acid, the cells must be washed for at least 1 hour in 70 per cent alcohol. On the other hand, when the fixative contains potassium dichromate, the tissues should be washed for at least 1 hour in water.

In general, this is the procedure for staining and mounting permanent slides:
1. Fix tissue and harden.
2. Dehydrate through series of alcohols.
3. Clear tissue.
4. Embed in paraffin.
5. Section with microtome.
6. Dissolve paraffin with xylol.
7. Pass through series of alcohols into distilled water.
8. Stain and counterstain.
9. Dehydrate by moving up the series of alcohols into xylol.
10. Mount in balsam.

Preparation of fixatives. There are several widely used fixatives which teachers and students will find desirable to prepare. After this section (on fixation) we shall follow through the next step, dehydration, and then proceed with subsequent procedures in preparing tissues for permanent, stained slides.

These fixatives are listed in alphabetical order. Consult textbooks on histological techniques, such as those listed at the end of this chapter, for more detailed studies. Note that smaller quantities than those given can be prepared by cutting the "recipe" in half, or in thirds.

ALCOHOL (ETHYL). A 70 per cent solution of ethyl alcohol is a common preservative for small forms and tissue specimens. (For ways to dilute alcohols to lower percentages, see p. 403.)

ALCOHOL (ABSOLUTE). Johansen[9] suggested a method for preparing absolute alcohol (theoretically 100 per cent alcohol, with all the water removed). Begin with 95 per cent ethyl alcohol. Heat some crystals of cupric sulfate

[9] D. Johansen, *Plant Microtechnique,* McGraw-Hill, New York, 1940.

until only a white powder remains. Add this anhydrous form to the 95 per cent ethyl alcohol. As long as there is still some water in the alcohol, the copper sulfate turns blue. Therefore, continue adding anhydrous sulfate until there is no change to blue. Then filter the alcohol quickly into a dry stock bottle and cork securely so that no moisture from the air enters the bottle. Vaseline the cork as an additional precaution. In fact, some workers keep a small bag of anhydrous sulfate suspended in the bottle to keep it free of water.

A sensitive test for water in absolute alcohol can be made by adding a few drops of alcohol to a solution of liquid paraffin in anhydrous chloroform. When moisture is present in the alcohol, the solution becomes clouded.

ALLEN'S FLUID. This fixative is recommended especially as an all-around general fixative. Combine the following:

water	75 cc
formalin (40% formaldehyde)	15 cc
glacial acetic acid	10 cc
picric acid	1 gm
chromic acid	1 gm
urea	1 gm

Fix small pieces of tissue for 24 hours and then wash in 70 per cent alcohol until there is no further loss of color.

BOUIN'S FIXATIVE. This is an excellent fixative for general use with both plant and animal tissue; however, it is difficult to wash out of tissues before staining. Its main advantage is that specimens may be stored in it for long periods of time. Combine the following:

glacial acetic acid	5 cc
picric acid (saturated aqueous)	75 cc
formalin (40% formaldehyde)	25 cc

Leave the tissue in the fixative for 24 to 48 hours; then wash in 70 per cent alcohol until the color is removed.

CARL'S SOLUTION. This is an excellent preservative for insect forms. A small amount of glycerin may be added to the solution to prevent hard-bodied insects from becoming brittle in the preservative. Combine the first three of these materials:

alcohol (95%)	170 cc
formalin (40% formaldehyde)	60 cc
water	280 cc
glacial acetic acid	20 cc

Add the glacial acetic acid to the solution just before using.

CARNOY AND LEBRUN'S FLUID. This is recommended often for hard-shelled specimens, such as some arthropods, for it has high penetrability. It also dissolves fat. (*Warning:* highly poisonous and inflammable.) Combine the following materials just before the fluid is to be used:

glacial acetic acid	33 cc
absolute alcohol	33 cc
chloroform	33 cc
mercuric chloride	(to saturate about 25 gm)

FORMALDEHYDE, ALCOHOL, ACETIC ACID (FAA). This is a good hardening agent for plant tissues. In fact, plant materials may be stored in this preservative for several years. Pieces of leaf tissue should be killed and hardened in this fluid for 12 hours, while thicker tissues, such as small stems and thick leaves, should be kept in it for 24 hours and woody twigs should remain in it for a week. Tissues need not be washed after preservation in FAA. Many small animal forms can also be fixed in this fluid. The alcohol content counteracts the swelling effects of formalin and glacial acetic acid. Combine these materials:

ethyl alcohol (95%)	50 cc
glacial acetic acid	2 cc
formalin (40% formaldehyde)	10 cc
water	40 cc

FLEMMING'S FIXATIVE. This is recommended especially as a fixative for small bits of tissue in preparation for careful histological study. Specimens are kept in the fixative for at least 24 hours. Combine these materials:

osmic acid (1%)	10 cc
chromic acid (10%)	3 cc
water	19 cc
glacial acetic acid	2 cc

Wash out the fixative with water for 24 hours, then transfer to 70 per cent alcohol.

GATES' FLUID. This fixative, mainly used for plant tissues, is recommended sometimes to show chromosomes in root tips. Prepare the solution in this way:

chromic acid	0.7 gm
glacial acetic acid	0.5 cc
water	100 cc

Leave the specimens in this fixative for 24 hours. Then wash out the fixative in running water.

GILSON'S FLUID. This is an excellent fixative for careful histological work, and especially recommended for the beginner. Avoid inhaling the fluid, for it is poisonous. Also keep steel instruments out of this fixative, or out of any other fixative which contains mercuric chloride (corrosive sublimate).

Specimens are kept in this fluid for 24 hours; they can remain in it for a month or so. Be sure to wash out the fixative in 70 per cent alcohol before proceeding further along in dehydration. Combine these materials:

alcohol (95%)	10	cc
water	88	cc
mercuric chloride	2	gm
nitric acid	1.8	cc
glacial acetic acid	0.4	cc

KLEINENBERG'S FIXATIVE. This is recommended especially as a fixative for chick embryos (p. 330) and many small marine organisms. Prepare as follows. To a 2 per cent aqueous solution of sulfuric acid, add picric acid until it is saturated.

LAVDOWSKY'S FIXATIVE. This is a general fixative especially useful in botanical work. Combine these:

potassium dichromate	5	gm
water	100	cc
mercuric chloride	0.15	gm
glacial acetic acid	2	cc

Again, avoid inhaling any of these fixatives which contain mercuric chloride (corrosive sublimate), and do not introduce steel instruments, such as tweezers, into the fluid.

Tissue may remain in the fixative for 24 hours. Then transfer tissue specimens into 70 per cent alcohol for at least 1 hour.

ZENKER'S FIXATIVE. This is widely used in histological work. It is also a fine preservative for small marine forms. Since it is not very stable, only small amounts should be made at any one time, or omit adding the glacial acetic acid until just before using the fixative. Mix together:

potassium dichromate	2.5	gm
water	100	cc
mercuric chloride	5	gm
glacial acetic acid	5	cc
sodium sulfate	1	gm

Fix the specimens for 24 hours. Wash out the fixative in 70 per cent alcohol for the next 24 hours. (Avoid using steel instruments and definitely avoid inhaling the fumes.)

There are other preservatives which may serve special uses in the laboratory or classroom. Some have found favor with technicians handling algae or fleshy fungi.

PRESERVATIVE FOR UNICELLULAR ALGAE. Sass[10] recommends the following preservative for storing unicellular algae, fleshy fungi, liverworts and mosses. Combine:

water	72 cc
formalin (40% formaldehyde)	5 cc
glycerin	20 cc
glacial acetic acid	3 cc

PRESERVATIVE #1 FOR GREEN PLANTS. This fluid is recommended often to prevent bleaching of chlorophyll in preserved plant specimens. Mix these ingredients:

alcohol (50%)	90	cc
formalin (40% formaldehyde)	5	cc
glacial acetic acid	2.5	cc
glycerin	2.5	cc
cupric chloride	10.0	gm
uranium nitrate	1.5	gm

The specimens may be stored in this preservative permanently, or they may be immersed in this solution temporarily before transferring to another preservative.

PRESERVATIVE #2 FOR GREEN PLANTS. This solution also prevents the bleaching of chlorophyll in plant tissues. You may want to add enough copper sulfate to the FAA fixative (p. 325) to make a saturated solution, so that one fixative, FAA, has been utilized for two purposes. Or you may prefer to make up this solution to have on hand, as follows: Dissolve 0.2 gm of copper sulfate in 35 cc of water. To this solution, add a solution composed of:

ethyl alcohol (95%)	50 cc
formalin (40% formaldehyde)	10 cc
glacial acetic acid	5 cc

Specimens may be stored in this preservative indefinitely. Occasionally transfer specimens into fresh liquid.

Dehydrating, clearing, and embedding tissues. In the fixative the tissues were killed quickly and also hardened. The next step is dehydration of the tissues. Water must be removed from the tissues, and then they are embedded in paraffin to give the support needed to cut thin

[10] J. Sass, *Botanical Microtechnique,* Iowa State College Press, Ames, 1951.

sections of tissue for examination under the microscope. Usually tissues are transferred from the fixative into 70 per cent ethyl alcohol, but the process depends on the kind of fixative the tissue has been killed in. Very delicate tissues are first washed in water and then transferred gradually, first into 30 per cent alcohol, then into 50 per cent, and finally into 70 per cent alcohol (so that diffusion currents do not distort the tissues). Keep the tissues in each of the different percentages of alcohol in the series for about 1 hour; in the 70 per cent alcohol for some 2 to 6 hours. (If the fixative contained picric acid, remove it quickly by adding a few grains of lithium carbonate to the 70 per cent alcohol in this washing.) Then transfer the tissues into absolute alcohol for 1 hour. Next, transfer them into a clearing agent to prepare them for embedding in wax. A clearing agent must be miscible with alcohol, for it replaces the alcohol in the tissues. Xylol is a rapid clearing agent.

Keep the tissues in xylol for 1 to 3 hours. If the xylol should become cloudy, return the tissues to absolute alcohol; for the cloudiness is an indication that the tissue has not been dehydrated completely. Incidentally, the best agent for removing water in the stock bottle of absolute alcohol is anhydrous copper sulfate (technique, p. 325).

When the tissues have been cleared, they are ready for embedding in melted paraffin. Keep the wax melted in a paraffin oven set at a temperature a few degrees higher than the melting point of the paraffin. Insert the specimens into square paper boats (Fig. 17-18) containing melted paraffin, and leave them there for 2 to 3 hours. Change the specimens into fresh wax within this period of time. When the wax is ready to be cooled, float the paper boat in a container of cold water, but do not submerge the boat so that water flows on top of the wax. Blow on the surface of the paraffin until a film begins to form. Or let the

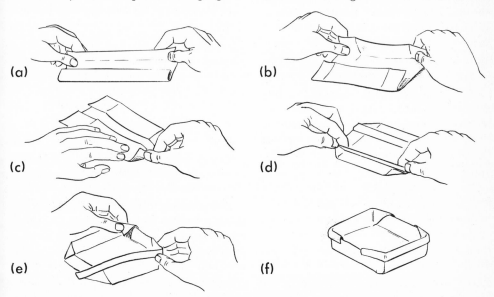

(a)

(b)

(c)

(d)

(e)

(f)

Fig. 17-18 Making a paper boat in which to embed bits of tissue in paraffin. (After P. Gray, *Handbook of Basic Microtechnique*, McGraw-Hill, 1952.)

paraffin solidify by simply removing it from the oven. When the paraffin has hardened sufficiently on the surface, submerge the boat in cold water and let it remain to harden throughout. Then remove the paper and trim the block of paraffin to a small size so that it fits on the holder of the microtome.

Sectioning and staining. To attach the block of paraffin to the holder of the microtome, melt the wax at one end of the block and press it against the holder. Spread melted wax around the edges. The cutting knife and block should be set so that sections from 6 to 10 microns can be cut (one micron equals 1/25,000 inch). As you cut, a ribbon of wax sections forms; lift off the sections with a spatula and float them on slightly warmed water which has been spread on slides already prepared with a thin film of albumen (see Mayer's albumen, p. 330). The water must be below the melting point of wax. Finally, the slides on which the sections are floating are dried for about 24 hours in an incubator set at 37° C. If this time is shortened there is danger that the tissues may be washed off the slides as the next steps are taken.

At this point, the prepared slides consist of slices of tissue imbedded in paraffin. In the next step, the wax must be removed before the tissue can be stained. First, the slides with the paraffin sections are heated a bit over an alcohol flame and then inserted into a jar of xylol to dissolve the wax. After 5 minutes, transfer the slides to absolute alcohol for 3 minutes, then for about 2 minutes in each of these alcohols: 70 per cent, then 50, then 30. Finally the slides are put into distilled water for 1 minute. Since most stains are aqueous, the sections are brought gradually through the alcohols into water.

Now the slides containing the sections of tissue (with the paraffin dissolved away) are ready to be stained. There are many stains which may be used. We shall take Harris hematoxylin, a nuclear stain, as an example of the general staining technique. First, add 2 drops of glacial acetic acid to the Harris hematoxylin (preparation, p. 329). Immerse the slides in the stain for 1 to 2 minutes. Transfer into tap water to wash out the acid; notice that the color fades. Wash for 5 minutes; then transfer slides to each of the following alcohols for 2 minutes: 30 per cent, to 50, to 70, to 90. Now to counterstain with eosin, a cytoplasmic stain, transfer the slides to eosin for 2 minutes and rinse in 95 per cent alcohol. Move the slides into xylol, where they may be left for some time. Finally, mount in Canada balsam.

There are many stains which may be used. Certain stains penetrate tissues better after use of a particular fixative.

Preparation of stains. There are basic (alkaline) dyes which stain acid structures within cells, and, conversely, acid dyes which stain basic structures. For example, acid dyes are held by plasma, cilia, and cellulose structures. Chromosomes, centrosomes, nucleoli, cork, cutinized epidermis, and xylem tissues of plants retain basic dyes.

Some basic dyes in frequent use are safranin, hematoxylin, methyl green, gentian violet, and Janus green B. Among the acid dyes are eosin, methyl orange, orange G, fast green, and light green. The stains described below are listed in alphabetical order. These are only a few among hundreds which are in common use, since this is only an introduction to histological techniques. Refer to the specialized texts listed at the end of the chapter for more detailed procedures with special stains, and general histological methods in use with plant and animal tissue.

ACID ALCOHOL. This is included here since it is used to decolorize stains. (It can also be used to clean coverslips.) Acid alcohol is prepared by adding 1 cc of 1 per cent hydrochloric acid to 99 cc of 70 per cent ethyl alcohol.

BORAX CARMINE. First, mix together 4 gm of borax in 100 cc distilled water. (Reduce the amounts if small quantities are needed.) Then add 3 gm of carmine and boil for about 30 minutes. After this solution has cooled, dilute with 100 cc of 70 per cent alcohol. Let this stand for a few days and then filter.

Specimens may be transferred into this stain directly from 70 per cent alcohol. Often the slides become overstained in this dye, but they may be decolorized by placing them in 70 per cent alcohol to which a drop of a 1 per cent hydrochloric acid solution has been added.

CARBOL FUCHSIN. A stable stain at room temperature. Prepare in two parts; combine:

basic fuchsin	1 gm
absolute alcohol	10 cc

Then mix with:

phenol	5 gm
distilled water	100 cc

CONKLIN'S HEMATOXYLIN. This is recommended especially as a stain for whole mounts of chick embryos (p. 330). Prepare as follows:

Harris hematoxylin	1 part
water	4 parts

To this add one drop of Kleinenberg's picrosulfuric acid (p. 326) for each cc of fluid.

DELAFIELD'S HEMATOXYLIN. First, dissolve hematoxylin in alcohol, then add the other ingredients.

hematoxylin	4 gm
absolute alcohol	25 cc

Add this to 400 cc of a saturated aqueous solution of ammonium alum. Expose the solution to light for a few days in a cotton-stoppered bottle; filter. Then add the following:

methyl alcohol	100 cc
glycerin	100 cc

The stain is ripened for 2 months at room temperature before it is ready for use. Finally store in well-stoppered bottles. Wash the specimens in water before transferring them into this stain. This stain and Ehrlich's and Harris' (below) may be purchased ready made.

EHRLICH'S HEMATOXYLIN. This solution is also ripened at room temperature for about 2 months. Transfer specimens from water to the stain. Mix these:

hematoxylin	2 gm
absolute alcohol	100 cc

Then add these substances in this order:

glycerin	100 cc
distilled water	100 cc
glacial acetic acid	10 cc
potassium alum	in excess

EOSIN Y. A plasma stain often used for whole mounts or for contrast. Make up a 0.5 per cent solution in distilled water.

ETHYL EOSIN. Prepare a 0.5 per cent solution in 95 per cent ethyl alcohol.

HARRIS' HEMATOXYLIN. Prepare two solutions; first combine:

hematoxylin	1 gm
absolute alcohol	10 cc

Then combine (heat is needed to dissolve the alum):

potassium alum (or ammonium alum)	20 gm
distilled water	200 cc

Mix the two solutions and bring to a quick boil; add 0.5 gm of mercuric oxide. Cool quickly.

METHYL GREEN SOLUTION (1%). This is a good nuclear stain for general use. Prepare a 1 per cent aqueous solution by dissolving 1 gm of the dye in 1 cc of glacial acetic acid. Then dilute with distilled water to make 100 cc.

METHYL ORANGE. This solution is widely used as an indicator. Prepare a 0.1 per cent solution by dissolving 0.1 gm of methyl orange in 100 cc of distilled water.

METHYL RED. This stain may also be used as an indicator. Prepare a saturated solution in 50 per cent ethyl alcohol.

METHYL VIOLET. This stain may be used to dye amphibian or human blood cells. Prepare as follows:

sodium chloride (0.7% solution)	100	cc
methyl violet	0.05	gm
glacial acetic acid	0.02	cc

When human blood cells are to be stained, prepare the stain in 0.9 per cent sodium chloride solution.

Other solutions needed in histological work. At times there may be reason to use some of the solutions (fixatives, stains, and so forth) which are gathered here. Many of these have been referred to in other sections of this book.

BALSAM (NEUTRAL). The slight acidity of samples of balsam is well known. This is an advantage when balsam is used as the mounting fluid after acid stains, but detrimental when the basic hematoxylin stains are used. Balsam may be neutralized by adding a small quantity of sodium carbonate. Let the fluid stand for about a month. The supernatant balsam should prove to be slightly alkaline.

FORMALIN. This is a 40 per cent solution of formaldehyde gas in water and is a stock solution.

A common fixative for small forms is a 10 per cent solution of formalin. This is prepared by adding 10 cc of stock formalin to 90 cc of water. This solution is often an ingredient of many fixatives; it may also be substituted in certain fixatives for glacial acetic acid.

Sometimes a 4 per cent solution of formalin is called for. In this case, add 4 cc of commercial formalin to 96 cc of water. (This is really a 1.6 per cent solution of formaldehyde.)

Avoid inhaling the fumes of any formalin solutions, for they irritate the mucous membranes.

LOEFFLER'S METHYLENE BLUE SOLUTION. This is a frequently used stain for bacteria. Add the stain to a slide for ½ to 3 minutes. Then rinse off in water. The stain, which keeps indefinitely, may be prepared by combining:

> methylene blue 30 parts
> (saturated alcoholic)
> potassium hydroxide 1000 parts
> (1:10,000 aqueous solution)

MAYER'S ALBUMEN. A dilute solution of albumen is spread as a film on a clean slide so that tissue sections or protozoa adhere to the slide throughout the transfers from one liquid to another. Combine:

> egg albumen 50 cc
> glycerin 50 cc
> thymol 1 crystal

(You can substitute for the thymol 1 gm of sodium salicylate; they are both antiseptics.) Shake the mixture vigorously so that the air bubbles become trapped in the solution. When they rise to the surface, remove the foamy mass and then store the clear fluid. It may be kept from 2 to 4 months without spoiling.

When the solution is to be used, add 3 drops of it to 60 cc of distilled water. With a finger, spread a very light film on a clean slide.

MOUNTING FLUID. At times this fluid may be used as a substitute for Canada balsam. How-

ever, it is poisonous and must be handled with caution. Mix together 2 parts of chloral hydrate to 1 part of phenol. Heat slightly until it becomes fluid.

Permanent slides of chick embryos

Since a 72-hour chick embryo is the easiest to fix and mount whole on a slide, we will give a general description of the preparation of a slide of this stage. Then students may want to work back to the 24-hour stage. Complete directions may be found in Rugh's embryology manual (see Bibliography).

One way to incubate fertilized chicken eggs, turn them, and float early embryo stages in bowls of warmed saline solution has been described (p. 174). Break open a 72-hour egg and float the embryo in warmed saline solution. Grasp the chalazae with forceps to float the embryo to the top of the mass of yolk. With sharp scissors cut outside of the area vasculosa and float this disc free of the underlying yolk (Fig. 17-19).

Lower a glass slide under water and float the blastodisc, yolk side uppermost, onto the slide. Flatten out the blastodisc on the slide and put a ring of filter paper large enough to encircle the area pellucida over that region to hold the embryo in position. Then lift out of the saline solution and gently pipette a fixative on the slide. Use Bouin's or Kleinenberg's picrosulfuric solution (pp. 325, 326). Place several such slides in Petri dishes of fixative for 8 to 10 hours. Then transfer the slides into a graded series of alcohols in this order: 30 per cent, to 50, to 70. Leave the slides in each alcohol for 1 hour. To the 70 per cent alcohol add a bit of lithium carbonate (or ammonium hydroxide, 3 volume per cent) to decolorize the bright-yellow picric stain. Then transfer the specimens back to fresh 50 per cent, then 30 per cent alcohol, and finally

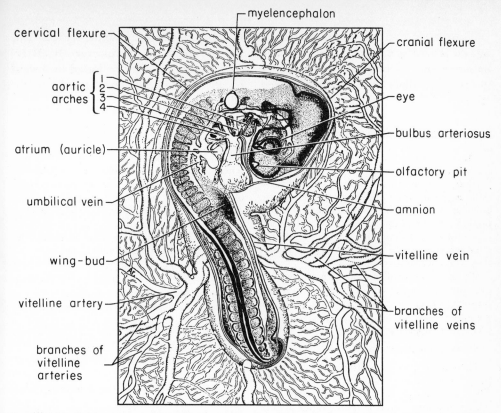

cervical flexure

myelencephalon

cranial flexure

aortic arches { 1 2 3 4

eye

bulbus arteriosus

atrium (auricle)

olfactory pit

umbilical vein

amnion

wing-bud

vitelline vein

vitelline artery

branches of vitelline veins

branches of vitelline arteries

Fig. 17-19 Chick embryo with adjacent portion of area vasculosa, with 35 pairs of somites (about 72 hours). (From R. S. McEwen, *Vertebrate Embryology*, 3d ed., Holt, 1949; after F. R. Lillie, *Development of the Chick.*)

into distilled water in preparation for staining.

Stain a 72-hour embryo with Conklin's hematoxylin (p. 329) for 5 minutes. For younger embryos less staining time is needed, possibly 2 minutes for a 24-hour embryo.

Then transfer the slides into tap water for a few minutes. Follow this with changes into 30 per cent alcohol, to 50 per cent; leave the slides ½ hour in each. Examine the slides under the microscope. Should the slides be overstained, destain them in acidified 70 per cent alcohol (p. 329). Then follow with a washing in slightly ammoniated 70 per cent alcohol (p. 323). The slides may remain in pure 70 per cent alcohol for several hours.

Finally transfer to 95 per cent alcohol and follow with two changes in absolute alcohol.

When the embryos are ready for mounting, transfer the slides from absolute alcohol into pure cedar oil for clearing. After 24 hours in cedar oil, the embryos should appear translucent. Next follow two transfers into xylol, ½ hour in each container. Then mount the embryos in balsam with small chips of glass tubing or pulled out tubing (so that the embryos will not be crushed). Add more balsam if needed. Flame a coverslip to dry any moisture on it, and lower it into the balsam. Let the slides remain flat for several days until the specimen hardens in place. Later remove excess balsam with xylol.

This is one method; there are many others. There are several fixatives and stains in use in preparing these chick embryos. The blastodiscs also may be fixed in Zenker's fixative (p. 326). Other stains may be preferred, and some workers clear the mount in oil of wintergreen. Alternate techniques may be found in several of the specialized texts listed in the Bibliography.

PEOPLE, PLACES, AND THINGS

Many of the techniques described here are specialized and practice is needed to gain skill. Students who may want help in gaining these skills may call upon a laboratory technician, a doctor, a member of a research staff of a hospital, a teacher in another high school or college biology department. You will find that these resource people are happy to help youngsters who have similar interests.

We know of several students who have been given access to a histology laboratory in which they have been helped by specialists. These youngsters have gladly washed glassware and done other chores for this privilege.

Books and pamphlets

These are only a few of the books which are pertinent to the work discussed in this chapter. These and many other references classified by subject and with complete bibliographical data are given in the Bibliography at the end of the book.

Bensley, R., and Bensley, S., *Handbook of Histological and Cytological Technique,* 1938.

Bullough, W. S., *Practical Invertebrate Anatomy,* 1950.

Conn, H. J., *Biological Stains,* Biotechnical Publications, Geneva, N. Y., 1946.

Gage, S., *The Microscope,* 17th ed., 1941.

Gray, P., *Handbook of Basic Microtechnique,* 1952.

Guyer, M., *Animal Micrology,* 1953.

Johansen, D., *Plant Microtechnique,* 1940.

Kudo, R. R., *Protozoology,* 1954.

Maximow, A., and Bloom, W., *A Textbook of Histology,* 1957.

Rugh, Roberts, *A Laboratory Manual of Vertebrate Embryology,* 1956.

Sass, J., *Botanical Microtechnique,* 1951.

War Dept., *Methods for Laboratory Technicians,* TM 8-227, Supt. of Documents, U.S. Govt. Printing Office, Washington, D. C., 1941.

Films and filmstrips

This partial list is intended only as a guide toward film and filmstrip selection. Refer to the more complete listing at the end of the book where films are classified by subject and where a key to abbreviations and the addresses of distributors are given. The cost of film rental, of course, may be subject to change. Films are sound and black and white unless otherwise specified. For films showing protozoa, bacteria, or tissue cells, refer to the films and filmstrips listed at the end of the related chapters.

Cells and Their Functions (f), Athena, $4.50 rental.

Cell: The Structural Unit of Life (f), Coronet, through film libraries, $2.00 rental.

Compound Microscope (fs), Visual Educ. Consultants, $3.00.

Compound Microscope (f, c), Film Distribution Service, Bausch & Lomb, free.

Eyes of Science (f, si), Film Distribution Serv., Bausch & Lomb, free.

Microscope and Its Use (f), Young America, $2.00 rental.

Seifritz on Protoplasm (f), Educ. Film Library Assoc., New York U., $6.00 rental.

The Thinnest Slice (f, s), U. of California Visual Institute, $2.50 rental.

Free and inexpensive materials

This is only a partial listing of free and inexpensive materials available to the teacher at this time. A more complete listing, including addresses, is given at the end of the book. Many of these materials are distributed to teachers without charge. Where there is a small fee, the cost is indicated, although the prices are subject to change. While we recommend the material for use in the classroom, we do not necessarily sponsor the products advertised.

Evolution of the Microscope, Microscopy in Medicine, American Optical Co., Public Relations Dept.

Eyes for the Little Worlds, Westinghouse Electric Corp. School Service.

Microscope—Its Applications, Leitz Inc.

Use and Care of the Microscope (also large chart) Bausch and Lomb Optical Co.

Use and Proper Care of the Microscope, American Optical Co., Public Relations Dept.

CHAPTER 18

Maintaining invertebrates

useful in the classroom

Many invertebrates and some classes of vertebrates can be cultured in the laboratory or classroom, providing living forms for activities in behavior, nature study, classification, reproduction, and variation, or comparative studies of organ systems, circulation of blood, and observation of the heart beat.[1] Furthermore, many of these animals serve as food for small vertebrates which often are reared in the laboratory.

Students usually bring in materials for identification when a resourceful teacher stimulates interest in living things. If a teacher brings in frog eggs and sets them out in aquaria or bowls in the classroom, or if he brings in patches of different mosses, a fern or two, and a lichen for a terrarium, youngsters will ask questions.

In many schools there are a few experts among the students who can give talks to classes or to clubs about the behavior of certain animals. There are students who would like to care for living materials (student squads, Chapter 22). Many students want to learn more about how to identify shells, or trees, or flowers; how to start an insect collection; how to set up a terrarium or an aquarium; how to get more plants without using seeds; how to photograph animals and flowers; how to make prints and enlargements; how to breed tropical fish.

In this chapter methods for collecting and cultivating the invertebrates will be described. As each phylum is mentioned, possible usefulness of these animals in the classroom is indicated. In the next chapter methods for maintaining living vertebrates are described. Chapter 20 deals with ways to cultivate plants. You may want to refer now to Chapter 15 for specific details for planning field trips, and tips on collecting different living organisms.

---

[1] You may want to read how other teachers develop concepts in these areas. For an example, look into the Resource Unit in Biology: *How Are Living Things Related?* L. Richardson, Portland Public Schools, Oregon, 1954.

Protozoa

Culturing protozoa is relatively simple if certain fundamental precautions are taken. The techniques which are described below have proved useful to the authors in their efforts to maintain living things for use in the biology classroom and laboratory. First, we shall describe the necessary general conditions for a culture center. Then we shall discuss specific culture methods for the more common, easily obtained forms of protozoa.

Suggestions for maintaining a culture center

In general, the room or portion of the laboratory where cultures are to be kept should fulfill these environmental conditions:

1. Keep cultures at a constant temperature within an optimum range of 18° to 21° C. These temperatures may be maintained during warm weather by stacking fingerbowls in a metal container, which is kept cool by putting it in a sink and circulating tap water to the level of the top dish. At temperatures above 25° C, cultures do not maintain themselves at maximum and may die off; below 15° C, development is very slow and the cultures may also die off.

2. Keep cultures away from fumes of concentrated acids such as nitric acid, hydrochloric acid, and sulfuric acid and such alkalies as ammonium hydroxide.

3. Try to keep the cultures at a hydrogen-ion concentration approximately neutral (pH 7).

4. Keep the cultures in medium light. Darkness is not detrimental. Direct sunlight is harmful, since the temperature of the culture may be raised above the optimum. (Of course, this does not apply to the culturing of green forms.)

5. Avoid sudden drafts near the cul-

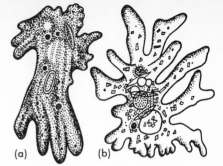

Fig. 18-1 Two species of *Amoeba* useful in the classroom: (a) *Amoeba proteus;* (b) *Amoeba dubia* (not to scale). (From G. G. Simpson, C. Pittendrigh, & L. Tiffany, *Life,* Harcourt, Brace, 1957.)

tures, since they may carry contaminants, such as some common chemicals in powdered form.

6. Keep glassware clean. Wash culture dishes with soap, and rinse repeatedly. For a final rinsing, wash in distilled water if the tap water is not free of copper and chlorine.

Rhizopods

Amoeba. The amoeba most commonly used in the classroom, *Amoeba proteus,* is not as common in nature as other amoebae. It may be found in ponds or pools which do not contain much organic matter, where the water is clear and not too alkaline, and where exceedingly swift currents are absent. Both *Amoeba proteus* and *A. dubia* (Fig. 18-1) are found among aquatic plants such as *Cabomba,* elodea, and *Myriophyllum.* Often scrapings from the base of a stalk of the cattail (*Typha*) or from the underside of a leaf of the water lily, *Nymphaea,* will yield many amoebae.

Place small amounts of these plants on which amoebae may be present into finger bowls, large Petri dishes, or flat jars. Cover the material with pond water in which the plants had been growing, or add spring water. Be certain to maintain them at room temperature. To each container add 2 to 4 uncooked rice grains. Amoebae generally appear in 1 week to 10 days in successful cultures. Examine with a binocular (stereoscopic) microscope to locate amoebae in the cultures.

Amoebae congregate on the bottom or sides of a container. They may be removed in either of two ways. Carefully pour off the excess fluid into another dish. Then with a pipette pick up the amoebae attached to the bottom and place them in fresh spring water to which a few uncooked rice grains have been added. When the rice grains begin to decay (bacterial action), small animals such as *Chilomonas* (Fig. 2-1) begin to increase. *Chilomonas* furnishes a good food supply for *Amoeba*.

If the animals are not congregated on the bottom, swirl the finger bowl with a rotating motion, thereby causing the heavier particles to fall into the center of the dish. You may then pick up the amoebae with a pipette.

The method we have just described is useful for temporary cultures in the laboratory. When amoebae are to be cultured continuously, the following methods have been successful.

Method A. This method involves the use of a hay infusion. Halsey[2] has described a typical method. Place eight 1-inch lengths of timothy hay stalks in 100 cc of spring water. Boil this for 10 minutes and let it stand for 24 hours. Then add large quantities of *Colpidium* or *Chilomonas*. Let this medium stand for 2 to 3 days, then inoculate with amoebae. As the culture develops, the food organisms (that is, the ciliated forms) decrease in number. When this happens, remove half of the culture medium and add an equal amount of fresh hay infusion to which *Colpidium* or *Chilomonas* have been added.

Add two grains of uncooked rice or boiled wheat, or four 1-inch lengths of boiled timothy hay for every 50 cc of culture medium which has been added. Cultures may last as long as 6 months. However, if large amounts of organic matter with accompanying large quantities of bacteria are present, they tend to cause the death of the amoebae.

Many methods described in the literature are similar to that of Halsey (see papers by Jennings,[3] Kofoid,[4] Hyman,[5] Dawson,[6] and LeRoy and Ford[7]). In all these methods a medium which has no specific chemical composition is used. While these methods are successful in the hands of some workers, they offer pitfalls for the beginner. In fact, the very simplicity of the method is its undoing. The beginner often needs a method which takes care of all the variables that may cause failure, namely, medium, food, temperature, pH, and so forth. Such a medium is described in method B.

Method B. Chalkley,[8] Pace,[9] Brandwein,[10] and Hopkins and Pace[11] have described methods which make use of synthetic pond water of a specific chemical composition, instead of natural pond

[3] H. S. Jennings, "Methods of Cultivating Amoebae and Other Protozoa for Class Use," *Jr. Appl. Micro. and Lab. Methods*, 6:2406, 1903.

[4] C. A. Kofoid, "A Reliable Method for Obtaining *Amoeba* for Class Use," *Trans. Am. Microscop. Soc.*, 34:271, 1915.

[5] L. Hyman, "Methods of Securing and Cultivating Protozoa: General Statement and Methods," *Trans. Am. Microscop. Soc.*, 44:216, 1925.

[6] J. A. Dawson, "The Culture of Large Free-living Amoebae," *Am. Naturalist*, 62:453, 1928.

[7] W. LeRoy and N. Ford, "Amoeba" in *Culture Methods for Invertebrate Animals*, J. Needham, ed.

[8] H. Chalkley, "Stock Cultures of *Amoeba proteus*," *Science*, 71:442, 1930.

[9] D. M. Pace, "The Relation of Inorganic Salts to Growth and Reproduction in *A. proteus*," *Arch. Protist.*, 79:133, 1933.

[10] P. F. Brandwein, "Culture Methods for Protozoa," *Am. Naturalist*, 69:628, 1935.

[11] D. L. Hopkins and D. M. Pace, "The Culture of *Amoeba proteus* Leidy Partim Schaefer," in *Culture Methods for Invertebrate Animals*, J. Needham, ed.

[2] H. R. Halsey, "Culturing *Amoeba proteus* and *A. dubia*" in *Culture Methods for Invertebrate Animals*, J. Needham, ed., Comstock, Ithaca, N. Y., 1937, p. 80.

water or hay infusion. (In some cases a buffer may be needed.) In our experience, these methods are superior to the previous ones described. Although more time is spent in preparing the culture medium, this is fully repaid by the quantity of animals found in each culture.

We have found the methods of Chalkley and one of ours (Brandwein) especially successful. The method described here is our modification of existing methods. This is selected merely because of our prolonged experience with it; it has also been successfully used by other teachers and students. The method has been used with many other protozoa and small invertebrates. Both methods depend upon a synthetic pond water prepared as follows.

SOLUTION A. Weigh out these salts and dissolve them in distilled water to make 1 liter of solution:

NaCl	1.20 gm
KCl	0.03 gm
$CaCl_2$	0.04 gm
$NaHCO_3$	0.02 gm
phosphate buffer (pH 6.9 to 7.0)	50 cc

This is *stock* solution A. For use, it should be diluted 1:10 with distilled water. (For each cc of stock solution A, add 10 cc of distilled water.)

Prepare a number of finger bowls by rinsing them in hot water, then in cold. Cover the bottom of each finger bowl with a thin layer (1 to 2 mm) of agar as follows. Prepare a 1 per cent aqueous solution of powdered nonnutrient agar in distilled water, or in solution A. Heat slowly until smooth. Pour this while fluid into finger bowls. While the agar is still soft, embed five rice grains in it.[12]

Introduce about fifty amoebae, together with 15 cc of the medium in which they have been growing, into each bowl and add about 30 cc of dilute solution A.

[12] The agar is not entirely necessary for the success of the method. It helps, however, to fix the rice.

For the next 3 days, add 15 cc daily of dilute solution A, until the total volume is about 90 cc. A few days after the cultures have been started, the layer of agar will separate from the bottom of the dish. Then amoebae may be found growing in layers on the upper and lower surfaces of the agar as well as on the glass surfaces.

After about 2 months of growth, the culture wanes and should be subcultured. This may be accomplished by dividing the contents of each finger bowl into 4 parts. Prepare fresh finger bowls containing a film of agar. Add one fourth of the old culture to each freshly prepared finger bowl, and an equal volume of dilute solution A.

When the original source of amoebae is limited, as it may be when collected in the field, it may be necessary to start small cultures in Syracuse dishes rather than the larger finger bowls. This apparently provides a better initial concentration of amoebae and makes the change of culture conditions less abrupt.

Prepare the Syracuse dishes with a thin layer of agar and embed two rice grains in each dish. Introduce the animals on hand with about 4 cc of the water in which they were collected; then add 4 cc of dilute solution A. In a successful culture a rapid proliferation of amoebae occurs. When some 200 organisms are present, add the culture to a larger container, a rice-agar finger bowl, with 20 cc of dilute solution A. *Caution:* It is detrimental to have large ciliates such as *Stentor, Paramecium,* large hypotricha, *Philodina,* or *Stenostomum* in cultures of amoebae. Microscopic worms, like *Nais* or *Aeolosoma,* or crustaceans like *Cyclops* or *Daphnia* are also harmful contaminants. Such cultures may as well be discarded. Moderate populations of *Chilomonas* and *Colpidium* are beneficial as food organisms for amoebae, but these forms should not be present in such amounts that the medium is clouded by their presence. At times mold, such as *Dictyuchus,* may grow about the rice, but this does not seem to be detrimental; in fact, amoebae may be found congregated in the mycelia.

Two other formulas are given for synthetic pond water which may be used as medium for amoebae.

CHALKLEY'S SOLUTION. Combine the following with 1 liter of water:

	grams
NaCl	0.1
KCl	0.004
CaCl$_2$	0.006

HAHNERT'S SOLUTION. Combine the following with 1 liter of water:

KCl	0.004
CaCl$_2$	0.004
CaH$_4$(PO$_4$)$_2$	0.002
Mg$_3$(PO$_4$)$_2$	0.002
Ca$_3$(PO$_4$)$_2$	0.002

Allies of Amoeba. Many teachers have found that a large amoeba, 3 to 4 mm in length, is superior to *Amoeba proteus* (600 microns) or *Amoeba dubia* (30 microns). This giant form is *Chaos chaos,* a form whose taxonomy is still a matter of controversy.

Chaos (Fig. 2-2). It can be cultured in Brandwein's solution, using the rice-agar method described earlier. In addition, add a pipetteful of *Paramecium, Blepharisma,* or *Stentor* (Fig. 17-3) or all three, as food. Since *Chaos* is omnivorous, its food vacuoles will be colored red by engulfed *Blepharisma* or green by trapped *Stentor.* Various stages of rotifers and small worms may also be found in the vacuoles of *Chaos. Chaos* is characterized by having many nuclei (as many as a thousand), and it may contain up to twelve contractile vacuoles. When it divides it often divides into three parts instead of two.

Arcella. This shelled relative of amoeba may be cultured by method A or B.

Difflugia. Various species of this amoeba, such as *Difflugia oblonga, D. lobostoma,* and

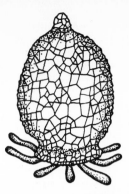

Fig. 18-2 *Difflugia,* a shelled relative of Amoeba. (From G. G. Simpson, C. Pittendrigh, & L. Tiffany, *Life,* Harcourt, Brace, 1957.)

D. constricta, may be cultured by using a number of green algae as food organisms, following the method described by Stump.[13] In this method such algae as *Spirogyra, Zygnema,* or *Oedogonium* are placed in shallow containers. Cover the algae with spring or pond water in Petri dishes or finger bowls. Thick cultures should develop in about 10 days. Add small quantities of fine sand for these organisms to build the intricate shells they carry about (Fig. 18-2). In our experience, this method of cultivation is subject to the same criticism as was method A. *Difflugia* can be readily cultured by method B, provided small amounts of fine sand are added to each culture.

Actinosphaerium. Culture these forms using method A or B. For this organism, best success has been obtained by assuring the presence of a moderate amount of *Paramecium.* To 30 cc of solution A in a rice-agar finger bowl, add 20 cc of a culture of *Paramecium* and inoculate with five to ten specimens of *Actinosphaerium.* Prolific cultures are usually obtained in about 10 days to 2 weeks. At this time, it may be necessary to subculture.

KNOP'S SOLUTION. Both heliozoans, *Actino-*

[13] A. B. Stump, "Method of Culturing Testaceae," described in *Culture Methods for Invertebrate Animals,* J. Needham, ed.

sphaerium and *Actinophrys,* may be cultured in Knop's solution. Prepare this modification of the solution by dissolving the following salts in distilled water to make 1 liter.

	grams
$MgSO_4$	0.25
$Ca(NO_3)_2$	1.00
KH_2PO_4	0.25
KCl	0.12
$FeCl_3$	trace

When these cultures are examined from week to week, a succession of living forms is found. In fact, the amoebae and related forms are the last to appear; that is, they begin to increase after the ciliates have reached a peak and the culture is "declining." In such a culture a frequent succession may be: small flagellates, *Colpoda,* hypotrichs, *Paramecium, Vorticella,* then *Amoeba.* Paramecia often appear in a new culture during its second week, and amoebae after 2 to 6 weeks.

Ciliates

Methods similar to those already described for subclass Rhizopoda may be used in collecting members of the class Ciliata. When only a small number of specimens have been collected, it may be necessary to use Syracuse dishes as described under method B in order to get concentrations for inoculation into larger finger bowls.

Four general methods may be used with success to culture most ciliates. Methods A and B have been described above for amoebae. When using method B, organisms should be subcultured every 2 weeks by dividing the liquid into two to four parts and adding fresh medium and rice grains.

Method C. Prepare a hay infusion in this way. First, boil 1 liter of pond water, spring water, or tap water (listed in order of best results). As the water comes to a boil, add a handful of timothy hay and boil for an additional 10 minutes. Then cool the mixture and allow it to stand for 2 days before inoculation with the ciliated forms such as *Paramecium* or *Stentor.* If a culture of *Chilomonas* is available, add a few pipettefuls to the cooled culture and use immediately.

Method D. In this method add five grains of wheat to each 100 cc of boiled, then cooled, pond water. Have this stand in exposed dishes before inoculating with ciliates such as *Paramecium.* Add several pipettes of *Chilomonas* if it is available. A population peak should be attained within 2 weeks.

Method E. Prepare a thin, smooth paste by grinding 0.5 gm of the yolk of a hard-boiled egg with a small amount of tap water or boiled pond water. Then add this paste to 500 cc of solution A, boiled pond water, or tap water.[14] Let this stand for 2 days or inoculate with *Chilomonas* and use immediately. It is now ready for the ciliated forms which are to be cultivated.

Method F. An excellent medium for most of the ciliates used in the classroom was described previously for amoebae as method B. The only modification is a variation in the number of uncooked rice grains. In culturing ciliates use about eight rice grains per finger bowl.

Method G. Add about ¼ package of dehydrated yeast (7.5 gm to package) to 250 cc of pond water, spring water, or tap water. Mix well and allow this culture medium to stand exposed to the air for several hours. Inoculate with the culture of protozoa you plan to maintain. Rich cultures develop within a week at room temperature. Keep the cultures covered after they have been inoculated with protozoa to prevent evaporation and contamination.

Paramecium grown in this medium often develop a darkened gray shade and have blackish food vacuoles.

[14] P. F. Brandwein, "Culture Methods for Protozoa," *loc. cit.*

Method H. In this method a pinch of skim-milk powder is added to 250 cc of spring water (or boiled, filtered pond water).[15] For careful work with protozoa, experimentation with volumes and weights may be necessary, but most protozoa tolerate a wide range of concentration of this milk powder.

Add a few pipettefuls of *Paramecium* to this culture medium and maintain at about 22° C. In 2 to 3 days there should be a rapid proliferation with an abundance of forms undergoing fission. A population peak is reached in 5 days with this medium and new cultures should be prepared within 2 weeks. At times, the addition of a pinch of milk powder to an old culture may be sufficient to renew the population peak for a short time.

Frings finds the protozoa reared in this medium to be large, with clear cytoplasm and clear food vacuoles; the macronucleus is usually visible. And other forms, such as *Colpoda, Oxytricha, Lacrymaria, Halteria* (Fig. 18-3), *Vorticella* (Fig. 9-2), *Colpidium, Euplotes,* and *Stylonychia* (Fig. 18-4) have been successfully cultured with this medium. Amoebae do not maintain themselves in it. On the other hand, plant forms such as *Monas, Chilo-*

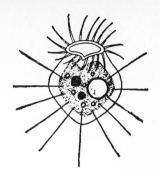

Fig. 18-3 *Halteria.* (From R. W. Hegner, *Invertebrate Zoology,* Macmillan, 1933.)

monas (Fig. 2-1), *Pandorina, Euglena,* and *Peranema* (Fig. 20-5), also thrive in this medium.

Method I. This method uses lettuce leaves rather than hay. Rub the outer dry leaves of lettuce through a fine-meshed wire strainer. Boil pond water, and when it cools, add 1 teaspoon of the lettuce to 1 liter of pond water. Boil this for 1 minute; let the jar stand covered, overnight. Later, divide the medium into finger bowls or baby-food jars and inoculate with a culture of *Paramecium.* Keep the containers covered.

In this method, DuShane and Regnery[16] suggest that a pinch of powdered milk be added to the culture after 12 days and repeated weekly. After a month's

[15] H. Frings, "Dried Skim Milk Powder for Rearing Protozoa," *Turtox News,* 26:1, General Biological Supply House, Chicago, Jan. 1948.

[16] G. DuShane and D. Regnery, *Experiments in General Biology,* Freeman, San Francisco, 1951.

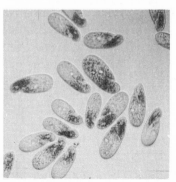

Fig. 18-4 (a) *Colpidium;* (b) *Euplotes* (stained); (c) *Stylonychia.* (Photos: a, b, General Biological Supply House, Inc., Chicago; c, D. F. Miller & J. G. Haub, *General Zoology,* Holt, 1956.)

growth, subculture by dividing the old culture into four parts and inoculate into fresh material.

Some specific ciliates. Of the methods which have been described, these are especially recommended for specific ciliates.

Paramecium and Colpoda. Use methods C, D, E, F, and I. Methods C and E are superior.

Paramecium bursaria. This green form is easily cultivated by method F. Keep the culture in medium light; these organisms congregate near the source of light. The alga *Chlorella,* containing chloroplasts (referred to by some botanists as green chromatophores), lives in a symbiotic relationship with this species of *Paramecium.*

Blepharisma. Use methods D and F. Method F seems to be superior.

Vorticella. A modification of method E is the most satisfactory for this stalked form (Fig. 9-2). Prepare the egg-yolk and tap-water medium as described (method E) and allow it to stand for 2 days. Do not add *Chilomonas.* Pour 40 cc of the supernatant fluid into a finger bowl and add *Vorticella.* The mature stalked forms adhere to the bottom of the finger bowls; young forms often form a thick layer on the surface of the culture.

Plan to subculture every 2 weeks. Scrape the bottom of the finger bowls to free the animals and divide the culture into four parts. To each bowl add 30 cc of fresh medium. When a very heavy population is desired, just pour off about 30 cc of the original liquid and add 30 cc of fresh fluid for replacement. In the same manner, remove contaminants by rinsing the bowls several times with solution A (since the *Vorticella* adhere to the bottom). Then add fresh medium.

Stentor. Both *Stentor polymorphus* and *S. coeruleus* may be cultured by method D, E, or F. However, method F is superior. Excellent cultures of *Stentor* may be ob-

tained when a pipetteful of *Paramecium* or *Blepharisma* (or both) as well as more *Chilomonas,* is introduced into the culture periodically.

Spirostomum. This elongated ciliate (Fig. 18-5a) may be cultured by using method D, E, or F. When the cultures become putrid, conditions seem to be favorable for this form.

Didinium. Introduce several of these animals (Fig. 18-5b) into a rich culture of *Paramecium* (prepared by method D or F). *Didinium* feed upon *Paramecium* and are found in a similar habitat. Within a week the *Paramecium* in the culture will probably have been consumed. Then inoculate the *Didinium* into fresh cultures of *Paramecium.*

You may preserve *Didinium* for later use by filtering an old culture through filter paper to retain the cysts. Then dry the filter paper in air and store in envelopes. When you wish to start a culture of *Didinium,* add a dried sheet of this paper to a thriving culture of *Paramecium.* You may prefer to allow a culture of *Didinium* to dry out in its container. When you wish to revive the culture, add a fresh *Paramecium* culture to the dish.

Colpidium. This ciliate (Fig. 18-4a) may be cultured in a medium made by boiling 100 cc of spring water or pond water to which 1.5 gm of whole rye grains have been added. After 10 minutes of boiling, filter the fluid, then cool it. Expose to air for a day, and then inoculate with about 10 cc of an old culture of *Colpidium.* At a temperature of about 22° C these cultures reach a peak in about a week.

Some interesting work has been done with bacteria-free cultures. Kudo[17] gives Kidder's formula for cultivating bacteria-free cultures of *Colpidium.* In this method, add 10 gm of brewer's yeast to 1 liter of distilled water. Then boil and filter

[17] R. R. Kudo, *Protozoology,* Thomas, Springfield, Ill., 1954.

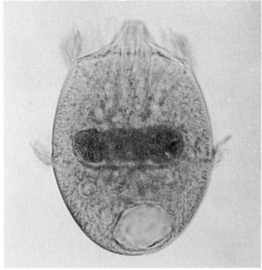

Fig. 18-5 *Left, Spirostomum (33X); right, Didinium (stained, 525X).* (Photos: General Biological Supply House, Inc., Chicago.)

through cotton. Again filter, this time through filter paper. To this solution, add 20 gm of Difco proteose peptone. Sterilize the whole solution for 20 minutes at 15 pounds pressure in an autoclave or pressure cooker. Inoculate with individual *Colpidium.*

Stylonychia and Oxytricha. Method F may be used; previous inoculation with *Chilomonas* is necessary.

Euplotes. For culturing this form (Fig. 18-4b), use either method D or F; inoculate with *Chilomonas* as a preliminary step.

One fact bears repetition. In raising certain carnivorous forms, the best results are produced when the food animal is raised separately and then added periodically to the culture medium. For example, we have said that *Stentor* grows best in media to which *Chilomonas* or *Colpidium* have been added. Similarly, *Didinium* cultures require *Paramecium* as a food organism, *Lionotus* feeds upon *Colpidium,* and *Actinobolus* consumes *Halteria.*

Flagellates

This class contains the protozoa with one or more flagella. Among the Masti-

gophora are some forms which may be classified as protozoa or as plant forms belonging to the Phytomastigina. An interesting feature of this group is lengthwise fission in asexual reproduction.

The procedures described for collecting Rhizopoda and Ciliata should be used here. In addition, the green-surface "blooms" which may be found in ditches or ponds may often contain large numbers of *Euglena, Chlamydomonas,* and similar flagellates.

In general, four of the methods which were described previously are recommended for cultivating flagellates. Of course, the forms which contain chlorophyll require moderate light.

Method B, described for rhizopods, and D, E, and F, described for ciliates, are also successful for flagellates.

Method J. An additional medium recommended for flagellates consists of a modification of method D (pond water and wheat grains). Boil four wheat grains in 80 cc of pond water. As soon as the medium is cool, add a few cc of pond water containing the flagellates which are to be cultured.

Method K. This method[18] uses a modification of Kleb's solution (below). To 100 cc of this solution in a glass battery jar, add 20 rice grains (which have been boiled for 5 minutes) and 900 cc of distilled water. Let this stand for 2 days. Keep the jar in indirect sunlight after you inoculate with an old culture of *Euglena.* Direct rays of the sun should not strike this culture for more than an hour a day. Inoculate the culture with *Euglena* three times at 3-day intervals. If an old culture of *Euglena* with encysted forms is available (these may be found on the sides of the jar) inoculate the cysts along with the motile forms. After 2 to 3 weeks, add an additional 10 mg of tryptophane powder which has been dissolved in 25 cc of the modified Kleb's solution.

MODIFIED KLEB'S SOLUTION. To make 1 liter of aqueous solution use the following:

	grams
KNO₃	0.25
MgSO₄	0.25
KH₂PO₄	0.25
Ca(NO₃)₂	1.00
bacto-tryptophane broth powder	0.01

Some specific flagellates

Euglena. For this flagellate use method K. The best methods for cultivating this animal are those of Jahn[19] and Hall.[20] These, however, require sterile conditions[21] and are tedious to prepare. Once they are established, the organisms may be maintained indefinitely in pure culture. Eventually, methods involving sterile

[18] P. F. Brandwein, "Culture Methods for Protozoa," *loc. cit.*

[19] T. L. Jahn, "Studies on the Physiology of the Euglenoid Flagellates" III. "The effect of hydrogen ion concentration on the growth of Euglena glacilis Krebs," *Biol. Bull.,* 61:387, 1931.

[20] R. P. Hall, "On the Relation of Hydrogen Ion Concentration to the Growth of Euglena anabaena var. minor and E. desos." *Arch. Protist.,* 79:239, 1933.

[21] A. K. Parpart, "The Bacteriological Sterilization of *Paramecium*," *Biol. Bull.,* 55:113, 1928; G. W. Kidder, "The Technique and Significance of Control in Protozoan Culture" in Calkins and Summer, *Protozoa in Biological Research,* Columbia U. Press, New York, 1941.

conditions may replace those we now employ.

Peranema. Method B yields excellent results; method J is also suitable.

Chilomonas. Raise this form with method D, E, or F, all of which yield excellent results.

Entosiphon. Use method J or B, both of which are equally successful.

In this discussion we have omitted the Sporozoa and Suctoria since they are not commonly studied in high school biology classes.

Uses of protozoa in the classroom

The organisms which have been described here have many uses in the classroom over the year. When cultures are maintained routinely, living materials are available at any time for such studies as these:

Microscopic examination (pp. 29, 30, 305, 313, 314; staining, p. 322)
Behavior (pp. 124, 126)
Food-getting (pp. 29, 230, 311)
Reproduction (pp. 153, 164)
Conservation (pp. 230, 248, 310)

Classification of protozoa

The study of protozoa is a specialized area of biology. When an unfamiliar protozoan moves into sight, you may want students to identify it. Students may become interested in studying a text on protozoology (see Bibliography) and examining the rich array of organisms illustrated as a guide for the identification of the unknown forms under the microscope.

In some circumstances, students may learn to use a key to identify organisms or as an introduction to a study of variations among living things (see Chapter 13). We shall not present detailed keys to classification of protozoa, but simply attempt, mainly with drawings, to focus observations on basic differences among

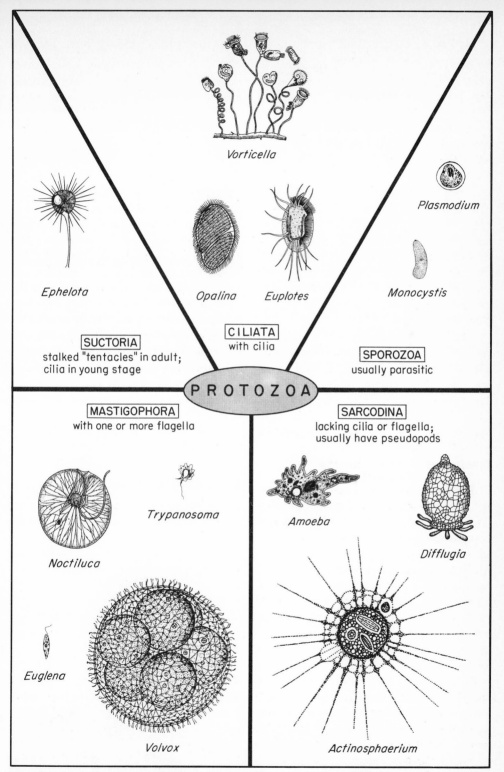

Fig. 18-6 A beginning classification of Protozoa. (Drawings from: G. G. Simpson, C. Pittendrigh, & L. Tiffany, *Life*, Harcourt, Brace, 1957; General Biological Supply House, Inc., Chicago; *Encyclopaedia Britannica*; R. R. Kudo, *Protozoology*, 4th ed., Chas. C. Thomas, 1954. Drawn not to scale, but in order of increasing size.)

the more common kinds of protozoans which might be found in quantity in pools of water, a ditch, or a container of rain water.[22] For example, if students examined with a microscope a drop of pond water rich in protozoans they might find some of the forms shown in Fig. 18-6. Sketches of these representative forms could be drawn on the blackboard for students to observe differences. What is one distinguishing characteristic of each type? Students easily distinguish that some forms are ciliated, some have one or more flagella, possibly some under view are amorphous masses of protoplasm with bulging false feet or pseudopodia, or some are highly organized cells with fine, spinelike projections.

Suppose we examine the flagellated forms closely. There may be single-celled types, such as *Euglena,* or colonial types, such as *Volvox.* Furthermore, some may have chlorophyll or other pigment (subclass Phytomastigina); or lack color bodies (subclass Zoomastigina) and be free living, or parasitic like Trypanosomes.

A more complex problem of variations exists among the ciliates. Have students look for differences among the members within the class Ciliata. The location of the "mouth" or peristome and the arrangement of cilia or long, fused cilia (membranelles) in relation to the peristome form the basic distinguishing features of the four subclasses of Ciliata; see *Paramecium, Euplotes,* and *Vorticella.*

Microscopic examination of the contents of the intestine of an earthworm may reveal the sporozoan *Monocystis* (Fig. 17-8). Prepared slides of plasmodia that cause malaria may also be studied at this time. You may also want to have students examine the flagellates (Zoomastigina) in the intestine of termites (Fig. 17-10).

Those students who want to go further in identifying genera of protozoans may consult the fine keys that are developed in textbooks of protozoology (see Bibliography).

Fresh-water invertebrates

Sponges. Only one family of sponges is found in fresh water, the Spongillidae. While marine sponges may be collected from considerable depths and dried for classroom use, they are difficult to keep alive without salt-water aquaria. In fact, fresh-water forms are also very difficult to keep in the laboratory. Specimens of fresh-water sponges may be found as crusty, brownish growths attached to submerged plants and rocks. Many have the texture of raw liver.

Spongilla (Fig. 18-7) is difficult to keep alive more than a few weeks in an aquarium and this is possible only when large specimens have been collected (as at the end of the summer and into fall). How-

ever, gemmules of these sponges may be cultivated in depression slides. Some will grow and attach themselves to the glass

Fig. 18-7 *Spongilla,* a freshwater sponge. (Photo: American Museum of Natural History, New York.)

[22] We pass lightly over two major types of protozoa: Sporozoa (many of which are parasitic), and Suctoria (which are not widely abundant).

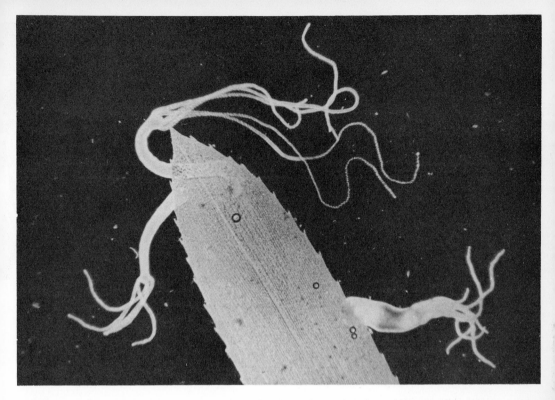

Fig. 18-8 Hydras attached to a submerged leaf. (Photo: General Biological Supply House, Inc., Chicago.)

surfaces. Keep them in darkness at 20° C.

Because sponges as a group have limited usefulness in high school biology, they are given only brief mention here. A text in zoology, such as any one of those listed at the end of this chapter, will furnish a description of the phylum.

Hydra. While many interesting examples of each phylum of invertebrates could be discussed, we are taking one type, a form which can be maintained under fairly simple conditions in the classroom or laboratory. Thus while many jellyfish forms may be collected and preserved for class examination, we will describe only one, *Hydra,* and the methods for its cultivation.

This fresh-water coelenterate (Fig. 18-8) may be found in lakes or ponds, attached to submerged stems of water plants or on the underside of floating leaves of water lilies and water hyacinths.

In the laboratory, transfer the plants upon which hydras are found into finger bowls or small aquaria. Be certain to use the water in which the hydras have been living, if available, or the water from a thriving aquarium. Add the aquarium water slowly, a glassful per day, to the original water in which the hydras were found, so that the organisms will become acclimated. Solution A may be used in the absence of satisfactory aquarium water.

Keep the containers in medium light or semidarkness, at a temperature below 20° C. Within a day or so the hydras will be found on the surface of the water. They can be picked up with a pipette and transferred into new containers to start fresh cultures. (If the hydras remain contracted and fail to expand, the water which has been added is not suitable. Do not put more hydras in such a tank.)

Keep the cultures in moderate light. Green hydras, *Chlorohydra viridissima,* in which an alga lives symbiotically in the gastrodermis or endoderm, require more light. (Incidentally, these algae are passed to the next generation in the cytoplasm of the hydra eggs.)

About twice a week feed the hydras a rich culture of *Dero, Tubifex,* or *Daphnia* (culturing, pp. 349–51). Well-fed hydras grow rapidly and reproduce readily.

On the whole, the most successful hydras for cultivation in the laboratory aquarium belong to the group *Hydra oligactis.* Adequate green water plants are needed for a rich supply of oxygen.

At times periods of depression beset hydras; tentacles are contracted and the body becomes shortened. Sometimes depression may be avoided by frequent changing of the water.

Uses in the classroom. A student project might develop in relation to a study of the means of preventing depression of hydras. There are other studies for the class:

1. For a study of food-getting. Examine how the hydra uses nematocysts (p. 311) to capture *Daphnia* (Fig. 18-16). Use starved hydras (forms which have not been fed for 24 hours).

2. In studies of regeneration (p. 155). Hydras might be used in club work or project activities to study the nature of polarity. For example, can tentacles grow on the "wrong" end?

3. In a study of sexual reproduction (p. 154).

4. To show tropisms (pp. 126, 311). Demonstrate the responses to touch, to food, to weak acids, and to light.

5. Or students might preserve some hydras for the school museum to be used only when living hydras are not available. First, narcotize the forms by adding crystals of menthol or of Epsom salts (mag-

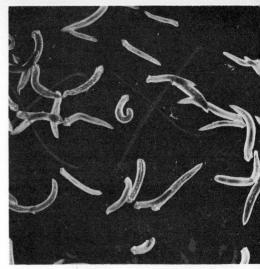

Fig. 18-9   *Planaria.* (Photo: Carolina Biological Supply Co.)

nesium sulfate) to the finger bowl of water containing the hydras. When they are elongated and quiet, place them in 70 per cent alcohol to fix and preserve them.

Planaria. Look for these small flatworms on the underside of submerged logs and under stones in ponds and lakes. Several varieties may be found in clear, running water, but the usual forms are the small blackish *Planaria maculata* and the brown *Dugesia tigrina* (Fig. 18-9). When you find some in a submerged log, wrap the whole log in wet newspaper and bring it into the laboratory. Submerge the log in a white enamel pan of water and peel off sections of wood. Usually the planarians float to the top. Planarians may also be baited by submerging a piece of raw beef liver or hard-boiled egg yolk (tied in cheesecloth) attached to a string, in a cold stream or lake. This method often attracts the larger form *Planaria doroto-cephalia.* Brush off the gathered forms into collecting jars and submerge your bait in another part of the lake or stream.

Transfer the collected plant materials into larger glass jars and keep them in moderate light. Soon planarians may be found clustering on the surface of the water or adhering to the sides of the jars. Then pick them off with a pipette and isolate them in separate culture containers.

Because planarians are photonegative, they should be maintained in black or opaque containers. Enameled containers are excellent. Frequently change the water with fresh additions of aquarium water or solution A. Keep them at a temperature below 35° C. Once a week feed them a diet of finely chopped raw beef liver, or bits of worms (*Tubifex* or *Enchytraeus* worms, pp. 348, 349). At other times, feed them bits of hard-boiled egg yolk. Remove the excess food with a pipette after several hours to avoid fouling the water.

Uses in the classroom. Planarians are classic material for studies in regeneration (p. 156). At times you may find planarians reproducing by fragmentation. They rarely reproduce sexually in the laboratory.

Use planarians to show tropisms (pp. 30, 126, 346). What happens when one is put on a slide and the glass is tapped? How do they respond to light?

For gross examination under the microscope, you may find it necessary to narcotize the animals before they are put on a slide. To a small watchglass or Syracuse dish of pond water containing a few planarians, add a small amount of chloretone, or a few crystals of Epsom salts or menthol (see p. 314). When the forms are quiet, lift them with a toothpick and arrange the animals on slides so that the proboscis is uppermost.

Rotifers. Half fill several jars with submerged plants, and fill them with pond water. In the laboratory, remove the covers and place the jars in moderate light. After a day or so these many-celled microorganisms (Figs. 17-9, 18-10) may be found congregated on the surface where there is an abundant supply of oxygen.

Use a pipette to pick the rotifers out of the jar. Then introduce them into finger bowls of pond water. Change the culture water frequently. Feed them cultures of *Euglena* or *Chlamydomonas* (culturing, pp. 341, 342). Keep the finger bowls stacked to prevent evaporation of the medium.

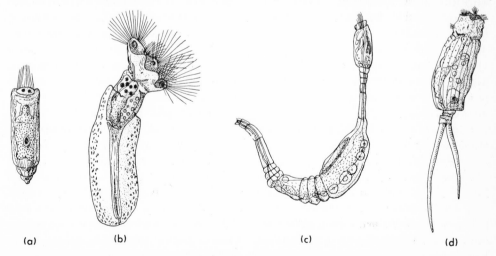

(a)   (b)   (c)   (d)

Fig. 18-10 Some rotifers: (a) male *Floscularia*; (b) female *Floscularia*; (c) female *Seison*; (d) female *Furcularia*. (General Biological Supply House, Inc., Chicago.)

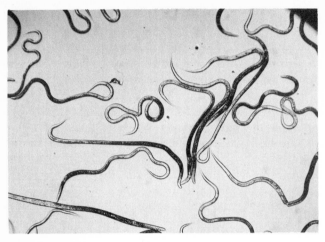

Fig. 18-11 Roundworms: vinegar eels (*Anguillula aceti*). (Photo: General Biological Supply House, Inc., Chicago.)

Vinegar eels. These nonparasitic roundworms (Fig. 18-11) feed upon the fungus "mother-of-vinegar." Because bottled vinegar has been pasteurized to inhibit the growth of these roundworms, bulk vinegar must be used as a source.

Add small quantities of bulk vinegar containing these worms to quart containers of pure, unadulterated cider vinegar. Then cover the cultures to prevent evaporation. Wide fluctuations in temperature are tolerated by the animals. About four times over the year subculture the stock, adding a bit of the old culture to fresh cider vinegar.

You may also purchase vinegar eels from a supply house (see listing, p. 479).

Uses in the laboratory. This small roundworm, *Anguillula aceti,* may be used in studies of relationships among organisms in a web of life (p. 228). Where parasitic roundworms are not available for study, these worms may be substituted as a representative of the group.

Earthworms. These annelids are readily collected at night and after a good rain, when they come to the surface.

Place several worms in wooden containers, such as cigar boxes. In the containers place 2 to 6 inches of moist rich soil or peat moss (sphagnum moss). Dampen the soil but avoid excess moisture. Keep the animals covered and in a cool place (at a temperature about 15° C). About twice a week feed them lettuce and bread soaked in milk. Bury the food.

Uses in the classroom. Earthworms are excellent organisms to use in studies of tropisms. When the cover is removed so that the animals are exposed to light, watch the rapid burrowing movements (see tropisms, pp. 125, 127).

Earthworms are also favorable material for dissection in many classrooms over the country. The reproductive, digestive, and circulatory systems, as well as the ventral nerve cord, may be studied as the worm is dissected (Fig. 16-1). Of course, earthworms may be cultivated as food for frogs and some reptiles maintained in the laboratory.

Enchytraeus. These white semiaquatic segmented worms may be purchased from a supply house or collected from samples of damp rich garden soil.

These annelids are cultivated in the same way as earthworms. Keep in covered containers which have 2 to 4 inches of rich garden soil. Feed them lettuce and potatoes boiled in their skins. Alternate this food with cooked oatmeal. On occasion, feed them bread soaked in milk. Keep

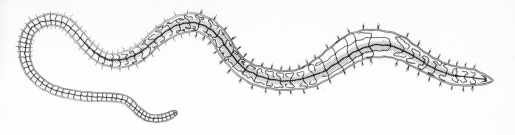

Fig. 18-12 Segmented worm: *Tubifex*. (After R. W. Hegner, *College Zoology*, rev. ed., Macmillan, 1930.)

several small cultures going rather than one large culture. The cultures should be kept at temperatures about 20° C and the food should be varied. Under these conditions, they multiply rapidly and many cocoons should be found among the masses of food.

Uses in the classroom. Enchytraeid worms are used mainly as food for other laboratory animals, such as fish, amphibia, and small reptiles.

They may also be used to demonstrate tropisms. Also prepare wet mounts to show contraction of muscle, such as peristalsis along the length of the intestine.

Tubifex and other aquatic worms. Any of the annelids described here may be purchased from biological supply houses which distribute living materials (see p. 479). *Tubifex* (Fig. 18-12) may be obtained readily from aquarium shops as well. In the field, *Tubifex* may be collected from the muddy bottom and decaying leaves of streams and ponds. They form tubes of mud held together by a secretion from epidermal cells. (*Tubifex,* and a related form, *Nais* (Fig. 2-3), are members of the family Tubificidae. These forms usually have a reddish color due to dissolved erythrocruorin in the blood.)

Members of the family Naididae, such as *Aulophorus* (Fig. 18-13) and *Dero*, carry on respiration through ciliated gills in the anal region. Naididae are abundant

in old cultures of protozoa. Under the microscope, *Aulophorus* can be distinguished from *Dero* by its two microscopic fingerlike terminal processes, as well as its gills, which are not found in *Dero*. The Naididae are larger than the Aeolosomatidae which are found in similar places, and they lack colored oil globules. The Naididae also lack dorsal bundles of setae in the anterior segments.

Fig. 18-13 *Aulophorus*, a segmented aquatic worm found in old cultures of Protozoa. (*Encyclopaedia Britannica;* from Marcus in Univ. São Paulo Pub.)

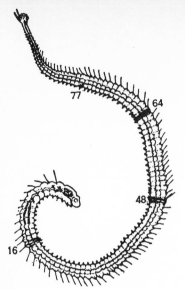

Fig. 18-14 *Aeolosoma,* a segmented aquatic worm. (*Encyclopaedia Britannica;* from Marcus in Univ. São Paulo Pub.)

and lakes, or they may be purchased from aquarium stores. *Planorbis* is the form with a shell coiled in one plane like a watch spring. It lays eggs in clusters of jelly. A popular form for aquaria is the imported red variety which lays pinkish masses of eggs. When both kinds are bred together, the common brown variety seems to be dominant. *Physa,* recognized by its sinistral spiral shell, lays eggs in long ribbons of jelly. *Lymnaea* is brownish-black in color with a dextrally coiled shell. It lays egg masses in jelly, usually found attached to stems of aquatic plants. A larger form, *Campeloma,* is a live-bearer and may be found in lakes or rivers attached to rocks or plants. Finally, *Helix,* the land snail, may be found in moist, but not too acid, soil such as that in gardens or some wooded areas.

Aeolosoma (Fig. 18-14) has minute yellow, greenish, or red globules in the epithelium.

Introduce *Tubifex* and *Nais* into well-established aquarium tanks which contain an inch or so of muddy soil.

Culture *Nais, Dero, Aeolosoma,* and *Aulophorus* by the methods described for maintaining protozoa, particularly method B or E.

Uses in the classroom. These aquatic worms serve several purposes in the laboratory and classrooms.

1. Regeneration experiments (p. 155).

2. Food supply for other laboratory animals, such as fish and hydras.

3. Circulation of blood, visible in some forms; and peristaltic contractions, especially clear in wet mounts of these worms, under low and high power (p. 71).

4. Asexual reproduction (fragmentation and transverse fission).

Snails. Among these fresh-water mollusks there are wide variations in shape (Fig. 18-15). Such egg-laying forms as *Physa, Planorbis,* and *Lymnaea* may be found attached to water plants in ponds

Raise *Helix* in a cool place in a moist terrarium with occasional feeding of lettuce. At times, also add whole oats rolled in calcium carbonate powder. Keep the aquatic snails such as *Planorbis* in an established aquarium. They normally feed upon algae, but when they increase in number they feed upon the aquatic plants.

Uses in the classroom. When the snails

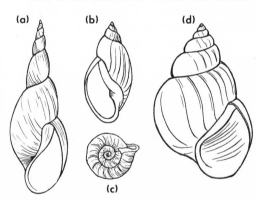

Fig. 18-15 Four snails which thrive in a classroom aquarium: (a) *Lymnaea;* (b) *Physa;* (c) *Planorbis;* (d) *Campeloma.* (General Biological Supply House, Inc., Chicago.)

reproduce, separate the developing eggs into covered Syracuse dishes. With a hand lens or binocular microscope, examine cleavage stages and ciliated veliger larvae. In the young embryos notice the beating heart. Here is a ready source of living material for studies of developing eggs (pp. 70, 164).

Snails should be kept in aquaria in class to hold down the abundant growth of algae and remove decaying materials in tanks.

Some small crustaceans

Daphnia. These small, laterally compressed water fleas (order Cladocera) may be collected from ponds, lakes, or streams by means of fine-mesh nets. They are characterized by a body enclosed in a transparent bivalve shell (Fig. 18-16). A cleft marks off the head from the rest of the body. Large second antennae are modified as swimming appendages to assist the four to six pairs of swimming legs. During the spring and summer, females are usually found. Eggs generally develop parthenogenetically at these times. In the autumn, males appear and the "winter eggs" are fertilized. Female *Daphnia* may be recognized by the curved shape of the end of the intestine. In the male the intestine is a straight tube.

A great many successful methods have been described for maintaining *Daphnia*,[23] using the fact that water fleas feed upon bacteria and nonfilamentous algae. Three methods which have proved successful are described below.

Using "green water." Fill large battery jars with tap water and let them stand overnight to permit evaporation of gases which may be harmful. Then put the battery jars in strong sunlight and inoculate them with nonfilamentous algae

[23] *Culture Methods for Invertebrate Animals,* J. Needham, ed.

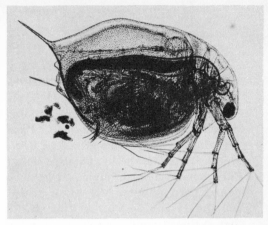

Fig. 18-16 *Daphnia* (water flea), a small crustacean found in lakes and ponds. (Photo: Carolina Biological Supply Co.)

from a "soupy green" aquarium. After this "green water" has been standing for about 2 to 3 days, add *Daphnia* and several cc of hard-boiled egg yolk mashed into a paste with a bit of culture medium. You may also add a suspension of yeast to stimulate growth. This method produces a luxuriant growth of *Daphnia*. The temperature range may vary between 12° and 24° C.

Using a modification of Knop's solution. In this method, a 6 per cent stock solution is prepared (see below). For immediate use, add 5 liters of distilled water to 1 liter of the stock solution. This will now be a dilute 0.1 per cent solution. When needed, this may be further diluted with an additional 4 liters of distilled water. Even this weak solution will maintain *Daphnia* adequately when the culture medium has been inoculated with nonfilamentous algae and allowed to stand in light until the water becomes tinged with a green color. About once a week, add a bit of hard-boiled egg yolk paste and a bit of yeast suspension.

MODIFIED KNOP'S SOLUTION. Combine these materials with 1 liter of distilled water and pour into several battery jars:

	grams
KNO$_3$	1
MgSO$_4$	1
K$_2$HPO$_4$	1

Then add 3 gm of calcium nitrate, Ca(NO$_3$)$_2$. As a result, a precipitate of calcium phosphate, Ca$_3$(PO$_4$)$_2$, is formed.

Using a culture of bacteria. Chipman[24] recommends the following method for culturing *Daphnia*. A rich growth of *Bacillus coli* is used as the food source. First, filter pond water through coarse filter paper. Then add about 90 gm of garden soil and 17 gm of cottonseed meal to 1 liter of this filtered pond water. Stir the mixture well and set it aside at room temperature for some 5 days. Fermentation takes place and gases are formed. At this time, decant off the supernatant fluid and strain through muslin. An almost pure culture of *Bacillus coli* is produced. Correct the pH to 7.2 by adding sodium carbonate. Use Hydrion pH paper for testing the pH (or use a pH-meter if available).

Now dilute this fluid with pond water (1 part of strained fluid to 100 parts of pond water). Inoculate this culture medium with *Daphnia*. Keep the cultures in large battery jars. Each week prepare fresh stocks of cottonseed meal. Then add a small amount of the old culture each time a new medium is established. In this way inoculation with the original kind of bacteria is achieved.

Uses in the classroom. These water fleas serve as excellent food for small fish, tadpoles, and hydras.

Introduce a drop of a culture of *Daphnia* on a slide containing one or two hydras. Under a microscope watch ingestion. What is the role of the nematocysts (see pp. 30, 311)?

Use *Daphnia* to clear an aquarium which has become soupy green.

[24] W. Chipman, Jr., "Culture Medium for Cladocerans," *Science*, 79:59–60, Jan. 19, 1934.

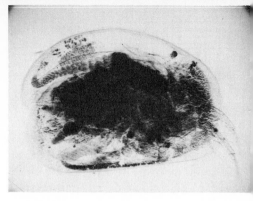

Fig. 18-17 *Cypris*, a small crustacean found in lakes and ponds (often mistaken for *Daphnia*). (Photo: General Biological Supply House, Inc., Chicago.)

Demonstrate the rapidly beating heart of *Daphnia* under low power (see p. 70). And you may want to demonstrate the effect of narcotic drugs on the heart beat as well. Use a hanging drop preparation (Fig. 17-7), or put bits of broken coverslips near the *Daphnia* as you prepare a wet mount. This will prevent crushing of the animals.

Small amounts of adrenalin and pituitrin cause a spontaneous shedding of the eggs from the dorsal brood sac.

Use wet mounts of *Daphnia* to study

Fig. 18-18 *Cyclops*, a small crustacean with a single compound eye. This female is carrying egg sacs. (General Biological Supply House, Inc., Chicago.)

Fig. 18-19 *Eubranchipus* (fairy shrimp), a small crustacean which swims ventral side up. (Photo: L. C. Peltier, courtesy *Nature Magazine*, Washington, D. C.)

circulation, respiratory system, and peristalsis.

Cypris. At first glance this form (Fig. 18-17) is often mistaken for *Daphnia.* However, it has an opaque shell which makes the study of body functions difficult.

Cypris is laterally compressed and completely enclosed in a bivalve shell. It usually has seven pairs of appendages, and its antennae protrude from the shells and are used in swimming.

They may be collected from ponds and streams by means of fine-mesh nets. The methods for collecting are the same, as a matter of fact, for all small crustaceans, and the culture methods are similar to those suggested for *Daphnia.*

Cyclops. This elongated crustacean (subclass Copepoda) lacks a shell and has no abdominal appendages (Fig. 18-18). It is characterized by the single compound eye located in the center of the head; it uses antennae for locomotion. During the summer months, females can be found carrying two brood pouches posterior to the body, as shown. *Cyclops* may be found in brackish water as well as fresh-water streams and lakes.

Culture methods are similar to those described for *Daphnia.* These forms are interesting for laboratory study and for introductory work with a microscope; they can be used as food for small invertebrates, fish, and amphibia.

Fairy shrimps. This small crustacean, *Eubranchipus* (Fig. 18-19), order Anostraca, is identified by its swimming motion. It swims with its ventral side uppermost. Its head bears stalked eyes and the body is transparent. It moves by means of thoracic appendages, as shown.

They are found in shallow, stagnant ponds which may dry up during the summer months. Culture them like *Daphnia* and the other small crustaceans.

Gammarus. These fresh-water shrimps (Fig. 18-20) are found abundantly along fresh-water streams and along the sea shore. They are members of the order Amphipoda, distinguished by laterally

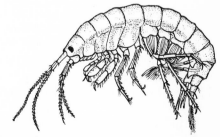

Fig. 18-20 *Gammarus,* a laterally compressed crustacean. (General Biological Supply House, Inc., Chicago.)

compressed bodies with gills borne on the legs. The first three pairs of legs are used as swimming legs, with the last three pairs modified as stiff processes used in jumping.

They are fairly easy to keep in the laboratory. Place them in an established aquarium. A bit of hard-boiled egg yolk (pea size) may be added every two weeks.

Reproduction in the fresh-water forms occurs in the spring and summer. *Gammarus* has been used in biology laboratories in studies of heredity. Eye color is studied most often.

Artemia. These brine shrimps (Fig. 18-21; larva, Fig. 11-24) are found in saline lakes, or they may be purchased as dried, resting eggs from aquarium shops or supply houses. They belong to the order Eubranchiopoda and are characterized by having ten to thirty pairs of leaflike swimming limbs. In development they have a nauplius stage like *Cypris* and *Cyclops*. (On the other hand, *Daphnia* has direct development.)

Artemia are sensitive to light and orient themselves so that the ventral surface is placed toward light. Thus they often swim with the ventral region uppermost. In the female, lateral egg pouches are conspicuous. After each molting, the females are ready for mating. Batches of eggs may be laid as often as every 4 or 5 days when ample food is available. Eggs laid with abundant secretion usually remain dormant for some time, often several months. Although a period of drying out is not necessary for hatching, the process often seems to shorten the time. Dried eggs retain their viability for several years, provided they are kept in a cool place. On the other hand, eggs which have a scant secretion when laid hatch out in 1 or 2 days as nauplius larvae.

Hatch the eggs of the brine shrimp by placing them in natural sea water. In 1

Fig. 18-21 *Artemia salina* (brine shrimp). (From R. W. Hegner, *College Zoology*, rev. ed., Macmillan, 1930.)

or 2 days the eggs hatch into larvae. You can prepare artificial sea water by adding about 3 to 4 gm of sodium chloride to 1 liter of pond water or aquarium water. Adults raised at higher salt concentrations (up to about 6 per cent) grow larger. However, sexual maturity is more rapid at lower salt concentrations.

Avoid overcrowding the larvae, and supply them with nonfilamentous algae. Algae scrapings from the sides of a tank have been found to develop as well in weak salt solutions. These may be added to the culture of *Artemia*. However, there must be an adequate oxygen supply as well as food for the nauplius larvae to mature rapidly. Keep the containers in moderate light at a temperature which remains below 25° C.

Woodlice. These land isopods (*Oniscus*) and the related genera *Porcellio*, the sow bug, and *Armadillidium*, the pill bug (Fig. 18-22), are all well adapted for their way of life and are widespread. They may be found under stones, boards, logs, in places which are dark, moist, and undisturbed.

The pill bug shows a characteristic response by rolling itself into a ball when it is disturbed. Both woodlice and pill bugs are found in the same ecological conditions and are cultivated in the same way.

Their usual ecological conditions are best duplicated in the laboratory in a terrarium containing damp, rich humus with small rocks or logs under which the organisms can hide. Supply these isopods with bits of ripe fruit (apples), bits of lettuce, and at times pieces of raw potatoes.

Fig. 18-22 *Left,* sow bugs *(Porcellio); above,* pill bug *(Armadillidium).* (Photos: Hugh Spencer; U.S.D.A.)

They will also accept small earthworms and insects.

Uses in the classroom. Isopods are interesting to have on hand in studies of adaptation of animals. Notice how their compressed bodies fit them for their environment. Use them in studies of tropisms (p. 124). Examine the contents of the intestine for flagellates (p. 311).

Marine aquaria

We have described the culturing of fresh-water invertebrates. More and more biologists are keeping marine aquaria (Fig. 18-23). These make especially fascinating studies for classes in inland cities. Synthetic sea water can be purchased along with small invertebrate animals and sea weeds as a kit from some biological supply houses (see listing of supply houses, p. 479). Use a hydrometer to establish the salt solution at a specific gravity of 1.017 to 1.022. Some salts must be replenished as they are absorbed by the organisms. Each month add a level teaspoon of a mixture of 3 parts rock salt and 1 part Epsom salt to a 20-gallon tank. Every 5 months add a small piece of plaster of Paris. (Avoid having brass, copper, or zinc in contact with sea water.)

Those who live along the coast may collect live specimens (gather only small ones) and prepare salt-water aquaria. Since sea plants are not good oxygenators, attach an aerator and pump. Collect small starfish, small clams or oysters, sea anemones, and sea weeds. Use fluorescent lights to prevent a change in the color of the water. (Incandescent lights seem to increase the growth of microorganisms, turning the water yellow.) Many sea worms thrive in these tanks. At feeding time remove the animals from the tank into smaller containers so that the aquarium does not become contaminated by uneaten food. Feed the starfish bits of clams or oysters.

Watch the means of locomotion of small starfish along the glass of the aquarium tank. Place a small oyster in another container, add a bit of lampblack to the water, and study the action of the incurrent and excurrent siphons as water moves in and out of the animal.

Marine aquarium

sea cucumber

sea urchin

starfish

Fig. 18-23 A marine aquarium and some animals which might live in it. (Photos: top three, Carolina Biological Supply Co.; right, American Museum of Natural History and U.S. Fish and Wildlife Service; bottom, General Biological Supply House, Inc., Chicago.)

scallop

clam

Insects

Some insects may best be collected as pupae, others in the adult or the larval stage. The work planned in the classroom will, no doubt, determine the kinds of insects to be kept. Following are some methods for keeping alive just a few kinds of insects; there are as many methods as there are kinds of insects (see Chapter 15).

Praying mantis. Collect egg masses in the fall or early spring. Or purchase some from biological supply houses. The egg cases are recognized as tan, foamlike masses attached to twigs (Fig. 2-4).

Keep the egg cases in covered terraria. With a gradual increase in temperature, hundreds of nymphs emerge. Supply the nymphs with dilute sugar solution or honey served in low, flat containers.

Uses in the classroom. In a study of reproduction among insects, the praying mantis illustrates an animal with incomplete metamorphosis: egg, nymph, adult. Some of the nymphs can be placed in corked vials and examined with a hand lens (pp. 166, 213).

Moths and butterflies. When pupal cases are collected in the fall, they should be stored in a cool place throughout the winter months. Place them in a box which can be left outside a window. In the spring put them into a small screened box or terrarium. Include twigs as supports for the emerging adults. Live pupae are generally heavier than dead or parasitized forms. (For instance, *Cecropia* moth pupae, a common form that students bring to class, is often parasitized by the Ichneumon fly.) Some teachers on the West Coast have their students observe metamorphosis of the mourning cloak butterfly (*Vanessa*). The changing of larvae into the chrysalis stage is almost completed within an hour. In seven days the butterfly emerges. Compare this develop-

larva   pupa   adult

Fig. 18-24 *Tenebrio* larva, pupa, and adult. The larvae are known as mealworms. (General Biological Supply House, Inc., Chicago.)

ment with that of the praying mantis or the grasshopper.

Uses in the classroom. In these living examples of insects, students may trace complete metamorphosis. At times, students may be fortunate enough to see a butterfly or moth emerge from a pupal case.

Directions have been given for raising fruit flies in class (see pp. 196–205).

Tribolium confusum. These beetles are often found in packaged flour and cereals. Keep both sexes in jars or finger bowls of slightly moistened whole-wheat flour, oatmeal, cornmeal, or bran. Where possible, adequate moisture may be supplied by attaching moist cotton to the cover of the container.

Metamorphosis is complete and takes about 5 to 6 weeks when cultures are kept at temperatures between 28° and 30° C. Start new colonies by placing pupae in fresh food medium.

Uses in the classroom. Tribolium beetles show all the stages in complete metamorphosis: egg, larva, pupa, and adult. They are also fine organisms around which students may design experiments in physiology, genetics, and behavior.

Tenebrio beetles. Larvae, called mealworms, of these beetles (Fig. 18-24) may be purchased from aquarium shops.

Culture the mealworms in battery jars half filled with moist bran or oatmeal, covered with fine mesh so that adult bee-

Fig. 18-25 *Left,* observation ant house; *right,* observation bee hive. (Photos: World of Adventure, Denver; U. of S. Calif.)

tles cannot fly off. When adult beetles develop, they should be fed bits of raw carrots or potatoes. At a temperature around 30° C, the complete life cycle may take 4 to 6 months.

Another method[25] describes the use of smooth galvanized iron boxes which are $2 \times 1\frac{1}{4} \times 1$ foot deep. On the bottom of the box spread a mash used to feed chicks. Over this, place a layer of burlap, then another layer of mash; alternate mash and burlap layers until some five or six layers of each are in place. This will support several hundred mealworms. In old cultures many eggs may be found. Start new cultures with a few organisms from the old cultures.

Uses in the classroom. While these beetles also show complete metamorphosis in a reproductive cycle, they are especially bred as food for laboratory fish, amphibia, and some reptiles.

Activities of social insects

Directions for making a beehive may be found in several texts on bees (see Bibliography). Some teachers purchase

[25] *Culture Methods for Invertebrate Animals,* J. Needham, ed.

an observation beehive (Fig. 18-25b) or wooden ant houses and observation boxes (Fig. 18-25a) from a biological supply house (listing, p. 479).

Making an ant colony. Students may prepare a makeshift observation ant colony for class use. Partially fill a battery jar or large box with slightly moistened sandy soil. Then place an ant hill you have collected from the field into the container. Include in the colony some workers and a queen. Keep the container covered or in the dark. Galleries made by the ants may be visible through the glass sides of the container. When possible place the jar in a basin of water so that a moat is formed, preventing the escape of ants.

Feed the ants on lettuce, carrots, potatoes, and bread crumbs as well as dilute molasses or honey. On occasion add some dead insects. But remove all excess food to prevent the growth of molds.

Keeping a termite colony. Colonies of termites may be kept in the laboratory for a continued study of social insects. A colony consists of a wingless large queen, winged males, wingless workers, and wingless soldiers. Inspect old tree stumps and wet logs for termite galleries. Gently strip off sections of the bark and wood to expose the insects and their eggs. Collect all stages with the wood in which they were thriving. In fact, move to the classroom as much of the log as is practicable.

In the laboratory remove the forms with a camel's-hair brush to avoid injuring them; their bodies are soft. Keep the insects, along with wood fragments, in covered finger bowls or Petri dishes. Add strips of moistened filter paper, then store in a dark place at room temperature. Keep moist by adding a few drops of water twice a week.

DeLong and Keagy describe several excellent methods[26] for making observation termite colonies in the laboratory. One simple method recommends the use of flat battery jars of the Delco type. A piece of balsa wood is placed inside along each of the two wide sides of the jar. Then the jar is filled about ¼ full of earth. Use thin strips of balsa wood to keep a space to accommodate free movement of termites between the balsa wood layers and the glass walls. When termites are introduced into the jar, they establish themselves within a few hours. Tunneling may be seen in a short time.

Uses in the classroom. These insects are splendid examples for a study of social life; they are also used in class as a source of the symbiotic flagellates which are found in their intestine. Prepare wet mounts of these beautiful flagellates as described on p. 311; also see p. 232.

CAPSULE LESSONS

Ways to get started in class

18-1. There are times when you want to develop a "parade of the animal kingdom" in class. This may be a survey of the kinds of animals which are available in the community. Try to use fresh materials, examine them under the microscope, keep them in vivaria or aquaria for observation. You may also want to survey animals by means of films, Kodachrome slides, or filmstrips.

In the catalogs of biological supply houses you will find long lists of slides of invertebrates, as well as vertebrate animals, and plants. The catalogs of film distributors offer a list of films and filmstrips which is phenomenal. Do you know these? *Beach and Sea Animals* and *Animal Life* (both Encyclopaedia Britannica); *Tide Pool Life* (Simmel-Meservey); *Wonders of the Sea* (Teaching Films Custodians); *Butterflies, Pond Insects,* and *Tiny Water Animals* (all three Encyclopaedia Britannica). A tremendous variety of animal life and functions is described in *Born to Die* (Skibo).

See also our film library (p. 464).

18-2. Are you familiar with the fine silent series produced by Rutgers University: several reels on the *Parade of Invertebrates* and reels on *Annelids, Mollusks,* and *Arthropods?*

18-3. Encourage students to bring in all kinds of living materials which you want to maintain. Form a club of museum curators to care for the living materials. In this way, living forms are available for study over the year, and in season. And your school may be in a position to help other schools in the vicinity if they call for living materials. (Student squads, p. 439.)

PEOPLE, PLACES, AND THINGS

Do you need help in identifying an insect, a specimen a student came upon on his way to school? Find out which people in your community have made a hobby of knowing the insects; there may be some who gather organisms at ebb tide along the beaches, or in desert areas, or in the woods. Who knows which insect pests which attack crops or garden plants or the shade trees? Is there a farmer who has a beehive?

There are many resources to tap: these people in the community, teachers at other schools and colleges. A museum or a zoological garden will help you identify many specimens. You

[26] D. DeLong and R. Keagy, "Termite Cultures in the Laboratory," *Turtox News,* 27:5, General Biological Supply House, Chicago, May 1949.

may also get help from biological supply houses in identification and also advice on ways to maintain organisms.

BOOKS AND PAMPHLETS

The literature in this area is specialized. In the Bibliography at the end of the book we have compiled a list of books, with complete bibliographical data, classified as nature study books and identification keys and guides. Also refer to the books in zoology and physiology for additional aids in this study.

Kudo, R. R., *Protozoology*, 1954.

Hall, R. P., *Protozoology*, 1953.

Miner, R., *Fieldbook of Seashore Life*, 1950.

Pennak, R., *Fresh-water Invertebrates of the United States*, 1953.

Smith, R., *Intertidal Invertebrates of central California Coast*, 1954.

FILMS AND FILMSTRIPS

Please refer to the listing of films at the end of the book in the section called Animals and Their Functions. This listing, however, is only a sampling of the films, filmstrips, and slides which are available for classroom use. You may send for catalogs from the distributors. A directory of distributors and their addresses is also listed at the end of the book.

FREE AND INEXPENSIVE MATERIALS

The quality of free materials available to the teacher in this area is excellent. A more complete listing, including addresses, is given at the end of the book. Your state department of agriculture offers many aids. For example, we have seen booklets from Illinois on identification of mushrooms, books from the Kansas Department of Agriculture on grasses, birds, and insects (including color plates). Many departments will put your name on their mailing list to receive announcements. Agricultural colleges often have a 4-H club bulletin series like those published by New York State College of Agriculture, Cornell University. There are fine pamphlets as, *Diseases and Insects in the Orchard, Pollination of Fruit Trees, Insect Control,* and many others.

You may have your name placed on the mailing list of the U.S. Department of Agriculture to receive announcements of their new publications and their Yearbooks. These cover all areas of biology.

Each of the biological supply houses offer aids for the teacher. We are familiar with only a few of the publications, but let us use them as an example of the quality of materials which teachers may receive. Many are free; in some cases, there are small handbooks available usually for about $1.00 or less. The following materials are available for the asking:

Carolina Tips, Carolina Biological Supply Co.

Turtox News; Turtox Leaflets (set of more than 50 leaflets), General Biological Supply House.

Ward's Natural Science Bulletin and leaflets on techniques, Ward's Natural Science Establishment.

Welch's *"A Living Biological Laboratory,"* Welch Manufacturing Co.

CHAPTER 19

Caring for vertebrates

useful in the classroom

The best ways for maintaining living things are those methods which reproduce the most favorable field conditions and eliminate natural enemies where possible. This is, in essence, the principle upon which the construction of vivaria is based.

Precautions similar to those for protozoa and metazoan invertebrates must be taken in caring for vertebrates. Here again, diet and temperature control are the factors most responsible for success in keeping vertebrates in a healthy state.

The purpose of this chapter will be to describe general methods which may be followed to advantage in the ordinary school laboratory. No attempt will be made to describe the methods of caring for many different kinds of vertebrates. The methods described will be suitable for many animals with demonstrated usefulness in teaching. Students quickly take over the coveted task of "zoo" and "vivarium" keepers. They learn a good deal in this way (student squads, p. 439).

(You may want to refer now to Chapter 15 for equipment needed in planning field trips.)

Fish

There is seldom a laboratory which does not have an aquarium. The aquarium probably furnishes the best single device for maintaining many of the animals in the laboratory.

Types of aquaria. The healthiest fish are those which are placed in an aquarium of appropriate size. Overcrowding is usually detrimental. A pair of fish 1 inch in length requires at least 1 gallon of water. A 5-gallon tank can house six pairs of fish, 1 inch or so in length, together with the needed plants and other animals. In our experience, 4- to 5-gallon tanks are the most suitable for aquaria. For demonstration or close study in the classroom the fish may be removed and placed in smaller tanks which are more easily handled.

For most purposes, rectangular tanks

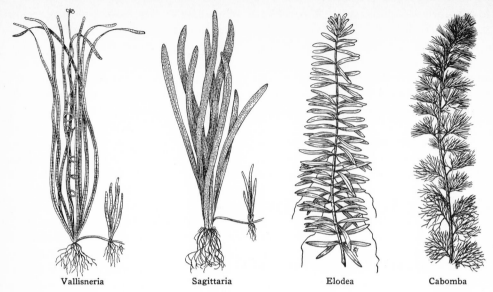

| Vallisneria | Sagittaria | Elodea | Cabomba |

Fig. 19-1 Plants for an aquarium. (General Biological Supply House, Inc., Chicago.)

with slate or glass bottoms and chromium or iron frames in which thick glass is fitted are desirable. Cheap tanks usually end up costing more than good ones (damaged tables, time spent in repair).

Certain tropical fish require heating and other arrangements. Their care is well treated in many texts. (See the list of books at the end of this chapter.)

How to prepare an aquarium. Before the animals are added, the tank should be prepared and planted. Proper, careful preparation and planting are necessary for success in maintaining animals.

First, wash the tank with soap and warm water. Avoid using very hot water; in many tanks the preparations used to cement the sides to the frame may soften. After several rinsings with cold water the aquarium should be ⅔ filled with cold water and allowed to stand for a day or so. At this time any leaks may be detected, and in addition, any soluble matter in the tank will be dissolved. This water should be discarded.

When the aquarium has been thoroughly cleaned, it is ready for plants and animals. Wash coarse sand (gravel) in boiling water. Then cover the bottom of the tank with a ½-inch layer of this sand. Embed a clean piece of clam shell at each end of the 5-gallon aquarium, to help neutralize acidity and furnish calcium salts for the shells of the snails. Over this, put another ½-inch layer of clean sand. Excessive growth of certain algae may be avoided by embedding a 2-inch square strip of copper (or several copper coins) in the sand. Next, lay a large sheet of paper on top of the sand before pouring water into the tank, to prevent the sand from becoming stirred. Add water to a level of 1 or 2 inches from the top, and remove the paper. Let the tank stand for 1 or 2 days to bring the water to room temperature, help dissolve air in the water, and rid it of chlorine.

It is good practice to add ½ gallon of established aquarium water to a freshly prepared tank. A tank to which this "conditioned" water has been added develops more quickly than a completely new one. Better still, add an entire gallon of a thriving *Daphnia* culture (see Chapter 18) to the newly prepared aquarium. When these are not available, the water should stand for two or three days. Then plants may be added together with the water in which they have been purchased or collected. Select rooted plants as well as floating plants for display and protection for young fish.

Plants for an aquarium. There is a variety of plants from which to choose. The common plants which have grown well in a tank are *Lemna, Vallisneria, Sagittaria, Anacharis* (elodea), *Cabomba, Myriophyllum, Ludwigia, Potamogeton, Chrysosplenium, Herpestis, Utricularia,* and *Cryptocoryne* (Fig. 19-1). It is recommended that the first plantings be of *Anacharis, Cabomba,* or *Vallisneria,* since these, in our experience, are the hardiest of the plants which may be purchased or collected. *Vallisneria*

roots readily; it is pleasing in display and does not tangle (so that a fish net may be used easily). *Potamogeton, Chrysosplenium,* and *Lemna* are still hardier, but the first two must be collected and have a tendency to grow rapidly and crowd the tank. This may be beneficial to the fish but may not be satisfactory for display purposes.

The water ferns *Salvinia* and *Marsilia,* and algae such as *Nitella,* will do well *after* the water has been conditioned.

In any event, it may be desirable to use a variety of plants for display (Fig. 19-2). Place plants in the background of the tank where they will not interfere with examination and handling of the animals. Then add a rock or two for scenic effect, but more important, to afford a hiding place for the animals,

Fig. 19-2 A thriving aquarium. (Photo: General Biological Supply House, Inc., Chicago.)

especially for gravid females.

Snails. Add two snails per gallon of water. They tend to keep the glass clean by removing encrusting algae. In addition, very young snails serve as food for some of the fish. *Lymnaea, Physa,* or *Planorbis* (Fig. 18-15) are suitable for this purpose. *Campeloma,* a very large snail, is excellent but requires more space than the others; three of them in a 5-gallon tank are sufficient.

Light. Keep the aquarium in medium light; strong light favors the growth of algae which turn the water green. In general, northern or western exposure is most suitable. When a southern exposure is the only available location, the portion of the aquarium facing the direct rays of the sun may be covered with paper, cardboard, or glazed glass, or painted green. Should algae turn the water green, add quantities of *Daphnia.* After the water is cleared the fish will feed upon the *Daphnia.* However, when there are many fish in the tank remove the fish before adding *Daphnia.* Otherwise the fish will eat the water fleas before they have a chance at the algae. Add more snails if there is an excessive growth of filamentous algae.

Feeding. There are many foods on the market; most of them consist of dried chopped shrimp, brine shrimp, ant pupae, or dried *Daphnia.* Others have dried vegetables added. Any one of these is satisfactory for tropical fish and native fish too, provided live food is added now and then. (Once a week is fine.) Some fish, like the Bettas, do very well on dried food, while others, like the Japanese medaka, reproduce regularly only when fed living food daily.

Native fish prefer living food but will accept dried food. *Enchytraeus* (white worms, see p. 348), either chopped or whole, *Tubifex* worms, *Daphnia,* and bits of fresh liver are acceptable.

Avoid overfeeding fish, for the excess food will foul the water, killing the fish. A pinch of dry food daily is enough for tropical fish about 3 or 4 inches long. During the first few days watch how much food the fish consume. Reduce the quantity the following day if food is not consumed. Remove the excess by siphoning. It is better to underfeed than to feed more than the animals take in a day.

Day-to-day care. Besides feeding the fish, keep the water level constant and remove dead plants or animals. When plants are growing rapidly some should be removed to prevent overcrowding. This is especially true of *Lemna* and *Salvinia,* two forms which grow profusely.

Also remove excess snails as they increase in number, for an excess will destroy plants. It is not necessary, especially for tropical fish, to change the water in the tank except where fouling or special care requires it. There is no cause for alarm if the water becomes yellowish or greenish; water that color is good, "conditioned" aquarium water. (A suitable pH range may be as wide as 6.8 to 7.2 for the average tank.)

Tropical fish. There are many tropical fish which add beauty and variety to a tank. Many hybrid forms have been developed as knowledge of the genetics of fish has accumulated. Only a few kinds of fish are described here as typical and useful in the classroom. Although the life histories of the "fighting fish" *Betta* (Fig. 19-3) and other bubble-nest builders are of unusual interest, they are not of general value for classroom use.

Guppy (Lebistes reticulatus) (Fig. 19-3). This is probably the commonest of the tropical fish, and perhaps the most successful to maintain for the beginner. It is hardy and can withstand low room temperatures. It is a live bearer (ovoviviparous) and reproduces readily.

Platy (Platypoecilus) (Fig. 19-3). These forms are not as hardy as the guppy but are interesting for display and study. They are also live bearers. A temperature range from 68° to 78° F is optimum for these fish.

Japanese medaka (Oryzias latipis). This fish does not need as careful temperature control as do other tropical fish, but it does need live food for regular reproduction. When it is fed *Tubifex, Daphnia,* or *Enchytraeus,* the female produces about eight to twenty eggs each morning. These eggs hang from the cloaca and can easily be removed if the fish is caught and transferred to a finger bowl of tank water. The eggs are clear and excellent for the study of embryological development. Students may examine these eggs under a binocular (stereoscopic) microscope or magnifying glass (see p. 168).

Native fish. Killifish (*Fundulus heteroclitus*), the red-bellied dace (*Chrosomus erythrogaster*), the stickleback, the banded sunfish (*Mesogonistius chaetodon*), and the blue-gill sunfish (Fig. 19-3) are desirable animals to have in the laboratory. These species should be kept separately in tanks well supplied with vegetation. In one sense they are easier to keep, since they can withstand a wide range in temperature.

In general, these fish will not accept the prepared foods although they may do so after some time. All living food and bits of raw meat, raw fish, or raw liver are readily accepted and eaten voraciously.

Goldfish (*Carassius auratus*) will thrive under the same conditions as tropical fish.

blue-gill sunfish (bream)　　　　goldfish　　　　platy

catfish　　　　Betta　　　　guppy

Fig. 19-3 Fish which should do well in a school aquarium. Note that the catfish shown is a special one for small aquariums. (Photos: Alan M. Fletcher; Innes Publishing Co.)

Small goldfish (Fig. 19-3) are preferable, since the larger ones require larger tanks. Goldfish do not need careful temperature control. Optimum temperature conditions range from 10° to 25° C (50° to 75° F). They are omnivorous and feed on plants in the tank and bits of boiled spinach in addition to other food.

Diseases of aquarium fish. Fungi, such as the water mold (*Saprolegnia*), and the protozoan called "water itch" (*Ichthyophthyrius*) are two of the many parasites which attack fish. When fish show gray patches on the fins or scales they should be isolated quickly, for these are symptoms of disease.

Fish which show these patches should be immersed in a 10 per cent solution of table salt. After 1 hour remove the fish and wash in ordinary water. Usually the patches disappear after this heroic treatment. Nevertheless, put the fish into a 0.5 per cent solution of potassium permanganate for 15 minutes. Then quarantine the affected fish in separate tanks and watch for the reappearance of the symptoms.

In actual practice, so little is known about fish diseases that it seems most desirable to discard fish which have become diseased. This has proved to be the best and the cheapest procedure (even after experts have prescribed the cure).

Amphibia

Salamanders and frogs are especially desirable to have on hand for studies both in natural history and in the development of eggs. Students may prepare vivaria so that the tanks duplicate the natural habitat of these animals.

Salamanders

Preparing vivaria. Long, low vivaria covered with glass are desirable. However, whatever type of container is used, there should be a pool with a "beach" for most kinds of salamanders (Fig. 19-4).

The vivarium must be cleaned as thoroughly as if it were to house fish. At one end of the tank put a small glass dish or noncorrosive metal pan to serve as a pool. Cover the rest of the tank with coarse pebbles together with a few pieces of charcoal. This should insure good drainage. Then build up this part of the tank with a loam soil rich in humus. Slant the layers of soil away from the small pool to a height of 3 inches and keep about 2 inches of water in the pool. Students can prepare an effective natural habitat by planting a "beach" around the pool. They may use layers of moss, such as *Sphagnum, Mnium, Dicranum,* or similar types. Place at least one rock in the water. Try planting the rest of the vivarium with small ferns, partridge berries, and a variety of other mosses which have different textures and shades of green.

Feeding. Almost all salamanders require living food such as *Daphnia, Tubifex, Lumbricus* (chopped), *Enchytraeus, Tenebrio* larvae, and *Drosophila*. On occasion, some forms such as *Triturus* (the red eft) may take fresh liver if it is dangled in front of

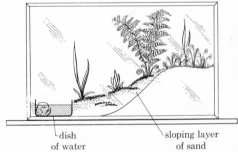

dish
of water

sloping layer
of sand

Fig. 19-4 Vivarium with a "beach" suitable for salamanders and frogs.

them on a string. But dead animals and food which has not been eaten must be removed within an hour or so to avoid fouling the tank.

Temperature. The best temperature range seems to lie between 15° and 18° C. However, many salamanders can survive at temperatures extending to 20° to 25° (note *Triturus,* below).

Diseases. In the laboratory many salamanders may be affected by such fungi as *Saprolegnia.* The infection is symptomized by patches of fuzzy white thread on the tail or over the entire body. While most animals infected by fungi do not recover, some first-aid measures may be attempted. Isolate the infected animal and place it in 5 per cent potassium permanganate for 10 minutes. After washing with cold water, place the animal in a jar of water to which a sheet of copper, copper wire, or copper filings have been added. Or add a drop of 1 per cent copper sulfate solution to 200 cc of water. Keep the animal in this solution for about 2 days. It may be necessary to disinfect the vivarium with 5 per cent formalin; then clean it thoroughly and replant it.

Red eft or water newt (*Triturus viridescens*). This salamander is the most easily reared. It can be easily handled, and its slow movements make it desirable for observation and study by students. Students may readily observe the two phases in the life cycle of the animal: the water and land phases. In the water phase, the animal is olive-green with carmine spots and yellow-speckled undersides. In this stage it may be kept with fish in an aquarium, although it is more desirable to keep it in a vivarium where it will remain in the pool of water. Water plants should be included in the pool. In this stage *Triturus* becomes sexually mature, and if both sexes are present fertilized eggs may be deposited on the water plants. Larvae hatch in water and metamorphosis into the red phase, the land stage, occurs. This is the beautiful creature which moves slowly over land and feeds on small insects and worms. After 2 to 3 years the red eft returns to the water and changes into the green phase.

In water, *Triturus* feeds on *Daphnia, Tubifex,* bits of *Enchytraeus,* and earthworms. On land, it feeds on *Drosophila* and *Tenebrio* larvae. (See Chapter 18 for ways to culture the "food" organisms.)

The amblystomas (tiger, spotted, and Jefferson's salamanders). These animals are readily kept in vivaria. The young stage (axolotl) remains in water and feeds on *Daphnia, Tubifex,* earthworms, and *Enchytraeus.* Adults feed voraciously on earthworms, insects, and *Tenebrio* larvae.

Other salamanders which may be kept in a similar tank are the red-backed *Plethodon cinereus,* the slimy *Plethodon glutinosios,* the dusky *Desmognathus fuscus,* the two-lined *Eurycea bislineata,* the red *Pseudotriton ruber,* and the Pacific salamander. (Over the country, these have different common names.) These woodland salamanders feed upon small pieces of liver and lean beef which should be offered to them on the end of a toothpick. There are a few forms such as *Amphiuma* and the red-bellied *Triturus pyrrhogaster* which thrive better in an aquarium. They may be fed the same diet as suggested previously.

Frogs

Egg-laying time among frogs (*Anura*). Frog eggs and tadpoles, as well as adult frogs, may be collected by students and cultivated in the laboratory or classroom for long-range enriching experiences. The time of egg-laying is different for each species and the surrounding temperature is a controlling factor. Therefore the time schedule given here may vary, progressing from the southern to the northern states.

As soon as the ice disappears, very early in March, *Rana sylvatica,* the wood frog, breeds, laying about 600 eggs. At this time the water temperature may be as low as 5° C. The eggs should be kept in water from 5° to 15° C. The common leopard frog, *Rana pipiens,* lays eggs in March and April; about 2000 are deposited at a time. The pond temperature at this time is about 15° C. Egg masses of *Rana palustris* are brownish in color and larger than those of *R. pipiens.* This species breeds in April.

The green frog *Rana clamitans* and *R. catesbiana* (bullfrog) are both summer breeders. The males of both species can be distinguished from the females by the presence of a yellow throat and tympanic membranes larger than the eyes. In the females these membranes are the same size as the eyes. The eggs of *Rana clamitans* do not tolerate temperatures below 12° C.

The spring peeper, *Hyla crucifer,* breeds in April and its eggs are laid singly. Pairs found in amplexus will deposit eggs in the laboratory. This is the best way to collect these eggs.

Toads lay eggs in long strings of jelly. Those of *Bufo fowleri* and *B. americana* are found in early June, of *Bufo californica* in May. The young develop rapidly.

Vivaria. The eggs should be kept in finger bowls or in shallow aquaria containing 5 or 6 inches of water. Such a tank can be well stocked with plants to provide sufficient oxygen (Fig. 19-4).

It has been best, in our experience, to hatch the eggs in finger bowls. Jelly masses can be cut with scissors so that about fifty eggs are put in each bowl. Remove the unfertilized eggs. These can be spotted readily, for the fertilized eggs orient themselves so that the pigmented portion is uppermost. Thus, within the jelly masses, when the black surfaces are uppermost the eggs are fertile.

Cleavage stages may be studied with a hand lens, a stereoscopic microscope, or a dissecting microscope. The rate of development of frog eggs usually varies directly with the temperature. Viable temperatures vary from 50° to 75° F. As tadpoles hatch out they still have considerable yolk sac, and no feeding is needed. However, as they grow older, add scraps of boiled lettuce or spinach. At times, raw lettuce and spinach are accepted, as well as aquatic plants. Change the water twice weekly. After several weeks, pieces of hard-boiled egg yolk or small bits of raw liver may be added to the water. But quickly remove the excess food to prevent fouling of the water. When the hind legs have appeared and the forelimbs are just breaking through the operculum and skin, place the tadpoles in a combination water-woodland vivarium (as described for salamanders); they are ready to undergo metamorphosis into land forms.

Tadpoles of the larger species, *Rana clamitans* and *Rana catesbiana,* as soon as they attain the size of ½ inch, should be transferred to a larger aquarium having a 6-inch water level. Tadpoles of *Rana clamitans* do not complete metamorphosis until the following year. Bullfrog tadpoles take 2 to 4 years for complete metamorphosis. Tadpoles may be kept in a "balanced" aquarium. When they are kept separately, they can be fed scraps of lettuce, liver, or hard-boiled egg yolk.

When a few frogs are kept for display purposes, a woodland vivarium is desirable. Such forms as bullfrogs are an exception; they fare better in 2 inches of water in a clean aquarium.

The problem of handling large quantities of frogs in the laboratory is a difficult one. The survival rate is high when they are kept at 10° C in a granite sink containing 1 inch of water. Cover them with wire mesh; change the water daily. Keep frogs away from zinc. Better still, when facilities are available, keep the water running slowly in the sink. An unused sink in which the drain can be stoppered with a closed wire mesh tube about 6 inches high is ideal. A slanted board should be provided so the frogs may leave the water.

Where a sink is not available, an alternate, but less desirable, method may be used. Keep the frogs in large aquaria with water at a level of 1 inch. Flush the frogs with a stream of water when the water in the tanks is changed each day; the water becomes fouled quickly. Dead frogs and frogs suffering from "red leg" should be isolated immediately, since the infection is highly contagious. In an attempt to reduce infection, add a dilute solution of table salt (0.2 per cent) to the water in which the frogs are kept.

Frogs which are most easily kept in beach vivaria as adults are *Rana pipiens, R. palustris,* and the green frog, *R. clamitans.* They accept *Tenebrio* larvae, small earthworms, flies, and similar living materials. *Rana catesbiana* should be kept in water which is 2 to 3 inches in depth. Provide a rock with a surface slightly above the water. These forms readily accept living things smaller than themselves, such as smaller frogs and earthworms.

The members of Hylidae, *Hyla crucifer* (spring peeper) and *Hyla versicolor* (tree frog), may be collected by students and kept in a beach vivarium. *Hyla crucifer* feeds on *Drosophila* and small mealworms. Provide a few stout twigs as supports for the tree frogs in the terrarium.

Among the toads (Bufonidae), *Bufo fowleri* and *B. americana* both require terraria similar to that of the Hylidae. However, it must be remembered that toads are active burrowers and they disrupt a well-managed terrarium.

Reptiles

Turtles

Vivaria. Most turtles, with the exceptions described below, should be kept in aquaria containing 2 to 4 inches of water. Cork floats can be added or a flat rock placed in one corner of the vivarium as a useful resting place. Students who care for the animals should change the water twice weekly to keep the water clear.

Painted turtles, wood turtles, and box turtles (Fig. 19-5) may be kept in water as described or in a beach vivarium. However, box turtles seem to prefer a moist terrarium or vivarium rather than water. Segregate snapping turtles, al-

Fig. 19-5   Box turtle and painted turtle. (Photos: U.S. Fish and Wildlife Service.)

though the small ones may be kept with other species.

Feeding. Most of the aquatic forms will accept bits of fish, ground raw meat, liver, earthworms, or dead frogs put in the water. Also most turtles will accept hard-boiled egg cut into slices, as well as lettuce and slices of apples. In addition, box and wood turtles take snails, slugs, and *Tenebrio* larvae.

When turtles become sluggish and show a tendency to hibernate they should be placed in a cool place. Forced feeding, especially at this time, is often detrimental.

Sex differences. The most uniform guide for distinguishing sexes in turtles is the shape of the plastron, the under shell. The plastron in the female of many species is slightly convex, while in the male, it is slightly concave. During the breeding season, there is a swelling of the anal region in the male. A distinguishing characteristic among box turtles is eye color. Males usually have red eyes; females have yellow eyes. The males usually have longer claws than the females.

Lizards and alligators

Small specimens of the American alligator and several kinds of lizards can be reared in the laboratory. The horned "toad" (*Phrynosoma*), the skink (*Eumeces*), and the chameleon (*Anolis*) are the lizards most useful in school.

Vivaria. Chameleons and the larger skinks should be housed in a large terrarium. Include some twigs so the animals have room to climb. Spray the plants in the terrarium daily to supply water for these lizards, since they seldom drink from a dish. They subsist mainly on live insects. It may be necessary to raise *Drosophila* for this purpose, especially during the winter months.

Young alligators survive in a vivarium of sand and rocks with a water trough embedded in the sand. Horned "toads" are maintained best in a similar desert vivarium containing about 5 inches of sand for burrowing, along with several rock piles for hiding. Embed a bowl of water up to the level of the sand. Students who care for the animals should provide several hours of direct sunlight but must also take care to ventilate the tank so that the temperature does not exceed 80° F.

Feeding. All these animals feed upon live insects, *Tenebrio* larvae, bits of earthworms, *Enchytraeus,* or similar living food. In addition, young alligators may take small frogs and fish. Chameleons and skinks may learn to accept small bits of raw liver or meat which are dangled before them. They do not feed regularly at low temperatures; 65° to 80° F is the most suitable range.

Snakes (nonpoisonous)

Every biology laboratory or project room should have one or two snakes on display. It is one way to break down the inordinate fear many students have of these animals. The most desirable forms are those which are easy to keep and to handle. These are the garter, ribbon, hognose, black, DeKay, and ring-necked snakes. Many others such as the bull, milk, water, and green snakes may also be maintained by interested students, but in our experience the first-mentioned are the easiest to keep.

Vivaria. Mesh cages much like those used for mammals are best for housing snakes, although the mesh should be of smaller gauge so that the smallest snakes cannot escape. In addition, bottom pans of zinc are needed. Door openings at the top of the cage are the most convenient to facilitate handling the animals. Into such a vivarium place a pan or bowl of water and a few rocks. Keep the snakes at a temperature between 70° and 80° F.

Where all-mesh cages are not available, use ordinary aquarium tanks with tightly fitting zinc mesh tops. You may need a weight to hold down the cover. An aquarium completely enclosed by glass is undesirable since there is no provision for ventilation. When cages of mesh are used for DeKay and ring-necked snakes, check carefully that the size of the mesh is small enough to prevent their escape. Snakes may be kept in such terraria as described for *Hyla* or *Bufo* (p. 368). All snakes should be washed weekly by flushing with water. Their cages should be cleaned at the same time.

Feeding. Most snakes described here will feed upon readily available food. DeKay and ring-necked snakes feed on insects such as *Tenebrio,* and small earth-worms; while hog-nosed, garter, and ribbon snakes accept entire, large earth-worms as well as insects, frogs or other amphibia, and lizards. Black snakes need live mammals. They may be fed a small rat every two weeks. On occasion, they will accept a dead animal if it is waved in front of them.

General care. Some students are experts at handling snakes; they can do much to help other students overcome their fears. When snakes are handled gently each day, they will in turn become gentle. Large snakes should first be handled with thick gloves. This may not be necessary as time goes on, as the snake shows signs of becoming accustomed to handling. Grasp a snake behind the head with one hand while the other hand is used to support its body.

Birds

Parakeets and canaries require little space and more or less routine care. Directions for maintaining these birds are given by the dealer at the time of purchase. In our experience, birds other than parakeets and canaries need more space and care than can be provided in the average classroom. However, where there are students who are expert in the handling of birds, this activity may become highly profitable.

On occasion a crow may be housed in a large cage. Young ones seem to find the surroundings agreeable and can be conditioned by students studying behavior.

Mammals

White rats and hamsters are the most satisfactory mammals to keep in the laboratory. Students become quite adept at handling them. Guinea pigs and rabbits do not, ordinarily, demonstrate anything for which mice and rats are not suitable, and they require much more space and care. The care of the rat will be described in some detail; that of the mouse is similar. However, good ventilation is needed when mice are reared since they have an offensive odor—most noticeable in close quarters.

Cages. Most of the cages available commercially are satisfactory (Fig. 19-6). The larger cages are best since they allow for exercise. The mesh should be large enough to allow droppings to fall through to a bottom pan (which should be made of a noncorrosive metal), as shown.

The door of the cage may be on the side or at the top. That on the top is the most convenient since it allows for better handling. However, such cages cannot

Fig. 19-6 Two commercial cages for housing small mammals. (Photos: Geo. H. Wahmann Mfg. Co.)

be stacked. Cages should be cleaned daily and fresh newspaper placed in the bottom pan. If cedar shavings are used instead of paper, the offensive odor of rats and mice is not as noticeable. Cleaning a cage the first or second day after delivery of a litter is not advisable. In fact, care must be taken for several weeks in order not to disturb unnecessarily the mother and young.

Male and female rats should be segregated when 50 days old and should be kept segregated until mating is desirable. Remove the male as soon as the female is pregnant.

The period of gestation is 21 days, and the young should be permitted to remain with the mother for about 21 to 24 days. At this time they should be weaned. When the young are kept with the mother for a longer period there is a severe drain on the female.

A pregnant rat should be given strips of newspaper or paper toweling for nest building. Once a nest is built it is not necessary to change the paper, although this can be done after the young have hair and their eyes are opened. This occurs after 16 to 18 days.

The sex of the young rats may be distinguished by the fact that the distance between the anus and the genital papilla is greater in the male than in the female.

General care. Students should feed the rats no more than once a day. They should be treated as pets (although many students will tend to overdo this). If they are, they respond satisfactorily and reproduce readily. Rough treatment may result in viciousness and cause the mother to destroy her litter. The rats should be handled gently and fondled, from birth. When this is done they do not bite, and in fact, they are so conditioned that they will run forward to be handled. Such animals are especially desirable for the classroom.

Care of the nursing mother. A gentle female rat will respond favorably to handling during the nursing period and will not resent handling of the young, provided it is done by one who has been responsible for her daily care. She should be fed whenever she is removed from her young. The female, especially at this time, may react unfavorably to strangers. A bit of chocolate or carrot given to the mother as she is returned to her young will help ease her distress.

Feeding. Rats should be fed a diet of bread, sometimes soaked in milk, in addition to lettuce, carrots, other vegetables, sunflower seeds, and similar foods. The bread should be broken and the carrots cut into portions equal to the number of rats in the cage. They will accept hard-boiled eggs. Two or three drops of cod-liver oil on the bread should be given twice a week. Provide a bowl of milk weekly.

Water must be supplied at all times. Water fountains, blown of one solid piece of glass, are available from biological supply houses (see listing at the end of book). Substitute ones may be made in the laboratory by inserting a 6-inch length of ¼-inch glass tubing, straight or bent, through a rubber stopper in a suitable 300-cc bottle. Fire-polish the protruding end to ⅛-inch opening and insert through the mesh of the cage (Fig. 19-7).

There are synthetic diets which may be used.[1] When the young are to be weaned, feed them milk, bread soaked in milk, and lettuce. After they are 30 days old they can be fed the same diet as the

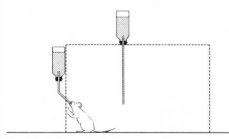

Fig. 19-7 Water bottle for mammals, two variations.

TABLE 19-1
Gestation periods of some mammals

	gestation period (in days)	Breeding age
White rats	21–22	Females may be bred when 4 months old. Wean the young and separate the sexes after 21 days.
Mice	20–22	Breed females when 60 days old. Wean the young after 21 days.
Guinea pigs	63	Breed when 9 months old. Wean the young and separate the sexes at 4 to 5 weeks.
Golden hamsters	16–19	Breed the females when 60 days old.
Rabbits	30–32	Females are ready for mating when 10 months old. Wean the young and separate the sexes after 8 weeks.

adults. Pellet foods may then be added to the diet.

Readers who seek information about the reproductive patterns of wild animals of their own community may want to look into Asdell's book, *Patterns of Mammalian Reproduction* (listed in the Bibliography), which covers mammalian reproductive cycles from the duckbills (Monotremes) to some of the higher hoofed forms.

CAPSULE LESSONS
Ways to get started in class

19-1. Students may form a "vivarium squad" (see Chapter 22), whose function is to maintain invertebrates and aquaria of different fish (in-

clude live-bearers such as guppies, as well as egg-layers) in the laboratory. They may also collect amphibian eggs in season and make them available to other students and classes.

19-2. Students may be interested in collecting reptiles. There are students who become experts on this subject. Have them as "guest speakers" in class programs or in assembly programs.

19-3. You may want to show films as vicarious field trips to survey animal forms and their

[1] Refer to the *Turtox Leaflets:* "Care of Rats, Mice and Guinea Pigs" and "The Care and Breeding of the Golden Hamster." Ralston Purina Company has a fine booklet, "Care and Feeding of Laboratory Animals."

adaptations. Vertebrates were included in some of the films listed at the end of Chapter 17. Also refer to the list of films and filmstrips at the end of the book. Here are a few of the useful films: *Mammals Are Interesting, Water Birds, Animals Growing Up,* and *The Zoo* (Encyclopaedia Britannica Films).

19-4. Some students may want to plan research projects involving some aspect of the biology of some of these animals. Many ideas have been presented in passing in the previous chapters. Fish genetics may be one problem; a study of parasites of frogs from different localities may be another. Behavior among members of another group may hold the interest of certain students.

PEOPLE, PLACES, AND THINGS

The suggestions we made in this section in Chapter 17 also hold this time. In fact, it may be easier to find people who are experts in handling fish; many students or members of their family have tropical fish. We have had students at times who have exchanged snakes with other enthusiasts or with a nearby zoological park.

Departments of Agriculture, a 4-H Club, or a local branch of the Audubon Society will help in identifying birds and suggesting ways to encourage birds to take up residence around school or a nearby area. Directions for building birdhouses are readily available. You may have bird-watching groups in your community. Someone may speak to the class or club on a topic of general interest.

If you wish to start to keep rats or hamsters, they may be purchased from a supply house. Or sometimes parents dispose of these pets when their youngsters "tire" of them (possibly the parents tire first). Your school may fall heir to these animals. At times you may get animals from a hospital, college laboratory, or research laboratory.

BOOKS AND PAMPHLETS

Refer to the Bibliography, classified by subject, at the end of the book, for books pertinent to the work discussed in this chapter.

FILMS AND FILMSTRIPS

You will find many slides available, whole series on birds and mammals, for example, which we have not had space to include in our film library at the end of the book. Send for catalogs from film distributors, and from biological supply houses which carry extensive selections of slides, charts, filmstrips, and films.

Only a sampling of different kinds of materials have been included in our film library.

FREE AND INEXPENSIVE MATERIALS

We have listed in the previous chapter a few of the biological supply houses which supply instructions for maintaining plants and animals. You will want to add to your list the publication *Care and Feeding of Laboratory Animals* available from the Ralston Purina Company (St. Louis 2, Mo.); perhaps you will also be interested in the booklet *Your Aquarium,* Innes Publishing Co., Philadelphia, $.30.

CHAPTER 20

Growing plants

useful in the classroom

Since there is no one best way to grow a specific plant, especially the algae and bacteria, a number of selected methods which have proven useful are given for some forms. A choice is included to meet the different needs of teachers.

Algae

Culturing

In view of their ability to carry on photosynthesis, it might seem that algae should respond readily to culture. This is not altogether true; while certain algae respond to specific methods, some species do not. Others, such as *Oscillatoria* and *Cladophora*, respond to a variety of methods.

Most of the algae useful in the biology classroom may be cultivated by one of the methods described in this section. The methods which have been found most suitable for each alga will be listed under its genus name in the summary.

General method: method A. One of the most successful methods for a great number of different algae is simple: Introduce the algae into an established aquarium in which fresh-water animals and plants have been thriving for at least 2 months.

Method B. Many solutions have been described as excellent for various algae. Here are a few which have given satisfactory results.

MOLISCH'S SOLUTION. Dissolve these materials in 1 liter of distilled water:

	grams
KNO_3	0.2
$MgSO_4$	0.2
K_2HPO_4	0.2
$CaSO_4$	0.2

Dissolve the calcium sulfate separately in 200 cc of water; then add to the other salts dissolved in 800 cc of water.

Both this and Benecke's solution, which we have found to be more suitable, are similar to Klebs' solution (p. 342), which differs mainly in that it uses both potas-

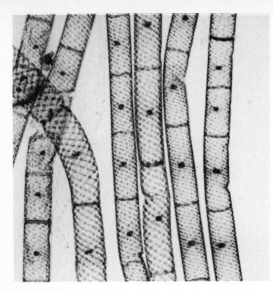

Fig. 20-1 *Spirogyra* (vegetative), a filamentous green alga containing one or several spiral chloroplasts. (Photo: General Biological Supply House, Inc., Chicago.)

sium nitrate and calcium nitrate.

BENECKE'S SOLUTION. Dissolve these materials in 1 liter of distilled water:

	grams
$Ca(NO_3)_2$	0.5
$MgSO_4$	0.1
K_2HPO_4	0.2
$FeCl_3$ (1% solution)	trace (1 drop)

KNOP'S SOLUTION. Use the variation described on p. 113.

In preparing these solutions, use distilled water, since tap water may be chlorinated or may contain copper, both highly toxic to algae.

The ability of these solutions to support the growth of various algae is greatly enhanced by adding to the culture jar 1 inch of soil taken from the pond where the algae have been growing. Good garden soil is a useful substitute. First, boil the soil in distilled water to destroy contaminating algae. Then you may have students add this, together with water, to the prepared container. Let the medium stand for a day or so before algae are added to the culture medium. Such soil-solution

cultures have been very satisfactory. You may need to subculture when the algae reach maximum growth.

For some as yet unknown reason, these methods and many others which have been tried fail when they are applied to culturing *Spirogyra* (Fig. 20-1), the alga most commonly used in class. Furthermore, it appears to die very quickly in its own pond water. The following method appears to be successful at times, although it is crude and is not useful for all forms.

Method C. We have found that when filaments of coarse-filamented *Spirogyra*, such as *S. nitida*, are introduced into a thriving culture of *Daphnia* (preparation, p. 351), rapid growth takes place.[1] (*Caution:* This method does not generally work with fine-filamented species.) In fact, the algae rapidly choke the container or aquarium in which the *Daphnia* are cultivated.

Keep the cultures in medium light, or in a north window. Each week add about 0.1 gm of fresh, hard-boiled egg yolk smoothed between the fingers into a paste. The species of *Spirogyra* containing two or more spiral chloroplasts seems to respond more vigorously than the species with single chloroplasts.

Recently it has been our experience to find that almost all the algae commonly used in elementary courses show vigorous growth when cultivated by this method. Discovering improved methods of culturing algae is very good project material for the gifted student.

A temperature range of 18° to 25° C is optimum in all the methods described. Higher temperatures are destructive, especially for methods A and C.

There are also methods described for the cultivation of algae on solid medium.

[1] P. Brandwein, "Preliminary Observations on the Culture of *Spirogyra*," *Am. J. Botany*, 27:3, 195–98, 1940.

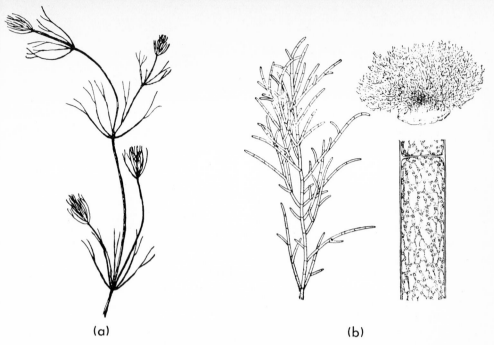

(a)   (b)

Fig. 20-2   (a) *Nitella;* (b) *Cladophora,* showing habit, portion of plant, and portion of chloroplast in young cell. (a, G. F. Atkinson, *Botany,* Holt, 1905; b, W. H. Brown, *The Plant Kingdom,* Ginn, 1935.)

When completely sterile conditions can be obtained, these methods are successful. However, for ordinary purposes they are tedious and undesirable.

Method D. For special techniques a solid medium may be needed. Here are two useful ones.

MODIFIED PFEFFER'S SOLUTION. Combine with 1 liter of distilled water:

	grams
$Ca(NO_3)_2$	1.00
K_2HPO_4	0.25
$Fe_3(PO_4)_2$	0.05
$(NH_4)_2SO_4$	0.50

When this solution has been prepared, add 15 gm of agar and 15 gm of fructose.

MODIFIED KNOP'S SOLUTION. Combine with 1 liter of distilled water:

	grams
$Ca(NO_3)_2$	1.00
KCl	0.25
$MgSO_4$	0.25
K_2HPO_4	0.25
$FeCl_3$	trace

To this solution add 20 gm of agar and 20 gm of glucose.

Summary of methods for specific algae

Here are listed some successful methods for maintaining certain algae.

Oscillatoria (Fig. 15-5): Use method A, B, or C.

Hydrodictyon (Fig. 15-5): Use method A or C. Method C gives a more vigorous growth.

Vaucheria (Fig. 15-7): Use method C. The form most commonly found is vegetative. Klebs induced formation of antheridia and oogonia within 4 to 5 days by placing *Vaucheria* in a 2 to 4 per cent cane sugar solution in *bright* light. *Vaucheria sessilis* is the common form found as green felt on flower pots in greenhouses. In ponds and lakes in the spring the more common form is *Vaucheria geminata.*

Chara: Use method C or B. *Chara* grows well when an inch of pond soil or sand is placed in the bottom of the culture jar.

Cladophora (Fig. 20-2b) and *Oedogonium*

(Figs. 11-48, 11-49): Use method A, B, or C. Methods A and C are most successful.

Spirogyra (Fig. 20-1): Use method C. Be sure the *Daphnia* are thriving in the culture before adding the spirogyra filaments.

Nitella (Fig. 20-2a): Use method C.

Desmids (Fig. 20-3): Use method B or C. Prepare the cultures in finger bowls.

Diatoms (Fig. 20-4): Collect diatoms from submerged rocks and stems of plants, or from the surface of mud in ponds and ditches in the spring. Diatoms abound in the brownish coating on rocks and stems which are slippery to the touch. Culture them like desmids in finger bowls (see above).

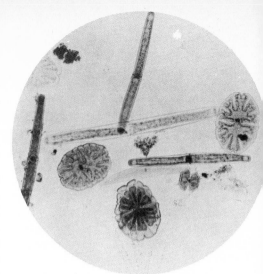

Fig. 20-3 Desmids. (Photo: General Biological Supply House, Inc., Chicago.)

Use of algae in the classroom

Algae of many kinds are used to show the structure of green plant cells (wet mounts, Chapter 17). It is unfortunate that *Spirogyra*, one of the most difficult to examine (with its complex strands of cytoplasm, spiral chloroplasts, and pyre-

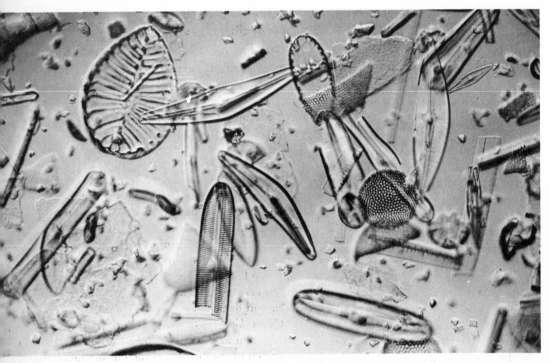

Fig. 20-4 Diatoms. (Photo: General Biological Supply House, Inc., Chicago.)

noids), and also difficult to keep in the laboratory, is the most commonly studied form in elementary work.

Protococcus (Fig. 15-8) or *Euglena* (Figs. 20-5b, 15-5) show a conspicuous chloroplast which you may want students to see in their work in cell studies. (A drop of Lugol's solution, p. 409, to a slide of *Protococcus* will also bring out the nucleus.) At times you may prefer to substitute *Peranema* (Fig. 20-5a) for *Euglena,* because its long flagellum is distinctly visible under low power. Although it has no chloroplasts (it is holozoic or saprozoic), it does undergo many changes in form and exhibits "euglenoid motion." One of the commonly occurring forms is *Peranema trichophorum,* which is some 60 to 70 microns long. *Euglena* may be used to show positive phototropic responses as well. Study diatoms under the microscope for the beauty of the sculpturing in their silicaceous shells. *Spirogyra* may be studied to show conjugation as well as plant structure, while such forms as *Vaucheria* are used in studies of the evolution of sexuality in plants.

Other purposes of the study of algae will, of course, depend upon the nature of the course. For instance, in most courses in biology few algae are studied; mainly *Spirogyra* and a casual study of

Fig. 20-5 Two flagellates: (a) *Peranema;* (b) *Euglena.* (General Biological Supply House, Inc., Chicago.)

some other forms to illustrate the phylum. On the other hand, some teachers use a variety of algae to illustrate different aspects of biology, e.g., *Volvox* to illustrate heterosexuality and the prologue to metazoan structure, *Spirogyra* to illustrate pyrenoid activity as well as conjugation, *Ulothrix* to show zoospores, *Oedogonium* to show heterospory, and so on. These varied purposes, although acknowledged, are outside the scope of this book.

Bacteria

Collecting bacteria

Because bacteria are found almost everywhere, they may be collected in many ways. When bacteria are to be studied as wet mounts, students may use sauerkraut juice or yoghurt as sources of harmless bacteria (see wet mounts and hanging drop preparations, pp. 307, 308). In this case, bacteria are available for immediate use. Or soak some beans or peas for several days; as they decay,

pipette off the fluid, which will be found to be teeming with large bacteria. Or, if you prefer, use the scum formed in the water of a vase of cut flowers. These kinds of bacteria may be examined adequately with the high power of a compound microscope when an oil immersion lens is not at hand.

Of course, special kinds of bacteria such as chromogenic, phosphorescent, or other specific genera of microorganisms may be obtained from biological supply houses (see listing, p. 479). Obviously there is no occasion to use pathogenic forms in a school laboratory. In addition, this is prohibited by law in many states. Furthermore, the literature in bacteriology indicates that under certain conditions some of the chromogenic forms are pathogenic and may cause serious infections.

In summary, the simplest means for collecting bacteria is to harvest them whenever substances are decaying. Put some timothy hay, meat, a piece of potato, beans, or peas into distilled water and leave it exposed to the air. After a few days stopper the test tubes or small flasks lightly with cotton and keep them in a comparatively warm place for the next few days.

Culturing bacteria

When bacteria are to be kept on hand permanently in the laboratory, there is the need to find suitable medium for culture and subculture. Or if you want to show how bacteria grow in colonies and that these are distinctive for each genus, you will need to use certain media and keep these under sterile conditions. Some ways to stain bacterial smears are described in Chapter 17.

A precaution. When bacteria are cultured in class or in the laboratory every precaution must be taken to avoid contamination with pathogenic forms. Treat each culture of bacteria as though it were pathogenic. Perhaps this needs a word of explanation. An old agar slant or Petri dish may have been exposed to the spray from a cough or someone's finger tips. The colonies which developed might be keyed out as nonpathogenic types. There may, however, be small numbers of pathogens which have failed to grow luxuriantly into conspicuous colonies because conditions were not optimum. (These bacteria may require a different pH, other salts, blood medium, and so on.) But they may be present in the culture nevertheless.

The methods below, therefore, include techniques for handling different kinds of bacteria as well as suggestions for avoiding contamination.

Preparation of culture medium for bacteria. For limited uses in the classroom, it is advantageous to purchase prepared sterilized test tubes of agar medium from supply houses. Or you may purchase dehydrated medium.[2] In the laboratory students can measure out accurately the necessary amount of dried medium. They should place this in a dry flask and add the needed amount of distilled water. Then the solution is sterilized (autoclaved). The next step is to pour plates or test tubes (see p. 383).

Some formulas for preparing a number of different kinds of culture media are described (for those who require special ingredients). The general procedures involved in handling bacteria are also described briefly. For more extensive work with bacteria the specialized references in the Bibliography at the end of the book may be helpful.

A suitable culture medium should contain a source of nitrogen such as peptone, inorganic salts, carbon, and possibly some growth-promoting substances. Certain bacteria require other substances for growth, such as serum or sugars or special salts. Meat infusions (where meat was soaked in water for many hours) have given way to beef extracts, which may be added as the medium is prepared.

MEAT EXTRACT BROTH. Weigh out the following materials and then combine with 1 liter of distilled water:

	grams
beef extract	3
peptone	10
NaCl	5

[2] Difco Laboratories, Inc., Detroit 1.

Heat this slowly to 65° C, stirring until the materials are completely dissolved. Then filter through paper or cotton and adjust the pH to 7.2 to 7.6, by adding a bit of sodium bicarbonate, so that a basic reaction with litmus is obtained. Pour this through a funnel into test tubes, filling them a third full; then stopper with cotton. Finally sterilize in an autoclave at 15 pounds pressure for 15 minutes. This quantity should be sufficient to prepare three dozen test tubes.

MEAT EXTRACT AGAR. A liquid broth may be solidified by the addition of agar or gelatin. For example, prepare the meat extract broth previously described. Now to 1 liter of the broth add 20 to 30 gm of agar. Heat slowly until the agar is dissolved. Then autoclave at 15 pounds pressure for 15 minutes. Filter the solution through cotton and adjust the pH to about 7.5; then sterilize the medium again. (The melting point of agar is about 99° C, and it solidifies at about 39° C.)

NUTRIENT GELATIN. While gelatin was one of the first substances added to solidify media, it has limited usefulness today because it melts at room temperature in warm weather. It has a use, however, for detecting bacteria which produce a protein-splitting enzyme.

Prepare 1000 cc (1 liter) of meat extract broth. To this add 120 gm of Bacto-gelatin and heat in a double boiler. Restore the volume with distilled water and adjust the pH to about 7.5 (add a bit of sodium bicarbonate).

Break a raw egg and mix a small amount of water with it. Add this to the solution to clarify it. Heat again very slowly until the egg becomes firmly solidified. Then filter the solution through cotton and pour it into test tubes (about 10 cc in each tube). Finally sterilize the tubes in an Arnold sterilizer (Fig. 20-7), for 20 minutes on three successive days. Cool the solution rapidly after each sterilization. Gelatin has a melting point of about 28° C (about 80° F). This should be sufficient for about three dozen test tubes.

POTATO MEDIUM. Use a cork borer to cut cylinders from large, washed and peeled potatoes. Then cut the cylinders obliquely into wedge-shaped portions and leave them in running water overnight to reduce their acidity. Now put a wedge of potato into each of several test tubes. (Or use slices of potatoes in covered Petri dishes.) Add 3 cc of distilled water to each and stopper the tubes with nonabsorbent cotton. Stand the tubes in a wire basket but avoid packing them. Push down the cotton

plugs so they won't pop out. Sterilize the tubes in an autoclave or pressure cooker for 20 minutes at 15 pounds pressure. Be sure to allow air to escape from the pressure cooker before closing the valve. If students use a double boiler, heat to boiling for 1 hour.

Students may either expose these tubes to air, or inoculate them by touching the surface of the potato wedge with a platinum or Nichrome wire loop (p. 384) laden with bacteria. Finally place the culture tubes or dishes in a warm dark place for several days. Colonies of bacteria appear as spots of different texture in white, cream, buff, yellow, orange, and other colors.

BLOOD AGAR. Sometimes it is desirable to devise experiments to show that while bacteria do not develop colonies on nutrient agar, this is no proof that bacteria are not present. Several kinds of bacteria will not grow on nutrient agar unless blood is added. Many types of bacteria found in the throat may be transferred by coughing into a sterile nutrient agar Petri dish. Recall the danger of using pathogenic bacteria and the need for use of caution in handling and disposing of the used plates and test tubes (see pp. 380, 383).

Cool some 95 cc of nutrient agar to about 45° C, and add 5 cc of sterile, citrated blood prepared by adding one cc of sodium citrate to 10 cc of blood. Then pour into sterile Petri dishes and immediately cover the dishes.

ROBERTSON'S MEDIUM FOR ANAEROBES.[3] Mix 1000 cc of distilled water, 500 gm of ground beef heart (from which fat and blood vessels have been removed), and 10 gm of peptone. Bring to a boil, and simmer for 2 hours, and adjust the pH to about 8 (with sodium bicarbonate). Pour off the broth into flasks and autoclave at 15 pounds for 15 minutes. Dry the meat portion by spreading it on clean filter paper and placing it in an oven at 56° C for some 48 hours. Into each test tube put a small amount of the dried ground heart and add about 10 cc of broth to each. Sterilize in an autoclave. When the broth is cool, adjust to a pH of about 7.5. Then resterilize the test tubes.

CARBOHYDRATE BROTH FOR FERMENTATION TESTS. Prepare this formula which has been

[3] War Dept., *Methods for Laboratory Technicians*, Tech. Man. 8-227, Supt. Documents, Govt. Printing Office, Washington, D. C., 1941.

suggested for work in bacterial fermentation.[4] Make a 0.5 per cent solution of the desired fermentable substance by first dissolving it in a small amount of hot water, then adding this to 1 liter of meat extract broth. Then add 1 cc of a 1.6 per cent alcoholic solution of bromcresol purple (p. 385).

Fill the fermentation tubes with about 6 cc of the solution and then sterilize them in an autoclave at 7 pounds for 10 minutes. Or use the Arnold sterilizer.

Sterilizing culture media. Naturally, when bacteria are to be cultured, conditions must be sterile; otherwise all kinds of bacteria and molds will contaminate the cultures. There are several ways to sterilize the materials you will need.

Dry heat. Glassware, including Petri dishes, test tubes, and flasks, may be sterilized by putting them in an oven at a temperature of 160° to 190° C for at least 1 hour. At temperatures over 175° C cotton and paper begin to char. When glassware is tightly packed in containers, it should be sterilized this way for at least 2 hours at the temperature mentioned above.

Steam under pressure (autoclave). Sterilize culture media and cotton and rubber as well as glassware in an autoclave (Fig. 20-6) set at 15 pounds pressure for 15 minutes. For small quantities of medium use a smaller pressure cooker. When large quantities of media are sterilized in flasks or bottles, keep them in the autoclave for ½ hour. Cover cotton plugs with paper to keep them dry.

When you begin to use the autoclave or pressure cooker, first check these points. After the materials are in the autoclave, open the escape or safety valve before turning on the steam. When the steam begins to flow, close the valve somewhat; when the steam escapes full force, close the valve so that only a small opening remains open for steam to escape. Regulate the valve to maintain the pressure desired.

[4] *Ibid.*

Fig. 20-6   Autoclave (pressure cooker), for sterilizing with steam under pressure. (Central Scientific Co.)

Steam without pressure (Arnold sterilizer). Certain kinds of media cannot be sterilized under pressure. Milk, nutrient gelatin, and any materials containing carbohydrates may be hydrolyzed or damaged by overheating. For these media use an Arnold sterilizer (Fig. 20-7). Bring the water in the pan to a boil. Put the media in the inner compartment and close it. Heat for some 30 minutes; then remove the media to room temperature. Repeat the boiling procedure on two successive days. This is known as intermittent sterilization.

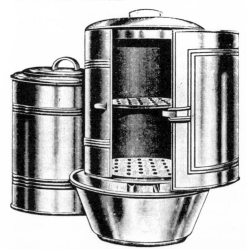

Fig. 20-7   Arnold sterilizer, for sterilizing with steam (no pressure). (Central Scientific Co.)

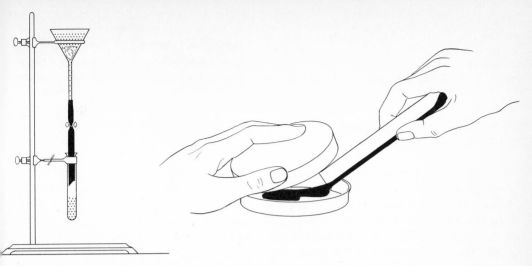

Fig. 20-8 Sterile technique: (a) filling sterile test tube with warm culture medium (use the pinch clamp to regulate the flow); (b) plating a sterile Petri dish with warm medium.

Sterilization with chemicals. Discarded cultures should be treated with steam under pressure or with a 2 to 5 per cent solution of cresol; or the surface of the dishes should be covered with Lysol. Laboratory table tops may also be disinfected with this solution. Wear rubber gloves to avoid burning the hands when using a strong disinfectant.

Boiling. Some materials may simply be boiled for 30 minutes for effective sterilization. For example, small pieces of glassware, syringes, and pipettes may be sterilized (for all effective purposes) in this way.

Filling test tubes. After the medium has been prepared, it must be poured into sterilized test tubes in such a way that it does not streak the sides of the tubes (Fig. 20-8a). And when the medium contains agar it must be poured quickly so that the agar does not have time to solidify.

Set up a warmed glass funnel in a ring stand and place a cotton filter in the bottom. Use a 4-inch square of cotton (absorbent) with the corners folded in toward the center to make a rounded filter. Wet the cotton and press it into place. Attach a rubber tube and a clamp to the funnel. Line up the test tubes in racks and insert the rubber tubing a third down into the test tube. Pour the medium into the funnel and use the clamp to control the quantity of medium which flows into each test tube. Fill some tubes ½ full, others ⅔ full, and replace each cotton plug. Finally sterilize all the test tubes, stand them in wire baskets, and put them in an autoclave for 20 minutes at 30 pounds pressure. Remove the test tubes from the autoclave; tilt the half full test tubes and set at an angle along a ledge so that they solidify with the medium slanted. This gives a larger surface area on which to streak bacteria. The test tubes which were filled ⅔ full are to be used to plate Petri dishes.

Plating. Sterilize Petri dishes by putting them in an autoclave for 15 minutes at 15 pounds pressure, or wrap them individually in paper and put them in an oven. When the paper begins to char a bit the temperature is high enough. Leave them in the oven for several hours. Petri dishes may be sterilized ahead of time in this way; when they are left wrapped in the paper they may be stored for several weeks.

Now the prepared test tubes (two-thirds full of medium) are ready for use. If the agar medium has solidified, stand the test tubes in boiling water.

Wet down the table tops by wiping them with a damp sponge. Avoid air drafts while plating. Light a Bunsen burner and work close to it. Remove one test tube of melted agar medium from the water bath, lift off the cotton plug, and bring the mouth of the test tube across the Bunsen flame to eliminate any contaminants around the mouth of the tube. Open the Petri dish slightly and quickly pour the contents of one test tube into the dish (Fig. 20-8b). Cover the dish quickly and tilt it around to distribute the medium in a uniformly thin film. Now set the dish aside to solidify. Proceed with the same technique until you have "plated" as many Petri dishes as you need. When they are all solidified, invert the dishes to prevent the condensing water vapor from falling back onto the agar surface. Then wrap each dish in paper until ready to inoculate them and refrigerate them to help prevent contamination. In this way plates may be saved for a week before they are to be used.

Inoculating culture medium. Petri dishes or test tubes may be exposed to air (to permit them to become contaminated), in order to show that bacteria and mold spores are ever-present in the air. But when it is desired to establish a pure culture, the procedure is to inoculate a new culture medium in sterile Petri dishes or test tubes with a bit of the old culture. A bit of the bacterial culture (together with its agar) is transferred on an inoculating needle, prepared as follows.

Hold the end of a piece of glass rod in a Bunsen flame until the glass is softened. Take a 3-inch piece of Nichrome wire (#24) or platinum wire in a forceps and insert it into the melted glass. When you want the needle for solid material, use a straight end of wire. When the medium is liquid, such as milk or broth, curve the wire into a small loop at the end. Fire-polish the other end of the glass handle.

To transfer or inoculate a fresh culture medium, the following procedure is useful. Heat the wire in a flame to red heat so that it is sterilized. Let the needle cool before touching it to the culture from which a transfer is to be made. Almost simultaneously, remove the cotton plug from the sterile culture tube or flask and hold it in the hand. Place the mouth of the tube in the flame for a moment. Dip the flamed, sterile needle tip into the old culture; remove the needle and insert it into the sterile new tube, flask, or dish (Fig. 20-9). Streak the needle along the entire length of sterile agar surface. It isn't necessary to press the needle into the agar. Again flame the needle before putting it aside in a needle holder. Then flame the mouth of the test tube again, and the plug (be careful that it does not catch fire) and replace the plug.

When you streak Petri dishes, raise the cover of the sterile Petri dish slightly and streak the surface in three equally distant parallel lines. Quickly replace the cover and invert the dish. Tape the dish and label its contents; place in an incubator at 37° C. Also put the test tubes in the incubator.

Broth-grown bacteria may be isolated in colonies by pouring a thin film of the broth over the surface of the sterile agar in a Petri dish. Do not invert these dishes. Be certain to keep the film thin. This is also the technique for isolating the kinds of bacteria in milk or tap water or other fluids.

Products of bacteria. The pH of a culture medium may be changed as a result of bacterial growth. You can determine

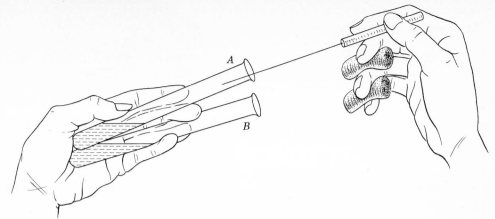

Fig. 20-9 One method of transferring a bit of established culture (A) into a new tube of medium (B).

what changes have occurred by adding a given quantity of an indicator to the medium when it is originally prepared. Table 20-1 gives three indicators which have been recommended.

Uses of bacteria in the classroom

Often we collect bacteria from water, soil, air, milk, or other materials if only to demonstrate that bacteria are found everywhere. We also try to show that bacteria are visible as colonies, and that bacteria may be identified by means of the color, shape, and texture of the colony as well as by their individual shape under the microscope (Fig. 17-17) and ability to hold specific stains. Furthermore, bacteria

are also identified by their reaction with certain media.

In the classroom teachers often set up demonstrations to reveal the conditions needed for bacterial growth, or test the action of penicillin or other antibiotics on the growth of bacteria (see p. 118, in Chapter 8). There are other experiments which students may devise to test the effectiveness of many antiseptics (see p. 119). They may devise an experiment to test the effectiveness of preservatives: heavy sugar solution, salts, drying, spices, vinegar, etc. More recently, teachers grow bacteria in agar to which radioactive phosphorus has been added. Later, radioautographs are made (p. 45).

TABLE 20-1
*Range of three indicators useful in testing culture media**

indicator	color change (acid to alkaline)	quantity per liter of medium (in cc)	pH range
Brom cresol purple (1.6% alcoholic solution)	yellow to purple	1	5.2–6.8
Brom thymol blue (0.04% aqueous solution)	yellow to blue	50	6.0–7.6
Phenol red (0.02% aqueous solution)	yellow to red	50	6.8–8.4

* War Dept., *Methods for Laboratory Technicians,* Tech. Man. 8-227, Supt. Documents, Washington, D. C., 1941.

Slime molds (Myxomycetes)

Collecting slime molds

The yellow plasmodia of slime molds may be found under the bark of fallen logs or under boards in swamps or moist woods. They may be found balled up or in the holes made by boring insects. A day or two after a rain is the best time to look for them. Whether they are to be considered animals (Mycetozoa) or plants (Myxomycetes) does not concern us here; questions relating to controversies dealing with the taxonomy of forms are beyond the scope of this book.

When conditions of moisture and food are adequate, the plasmodia of slime molds will increase in size and their nuclei will divide repeatedly, so that ultimately the mycetozoan (or the myxomycete, if you are a botanist by inclination) may be several inches in diameter and contain some thousand nuclei. Cell walls are lacking, and slow, amoeboid movements can be observed under the microscope.

Small plasmodia may be obtained from the spores of the fruiting bodies of *Physarum* (Fig. 20-10), *Didymium,* or *Fuligo.* These fruiting bodies may be crumbled on filter paper or on solid agar.

Culturing slime molds

(a) Camp[5] cultures slime molds on paper toweling and pulverized oatmeal, as follows. Wrap a finger bowl or similar container in filter paper to make a "drum." Then place this prepared finger bowl flat within a larger battery jar; the filter paper which is exposed should have a flat and smooth surface. It is better to have the open or upper side of the finger bowl on top. Then add 1 inch of water down the side of the battery jar. The fil-

[5] W. G. Camp in *Bull. Torrey Bot. Club,* 63:205–10, 1936.

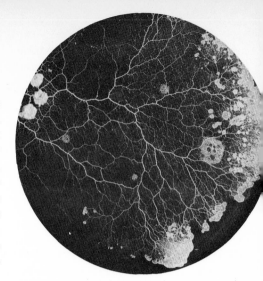

Fig. 20-10 Plasmodium of a slime mold (*Physarum polycephalum*). (Photo: General Biological Supply House, Inc., Chicago.)

ter paper now acts as a wick and draws moisture to the top of the "drum" (Fig. 20-11).

Place the plasmodia on the filter paper; then sprinkle about 0.1 gm of pulverized oatmeal (rolled oats which have been ground in a mortar will suffice) onto the paper. Next cover the battery jar with a glass plate. Within 24 to 48 hours the oatmeal should be consumed by the spreading plasmodia. Avoid overfeeding, but as the plasmodia grow and spread over the paper, add larger quantities of oatmeal.

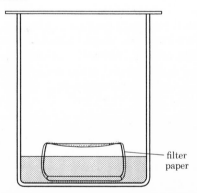

Fig. 20-11 Culturing slime molds on oatmeal on top of wet filter-paper "drum."

In fact, when the plasmodia have spread over the entire surface of the paper, place paper toweling on the inner surface of the battery jar so that, in effect, the inner surface is lined with paper. Then the toweling will also act as a wick to draw water. The plasmodia will move across the water moat between the filter paper and the toweling and begin to spread along the toweling. Place the oatmeal, however, on the central filter paper. Then after the plasmodia have spread over all the paper, remove the toweling and dry at room temperature. On the paper the yellow plasmodia quickly form sclerotia.

This dried paper may be cut into squares and stored in envelopes in a dry place. The plasmodia will remain viable for at least a year or two and may be used to prepare fresh cultures within this time. To do this, place a square of paper on wet filter paper on the finger bowl arrangement already described. Allow 24 hours for the plasmodia to form and place oatmeal powder in small quantities for food. Increase the amount of oatmeal as the plasmodia grow.

(b) Students doing a project on plasmodia may prefer to crumble these fruiting bodies on a medium containing agar.

AGAR MEDIUM FOR PLASMODIA. Soak 6 gm of oatmeal in 200 cc of water for 1 hour. Then strain the liquid. To 100 cc of the clear filtrate add 1.5 gm of plain agar, and heat until the agar is completely dissolved. Then pour a thin layer into each of several Petri dishes. It is not necessary to sterilize the agar preparations. Inoculate these dishes and keep them in a warm, dark place. Within some 3 days active plasmodia should be seen.

Other methods of culturing myxomycetes have been described by Howard[6] and many other workers in this area.

Fungi

Collecting molds and yeasts

For an unassorted culture of molds, expose a piece of moist bread or fruit (apple or orange) on which some dust has been scattered. Place the bread in Petri dishes or larger covered containers which have been lined with moist blotting paper, and place them in the dark. A good yield of sporangia of *Rhizopus,* the common white mold, should develop within a week. When the bread remains for a longer time, other fungi such as *Aspergillus* and *Penicillium* (Fig. 20-12) begin to appear.

Several other methods are described in the following pages. For example, dung media will yield many forms, such as *Mucor* (which is a close relative of *Rhizopus*), *Pilobolus,* certain Ascomycetes, and Basidiomycetes. Cheese, such as Roquefort, when covered with a bell jar, or placed in a moist chamber, will yield *Penicillium*. This form may also be found growing on citrus fruit.

Yeasts may be found on the surface of dill pickle or sauerkraut juice or on the

[6] F. L. Howard, "Laboratory Cultivation of Myxomycete *Plasmodium*," *Am. J. Botany,* 18:624–28, Oct. 1931.

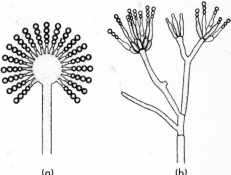

(a)   (b)

Fig. 20-12 Mold plants: (a) *Aspergillus;* (b) *Penicillium.* (From C. L. Wilson & W. E. Loomis, *Botany,* rev. ed., Dryden, 1957.)

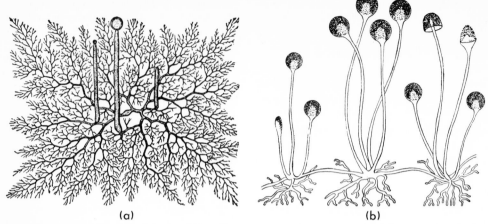

Fig. 20-13 Two common molds: (a) *Mucor;* (b) *Rhizopus.* (a, W. H. Brown, *The Plant Kingdom,* Ginn, 1935; b, W. G. Whaley, O. P. Breland, et al., *Principles of Biology,* Harper, 1954.)

surface of bruised fruits, especially grapes. You may also purchase yeast in dried form and add it to a culture medium.

Culturing molds

Most species of *Rhizopus* grow best at 30° C. in moderate light. *Rhizopus* and *Mucor* are often confused but may be distinguished in this way. The sporangiophores in *Rhizopus* arise in a fascicle from a node on a stolon, while in *Mucor* there are single sporangiophores arising from mycelia (Fig. 20-13).

Asexual spores are abundant; you can also show a type of sexual reproduction called conjugation. Two different mating strains are needed, a plus and a minus strain (purchase from a biological supply house, p. 479). When a plus strain is streaked across a moistened slice of bread or agar dish and a minus strain streaked at the opposite end, zygospores (sexual spores) form along the center of the bread (Fig. 11-46a)

OATMEAL AGAR. Where pure cultures of one type of mold are desirable, sterile conditions must be observed. In this method, grind 5 gm of oatmeal into 200 cc of water and boil this for 20 minutes. Then pour off the supernatant fluid through gauze to avoid including the oat residue. Add 4 gm of agar to the fluid and boil

to dissolve. Finally, pour into sterile Petri dishes, cool, and later inoculate with spores of selected fungi.

POTATO-DEXTROSE AGAR. Peel and slice about 100 gm of white potatoes and boil for 1 hour in 350 cc of distilled water. Strain through cheesecloth and restore the liquid to the original volume by adding more distilled water. To this 350 cc of potato filtrate add 1 gm of dextrose and 10 gm of agar. Boil this for ½ hour in a double boiler. Strain and sterilize; then pour the liquid into sterile Petri dishes. Later, inoculate with desired mold specimens in order to grow a pure culture.

A potato-agar medium may be prepared omitting the dextrose.

PRUNE AGAR.[7] Boil about 5 prunes in water for 1 hour. Then pour off the supernatant liquid and make up to 200 cc. To this add 80 gm of cane sugar and 10 gm of agar. This quantity (i.e., 200 cc of fluid) will be enough for about seven Petri dishes. Multiply all amounts for larger quantities of the medium.

PEA AGAR. Boil about eighty dried peas for an hour; then pour off the liquid and make up to 200 cc. To this add 5 gm of agar. Boil in a double boiler as described previously, then strain and sterilize. Plate the medium in sterile Petri dishes.

DUNG AGAR. Soak some 200 gm of horse, cow, or rabbit dung in water for 3 days. Then pour off the liquid and dilute with water until the liquid is straw colored. To this add agar,

[7] H. C. Gwynne-Vaughan, and B. Barnes, *The Structure and Development of the Fungi,* Cambridge U. Press, New York, 1927.

about 2.5 gm for every 100 cc of diluted fluid. Boil the materials as described previously and plate into sterile culture dishes.

Media without agar. Since it is often difficult to remove molds from solid media without damage to the rhizoids, several culture methods which omit agar have been developed. Klebs' solution (p. 342) can be considered one of these. (Dilute the stock solution 1:10 with distilled water.)

Another simple liquid culture medium is 5 per cent glucose solution.

Johansen recommends another medium.[8] Dissolve the following in 1 liter of distilled water:

	grams
sucrose (cane sugar)	30.0
NH_4Cl	6.0
$MgSO_4$	0.5
K_2HPO_4	0.5

BARNES' MEDIUM.[9] Dissolve the following in 100 cc of distilled water:

	grams
K_3PO_4	0.1
NH_4NO_3	0.1
KNO_3	0.1
glucose	0.1

(If desired, 2.5 gm of agar may be added to this glucose-salts solution.)

Sabouraud's medium for fungi. A useful medium for many kinds of fungi grown in the laboratory is Sabouraud's medium. Mix together and bring to a boil 10 gm of peptone, 20 gm of agar, and 1 liter of tap water. To this add 40 gm of maltose; filter if necessary. No adjustment for pH is needed. Finally sterilize for 30 minutes at 8 pounds pressure and pour into Petri dishes, test tubes, or Syracuse dishes.

Summary of methods for specific molds

As a short summary, let us see which specific molds thrive best on the culture media described. *Rhizopus,* for example, grows well with methods using bread and the potato-agar method (with or without sugar). For careful work the latter method is recommended.

The prune-agar method is recommended for culturing *Aspergillus.* This mold is also cultured readily on bread which has been exposed to the air for several hours and then soaked in a 10 per cent solution of cane sugar, grape juice, or prune juice. Keep in a covered jar at room temperature.

Penicillium is best kept on its source, Roquefort cheese or citrus fruit. For pure cultures use the prune-agar method. Some teachers prefer to culture this mold in flasks.

Molds such as *Saprolegnia* (water mold) grow abundantly on decaying insects or small fish. When dead flies are put in pond water they soon develop a fuzz of mold growth, and sporangia develop in 24 hours.

Small hymenomycetes among the Basidiomycetes may be kept in flasks containing dung agar. Spores may be collected from the hymenium of the desired species. Such forms as *Marasmius, Clitocybe,* and *Armillaria* have responded to this method.

Other forms, like *Dictyuchus,* may be found and cultured in pond water to which wheat or rice grains have been added. The water must be changed when it becomes cloudy.

Neurospora may be cultured easily in a commercially prepared medium such as Difco's Bacto-Neurospora Culture Agar (see directory of supply houses, p. 479). This powdered medium, which contains yeast extract, peptone, and maltose, is rehydrated by adding 1000 cc of distilled water to 65 gm of the medium. It is then heated to boiling and sterilized in an autoclave for 15 minutes at 15 pounds pressure.

[8] D. Johansen, *Plant Microtechnique,* McGraw-Hill, New York, 1940.
[9] H. C. Gwynne-Vaughan and B. Barnes, *op. cit.*

Culturing bread molds on slides

Vernon recommends this method[10] whereby slides for individual students in class can be prepared. Boil together 6 gm of oatmeal, 1 gm of agar, and 100 cc of distilled water. Then place a drop of the hot liquid on each of several glass slides. Cover with a coverslip until the medium has hardened. When cooled, remove the coverslip and cut the film of agar into several sections, separating each from the other to form little grooves. Inoculate with mold spores, similar or of different kinds, and ring the coverslips with Vaseline. Keep the slides in a moist chamber. Aerial hyphae and sporangia or conidiophores will grow into the grooves, and they can be studied under the microscope.

[10] T. R. Vernon, "An Improved Type of Moist Chamber for Studying Fungal Growth," *Ann. Botany,* 45:733, 1931.

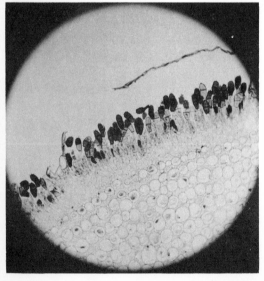

Fig. 20-14 Parasitic fungi: downy mildew on grape; powdery mildew of willow; wheat rust; microscopic view of wheat rust. (Photos: Dr. T. Sproston, U. of Vermont; Dept. Plant Pathology, Cornell U.; U.S.D.A.; General Biological Supply House, Inc., Chicago.)

Some parasitic fungi

Blackberry rust is one of the easiest of the parasitic fungi to keep in the laboratory. Plant blackberries infected by rust in a window box; the rust, since it is autoecious, maintains itself on the plant.

Students may collect several kinds of fungi, such as the powdery mildews which are parasitic on leaves of poplar, Virginia creeper, lilac, and willow (Fig. 20-14). Others are found on cherry and apple leaves. Keep the leaves dried in envelopes until they are to be used; then soak the leaves in tap water for several hours and mount the scrapings carefully on clean slides in a drop of the fluid. Wheat rust (Fig. 20-14) is also a parasitic fungus which may be studied.

Culturing yeast cells

To show budding as a means of asexual reproduction use *Saccharomyces ellipsoideus,* which is found on grapes, or *S. cerevisiae,* which is the commercial yeast. Prepare a 5 to 10 per cent aqueous solution of molasses or diluted grape juice. Add half a package of dried yeast to 500 cc of the medium. To this add 1 gm of commercial peptone, or about twenty beans or peas, for rapid fermentation.

Insert a cotton plug into the container and set aside in a warm place (25° to 30° C). Within 6 to 24 hours rapidly budding cells should be found (Fig. 11-7). Spore production is not typical in these species, although spores may be found on occasion on the surface of cakes of yeast (formerly used instead of dried yeast) which have been refrigerated for a week.

The method for staining cells with methylene blue, described in Chapter 17, may be used to dye these yeast cells. Students may notice that there is a very slow diffusion of methylene blue into the cells so that living cells are stained selectively.

Lichens

Some lichens such as the red-topped *Cladonia* or the gray crusty *Parmelia* and *Physcia* are found on the bark of trees, especially fallen tree logs and tree stumps (Fig. 14-8). Sections of bark covered with lichens may be put into a terrarium. Avoid excess moisture, as molds grow readily. Keep the terrarium uncovered.

Students may put dry, brittle specimens in water; after a few hours of soaking the lichens will probably become quite flexible and green.

Lichens are useful for study since they illustrate an interesting example of symbiosis (cooperative living of an alga and a fungus, see p. 231). Bits of the material may be teased apart in a drop of glycerin or water on a glass slide for examination under the microscope. The algae carry on photosynthesis, while the fungi are better able to hold the water needed for food-making. You may see ascospores too.

Bryophytes

Collecting and culturing mosses and their relatives

Mosses and liverworts can be collected with small amounts of soil and wrapped in waxed paper or newspaper. In the laboratory or classroom they can be kept in terraria. Students may cultivate the protonemata which grow from spores on sterile agar (Fig. 11-45).

A terrarium which is to be used for mosses can be prepared by students in this way. Place a layer 1 inch deep of coarse gravel or pebbles on the bottom of a tank. Over this spread a ½-inch

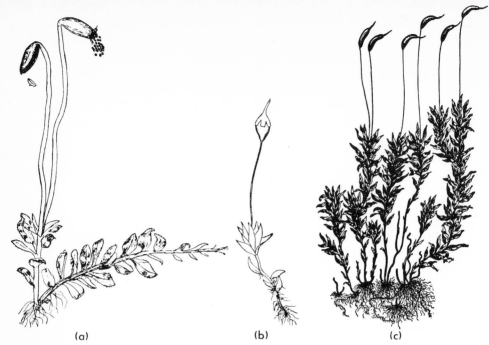

Fig. 20-15 Several common mosses: (a) *Mnium affine;* (b) *Physcomitrium pyriforme;* (c) *Catharinea undulata.* (a, G. F. Atkinson, *Botany,* Holt, 1905, c, W. H. Brown, *The Plant Kingdom,* Ginn, 1935.)

layer of sand. Then add a third layer, a cover of garden loam about 1 inch deep. The mosses which have been collected from the field are now sodded in this bed. The water level within the terrarium should be halfway up the gravel layer, and the tank should be covered with a glass. Keep the tank in medium light. When molds show a tendency to grow in the tank, reduce the amount of water and remove the cover until they disappear.[11] Subsequently, keep the terrarium with the least amount of water needed to keep the plants alive. During the winter months supply light from an electric light bulb.

Mosses such as *Mnium* (Fig. 20-15a), *Bryum, Fissidens, Dicranum,* and *Polytrichum* may be kept in this way. Liverworts like *Pellia, Pallavacinia, Riccia, Marchantia,*

Conocephalum, and Lunularia have grown abundantly under identical conditions. On the other hand, *Funaria* and *Polytrichum* can withstand a drier terrarium. Finally, the aquatic liverwort, *Ricciocarpus,* grows abundantly in an ordinary aquarium.

Culturing moss protonemata

Several nutrient solutions may be used with equal success. Three of these will be described. Spores of mosses germinate in the liquid, or the medium may be solidified by adding agar.

Using Knop's solution. Crush a dry sporangium of *Funaria* or *Catherinea* (Fig. 20-15c) and liberate the spores onto the surface of some Knop's solution which has been diluted to one third of its original strength (p. 113). The solution may be kept in Petri dishes or similar containers in moderate light. Spores ger-

[11] Sometimes sprinkling the terrarium with a small amount of powdered sulfur will destroy the growth of molds.

minate in 2 weeks, while branched protonemata are formed in 4 weeks.

Using a solid medium. This seems to be preferred by some workers. Prepare 98 cc of dilute Knop's solution (one third its original strength). Then add 2 gm of agar. Boil this until the agar is dissolved and then restore the volume up to 100 cc with distilled water. Filter through absorbent cotton into Petri dishes so that a film of about ⅛ inch thick is formed. Cover the Petri dishes and allow the agar to cool and solidify. Crush a clean sporangium over the medium, replace the cover, and place the Petri dishes in subdued light.

Several cultures should be prepared, since some may become contaminated. Germination usually takes place in about 10 days. Buds and young gametophytes appear within 2 to 3 months. Students can prepare better cultures by using sterile medium and sterile dishes. And the unbroken sporangia may be sterilized in sodium hypochlorite solution (Clorox and oxolchlorite are commercial preparations). Rinse the sporangia in sterile water, transfer to the agar plates, and crush with sterile forceps. We find that spores of *Funaria* grow especially well in the laboratory.

Using Benecke's solution. Instead of Knop's agar nutrient, students may want to try a modification of Benecke's solution prepared as follows in 100 cc of distilled water:

	grams
NH_4NO_3	0.2
$CaCl_2$	0.1
K_2HPO_4	0.1
$MgSO_4$	0.1
$FeCl_3$	trace

Dissolve 0.2 gm of agar in 100 cc of the solution. The treatment of spores is similar to that described previously for the Knop's agar medium.

Using Shive's solution. Prepare several Petri dishes with a thin layer of Shive's solution to which agar has been added. Blow the spores from crushed moss capsules over the surface. Then cover the Petri dishes and keep in moderate light.

SHIVE'S SOLUTION. Dissolve the following in 1 liter of distilled water:

	grams
$Ca(NO_3)_2 \cdot 4H_2O$	1.06
KH_2PO_4	0.31
$MgSO_4 \cdot 7H_2O$	0.55
$(NH_4)_2SO_4$	0.09
$FeSO_4 \cdot 7H_2O$	0.005

MODIFIED SHIVE'S SOLUTION. Bonner and Galston[12] recommend that minor elements be added to Shive's solution. One cc of the following solution should be added for each liter of Shive's solution. Prepare the solution of minor elements by dissolving the following in 1 liter of distilled water:

	grams
H_3BO_3	0.6
$MnCl_2 \cdot 4H_2O$	0.4
$CuSO_4 \cdot 5H_2O$	0.05
$ZnSO_4$	0.05
$H_2MoO_4 \cdot 4H_2O$	0.02

Flowerpot culture method

Protonemata of mosses may be cultured using the method described for growing fern prothallia (p. 395). Gametophytes should appear within three weeks (life cycle, Fig. 11-45). If you also want to grow sporophytes, flood the gametophytes with water for about 1 hour so that fertilization may occur. Then let the excess water run off.

Students can examine the protonema stage under the microscope. They can mount it directly in a 10 per cent glycerin solution on a clean slide. The color of chlorophyll remains well preserved, but for a permanent slide the coverslip should be sealed.

Mount the gametophyte of the moss *Funaria hygrometrica* in water. Examine

[12] J. Bonner and A. Galston, *Principles of Plant Physiology*, Freeman, San Francisco, 1952.

the "typical" plant cells with many chloroplasts and prominent cell walls. Students may notice that the gametophyte is just one layer of cells in thickness. Or mount leaves of the moss *Mnium,* which is also a single layer of cells in thickness.

Pteridophytes

Collecting ferns

Terrestrial ferns may be kept in the laboratory if care is taken in transplanting them. Students should uproot the rhizome and the roots of ferns along with the soil in which they are growing. For large ferns, such as those of the Osmundaceae (for example, the cinnamon fern, *Osmunda cinnamomea*) dig in a circle whose radius is 6 inches, using the frond as the center of the circle. The rhizome extends about 6 inches into the soil. For more delicate ferns, dig within a radius of 3 inches. Students will need to pack the roots and the rhizomes together with the soil attached to them in moist newspaper, waxed paper, or plastic bags, then transport the entire plants in a plant carrying case (vasculum) if possible.

Culturing ferns

Add some charcoal

Transplant the ferns into clay pots in which they fit without crowding. Before transplanting, prepare the pots with 1 inch of coarse gravel, broken tile, or clay pot on the bottom, and then about 1 inch of garden loam. Put the fern on top of this, and continue to add soil made up of equal parts of sand, peat, and garden loam. If the ferns were removed with enough soil around the roots and rhizomes, then the rhizomes probably have not been injured. Keep the plants in medium light and provide moisture by standing the flowerpots in water. Keep the soil moist but not wet. Such forms as the bracken fern (*Pteris aquilina*) and the hay-scented fern (*Dennstaedtia punctilobula*) can withstand fairly bright light but should not be put in direct or strong sunlight.

Water ferns such as *Salvinia, Azolla,* and *Marsilia* may be grown in aquaria which have been in use for a month or so. *Azolla*

Woodland terrarium   Desert terrarium

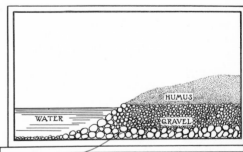

Add some charcoal

Bog terrarium

Fig. 20-16 Wardian case in which tall ferns thrive; and three habitat terraria that students can make. (General Biological Supply House, Inc., Chicago.)

Fig. 20-17 Three common ferns, each with diagram of fruiting frond: (a) Christmas fern (*Polystichum acrosticoides*); (b) common polypody (*Polypodium vulgare*); (c) cinnamon fern (*Osmunda cinnamomea*). (Photos: a, U.S.D.A.; b, c, Hugh Spencer; drawings, General Biological Supply House, Inc., Chicago.)

requires strong light, while *Salvinia* and *Marsilia* grow better in medium light.

Most of the small ferns need constant humidity, a condition which is best duplicated in the laboratory terrarium (Fig. 20-16). In this way students may grow Maidenhair and Royal Osmunda with success. A suitable terrarium soil consists of 1 part of coarse sand, 1 part of fine peat moss, and 2 parts of good garden loam.

Several common ferns, with their fruiting fronds, are shown in Fig. 20-17.

Culturing fern prothallia. Because it takes at least 6 weeks for fern gametophytes to grow, sow the spores well in advance of the time you will want gametophytes (see life history, Fig. 11-44).

Flowerpot culture of ferns. In this method and the following one, use flowerpots as the container plus some means for keeping moisture. Fill a large flowerpot with broken pieces of tile or porous clay flowerpots up to within 2 inches of the top. Then cover this with 1 inch of rich loam, and then a ½-inch layer of washed sand.

Sterilize the entire pot by placing it in boiling water for a few minutes, or pour boiling water over the pot and its contents. However, keep the surface layer of fine sand intact. Next crush the sori found on the underside of ripe fern fronds (Fig. 20-17). Or spread ripe fern fronds on paper for a few days; the spores fall on the paper. Then sprinkle these spores over the sand surface of the flowerpot. Cover the pot with a glass plate to retain moisture and prevent contamination. Next stand the pot in a saucer of water.

Add water to keep the level in the saucer and stand the pot in medium light. Should "damping off" by fungi (or mildewing) occur because the soil is too moist, students may water the pot with 0.01 per cent potassium permanganate solution.

Prothallia will develop from spores in about 3 to 4 weeks, producing a five- to ten-cell stage. Then the prothallia may be separated and subcultured in freshly prepared containers.

When gametophytes have been growing for about 5 months, they may be used to get sporophytes. Transfer them to the surface of sterile leaf mold packed into clay saucers. Water frequently and keep a constant humidity. Within a few months sporophytes should begin to develop.

Costello's method. In this method fern prothallia grow over an inverted flower-

Fig. 20-18 Fern prothallia growing in nutrient solution. (Photo: Carolina Biological Supply Co.)

pot. Clean a 4-inch clay flowerpot and fill it with sphagnum moss (peat moss) or paper toweling; moisten this and pack tightly. Immerse all the materials for 10 minutes in boiling water to sterilize them. Then allow the pot to cool, and invert it into a flowerpot saucer filled with water or Knop's solution diluted to half its original

Fig. 20-19 Relatives of the ferns: *left*, club moss (*Lycopodium*); *right*, horsetail (*Equisetum*). (Photos: A. M. Winchester; Hugh Spencer.)

strength. The contents of the pot now act as a wick to draw up water.

Dust fern spores over the moist surface of the inverted flowerpot. Cover with a battery jar or bell jar and place the device in a cool place in medium light. Within 10 to 20 days, small prothallia should be growing on the outer surface of the flowerpot.

Agar medium. The sterile agar method found suitable for moss protonemata may be used here. Use Benecke's or Knop's solution. However, if small sporophytes are desired, wide-mouthed low jars may be used instead of Petri dishes. You may also grow fern prothallia on agar slants in test tubes or flasks.

Other methods. At other times, students may want to sow spores on Knop's agar solution on slides so that the growth of young prothallia may be studied under the microscope; Vaseline the coverslips and keep them in a moist chamber. Or prothallia may be grown in nutrient solution (Fig. 20-18).

Other Pteridophytes

The club mosses, including the two common genera, *Lycopodium* (Fig. 20-19) and *Selaginella,* and the horsetails, of which there is only one genus, *Equisetum* (Fig. 20-19), may be collected and kept in a terrarium in which ferns grow.

Students may want to try to grow the horsetail, *Equisetum,* in the laboratory. Spores germinate quickly when they are shed. Shake the spores onto soil and cover with a pane of glass. For best results, the soil should be sterilized, either by heating it in an oven or by watering it well with a dilute potassium permanganate solution (on the average some 5 small crystals to 1 liter of water). In about 3 to 5 weeks, antheridia should be visible and archegonia a little later.

Spermatophytes

Culturing seed plants

While most seed plants grow readily in porous flowerpots of suitable size, several precautions must be followed. These will not be developed at great length here, for there are excellent books which deal with the care of specific house plants (see Bibliography). Let us consider briefly a few of the pitfalls.

1. Do not overwater plants. The soil should not be wet (nor should it be very dry). One of the best ways of watering plants is to immerse the entire flowerpot in water for 10 minutes. In most cases this treatment is sufficient to ensure moisture for the roots for from 4 to 5 days.

2. Do not place plants over a radiator. In many cases, this is the reason for poor growth of plants in the classroom and laboratory. Neither should a plant be kept too near the window, for in winter the side nearest the window is subjected to excessive cooling.

3. Examine the undersides of leaves for insect pests, such as aphids, mealy bugs, and other scale insects. When these are found they should be washed off with soap and warm water. Spray with a nicotine-soap solution.

4. Every month or so, water the plants with about 100 cc of Knop's solution (or add commercial mineral preparations). This will replenish the soil.

5. A good garden soil will bring about the greatest growth. But it is equally important that each flowerpot have broken tile or broken clay at the bottom to ensure drainage.

6. When the plant has outgrown the pot, it should be repotted. Carefully re-

move the roots and the soil. Tap the flowerpot to release the plant.

7. Good growth will be assured if the plants are kept in a Wardian case.

8. The number of plants may usually be increased by vegetative propagation. Chapter 11 describes several methods which may be used.

What kinds of plants should you buy?

Not all seed plants require equal amounts of light. In fact, teachers may be hard put to know the kinds of plants to grow in a northern exposure where there is little or no sunlight. A quick reference to the following lists[13] may help to establish a cheerful atmosphere in the classroom. Most of these plants are also useful in teaching biology.

Plants for full sunlight

Cactus	*Zygocactus truncatus*
Echeveria	*Echeveria,* sp.
Geranium	*Pelargonium*
Kalanchoë	*K. coccinea*
Oxalis	*O. rosea*
Patience plant	*Impatiens sultani* (or *Holstii*)
Primrose (fairy)	*Primula malacoides*
Spiraea	*Spiraea*

Plants for sunlight (2 to 4 hours)

African violet	*Saintpaulia*
Asparagus "fern"	*Asparagus plumosus*
Begonias	Many varieties, *argenteo-guttata*
Coleus	*Coleus Blumei*
House iris (Apostle plant)	*Marica Northiana*
Nephthytis	*N. Afzelii*
Pick-a-back	*Tolmiea Veitchii*
Peperomia	*Peperomia maculosa* (and *arifolia*)
Strawberry begonia (saxifrage)	*Saxifraga*
Spider plant	*Anthericum,* sp.

[13] Personal communication from Marvin Brooks, 1947, then Director of Gardening, New York City Board of Education.

Plants for windows without sun (northern exposure)

Aloe	*Aloe arborescens*
Aspidistra	*Aspidistra lurida*
Begonia	*Begonia rex*
Boston ferns	*Nephrolepis exaltata bostoniensis*
Chinese evergreen	*Aglaonema modestum*
Chinese rubber plant	*Crassula arborescens*
Date palm	*Phoenix dactylifera*
Dumbcane	*Dieffenbachia seguine*
Gold-dust Dracaena	*Dracaena Sanderiana*
Grape ivy	*Vitis*
Hen and chickens	*Sempervivum,* sp.
Holly fern	*Cyrtomium falcatum*
India rubber tree	*Ficus elastica*
Ivy, English	*Hedera Helix*
Philodendron	*Philodendron cordatum*
Stonecrop (Live-forever)	*Sedum,* sp.
Snake plant	*Sansevieria*
Tradescantia	*Tradescantia zebrina*

Germinating seeds

There are times when students may want to germinate seeds in the classroom either for class study or for individual projects. Seeds of gymnosperms germinate slowly, often requiring 2 weeks to several months. Seeds of maples, oaks, or tulip trees grow more rapidly. When rapidly growing seeds are desired, use radish or mustard seeds, for they germinate within 24 hours. The larger seeds of beans, peas, corn grains, squash, and castor beans germinate in 1 to 2 days. When seeds are soaked overnight at room temperature (before sowing) germination is hastened.

All the stages in the germination of seeds can be observed by students. Line a small pan or cheese box with filter paper or use sand. Sow soaked seeds and dampen the paper or sand. Cover with a glass aquarium and keep in moderate light. (See p. 109 for methods of disinfecting seed surfaces.)

Seeds can also be germinated on

sphagnum moss to prevent "damping off." Dried sphagnum purchased from a florist can be shredded and is then ready for use. Plants may be grown in the shredded sphagnum without adding soil.

Plants which are ordinarily difficult to root have been grown successfully in vermiculite[14] (an insulating material sold by building supply dealers), which has the property of expanding into fluffy material when heated. It is also sterile when fresh and has extensive adsorbent surfaces that hold good quantities of water as well as air.

Youngsters can germinate seeds by placing them between blotting paper and the glass walls of a tumbler when they want to study the parts of a developing seed. In this way they may study the developing root system as well as the shoots. For other demonstrations using germinating seeds, refer to Chapter 8, p. 108.

Conditions for germination of some common seed plants are given in Table 20-2.

[14] F. C. Bradford, "Short Cuts for the Gardener" in *Science in Farming,* Yearbook, Dept. of Agriculture, Supt. Documents, U.S. Govt. Printing Office, Washington, D. C., 1943–47.

Key for Table 20-2

F—Several pieces of wet filter or blotting paper placed below and above the seeds. Petri dishes are excellent.

S—Washed sand, thoroughly moistened but not wet. The seeds are imbedded ½ to 1 inch below the surface.

P—Loam soil in a pot. The seeds are planted ½ to 1 inch below the surface. The soil should be loose.

* H. C. Muller, "Methods for Establishing the Viability of Seeds of Various Plant Species," Abderhalden's *Handbuch der Biologischen Arbeitsmethoden,* vol. XI:2, Urban & Schwarzenberg, Berlin, 1924.

TABLE 20-2
Conditions for germination of some plants*

plant	medium	temperature (degrees C)	length (in days)
Abies (fir)	F, S	20	10 to 28
Achillea (yarrow)	F, P	20	4 to 10
Allium (onion)	F, S, P	10–20	5 to 14
Alnus (alder)	F, S, P	20–30	6 to 21
Asparagus	F, S, P	20	10 to 28
Avena (oats)	S, P	20	4 to 10
Beta (beet)	S	20–30	7 to 14
Betula (birch)	S, P	20–30	30
Brassica (mustard)	F, P	20–30	3 to 10
Capsicum	F, P	20–30	14 to 28
Cucurbita	S	20–30	5 to 14
Daucus (wild carrot)	F, P	20–30	6 to 21
Fagus (beech)	S, P	20	6 to 28
Hordeum (barley)	S, P	20	3 to 10
Helianthus (sunflower)	F, S, P	20–30	4 to 10
Larix (larch)	P	20	10 to 28
Lathyrus (pea)	F, S	20	5 to 10
Linum (flax)	F, P	20–30	3 to 10
Lotus	F, S, P	20	6 to 14
Lupinus (lupine)	S	20	4 to 10
Lycopersicum (tomato)	F, P	20–30	3 to 10
Medicago (alfalfa)	F, P	20	3 to 10
Nasturtium	F, S, P	20	4 to 10
Nicotiana (tobacco)	F, P	20–30	5 to 14
Pastinaca (parsnip)	F, S	20–30	5 to 14
Phaseolus (bean)	S	20	4 to 10
Phleum (timothy)	S	20	4 to 10
Picea (spruce)	P	20	7 to 28
Pinus nigra (Austrian pine)	P	20	14 to 42
Pinus Strobus (white pine)	F, P	20–30	14 to 60
Pinus sylvestris (Scotch pine)	P	20	14 to 28
Pisum arvense (garden pea)	S	20	3 to 10
Quercus (oak)	S	20	28
Raphanus (radish)	F, P	20–30	3 to 10
Rumex Acetosella (sourgrass)	F, S, P	20	5 to 14
Secale (rye)	F, S	20	3 to 10
Spinacia (spinach)	S	20–30	4 to 14
Trifolium, sp. (clover)	F, S, P	20	3 to 10
Triticum (wheat)	S, P	20	3 to 10
Zea (corn)	S, P	20–30	4 to 10

Seed plants: special methods

Insectivorous plants. Insectivorous plants (Fig. 14-8) need special care. They should be placed in a glass-enclosed chamber (to maintain humidity). Feed sundew (*Drosera*) on fruit flies. For *Dionaea*, the Venus fly-trap, drop *Tenebrio* larvae (mealworms) into the traps. Or bits of meat may be substituted. The pitcher plant (*Sarracenia*) will survive in such a terrarium without insect food. Water the plants once a month.

As the plants spread, and give rise to others, they may be repotted in a soil prepared by thoroughly mixing together 3 parts garden loam, 1 part peat moss, and 1 part sand. The peat moss (sphagnum) will supply the needed acid condition.

Cactus plants. Cactus plants require still a different treatment. *Opuntia,* the pear cactus, may be planted in ordinary garden soil but should be watered only once every 2 weeks. Other cactus plants, such as *Cereus, Echinocactus, Phyllocactus,* and related forms, should be potted in soil made up of 4 parts sand and pebbles and 1 part garden loam. A good watering every 3 weeks is sufficient.

Dodder (*Cuscuta*). This is a bright orange-colored seed plant which is often parasitic on clover, goldenrod, and other plants (see Fig. 14-2). There is enough food in the seed for the young plant to begin to develop a slender stem and roots by which it becomes attached to a host. Leaves are reduced to scalelike structures. Then it sends wedgelike haustoria into the host's stem, forming a junction with the vascular system of its host. Finally, its connection with the ground is severed and it depends upon the host. Dodder forms abundant white flowers which hang in clusters in late summer.

Collected specimens wilt quickly but may be preserved in 70 per cent alcohol.

Pressed specimens may be useful for temporary display. Hold the specimens on mounting paper with cellophane tape.

Mistletoe (*Phoradendron*). This seed plant grows on branches of ash, elm, and hickory as well as many other trees. Mistletoe has green leaves and carries on photosynthesis, but probably absorbs water and salts through its roots, which are embedded in the tree branches. Thus it may be considered a partial parasite. Collect specimens and preserve in the dry state on mounting paper.

Indian pipe (*Monotropa*). This seed plant lacks chlorophyll and thus appears as a stark white stem with scalelike leaves (Fig. 14-5). It gets its food from humus and is a saprophyte, not a parasite.

When picked, the plant wilts quickly, developing a black-purple pigment. If the plants have been carefully transported undisturbed with their original soil and put into a Wardian case (Fig. 20-16), they may remain white for several weeks. Specimens may be preserved in alcohol or formalin.

Wolffia. In this smallest of flowering plants, the plant is reduced to an oval or rounded green body (the stem). There are no leaves or roots present (Fig. 20-20a).

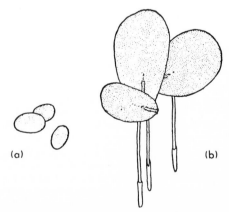

Fig. 20-20 Tiny floating seed plants: (a) *Wolffia*, the smallest of all; (b) *Lemna* (duckweed), often found with *Wolffia*. (From R. D. Gibbs, *Botany*, McGraw-Hill, 1950.)

Absorption takes place through the underside of the stem. New fronds grow out from depressions on the underside of one end of the oval frond.

Wolffia is found floating on the surface of lakes and ponds, at times very abundantly. The plants multiply rapidly and lend a pleasing appearance to aquaria in the laboratory and classroom. Students may devise individual projects studying the growth of these plants under a variety of conditions. It is relatively easy to measure the growth of these simple plants.

Lemna (duckweed). *Lemna* (Fig. 20-20b), as well as a closely related form, *Spirodela,* are found as small floating plants in lakes and ponds. The broad leaflike expansions are not leaves but stems. A single rootlet lacking root hairs extends from the underside of the frond. They grow well on the surface of an aquarium and add an attractive touch. However, they are not good oxygenators.

CAPSULE LESSONS
Ways to get started in class

20-1. Have students plan a field trip to explore the school grounds. Examine many kinds of flowering plants such as magnolia, *Forsythia,* cherry, dandelion, and other plants in special biomes. (Suggestions for developing the school grounds and for nature trails are described in Chapters 14 and 15.)

Have the class undertake a project such as this one: Develop a mimeographed sheet which outlines a specific trail and identifies plants along the way.

20-2. Have each student bring in a plant specimen for identification. Develop the story of plants from one-celled forms to seed plants. Teach students to use a key (p. 218) in identifying plants as a club activity or a small group project. Prepare a large bulletin board and mount dried specimens or drawings on it. In season, maintain flowering twigs in containers of water in a hall cabinet. Other plants may be kept in a terrarium.

20-3. As a project, have students put name plates on the trees and shrubs in the school lawn.

20-4. When a field trip is planned, arrange to transplant ferns, mosses, possibly some spring flowers, and small evergreens to a similar environment around the school grounds.

20-5. You may want to introduce students to plants which cannot be found on a field trip on the school grounds. Take a vicarious field trip by means of a film and study *Plant Traps, Fungus Plants,* or *Dodder* (all available from Encyclopaedia Britannica). Or explore the films *Life Cycle of a Yeast Cell* (Southern Illinois University) or *Life of Plants* (United World). Refer to our film library for additional films. Also check the catalogs of biological supply houses (p. 479) for an abundant source of slides of all kinds of plants (and animals too).

20-6. You may want to refer to the suggestions for capsule lessons given at the end of Chapter 14. Many of the ideas used plants and animals in illustrating the balance in nature. The materials needed for field trips are indicated in Chapter 15.

PEOPLE, PLACES, AND THINGS

Botany is not your specialty? Suppose a student wants to work on a project in some specialized area in plant hormones or plant genetics. You may look into *Biological Abstracts,* which prints short summaries of work published by research people in every field of biology. This is one way to discover who the active workers are in a special field of biology.

If there is a botanic garden or an agricultural college nearby, you may be able to plan a trip, borrow living materials or a film, or arrange to have someone sponsor a gifted student.

Books and pamphlets

These are only a few of the books which are pertinent to the work discussed in this chapter. These and many other references classified by subject and with complete bibliographical data are given in the Bibliography at the end of the book. Guides to specific plant phyla are included in the Bibliography.

Christensen, C., *Molds and Man,* 1951.

Cobb, B., *A Field Guide to the Ferns and Their Related Families,* 1956.

Cope, J., and Winch, F., *Know Your Trees,* Cornell 4-H Club Bulletin 85, Cornell U., Ithaca, N. Y., 1955.

Gibbs, R., *Botany: An Evolutionary Approach,* 1950.

Graves, A., *Illustrated Guide to Trees and Shrubs,* 1956.

Hill, A., *Economic Botany,* 1952.

Hottes, A., *The Book of Shrubs,* 1952.

Jepson, W. L., *Manual of the Flowering Plants of California,* 1957.

Lee, R., *Sequence of Bloom of Perennials, Biennials and Bulbs,* Cornell Miscell. Bull. 21., Cornell U., Ithaca, N. Y., 1955.

Moldenke, H., *American Wild Flowers,* 1949.

Muenscher, W., and Winne, W., *Common Poisonous Plants,* Cornell Extension Bull. 538, Cornell U., Ithaca, N. Y., 1955.

——— and Schumacher, G., *List of Names, Common and Scientific, of the Weeds of New York,* Cornell Extension Bull., Cornell U., Ithaca, N. Y., 1955.

Peltier, G., Georgi, C., and Lindgren, L., *Laboratory Manual for General Bacteriology,* 1952.

Post, K., *Indoor Gardening,* Cornell 4-H Club Bull. 70, Cornell U., Ithaca, N. Y.

Sass, J., *Botanical Microtechnique,* 1951.

Stiles, W., *An Introduction to the Principles of Plant Physiology,* 1950.

Stefferud, A., *How to Know the Wild Flowers,* 1950.

U.S. Dept. of Agriculture, *Plant Diseases,* Yearbook for 1953.

Walker, J., *Diseases of Vegetable Crops,* 1952.

Wherry, E., *Wild Flower Guide,* 1948.

———, *Our Smallest Servants,* Charles Pfizer & Co., New York, 1955.

FILMS AND FILMSTRIPS

We lack the space to indicate the vast array of 2″ x 2″ slides in black and white and in color which are available from biological supply houses in many areas of biology. These companies (listed with their addresses in the directory at the end of the book) will be happy to send their catalogs for your perusal.

Similarly, there are many, many films and filmstrips available. We have given a representative number of these in the list at the end of the book under the topics of Plants and Their Functions, Health and Disease Prevention, Reproduction in Plants and Animals, Conservation.

FREE AND INEXPENSIVE MATERIALS

Your state department of agriculture has many bulletins which are available for teachers. In fact, teachers may also order a certain number of tree seedlings if they are doing useful work in that area. Also have your name placed on the mailing list of the U.S. Department of Agriculture for notification of their available publications. Many state universities have an agricultural college which publishes materials available to teachers in that state, either free or at a small cost.

Many of the large pharmaceutical firms have splendid booklets available. Pfizer's *Our Smallest Servants* is one example. There has been a tremendous number of fine books which have been reprinted in soft-cover editions. For example, there are field guides to birds, to insects, and to flowers, available in editions which cost from $0.35 to $0.50. You may want to select titles from the list of science paperbacks, *An Inexpensive Science Library,* prepared by the AAAS.

We have mentioned before, but it bears repetition, that the biological supply houses publish directions for caring for plants and animals. Some of these are free leaflets; other directions are included with the specimens when they are purchased from the company. Several companies also print small bulletins that they sell. See also the listing of free and inexpensive materials at the end of the book.

CHAPTER 21

Additional tools for the teacher

In this section some skills, general or technical, are described; others are merely indicated. In a sense, some are in the nature of a specialty beyond the scope of this book (for example, making slides and films, or a complete description of steps in mounting specimens in plastic or preparing a skeleton of an animal). In many cases we indicate the road, where to find information in these specialties.

The organization of the materials in this chapter follows this pattern:

A. Preparing solutions
B. Making visual "props"
C. Working with glass

Preparing solutions

It did not seem useful to us to describe in detail the preparation of certain indicators or solutions at the point where they were first mentioned. You will find these solutions here—in alphabetical order. A number of other general preparations useful in the laboratory have been included. First, however, we shall discuss how to make up solutions of various strengths.

Strength of solutions

Percentage by weight. In common practice, when preparing a dilute solution, such as a 1 per cent solution of sodium chloride, 1 gm of the salt is added to 100 cc of water. (Actually, this is slightly less than 1 per cent.) However, when the concentration is over 10 per cent, the error involved in doing this becomes significant, and so we need more precision. To make a 10 per cent solution (accurately enough for most purposes) of sodium chloride we would add 10 gm of salt to a graduate cylinder, then add water up to the 100-cc mark.

Percentage by volume; making dilutions. Measure out the number of cubic centimeters of the higher-percentage solution equal to the percentage needed for the new solution. (For example, when you have 70 per cent alcohol on hand and want to prepare 50 per cent alcohol, measure out 50 cc of the 70 per cent alcohol.) Then add enough distilled water to bring the volume to a number of cc equal to the percentage of the original solution (in this example, to 70 cc). In another case, suppose that you have 95 per cent alcohol and want to prepare 70 per cent. Measure out 70 cc of the 95 per cent alcohol and add 25 cc of distilled water to make the total volume in cc equal to the percentage of the alcohol on hand.

Molar solutions. A *molar* solution is a solution containing one gram-molecule of the dissolved substance per liter of *solution* (not solvent). To prepare a molar solution dissolve a number of grams equal to the molecular weight of the substance in water (or other solvent) and make up to 1 liter.

For example, sodium chloride has a molecular weight of 58.45. A molar solution of sodium chloride (written $1M$ NaCl) will contain 58.45 gm of sodium chloride in 1 liter of solution. A molar solution of hydrochloric acid ($1M$ HCl) would contain its molecular weight in gm (36.5) in 1 liter of solution.

We can make dilutions of molar solutions, such as $0.5M$, $0.1M$, and so on. A $0.1M$ solution of hydrochloric acid contains $36.5 \times 0.1 = 3.65$ gm of HCl per liter of solution. A $0.4M$ solution of sodium chloride would contain $58.45 \times 0.4 = 23.38$ gm of NaCl per liter of solution.

Normal solutions. One gram-equivalent of a substance in 1 liter of solution will result in a *normal* solution of that compound. A gram-equivalent is the amount of the substance equivalent to one gram-atom of hydrogen (1.008 gm). Thus a normal solution of an acid contains a gram-atom (1.008 gm) of reacting hydrogen per liter of solution; any other normal solution can then replace or react quantitatively with an equal volume of such a solution.

To prepare normal solutions study the formula of the acid, base, or salt to be dissolved. When there is one hydrogen

TABLE 21-1
General solubility rules

Soluble in water

Compounds of sodium, potassium, and ammonium.

Sulfates (except lead and barium sulfate; calcium, strontium, and silver sulfate are slightly soluble).

Chlorates, nitrates, and acetates.

Chlorides (except silver and mercury chloride; lead chloride is slightly soluble).

Insoluble in water

Phosphates, carbonates, oxides, sulfides, sulfites, and silicates (except those of sodium, potassium, and ammonium).

Hydroxides (except those of sodium, ammonium, potassium; calcium, barium, and strontium hydroxides are slightly soluble).

---

atom or one hydroxyl group or one of any ion which will combine with one hydrogen or hydroxyl, a normal solution is the same as a molar solution.

When two hydrogen atoms are present, as in H_2SO_4, a normal solution contains half as much H_2SO_4 as a molar solution, because there are two gram-equivalents in every gram-mole. This is also true for $Ca(OH)_2$, and a normal solution is prepared by making a $0.5M$ solution of calcium hydroxide.

A normal solution of $FeCl_3$ (which has three chlorines, each of which could react with one hydrogen) would be a $.33M$ $FeCl_3$ solution.

In general, a normal solution is prepared by dissolving in 1 liter of solution a quantity of the acid, base, or salt determined in the following way:

$$\frac{\text{no. of gm required for } 1M \text{ sol'n}}{\text{no. of equiv. to 1H in each molecule}}$$

or

$$\frac{\text{molecular weight of substance in gm}}{\text{valence}}$$

Rules of solubility. In preparing solutions such as nutrient solutions for microorganisms or for studies in hydroponics, it is useful to know which salts are more soluble than others (Table 21-1).

Some solutions in general use

ACID STARCH SOLUTION. Immediately before the acid starch solution is needed, add 5 drops of yellowish nitric acid (containing nitrous acid) to 10 cc of a starch solution.

In an alternate method, add 1 cc of dilute $NaNO_2$ solution and one cc of dilute H_2SO_4 to 10 cc of the starch solution just before it is to be used.

ADHESIVE, GLASS TO METAL. When students build an apparatus which uses a combination of metal and glass, a solution of sodium silicate has been recommended as an adhesive.[1] A paper gasket might be soaked in a solution of sodium silicate and inserted between the edges of glass and metal cutout.

ANTICOAGULANT #1 FOR BLOOD. Add 1 cc of this solution to 10 cc of blood. Dissolve in 100 cc of distilled water:

	grams
potassium oxalate	2
NaCl	6

ANTICOAGULANT #2 FOR BLOOD. Add 200 mg (0.2 gm) of sodium citrate to 10 cc of blood.

AQUARIUM CEMENT. For repair of aquariums, this type of cement has been recommended; it will stick to glass, metal, stone, or wood. The first four ingredients may be mixed together in the dry state. Add enough linseed oil to make a stiff putty just before using. Allow 3 to 4 days for this cement to harden after it has been forced into crevices and smoothed over with a spatula. The following measurements are given as parts by weight.[2]

	parts
litharge	10
plaster of Paris	10
powdered rosin	1
dry white sand	10
boiled linseed oil	

BENEDICT'S SOLUTION (QUALITATIVE). This is used in a test for the presence of simple sugars in foods, blood, and urine. In the presence of simple sugars, a yellow or reddish precipitate of cuprous oxide forms when the reagent is

heated with the "unknown." The test will detect 0.15 to 0.20 per cent dextrose.

This solution can be purchased ready made or it can be prepared as follows.

Dissolve the carbonate and the citrate in 700 cc of water, slightly warm to speed solution. Then filter. Dissolve the copper sulfate in 100 cc of water and slowly pour into the first solution. Stir constantly; let this cool and add distilled water to make 1 liter.

	grams
sodium or potassium citrate	173.0
Na_2CO_3 (crystalline)	200.0
(or 100 gm anhydrous)	
$CuSo_4$ (crystalline)	17.3

BIURET REAGENT AND PAPER. Biuret reagent is prepared by adding 25 cc of a 3 per cent solution of copper sulfate per liter of 10 per cent potassium hydroxide.

Walker's modification of the Biuret reagent is prepared as follows.[3]

Add 1 per cent copper sulfate solution, a drop at a time, with stirring, to a 40 per cent (approximate) solution of sodium hydroxide until the mixture becomes a deep-blue color.

Then, filter paper may be immersed in the reagent, dried, and cut into small strips for use in tests for proteins.

BUFFER SOLUTION. The following salts should be weighed out and added to 1 liter of distilled water:

	grams
NaH_2PO_4	28.81
Na_2HPO_4	125.00

If a buffered solution of sodium chloride is needed, add 8.5 gm of sodium chloride to 20 cc of this buffer solution, and make up to 1 liter with distilled water.

COBALT CHLORIDE PAPER. Immerse sheets of filter paper in a 5 per cent aqueous cobalt chloride solution. Remove them and blot dry between other sheets of filter paper. Then dry them in an oven at 40° C. Cut the papers into strips. For immediate use, dry these strips quickly by putting them into a dry test tube, and heating them over a flame until the paper turns from pink to blue.

Store cobalt chloride paper in wide-mouthed, tightly stoppered bottles containing a layer of anhydrous calcium chloride covered with cotton. Should the blue papers change to pink,

[1] H. Bennett, ed., *Chemical Formulary,* Chemical Publishing Co., New York, 1951.
[2] *Ibid.*

[3] P. Hawk, B. Oser, and W. Summerson, *Practical Physiological Chemistry,* Blakiston (McGraw-Hill), New York, 1954.

indicating the presence of moisture, heat them again in a dry test tube.

FEHLING'S SOLUTION. Either purchase, or prepare both solutions separately and store them separately in rubber-stoppered bottles. In testing for the presence of simple sugars add an equal amount of each solution to a test tube of the substance to be tested, and heat. A heavy yellow or reddish precipitate forms (cuprous oxide) if simple sugars are present.

Solution 1

$CuSO_4$	34.65 gm
distilled water	500 cc

Solution 2

KOH	125 gm
potassium sodium tartrate	173 gm
distilled water	500 cc

FERTILIZER FOR ACID-LOVING PLANTS.[4] Combine the following fertilizer ingredients. Then mix each pound of this with 5 cubic feet of redwood or cypress sawdust.

	parts
$(NH_4)_2SO_4$	26
superphosphate	31
potash	190

For a planting mixture, use half garden loam and half this mixture.

GRAFTING WAX #1 (LIQUID).[5] Reduce the quantities given to suit your specific needs.

rosin	4 lb
tallow	0.5 lb
isopropyl alcohol	0.75 qt
turpentine	0.25 pt

Melt together the rosin and tallow, then cool a bit and dilute with alcohol and turpentine. Store in a tightly stoppered bottle.

GRAFTING WAX #2 (LIQUID)

rosin	4 lb
beeswax	1 lb
raw linseed oil	1 pt

Melt the rosin and add beeswax. Let this melt slowly; add linseed oil and mix thoroughly. After it has cooled, store it in a cool place.

GRAFTING WAX #3 (MALLEABLE)

	parts
rosin	4
beeswax	2
tallow	1

Heat these ingredients together, and pour

[4] H. Bennett, ed., *Chemical Formulary*.
[5] *Ibid.*

the melted material into water. When cool, shape into balls with the fingers.

HAYEM'S SOLUTION. This solution is used as the diluting fluid in preparing blood for red blood cell counts. It is often used as a stain for blood smears when 0.05 gm of eosin is added to the solution indicated here. Before making the smear, mix 1 part of blood to 100 parts of this stain. Then make the blood smear on a clean slide (p. 318).

Weigh out these salts and add them to 100 cc of distilled water.

	grams
$HgCl_2$	0.25
Na_2SO_4	2.5
NaCl	0.5

HOLTFRETER'S SOLUTION. Young amphibian embryos may be maintained in this solution or mounted in it for study. Prepare the following solution in 100 cc of distilled water.

	grams
NaCl	0.35
KCl	0.005
$CaCl_2$	0.01
$NaHCO_3$	0.02

INDICATORS. Indicators are dyes which are used to test the pH of a solution. As the hydrogen-ion content of the solution changes, rearrangement of the indicator molecule occurs, resulting in a change in color.

Table 21-2 indicates the range of use of indicators from small variations within the acid or alkaline range and from one end of the scale to the other. Notice that some of the indicators commonly used in demonstrations are those which show a shift in pH around neutral (7). The strength and solvent recommended are generally given on the bottle of indicator dye. The dilution for some of the common indicators follows.

Phenolphthalein. Prepare a stock solution of 1 per cent by dissolving 1 gm of phenolphthalein in 60 cc of absolute alcohol; add 40 cc of water. Or add 1 gm to 100 cc of 95 per cent alcohol. For use, a 0.5 per cent solution in 50 per cent alcohol may be prepared. A 0.1 per cent solution is used for very sensitive tests.

Alizarin red. Water; 1 per cent.
Methyl red. Water; 0.02 per cent.
Methyl orange. Water; 0.02 per cent.
Neutral red. A 1 per cent solution in 50 per cent alcohol.
Congo red. Alcohol; 0.5 per cent.

TABLE 21-2   Range of certain indicators*

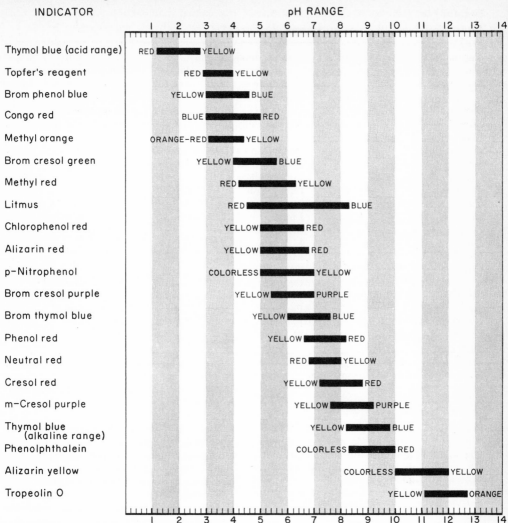

INDICATOR — pH RANGE

- Thymol blue (acid range): RED ▬▬ YELLOW
- Topfer's reagent: RED ▬▬ YELLOW
- Brom phenol blue: YELLOW ▬▬ BLUE
- Congo red: BLUE ▬▬ RED
- Methyl orange: ORANGE-RED ▬▬ YELLOW
- Brom cresol green: YELLOW ▬▬ BLUE
- Methyl red: RED ▬▬ YELLOW
- Litmus: RED ▬▬ BLUE
- Chlorophenol red: YELLOW ▬▬ RED
- Alizarin red: YELLOW ▬▬ RED
- p–Nitrophenol: COLORLESS ▬▬ YELLOW
- Brom cresol purple: YELLOW ▬▬ PURPLE
- Brom thymol blue: YELLOW ▬▬ BLUE
- Phenol red: YELLOW ▬▬ RED
- Neutral red: RED ▬▬ YELLOW
- Cresol red: YELLOW ▬▬ RED
- m–Cresol purple: YELLOW ▬▬ PURPLE
- Thymol blue (alkaline range): YELLOW ▬▬ BLUE
- Phenolphthalein: COLORLESS ▬▬ RED
- Alizarin yellow: COLORLESS ▬▬ YELLOW
- Tropeolin O: YELLOW ▬▬ ORANGE

* Data from P. Hawk, B. Oser, and W. Summerson, *Practical Physiological Chemistry*, Blakiston (McGraw-Hill), New York, 1954.

TABLE 21-3   pH values of 0.1N solutions of a variety of acids and bases*

acids (order of decreasing strength)	pH value	bases (order of increasing strength)	pH value
Hydrochloric acid	1.0	Sodium bicarbonate	8.4
Sulfuric acid	1.2	Borax	9.2
Phosphoric acid	1.5	Ammonia	11.1
Sulfurous acid	1.5	Sodium carbonate	11.36
Acetic acid	2.9	Trisodium phosphate	12.0
Alum	3.2	Sodium metasilicate	12.2
Carbonic acid	3.8	Lime (saturated)	12.3
Boric acid	5.2	Sodium hydroxide	13.0

* Data from *Handbook of LaMotte Chemical Control Units for Science and Industry*, 13th ed., LaMotte Chemical Products Co., Towson, Baltimore, 1944.

TABLE 21-4
Approximate pH of some common substances*

Apples	2.9–3.3	Human duodenal		Pickles, sour	3.0–3
Apricots (dried)	3.6–4.0	contents	4.8–8.2	Pimento	4.7–5
Asparagus	5.4–5.7	Human feces	4.6–8.4	Plums	2.8–3
Beans	5.0–6.0	Human gastric		Pumpkins	4.8–5
Beer	4.0–5.0	contents	1.0–3.0	Raspberries	3.2–3
Beets	4.9–5.6	Human milk	6.6–7.6	Rhubarb	3.1–3
Blackberries	3.2–3.6	Human saliva	6.0–7.6	Sauerkraut	3.4–3
Bread, white	5.0–6.0	Human spinal fluid	7.3–7.5	Salmon	6.1–6
Cabbage	5.2–5.4	Human urine	4.8–8.4	Shrimp	6.8–7
Carrots	4.9–5.2	Jams, fruit	3.5–4.0	Spinach	5.1–5
Cherries	3.2–4.1	Jellies, fruit	3.0–3.5	Squash	5.0–5
Cider	2.9–3.3	Lemons	2.2–2.4	Strawberries	3.1–3
Corn	6.0–6.5	Limes	1.8–2.0	Sweet potatoes	5.3–5
Crackers	7.0–8.5	Magnesia, milk of	10.5	Tomatoes	4.1–4
Dates	6.2–6.4	Milk, cow	6.4–6.8	Tuna	5.9–6
Flour, wheat	6.0–6.5	Molasses	5.0–5.4	Turnips	5.2–5
Ginger ale	2.0–4.0	Olives	3.6–3.8	Vinegar	2.4–3
Gooseberries	2.8–3.1	Oranges	3.0–4.0	Water, distilled	
Grapefruit	3.0–3.3	Peaches	3.4–3.6	(carbon-dioxide-free)	7
Grapes	3.5–4.5	Pears	3.6–4.0	Water, mineral	6.2–9
Hominy (lye)	6.9–7.9	Peas	5.8–6.4	Water, sea	8.0–8
Human blood plasma	7.3–7.5	Pickles, dill	3.2–3.5	Wines	2.8–3

* Data from *Handbook of LaMotte Chemical Control Units for Science and Industry*, 13th ed., LaMotte Chemical Products Co., Towson, Baltimore, 1944.

IODINE–POTASSIUM-IODIDE SOLUTION. Dissolve 3 gm of potassium iodide in 25 cc of water. Then add 0.6 gm of iodine and stir until dissolved. Make up to 200 cc with distilled water. Store in a dark bottle.

IODINE, TINCTURE OF. Dissolve 70 gm of iodine and 50 gm of potassium iodide in 50 cc of distilled water. Then dilute to 1 liter with 95 per cent alcohol.[6]

LIGNIN TEST. A saturated solution of phloroglucin[7] (1,3,5-trihydroxybenzene) in alcohol is recommended as a test for the presence of lignin. First, mount plant tissue sections in this solution for a few minutes, then transfer to a drop of water (containing a minute trace of hydrochloric acid). If lignin is present it stains a bright reddish-violet color.

[6] Iodine stains may be removed from clothing by washing the stain with a 10 per cent solution of sodium thiosulfate in water. Then rinse in water.

[7] F. Emerson and L. Shields, *Laboratory and Field Exercises in Botany*, Blakiston (McGraw-Hill), New York, 1949.

LIMEWATER. To distilled water add an excess of calcium hydroxide or calcium oxide. Cork the bottle, shake well and let it stand for 24 hours. Then pour off the supernatant fluid (filter if necessary) and keep well stoppered.

The limewater should remain clear. When carbon dioxide is added, a milky precipitate of calcium carbonate is formed:

$$CO_2 + H_2O \longrightarrow H_2CO_3$$
$$Ca(OH)_2 + H_2CO_3 \longrightarrow CaCO_3 + 2H_2O$$

LOCKE'S SOLUTION. This solution may be used to mount fresh mammalian blood samples. It is also a component of some special culture media for protozoa. Dissolve the following in 1 liter of distilled water.

	grams
NaCl	9.0
$CaCl_2$	0.2
$NaHCO_3$	0.2
KCl	0.4
glucose	2.5

This solution should be sterilized in an autoclave or an Arnold sterilizer.

LUGOL'S SOLUTION. This solution is used as a test for the presence of starch in food samples or in leaves, and as a stain, especially for flagella, cilia, and the nuclei of cells.

Dissolve 10 gm of potassium iodide in 100 cc of distilled water; then add 5 gm of iodine.

Gram's iodine stain solution may be made from this formula by adding 14 times its volume of water.

For very delicate work, this solution may be diluted 1 part to 10 parts of water.

LUBRICANT, STOPCOCK. Glycerin prevents sticking of ground-glass parts and is also useful in sealing ground-glass joints to prevent leaking of substances which are insoluble in it (such as ether).

MILLON'S REAGENT. This reagent is used as a test for proteins. Dissolve 100 gm of mercury in 200 cc of nitric acid (specific gravity 1.42). Dilute the solution with 2 volumes of distilled water.

MOTION-PICTURE FILM CEMENT. This type of cement has been recommended for splicing on direct positive safety film.[8] It evaporates very quickly; keep the solution in a tightly sealed bottle.

	cc
acetone	20
Duco cement	10
propylene oxide	10

NONCURLING SOLUTION FOR PHOTOGRAPHIC PRINTS.[9] Immerse prints after washing in a solution made by combining 12 parts glycerin, 5 parts alcohol, and 83 parts water.

PHYSIOLOGICAL SALINE SOLUTION (FOR COLD-BLOODED ANIMALS). Use as a mounting fluid in the preparation of temporary wet mounts. Prepare a 0.7 per cent solution of sodium chloride in distilled water.

PHYSIOLOGICAL SALINE SOLUTION (FOR WARM-BLOODED ANIMALS). Prepare a 0.9 per cent solution of sodium chloride (dissolve 0.9 gm in 100 cc of distilled water).

POTASSIUM PYROGALLATE SOLUTION. This solution is used to remove oxygen from air. Prepare the solution by combining 1 part by weight of pyrogallic acid, 5 parts of potassium hydroxide, and 30 parts of water.

RINGER'S SOLUTION #1 (FOR FROG TISSUE). This solution, isotonic for frog tissue, may be used as a mounting fluid for living frog tissue. The heart of a dissected frog will continue to beat for several hours if bathed in this buffered solution. Dissolve the following salts in 1 liter of distilled water:

	grams
KCl	0.14
$NaCl$	6.50
$CaCl_2$	0.12
$NaHCO_3$	0.20

RINGER'S SOLUTION #2 (FOR MAMMALIAN TISSUE). This solution, isotonic for mammalian tissues, may be used as mounting fluid for examination of living tissues. Prepare this solution in 1 liter of distilled water.

	grams
KCl	0.42
$NaCl$	9.0
$CaCl_2$	0.24
$NaHCO_3$	0.20

SEED DISINFECTANT. In a description of seed germination (p. 108), we spoke of dipping seeds in Clorox (1 part to 6 parts water) or dilute potassium permanganate solution (p. 397). Dip seeds briefly into alcohol (a wetting agent), and then into Clorox for 15 minutes.

As an alternate technique, this disinfectant has been suggested in the literature.[10] Dissolve 0.4 ounce of mercuric chloride in 0.2 quart of boiling water first; then add 3 gallons of water to this solution. (*Caution:* mercuric chloride is poisonous.)

Place the seeds in a cheesecloth bag and immerse in the liquid. For most seeds a 5-minute immersion is sufficient. More hardy seeds can be immersed up to 10 minutes in this disinfectant. Then wash the seeds several times in water for 15 minutes; spread them out to dry.

STARCH PASTE (1%). Add a small amount of cold water to 1 gm of arrowroot starch and stir into a paste. Then add this to 100 cc of boiling water; stir constantly. Bring this to a boil and then let it cool. This is a satisfactory strength for general use in demonstrations of salivary digestion.

SOIL ACIDIFIER.[11] Prepare the following and add it to the soil until the desired pH is obtained.

	parts
flowers of sulfur	1
$(NH_4)_2SO_4$	1
$Al_2(SO_4)_3$	1

[8] H. Bennett, ed., *Chemical Formulary.*
[9] *Ibid.*

[10] *Ibid.*
[11] *Ibid.*

WOOD STAIN (ACIDPROOF). Laboratory desks and tables may be protected against the action of strong acids. Commercial preparations are available, but the one described here is simple and inexpensive. It is necessary to remove varnish, paint, grease, or other chemicals. Then with a paint brush apply two coats of boiling hot solution 1. Allow the first coat to dry before applying the second layer. Then apply two coats of solution 2 in the same manner.

Solution 1
$CuSO_4$	125 gm
$KClO_3$	125 gm
water	1 liter

Solution 2
aniline oil (fresh)	150 gm
HCl (conc.)	180 cc
water	1 liter

When the wood surfaces are completely dry, wash off the excess chemicals with hot soapsuds. Then apply a finish of linseed oil, rubbed well into the wood. Later apply other coats of linseed oil and rub down well whenever the wood surface needs it.

Addenda

Making dissection pans. Use rectangular metal cake pans of a uniform size. Melt together equal parts of paraffin and beeswax over a low flame. If a black wax is desired, add lampblack to the melted preparation. Then pour into metal pans to a depth of ½ inch and set aside to harden. Avoid stirring, for this creates air bubbles. Should air bubbles apppear, they may be broken with a dissection needle while the wax preparation is still warm.

Labeling rock specimens. Sufficiently large rock specimens may be labeled by painting on a plaster of Paris surface, as follows.[12] Mix plaster of Paris and water to a creamy consistency. Apply a thin, smooth layer on the side of the specimen which is to be labeled. When the plaster has "set," apply a thin solution of glue

as sizing over the surface. Labels may be printed with a permanent ink on the sized dry surface of the plaster. Then protect the label by brushing over the dry ink with melted paraffin. Very small specimens may be partly embedded in plaster.

Permanent labels for specimen bottles. Sometimes, to avoid smearing of labels, it is advantageous to place a printed label inside a jar containing specimens preserved in alcohol.[13]

Print labels with India ink and set aside to dry until the ink no longer glistens; dip them into a jar containing 5 or 10 per cent glacial acetic acid (use forceps). Then drain the labels on blotting paper and insert into the specimen jars containing 70 per cent ethyl alcohol. Rather strong paper should be used for labels, because glacial acetic acid tends to soften it.

Preparation of skeletons. There may be students who want to prepare a skeleton of a small bird or mammal. A full description of the technique is beyond the scope of this book. However, students can get assistance from the biological supply houses. In general, the technique involves these procedures: (a) cut away as much of the flesh as possible from the bones and let the bones dry; (b) scrape the bones clean with special bone scrapers, and place the skeleton in an ammonia bath for several days; (c) bleach the skeleton in sodium hypochlorite, and finally dry it; (d) then treat the skeleton with carbon tetrachloride so that the oils can be removed from the bones. Note that good ventilation, preferably a hood, is needed for each of these steps. All this is preliminary to the mounting of the bones to make a skeleton.

[13] G. J. Spencer, "Rendering India Ink Labels Permanent in Alcohol," *Turtox News*, 26:1, Jan. 1948, General Biological Supply House, Chicago.

[12] *Ibid.*

Making visual "props"

An effective teacher in the classroom evokes images for children—with words, sometimes with gestures, other times with useful props. There are many kinds of props or aids. Where possible, use living materials—the real props. These may be brought to class, or youngsters may go to the living materials through field trips.

A model, three dimensional, may be the next best experience. A slide, a photograph, a chart, a drawing on the board —all two-dimensional—also provide effective next-best experiences.

Only a brief introduction to the making of models, charts, and other props is presented here.

A visual aid should be simple and used sparingly, to clarify some confusion, to bring the attention of all students to the same thing, for review in a new view of the work, or as part of an evaluation of learning. Visual aids should not be "inserted" into a lesson because a good model of some sort is part of the equipment of the department. Students can become overwhelmed by seeing many charts or models, complex in design, in one period. (All of us know of some favorite piece of demonstration material we have which we think couldn't be simpler or more to the point. Yet we have found that all students do not have the same perception. They lack a common frame of reference. You may have found yourself explaining the model.)

Models

Real materials. A hen's egg may become a simple model. (Boil it first as a safety measure!) Use it to ask: what kind of an animal arises from this egg? What does it contain that enables it to develop into a chicken, not an eagle? More than

that—the egg develops into one kind of chicken—a Plymouth Rock, not a Leghorn.

Other times, students may bring in the models for the lessons: a beef heart, a sheep's brain or eye, frogs, insects, a beef or hog kidney, beef lungs with trachea, arteries and veins, seeds, flowers and fruits, leaves showing variations, cocoons, water from a pond, guppies, starfish, and many more which have been indicated in this book. On field trips students may study the dynamic interrelationships among many living things.

Sometimes professionally made models supplement the use of real materials. Many times they simplify a concept by reducing the real thing to its essentials.

Models in clay. A ball of plasticine may represent a fertilized egg. What will it develop into? How does this one cell develop into many cells? Students can model several stages in cleavage. With a knife divide the ball in two, then each of these in two, to represent the four-celled stage. The next cleavage is in a horizontal plane. Each of the four cells divides and a ball of eight cells results. They can also show the depression of the neural tube and how it is formed from the outer ectoderm of the embryo.

Clays in different colors make effective models. Each student in class may model pairs of chromosomes in clay. On a sheet of paper they can demonstrate mitotic divisions and the differences between mitosis and reduction division.

Students have modeled many tissue cells, the heart, the entire respiratory and digestive systems in clay. However, the models fall apart fairly easily so that clay seems to be most useful in manipulating models in class before the eyes of students. However, some students have successfully portrayed dioramas—farming practices which favor conservation of land, life in the past among the dinosaurs, and many other similar ideas.

Models in glass. You may draw an air sac of the lungs on the board, using colored chalk. However, a round-bottomed Florence flask is a useful model in three dimensions. Have students draw capillaries on it with a glass marking pencil as they explain the exchange of gases between the capillaries and the air sac. Or tie a meshwork of string around the bulb of the flask to represent a capillary network.

A villus can be made by inserting a small test tube (a "lacteal") into a larger test tube (the outer membrane of the villus).

Pieces of string, wire, and odds and ends. Tease apart some fibers in a square of gauze. Doesn't this resemble a capillary bed? Or use a length of hemp cord. Separate the fibers in the center section to represent capillaries. Students may dip one end of the cord in blue ink, the other end in red ink. This gives an idea of the conventional artery-capillary-vein representation.

Recall the rubber change mat in stationary stores? All the rubber projections may be considered villi in the lining of the small intestine.

We say that food materials pass along some 25 to 30 feet of digestive tract. Have you ever brought to class a length of clothesline and asked students to estimate 30 feet? Have students stretch out the clothesline along the length of the room to show 30 feet. Now, what happens to food as it passes along this long tube?

In an earlier section (see Fig. 11-18) a description was given for showing animated "chromosomes" in mitosis, using short pieces of electrical wiring, rubber bands, and string.

How are genes arranged on a pair of chromosomes? Are the same genes in all the different pairs of chromosomes? Wooden beads of different colors may be threaded on wires. Make up pairs of different lengths with different colored beads. The plastic beads women have been wearing recently which fit into each other (and are not on thread) can be pulled apart and remade into strings of beads of any length. These are an excellent prop. Many chromosome aberrations can be demonstrated with these beads. With different colored plastic beads students could show translocation of chromosome parts, fragmentation, crossover, and with the help of some modeling clay or glue, nondisjunction of chromosome pairs. A dab of colorless nailpolish will hold the bead pairs together effectively.

Here is another simple device often used. Bring in a roll of the candies (Reed's) which are biconcave discs. These may represent red blood cells.

A cell model. Students may use agar to make a model of a cell. Prepare some agar in cold water, bring it to a boil, then let it cool. The agar may be packed in a cellophane "cell membrane." Embed colored marbles or other small particles in the cooling agar to represent nucleus, centrosome, and so on. Or use green peas for chloroplasts if a plant cell is desired. Students can improvise in many ways. Suppose an indicator, such as phenolphthalein, is included in the agar medium as it is prepared. Later on, if ammonium hydroxide were placed near the finished model of the "cell," diffusion of the alkaline into the "cell" would produce a pink color within the "cell." This is a useful demonstration of diffusion through a cell membrane.

An artificial cell. To a test tube containing a small amount of dilute albumen from a raw egg, add a few drops of chloroform. Shake the materials together, mount a drop on a slide and observe the artificial "cells" which form.

There are times you may have reason to show this demonstration to provide an image for students. All these materials are, of course, nonliving, but this demonstration may help to visualize how a cell grows. Place a crystal of copper sulfate in a solution of potassium ferrocyanide. As the copper sulfate passes into solution, a membrane is formed around the crystal. This is a membrane of copper ferrocyanide formed on contact with the surrounding potassium ferrocyanide. Watch the membrane expand and simulate the growth of a cell as water continues to pass through the membrane in one direction only. Note that the equal expansion in all directions is due to the entrance of water, not to the formation of new material (corresponding to new protoplasm which would occur in a living cell).

Models of plaster of Paris. Plaster of Paris may be poured into a mold shaped of plasticine, cardboard, or metal tins. Shape the plasticine to form a mold for a cell, such as an epithelial cell. If there are any parts which are to protrude in plaster, they should be indentations now in the plasticine. For example, indent the region where a nucleus should be in the cell. Build up a cuff, the outer edges of the cell mold, about an inch and a quarter high. Vaseline the clay if needed. Then prepare the plaster of Paris. Add enough plaster of Paris (a good quality such as dental plaster) to water to form a consistency thick and creamy, but thin enough to pour. Stir carefully to avoid including air bubbles in the plaster. Pour in the plaster of Paris slowly so that air bubbles do not rise. Allow this to set and harden. Later peel away the clay mold. These plaster models may be smoothed down with fine sandpaper; they may be shellacked and painted different colors.

Professional-looking models may often be made (as a club activity). These may become part of the stock of the science department. In the legend accompanying the photographs in Fig. 21-1 are the directions for especially fine models. Latex models may also be made; they have the advantages of being lighter in weight and less fragile. Or you may want to use the rubber liquid now available at arts and crafts suppliers; this liquid may be used to make molds of various sorts. The advantage of these rubber molds is that they can be used again and again.

Models in papier mâché. In this method, strips of toweling or newspaper are dipped into a thin paste made of flour and water. Or strips of newspaper soaked in water may be worked over to make a malleable thick paste. Add 1 per cent phenol to prevent spoilage. Then this newspaper mash is added to flour and water to make a material that has adhesive properties. A dinosaur or a cell or cleavage stages may be modeled of cardboard and wire props. Then apply the mash of flour-soaked newspaper or apply overlapping strips of toweling soaked in flour paste. Successive layers are applied after each preceding layer has dried thoroughly. About six to seven layers are needed. When the model is thoroughly dry it can be smoothed with fine sandpaper. These models may be painted in bright colors.

Models in wood. Some students are talented in working with wood. Fine lightweight models may be made of balsa wood. Students have made three-dimensional models of microorganisms, cells,

1. The subject, an early embryo stage, is modeled in Plasteline (this one by Dr. J. Wilson, U. of Rochester Medical School) and then shellacked.

2. When dry, the model is covered with tissue paper (to protect it) and then completely covered with a ¾-inch layer of modeling clay.

3. A cardboard wall divides the clay layer into 2 equal parts. A coat of lard oil is brushed over all.

7. The 2 halves of the jacket are tied together tightly, and molding glue is poured in, completely filling the space between the jacket and model.

8. One half of the jacket is removed, by prying with a screw driver. Then the glue is cut through along the plaster edge, so that the free half of the glue mold can be removed.

9. Then the Plasteline model is removed, and the inside of the glue mold is dusted with French chalk, then brushed with a saturated alum solution.

Fig. 21-1 Making professional-looking plaster-of-Paris models. These photographs and directions were supplied by Ward's Natural Science Establishment, Inc.; further instructions for sandpapering and

and the heart. These had the added advantage of hinged halves so that the model could be opened, revealing brightly painted interiors—a section through an amoeba or the chambers of the heart or the tubes of the kidneys.

With a jigsaw some students can cut two-dimensional models—or rather plaques—of organs of the body, or of tissue cells.

Models in clear plastic. Attractive, convenient models are available of plant and animal specimens mounted in clear plastic as in Figs. 21-2 and 21-3. You may purchase models which include representatives of the basic plant and animal phyla. Some students may want to try to duplicate these professionally made models. The supply houses sell the materials which are needed and provide complete

4. A ¾- to 1-inch layer of plaster is then built on one side up to the dividing wall. When it has set, the wall is removed and the edge of the plaster is smoothed.

5. Registration notches are cut in the edge, which is then brushed with lard oil, and plaster is applied to the other half in the same way.

6. The 2 halves of the jacket are separated, and the clay and tissue paper removed. A notch is cut in the top of each half. The inside of the jacket is shellacked, and, when dry, oiled and placed around the lightly oiled model.

0. After it has cured for an hour, the inside of the mold is brushed with a mixture of stearine and kerosene, the halves are tied together, and plaster is poured in through the bottom.

11. It must be removed as soon as set, or the heat will melt the glue. The 2 halves of the mold are carefully separated, and the cast is removed.

12. The finished model. The glue mold can be used to make up to 20 casts, with care, by repeating the last two steps.

---

applying lacquer, and formulas for the various materials used can be obtained from their Bulletin No. 2, *How Models Are Made*.

instructions. Clear plastic is a tricky medium to work in, but some students have, after practice, made better-than-average models which could be used in teaching. A summary outline of the basic steps in the process is indicated here to give a notion of the procedure.[14]

Specimens are fixed in Bouin's fixative or formaldehyde. Then the fixative is washed out with water. Next follows staining; acid carmine is a successful stain to use. Then the specimens are transferred through the alcohols for dehydration: 70 per cent, 85, 90, then absolute alcohol. Now the procedure begins to differ from regular microscope work. The alcohol is removed by transferring the specimens

[14] T. Romaniak, "The Use of Unsaturated Polyester Resins for Embedding Biological Material," Ward's *Natural Sci. Bull.*, vol. 20:3, Jan. 1947, Rochester, N. Y.

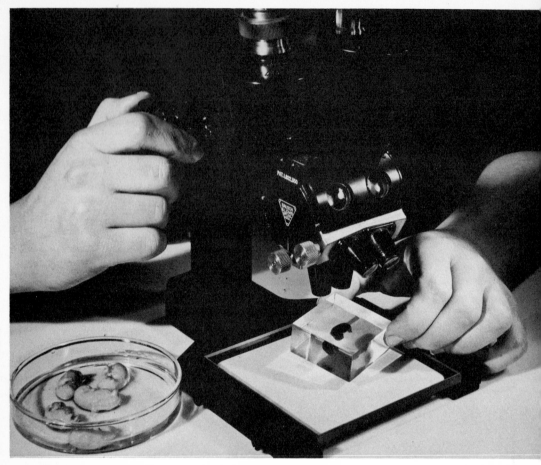

Fig. 21-2 Examining a plastic-mounted specimen under a binocular microscope. (Ward's Natural Science Establishment, Inc.)

to anhydrous ether. Then the specimens are transferred to the uncatalyzed monomer and put into a vacuum dessicator to remove the ether. After the slow impregnation of plastic into the specimens, a catalyst is added to the plastic. Now, additional plastic is poured into a tray until it gels sufficiently to support the specimens. After several hours a second layer is poured over the first. Finally the specimens are transferred into the plastic; this is placed in an oven for several hours. Then the blocks of plastic are left to cool, and finally buffed and polished.

Slides

In the catalogs of the biological supply houses you'll find a full library of slides (mainly 2 inches × 2 inches) both black and white and color, in botany, zoology, and human anatomy and physiology. Some professional slides, for instance, of tissue cells, may be flashed on the blackboard. A student can outline the cells in chalk on the board. Turn off the projector, turn on the lights, and the image is now on the blackboard where it can be studied in detail for an extended time. This may

Fig. 21-3 A variety of specimens mounted in plastic is available. (Photos: top, Ward's Natural Science Establishment and Carolina Biological Supply Co.; bottom, General Biological Supply House, Inc., Chicago.)

be a useful step toward developing a point in a lesson.

Students may also be taught to give demonstrations with their talks to the class. When they give a report you may be able to make a projector available. With a glass-marking pencil on dry, clear glass slides (2 × 2 or 3¼ × 4) have students make simple diagrams which can be projected for all to study. More successful slides may be made on ground glass, using pencil, India ink, or crayons. In elaborate attempts, students may get a three-dimensional effect with shading. Some

crayons may be moistened, very slightly, with water to give a smooth, blended color effect.

Sometimes students may want to press a small, thin specimen between two slides and bind the edges with gummed tape.

Making charts

Drawings may be made on the blackboard using different colored chalk. These drawings are effective when developed with the class as part of the lesson.

Other kinds of drawings may be made on window shades using inks and crayons or on muslin, using wax crayons. When the wax-crayon drawing is finished, cover it with brown wrapping paper and iron the paper. The wax melts and is absorbed into the muslin. (Be careful to protect the ironing-board cover with paper too.) These charts can be washed when needed. Their main advantage is that they can be folded and kept in envelopes in a filing cabinet. Sew a 1-inch hem at the top of the chart and have metal eyelets inserted so that it may hang from hooks, or use thumbtacks. If you have a storage cabinet for other charts you may prefer to nail the muslin charts onto wooden rods like professional charts.

Supply houses offer professional charts of all kinds, and they also offer teachers leaflets and bulletins on ways to make good-looking charts. All your charts may be stored in a cabinet such as the one in Fig. 21-4. Here a label is affixed to one end of the chart along with a loop of wire. Hang the charts according to your own

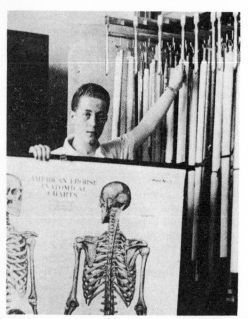

Fig. 21-4 Cabinet for storing charts. (Photo: Forest Hills H. S.)

filing system. These charts last longer in such a cabinet since they are not handled or knocked about.

A picture file

Students accept the responsibility for keeping a bulletin board interesting with current topics. You may want to train a squad of students to maintain a picture file. Give them file folders and space. Excellent pictures (and reference reading materials) may be found in *Life, Natural History, National Geographic,* and similar magazines and bulletins. Valuable reprints are available from *Life.*

Very shortly, students will have timely bulletin boards for any topic in the year's work: behavior, physiology, heredity, disease prevention, conservation, reproduction, and evolution.

Blueprints of leaves

As a project some students may develop a file of leaves. This is one step in learning to identify plants, and attractive display materials may be prepared. One way is to prepare leaf skeletons which can be taped between two glass slides and projected for the class to study. In another method, which young children also enjoy, blueprints are made of leaves, as follows. Tape one side of a 6-inch × 6-inch square of cardboard to one side of a sheet of glass cut to the same size. Insert a sheet of blueprint paper of the same size or smaller between the glass and cardboard backing. Lay a leaf on the blueprint paper and hold it flat by pressing the glass over it. Expose this to sunlight. A few trials will indicate the length of time needed. Remove the blueprint paper and rinse in water. Allow to dry, then flatten under a weight.

Outlines of leaves may be made on photographic paper, but the developing of the print is more time-consuming.

Working with glass

Cutting glass. Students will be most successful when working with thick-walled glass tubing about 6 mm in diameter. With this tubing they may make capillary pipettes and glass bends.

Glass is cut by applying one firm scratch with a triangular file on a section of glass held securely on the top of a table. Then hold the tubing as in Fig. 21-5. (As a precaution, students should wrap each end with paper toweling or a soft cloth.) Hold the scratch away from the body; place the thumbs behind it. Pull on the tubing and at the same time exert a forward push with the thumbs. An even break in the tubing should result. Fire-polish the cut ends in a flame. The bore of the opening of the tubing may be altered while the glass is heated. Over-melting of the glass will reduce the size; the opening can be increased by inserting the round end of the triangular file into the melted glass opening.

Making a capillary pipette. Cut glass tubing into sections about 7 to 9 inches in length; fire-polish both ends. Many of these can be kept on hand until they are needed for making pipettes.

Rotate between thumb and first two fingers of both hands, a center section of a length of glass in a flame until the glass is soft; remove from the flame and pull out. Hold in position or place on asbestos sheet until hardened. Too rapid a pull will produce fine capillary sections. Cut off the lengths desired and carefully fire-polish.

When a long, tapered capillary tube is desired, rotate the glass tubing over a wing top or flame spreader.

The pulling out of soft glass test tubes has been described in making a micro-aquarium (see Fig. 6-4).

Bending glass. A good bend retains the same size bore throughout the bend. Rotate tubing or glass rod holding both ends lightly, and turn the tubing evenly so that all sides are heated equally. Use a wing top when a broad U-shaped bend is desired so that a larger area of glass may be heated. Remove the tubing from the flame when it starts to sag and bend to the desired shape, applying equal pressure with each hand. Hold the tubing in one plane until it hardens. Some workers remove the sagging tubing from the flame and take advantage of the natural sag by raising the ends upward so that the sag hangs down in a bend. Others lay the sagging tubing on asbestos and make the bend from a flat surface, thus ensuring that the bend is in one plane. A good right-angle bend can easily be made in this way by using the corner of the asbestos pad as a pattern for the right angle. When bends of a specific angle are needed, cut a pattern, or draw one on asbestos. In any event, set the tubing aside on asbestos to cool. Students should learn to touch glassware cautiously before they grab it—hot glass looks exactly like cold glass!

Glass rods can be drawn out to varying thicknesses. Fine threads of glass are

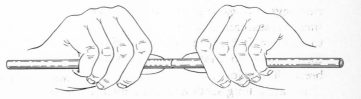

Fig. 21-5 Correct way to hold glass tubing to break it; it has already been scratched.

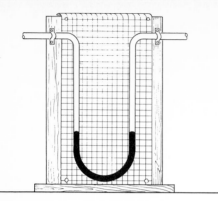

Fig. 21-6 A U-shaped tube mounted against graph paper to serve as a simple manometer. It may be filled with mercury, as shown, or with colored water.

used for glass needles for careful work in embryology where bits of tissue are transplanted from a young embryo into an older one. Glass stirring rods may be made easily; cut glass rods to desired lengths (depending on the size of the beakers used) and heat both ends (one at a time) to melting; while the rod is hot, press against a sheet of asbestos or a stone-topped table to flatten the ends a bit.

A U-shaped tube: a simple manometer. Sections of glass tubing may be used as a manometer. Students may make one from 1-mm glass tubing. Heat the tubing over a flame spreader or wing top and shape into a symmetrical U-tube. At each end of the tube make a right-angle bend, add mercury or colored water, and mount the "manometer" on a board against a sheet of graph paper (Fig. 21-6).

Rubber tubing can be attached to one end in use.

Curved pipette. The curved pipette shown in Fig. 21-7 is useful in transferring eggs of frogs or snails, protozoa, or small crustaceans from one finger bowl to another. It fits into the curve of the finger bowl, so that the tip does not break off so readily.

Rotate a long section of glass over a

fish tail or flame spreader. When the glass begins to sag, remove the tubing and begin to make a U-shaped bend. However, quickly flick the wrists so that the palm of each hand is turned slightly inward forming a slight curve in another plane. After the glass cools, cut it in the center of the U-bend so that two pipettes result. Fire-polish the ends. The size of the bore should be made to fit the materials to be transferred, e.g., large if frog eggs are to be transferred.

Making a wash bottle. A wash bottle containing distilled water is a useful piece of equipment for careful work in the laboratory.

Students will need a flat-bottomed Florence or Erlenmeyer flask, a two-hole stopper, several lengths of glass tubing, and a 4-cm section of rubber tubing to which the small glass nozzle is attached.

Prepare the glass bends and assemble as shown in the completed wash bottle (Fig. 21-8). Both the glass tubing and the stopper should be wet while the glass tubing is being inserted into the stopper. Students should use toweling and hold the tubing next to the region inserted into the stopper. With a gentle twisting motion, the glass tubing can be inserted into the stopper. The tubing is safer to handle when the ends have been fire-polished beforehand.

Cleaning glassware. Most glassware can be washed with warm, soapy water, but when experiments call for chemically clean glassware, extra precautions must

Fig. 21-7 A curved pipette convenient for transferring delicate specimens out of small finger bowls.

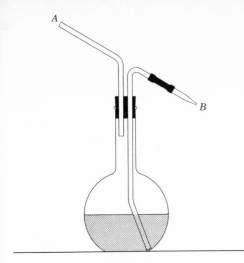

Fig. 21-8 A wash bottle can be used in two ways: water can be simply poured out of A; or a fine stream of water can be obtained from B by blowing into A.

be taken. After glassware has been washed by ordinary means, place it in a hot dichromate cleaning solution. This is prepared by pouring 1 liter of concentrated sulfuric acid into 35 cc of a saturated aqueous solution of sodium dichromate. (*Caution:* Never pour the aqueous solution into the acid; avoid spilling on clothes or skin.)

After the glassware has been standing in this solution for several hours or overnight, it should be rinsed continuously in warm tap water until all the chemical solution has been removed.

Glassware is clean when water completely wets the glass, forming a continuous film; on glassware which is not clean, water collects in drops on the surface.

Greasy and tarry materials on glassware may be removed by soaking the glassware in an alcohol sodium hydroxide solution. This is prepared by dissolving 120 gm of sodium hydroxide in 120 cc of water, and diluting to 1 liter with 95 per cent ethyl alcohol. Afterwards, rinse the glassware in tap or distilled water.

Repairing damaged glassware. At times, some sharp, uneven edges of pipettes, flasks, beakers, and test tubes may be repaired for subsequent use by filing the chipped edges or rims, and then fire-polishing. It may be necessary to shape the opening with the blunt end of a glass file.

Large battery jars which have become cracked and useless for holding liquids may have a life as a terrarium if they are inserted into a block of plaster of Paris for support.

It should become a uniform practice in the laboratory and classroom to dispose of broken or cracked (beyond repair) glassware in crockery jars or in other special containers. Glassware should not be discarded haphazardly in waste-paper baskets.

Cutting glass with wire. Long-necked glassware or tubes which have been chipped can be cut off to serve other uses in the laboratory. Nokes[15] describes this method for preparing electrically heated wire to cut glass.

Build (or buy) the wood stand as diagramed (Fig. 21-9). Connect a length of #24 B & S gauge Nichrome wire between the two supports. Connect this with a suitable resistance to the main supply of electricity or to batteries.

Make a circular cut with a glass file around the circumference of the tube to be repaired. Then roll the tube along the hot wire so that the entire scratch or cut is heated. When the crack is completely made, the tube can be removed. Soft glass, up to a diameter of 2 cm, may be cut in this way. Larger glass tubes may need heat applied to the entire circle at the same time. Here a loop of Nichrome wire, attached to insulated handles, is more desirable.

[15] M. O. Nokes, *Modern Glass Working and Laboratory Technique,* Chemical Publishing Co. New York, 1950.

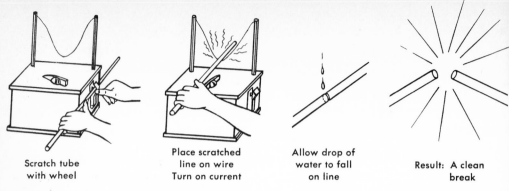

| Scratch tube with wheel | Place scratched line on wire Turn on current | Allow drop of water to fall on line | Result: A clean break |

Fig. 21-9 Using electrically heated wire to cut glass. The unit shown operates on 115-volt AC; a transformer controls the temperature of the cutting wire. (From W. M. Welch Manufacturing Co., Chicago.)

PEOPLE, PLACES, AND THINGS

We find that teachers are always looking for new ways to develop a concept in the science classroom. Do you belong to a professional science teachers' organization? Many groups of teachers plan techniques meetings in which they share successful demonstrations and ask help for improving some other less successful techniques. Along with the professional journals of such organizations as the National Science Teachers' Association and the National Association of Biology Teachers, local groups of teachers often publish a small newsletter in which they exchange techniques and ideas for project work with students.

We know of a school where the science department worked closely with the shop department in creating a science-shop course in which practice was given in the use of tools, wood lathes, jigsaws and the like. Such a course might be planned for teachers in a community, and also opened to students who plan to major in science. Students who plan to specialize in science need practice in manipulative skills.

JOURNALS

The American Biology Teacher, National Association of Biology Teachers, Bryan City Schools, Bryan, Ohio, 8 issues yearly.

The Science Teacher, National Science Teachers Association, 1201 Sixteenth Street N. W., Washington 6, D. C., 6 issues yearly.

We have already mentioned the fine free bulletins published as a service for science teachers, those of Ward's Natural Science Establishment, General Biological Supply House, and Welch Scientific Company (see the Directory at the end of the book).

CHAPTER 22

Science facilities

for a science program

This chapter examines some of the patterns of managing science classrooms and laboratories and providing facilities for storing materials, such as special shelves, cabinets, and closets. One advantage in having facilities to permit storage and good housekeeping is that students can offer superior service as laboratory aides for many kinds of work going on in classrooms and laboratories. Many of the kinds of activities in which students can share work in class and in the laboratory under a teacher's supervision are described here in detail.

There is the constant need to observe specific safety requirements in using certain chemicals and equipment in class, in transporting materials through corridors to classrooms, and in storing chemicals and glassware.

These areas will be discussed in this order:

A. Space for work
B. Space for storage
C. Equipment and supplies
D. Student squads
E. Safety

Space for work

In older schools, teachers have used their own good devices to find ways to make over old things. Gradually they have ordered new equipment. They have improvised, as well. For example, in rooms which are not equipped with gas, teachers use cylinders of propane gas to which a burner attachment is fitted (Fig. 22-1).

When a room is not equipped with running water, some teachers use a large battery jar of water, a water wash bottle, or for prolonged use, a carboy of water with a rubber extension tube and clamp.

Students willingly bring to class equipment to augment the facilities of the school. In this way aluminum-foil dishes, baby-food jars, plastic boxes, and large glass jars are available in place of more expensive glassware.

Some schools have solved their individual problems concerning older class-

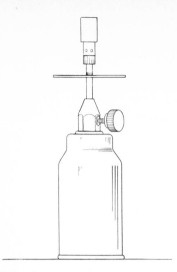

Fig. 22-1 One type of propane burner useful when a gas supply is not available in a classroom.

have for a greenhouse or a nature room of some kind?

The kinds of activities you plan will decide the work space needed. In the following sections are suggestions for kinds of work space that teachers over the country find necessary in creative science teaching.

Classrooms and laboratories. If you were given the responsibility for ordering classroom furniture you would be likely to study supply house catalogs and those of companies which deal exclusively with school furniture. Specific recommendations are given for space per cubic centimeters for each student; chairs and tables of different heights are needed to provide for the many individual differences in maturation among high school students.

rooms not equipped for science teaching by purchasing a transportable demonstration table such as that in Fig. 22-2. These units, along with the more elaborate kind shown in Fig. 22-3, give teachers an opportunity to provide more demonstrations and experiments in class.

Newer schools are equipped with outlets in classroom and laboratory for water, gas, often a vacuum jet, and one for compressed air. The trend in newer schools seems to be toward a combination class and laboratory so that the room serves multiple purposes (Figs. 22-4, 22-5).

Science teachers are often asked to suggest plans for classrooms (or lists of ideas they would want to see in practice) which may be incorporated in blueprints for a new school.

What facilities would you request for a new school? What kind of tables and chairs, and for what age group? Do you favor separate adjoining closets or closets and cabinets in a central supply laboratory? Do you prefer a combination classroom-laboratory? Is there space for a darkroom? What provisions would you

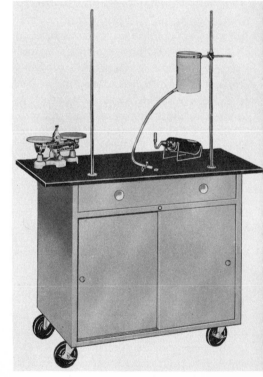

Fig. 22-2 A unit demonstration table which can be transported from one classroom to another. (Photo: W. M. Welch Mfg. Co.)

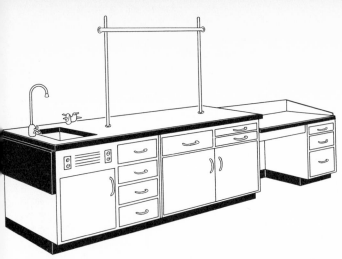

Fig. 22-3 Compact demonstration unit, including teacher's desk. (Sheldon Equipment Co.)

If space is limited, there is an advantage in having a laboratory arrangement at one side of a room and movable tables and chairs at the other side. In this way, students may be grouped at either end and the teacher and students do not have to speak and be heard across a large room.

Much has been written on kinds of furniture and floor layouts for science rooms which include cabinets and closet space, provisions for bulletin boards, and shelves for aquaria. Perhaps the last word has been said for a long time to come in

the well-conceived, comprehensive book from which several of the figures used here have been taken, *School Facilities for Science Instruction* (John Richardson, ed., 1954; National Science Teachers Association, 1201 Sixteenth St. N. W., Washington 6, D. C.). In this reference are chapters dealing with facilities for general science, biology, chemistry, physics, and special courses in science. There is also a chapter on planning for elementary science facilities, an excellent bibliography for extensive research in this area, and a splendid listing of suggested equipment

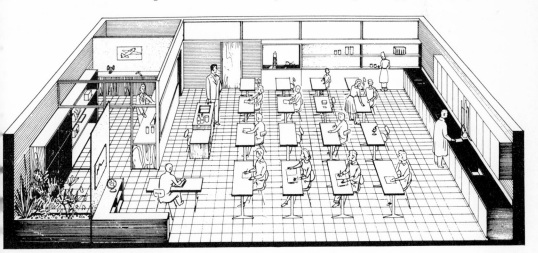

Fig. 22-4 Schematic drawing of combination classroom-laboratory. (From J. S. Richardson, ed., *School Facilities for Science Instruction*, NSTA, 1954.)

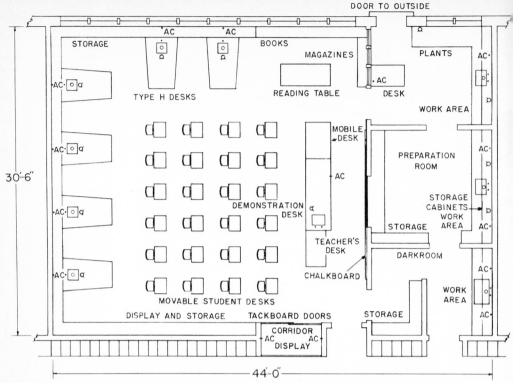

Fig. 22-5 Two floor plans for science classroom-laboratories.

and supplies for all the sciences.

Increasing numbers of teachers are using methods of teaching which give scope to budding potentialities of young people. In the following section some of the varied kinds of work going on in schools is indicated. Facilities need to be planned to enable teachers and students to work together in these pursuits.

Greenhouse. Many students find work in a school greenhouse an enriching experience. This work may be an extension of class activities or a means for supplying classrooms with living materials for study.

They may learn to grow algae, mosses, ferns, and seed plants. They can gain success in raising plants by vegetative propagation. Some may go into soil testing techniques while others begin studies in plant physiology.

In many schools over the country a

greenhouse is associated with student project work, field-work activities on the school ground, or at school camps. (See Chapters 15 and 20 for methods of collecting and maintaining plants.)

School grounds. Very often teachers of biology are asked to contribute ideas for landscaping the school grounds. When flowering trees and shrubs are specially selected for planting around school, a teacher can conduct a short field trip (within a class period) to introduce the topic: how flowers function in plant reproduction. (This notion is developed further in Chapter 20 in the section on field trips.) At other seasons they may study seed formation, devices for seed dispersal, variations, and plant communities.

In fact, some teachers have laid out nature trails, have built artificial lakes which have later been stocked with plants and animals, and have, in general, stim-

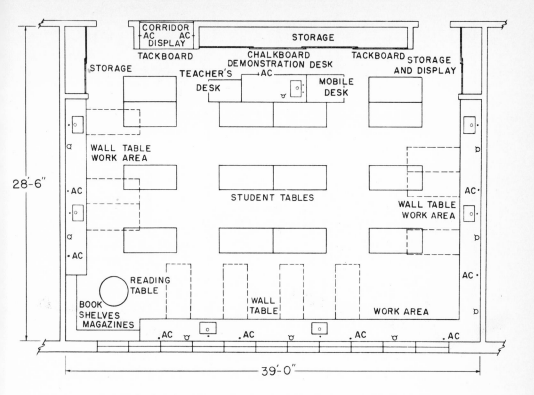

ulated the study of field biology. Clubs or classes in gardening are popular in many communities.

School camps. In some communities there is a cooperative bond between community and school to bring many first-hand outdoor nature experiences to students. Certainly students gain a greater appreciation of the biological world around them and the interacting factors in the conservation of living things. Often these are week-end excursions chaperoned by teachers and parents. When the school owns a camp, or rents one out of season, many long-range activities can be planned.

School nature museum. Almost every teacher of biology grows some kinds of living things, and students have similar interests. When both students and teachers pool their techniques, a small space can be found to exhibit living things for the whole school. Descriptions of relationships

(classification), and interesting facts about the plants and animals can be typed as legends on library cards. This area can grow into a permanent, living nature museum. Students can be trained as curators (see student squads, p. 442).

Living culture center. Many of the organisms for a school nature museum may be drawn from stocks that are maintained all year round in the biology classrooms or laboratories. In fact, a living culture center which maintains protozoa cultures and representative members of the invertebrates and vertebrates may serve the elementary and junior high schools in the community. Students who work on individual projects may also get their supplies of organisms from the school living culture center.

Just as space and facilities are needed for a greenhouse, there is need to plan for an animal room—a place for tanks

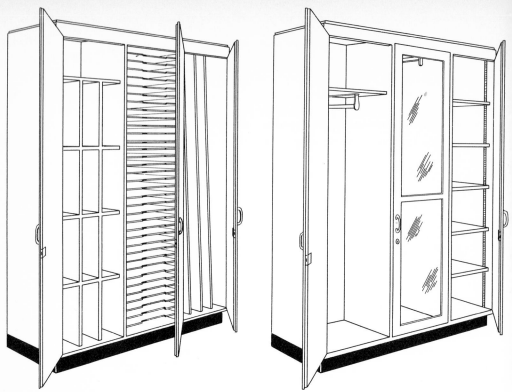

Fig. 22-6 Two cabinets for general storage, including projectors and microscopes.

and cages to house fish, amphibia, reptiles, hamsters, white rats, and sometimes, as temporary guests, pigeons or parakeets. (Directions for collecting and maintaining invertebrates are given in Chapters 15 and 18, vertebrates in Chapter 19.)

Project room. In some schools, teachers have set aside space for individual students to pursue an interest, a research problem, a prolonged "original" experiment in science (pp. 10, 11). Over a year or more these young people use the methods of scientists. They need shelves to store materials, a work desk, and locker space for storage of their equipment (see Figs. 22-7, 22-9). There should be adequate electrical outlets and provisions for gas and water. A book shelf or cabinet for science reference books in the same room is a convenience.

Science library and committee room. When space is not the limiting factor there should be room for a small science library and a separate place for students to meet for conferences or committee work associated with their classwork. This library does not compete with the school library but contains more advanced texts and magazines for students engaged in individual research work. Suggestions for books to purchase may be found in the Bibliography at the end of the book.

Film room. Many schools set aside a room to accommodate all the classes in the school. This room is equipped with dark shades, drapes, and a large screen. Specially trained student squads (described on p. 444) run the projectors (silent, sound, lantern, 2″ × 2″, opaque, microprojector, and so forth). These students also keep the equipment in good condition in adequate storage facilities near the film room (see p. 445).

Catalogs of slides, films, and filmstrips may be obtained from supply houses (see p. 497 for addresses) and from film companies (addresses, p. 464). You may also want to check on the availability of free films from industry (consult general listings of films and of sources of free and inexpensive materials at the end of the book).

Darkroom. Many young people today are camera enthusiasts and develop their own pictures. Thoughtful planning of space may give rise to a spare closet which can be converted into a darkroom.[1]

Teacher's corner. Provisions for a small, snug, confined area for the teacher reap high returns in teacher efficiency. While an "office" sounds formidable to some, a small nook to which a teacher may repair to meet a student or colleague in semi-privacy, to work over records, to read, relieves the teacher of the strains which mount from the continued buzz and activity of many busy people in a school day.

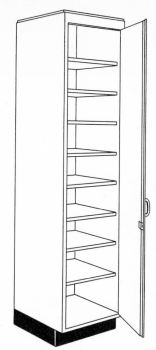

Fig. 22-7 Cabinet for storage of glassware.

Facilities for storage

Closed storage spaces, that is, compact closets and cabinets, are in greater demand than open shelves. In this way equipment and supplies do not accumulate dust and they are not exposed to fumes or fluctuations in humidity and temperature.

Demonstration materials such as models, skeletons, glassware, and projectors may be stored in cabinets such as the ones shown in Figs. 22-6 and 22-7. When charts are stored in a hanging position (see Fig. 21-4), many charts can be stored conveniently and they are not exposed to wear. Each chart can be wired at one end and hooked onto the sliding arms of the cabinet. When each arm holds the charts dealing with a given topic in biology, students as aides in the laboratory (p. 439) can find the charts quickly when they are preparing a teacher's order for the day.

Teachers have found the wooden slide box shown in Fig. 22-8 (left), convenient for storing prepared slides for microscopic examination. However, when slides are stored flat, as in the cabinet shown in Fig. 22-8 (right), they take less space, there is no slipping of specimens in the mounting fluid, and all the slides are visible at a glance so that selecting the desired slides for a day's lesson can be done quickly by a student on a squad. Broken slides can be detected at the end of a class period.

---

[1] The companion volume, A. Joseph, P. F. Brandwein, and E. Morholt, *Teaching High School Science: A Sourcebook for the Physical Sciences,* Harcourt, Brace, 1958, describes improvised darkrooms and other photographic devices.

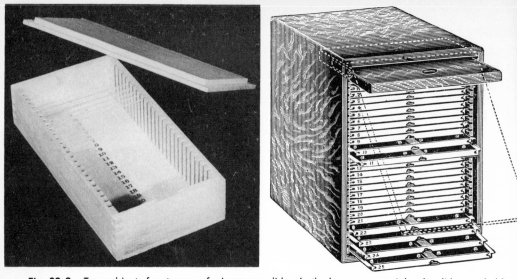

Fig. 22-8 Two cabinets for storage of microscope slides. In the larger one at right, the slides are held flat and visible. (Photo: General Biological Supply House, Inc., Chicago; drawing from *Turtox* catalogue.)

Fig. 22-9 Cabinet for storage of microscopes.

Fig. 22-10 Cabinet for compact filing of film reels.

Microscopes can be stored and easily counted in a cabinet made up of individual sections (Fig. 22-9). There is less chance for tumbling or knocking of the microscopes in this type of storage cabinet. Stereoscopic microscopes can be stored in individual cases.

In a cabinet such as that in Fig. 22-10, films may be stored. Lantern slides or 2″ × 2″ slides may be stored in grooved boxes.

The cabinet in Fig. 22-11 has many drawers in which rocks, fossil specimens,

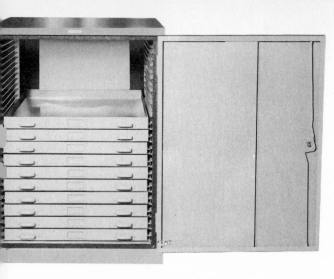

Fig. 22-11 Cabinet for storage of rock specimens or other small objects. (Photo: Chas. J. Lane Corp.)

or small demonstration objects may be stored.

Open-shelf storage space may be covered with transparent plastic sheeting to reduce the accumulation of dust.

Chemicals, especially acids, strong bases, and substances like chloroform, ether, iodine, and hormones should be stored in facilities which can be locked. A part of a storeroom may have a special soapstone section which is locked by doors of metal wiring.

Equipment and supplies

In the previous section we have described basic facilities for effective work in biology. What kinds of equipment and supplies does a teacher of biology need?

Table 22-1, a list of suggested equipment and supplies, with the approximate cost of each item, has been gleaned from many sources and from our own experiences over twenty years in the classroom. While *these prices are subject to great change* with time, they give a useful estimate, a yardstick, albeit a rough one, which teachers may use in planning orders to submit to their administrative officers. Usually teachers are given a budgetary allowance and must order wisely.

The quantity of material to be ordered depends upon which activities are to be carried on and how they are to be done —as a classroom experiment by all students, by groups of four students working together, by an individual as a project, or as a class demonstration. The amount of material also depends on the annual budget for equipment and supplies.

Some teachers may find Table 22-1 useful for taking inventory as a first step in planning a science program. Since each teacher will select those activities from this text which fit his own school situation, not all the materials listed here will be needed.

Many of the materials may be purchased in local hardware stores and aquarium shops; some may be brought to class by students and teachers from home supplies. Many of the fresh materials may be collected in season by students on field trips. Other materials and basic equipment you will need to order from supply houses (listing, p. 479).

TABLE 22-1 Checklist of supplies

Apparatus and equipment	approx. unit cost	on hand	students supply	field trips	quantity to order
aquarium tanks					
5 gal	$ 6.00				
10 gal	12.50				
aquarium heater					
thermostat	9.00				
air pump	15.00				
asbestos sheets	.28/doz				
balances					
analytical					
(sensitivity 0.1 mg)	110.00				
Harvard trip scale					
(sensitivity 0.1 gm)	20.00				
laboratory scale					
(dial type)	10.00				
single beam (2000 gm)	19.00				
triple beam (1610 gm;					
sensitivity 0.1 gm)	22.00				
spring (9 oz; 250 gm)	2.25				
balloons	.05				
battery jars					
1 qt	1.05				
2 qt	1.50				
1 gal	2.15				
3 gal	7.00				
beakers, Pyrex					
Griffin, low form					
50 ml	.28				
100 ml	.30				
250 ml	.28				
1000 ml	.82				
Griffin, with handle					
3000 ml	3.75				
Berzelius, tall form					
100 ml	.33				
500 ml	.46				
beakers, polyethylene					
400 ml	1.00				
bell jars					
open-top	14.00				
closed-top	12.00				
blotting paper	.25/doz				
boilers, double	5.00				
bottles					
wide-mouth, 125 ml	1.20/doz				
extra-wide-mouth					
200 ml	4.55/doz				

Apparatus and equipment	approx. unit cost	on hand	students supply	field trips	quantity to order
glass-stoppered, penny-head shape 500 ml	10.25/doz				
glass-stoppered, flat-top 500 ml	12.00/doz				
bottles, acid storage 2500 ml	1.60				
bottles, balsam	1.10				
bottles, dropping, Barnes (square, pipette closure)	.25				
channeled stopper	.75				
bottles, reagent 125 ml	.48				
250 ml	.60				
bottles, wash, Pyrex 500 ml	1.38				
bottles, polyethylene 6 oz	.40				
16 oz	.76				
brushes, camel's-hair	.10				
buckets, galvanized iron	1.25				
polyethylene, 11 qt, cover	3.80				
burners					
alcohol (Pyrex)	.80				
alcoburner	10.25				
Bunsen	1.80				
Fisher	3.00				
fuel—propane cylinder and burner top	6.00				
wing top	.18				
cages					
ant nest	6.00				
breeding cage, plastic, terrestrial insects	2.05				
collapsible breeding cage	15.50				
rats, small animals	9.60				
rabbit, guinea pig	19.00				
carbon paper	.25/pkg				
cardboard					
centrifuges, hand, 2000 rpm	20.50				
cheesecloth	.15/yd				
clay, modeling	.50/lb				
Coplin jars, 10-slide capacity	.90				
cork, thin sheets, 4″×12″×¼″	.80				

Apparatus and equipment	approx. unit cost	on hand	students supply	field trips	quantity to order
corks, assorted (0 to 11)	1.35/100				
cork borers	2.00				
cotton, absorbent	2.15/lb				
cotton, nonabsorbent	.90/lb				
coverslips	1.98/oz				
cylinders, graduate					
25 ml	.80				
100 ml	1.20				
500 ml	2.60				
dissecting trays (waxed)	1.10				
dissecting pins	1.50/500				
drying tubes, calcium chloride U-tube	.35				
evaporating dishes porcelain, 75 mm	.42				
fermentation tubes	.98				
files, triangular, 6 in	.32				
filter paper	.40/pkg				
finger bowls, culture dishes					
4½″ × 2″	.80				
8″ × 3″	2.80				
fire extinguisher	27.00				
fish food	.25				
flasks, Erlenmeyer					
250 ml	.36				
500 ml	.45				
1000 ml	.72				
flashlights	1.50				
flowerpots (assorted sizes)	.10 to .60				
funnels, 90 mm, short-stem	.85				
glass cutters	.72				
glass-marking pencils	.18				
glass squares					
2″ × 2″	.10				
4″ × 4″	.20				
10″ × 10″	.50				
glass tubing, different bores	1.50/lb				
hot plates, electric	21.80				
humus	.10/lb				
Hydrion test kits, pH 1–11	1.50				
hydrometers, universal	3.00				

Apparatus and equipment	approx. unit cost	on hand	students supply	field trips	quantity to order
incubators	40.00				
inoculating needles					
Nichrome wire	.45				
platinum wire	2.10				
injection syringes and					
needles (10 cc)	3.50				
insect display cases					
Schmitt box	7.50				
Riker mounts	1.30				
insect killing bottles					
CCl_4	.60				
cyanide	.75				
insect mounting pins	.80/100				
insect spreading boards	1.85				
jars, display and storage					
wide-mouth, screw-top					
4 oz	.12				
8 oz	.15				
½ gal	.38				
16 oz, tall	.19				
jars, culture, cover-knob					
countersunk, loose-fitting					
2 pt	1.20				
6 pt	2.25				
jars, tall storage, ground-					
glass cover					
8 oz	1.90				
16 oz	2.38				
kits, dissecting	1.90				
kits, first-aid	15.50				
labels, Dennison	.25/box				
lens paper	.20/pkg				
magnifiers, lens and tripod					
(7x)	1.50				
three lenses (5x, 7x, 10x,					
11x, 13x, 16x, 20x)	3.75				
matches	.20				
medicine droppers	.04				
membranes, goldbeater's	.10				
microprojectors	160.00				
microscopes, binocular (stereo)					
(objectives 1x, 2x, 3x; eye-					
pieces 9x, 10x)	466.00				
compound	110.00				
dissecting (Barnes)	11.00				

Apparatus and equipment	approx. unit cost	on hand	students supply	field trips	quantity to order
microscope slides					
plain	1.60/½ oz				
concavity	.20 ea				
microscope slide boxes					
25 slide	.45				
100 slide	2.30				
microscope substage lamps	5.00				
microtomes (hand)	40.00				
mortars and pestles	1.20				
nets					
aquatic	6.00				
dip	5.50				
fish	.25				
insect	2.75				
plankton	16.00				
sweeping	5.00				
needles, disposable, blood typing					
Petri dishes					
(10 x 75 mm)	.50				
(15 x 100 mm)	.60				
plant presses	5.50				
plastic sheeting	.40/yd				
Riker mounts (6½″ × 8½″)	1.05				
ring stands	1.60				
clamps	.80				
support stand rings	.85				
rubber sheeting (dam)	.34/sq ft				
rubber stoppers (assorted, solid, one-hole, two-hole)	1.70/lb				
rubber tubing					
³⁄₁₆″	.12/ft				
¼″	.16/ft				
sand, aquarium	.15/lb				
seed germinating dishes, clay	.60				
soil pH testers	1.50				
sponges, plastic	.10				
Stender dishes	.54				
sterilizers					
Arnold steam	26.00				
pressure-autoclave type	33.00				
Syracuse dishes	3.00/doz				

Apparatus and equipment	approx. unit cost	on hand	students supply	field trips	quantity to order
test tubes					
Pyrex, 150 × 18 mm	.06				
200 × 25 mm	.13				
soft glass, 100 × 3 mm	.03				
150 × 19 mm	.06				
test-tube supports					
12 tubes, wood	1.40				
metal	.60				
thermometers, double scale	1.66				
Thermos bottles	2.50				
thistle tubes, Pyrex	.27				
tongs, crucible	.60				
triangles, galvanized	.20				
tripods	1.70				
vasculum	6.00				
vials					
shell for taper corks	.47/doz				
23 × 85 mm screw-cap	1.27/doz				
volumetric pipettes, 25 cc	1.05				
watch glasses					
75 mm	.08				
150 mm, Pyrex	.26				
water baths, copper, 6 in	3.25				
waxed paper cups	.20				
weights	5.65				
wicks	.43/doz				
wood splints	.50/500				
Y-tubes					
glass	.23				
brass	.78				

Fresh materials

Animals, such as protozoa, other invertebrates, and vertebrates

Plants, all phyla

Organs of animals—such as brain of sheep; uterus of pig; lungs and trachea, kidney, and liver of chicken or cow.

Fertilized eggs of frogs, chickens, etc.

Chemicals and stains

Space prohibits the listing of all the kinds of chemicals and stains useful in the

Apparatus and equipment	approx. unit cost	on hand	students supply	field trips	quantity to order
laboratory. When teachers consult the laboratory catalogs of supply houses they will find sections set aside giving prices for given quantities of these materials.					
Models and charts Protozoa and algae					
Cells and tissues, plants and animals; mitosis; life histories					
Organs and organ systems of plants and animals					
Variations and genetics					
Prepared slides Stained slides of cells and tissues of plants and animals					
Slides for projection Slides (2″ × 2″) of representative plants and animals, of organs and tissue cells; examples of variations.					
Lantern slides of plant and animal specimens; illustrations of laws of heredity, variations, etc.					
Films and filmstrips					
Books					

Using student resources

Individual students have certain talents which a teacher can put to use in many ways. In fact, almost every teacher has a student following of a sort. In the beginning, a teacher may plan a program of activities with this unorganized group of students who probably share many interests in common. In this way a squad of students may be born.

How can a squad, that is, a small group of students, help an individual teacher, or several teachers who make up a department? And how, in turn, does this activity help these students themselves grow in competence?

Co-curricular and extracurricular activities in school provide opportunities for boys and girls to practice some of those so-called required learnings or developmental tasks that they all need to develop—skill in getting along with others, peers and adults; trying out one's abilities; getting practice in making judgments; self-evaluation concerning possible success in science as a vocation; manipulating tools of the scientist; gaining specific skills and a better understanding of what science is.

Many kinds of activities in which students may share are listed here. They vary in need for special skill or high ability. However, each kind of job has a status-giving quality for some child and may help him retain his individuality. Often through these informal relationships teachers come to know their students better; this rapport places the teacher in an effective role as friend and counselor.

Aside from the personal satisfaction to a student, or the gain in some skill or knowledge, many teachers describe students' work in anecdotal accounts which are filed with the permanent cumulative records of students. These are useful later on as recommendations for college, or for future employers. Several schools have student governments which sponsor school service programs and allot service points for all kinds of work done in the school and community. The accumulation of 50 points may lead to a certificate, 75 points to a service pin presented at commencement.

What are some ways that teachers have used students as resources to increase the effectiveness of activities in the laboratory and science classroom? Let us describe the work of students in squads in the laboratory.

Laboratory squads

In practice, probably the most pressing need for most science teachers is assistance in the daily routine of getting out materials, setting up demonstrations or experiments, purchasing perishable materials, dismantling equipment, washing glassware, and getting materials stored away according to some kind of organized system so that they can be found again. Student assistants, as *organized* laboratory squads, can be trained in these routine tasks. The work may be done before school, during school hours, or after school. Students can be helpful in the bookkeeping job required for keeping track of equipment, mainly expendable materials. This is a great help when it comes to ordering supplies and taking inventory.

In a small school the science teacher probably prepares his demonstrations on the run, for he carries a heavy teaching load. A squad of students can assist him at some assigned time that both teacher and students can arrange. Students must work under a teacher's supervision.

In larger schools there are many procedures in use. Where there are several science teachers sharing a common stock of materials and equipment, there is often one teacher in charge who has responsibility for ordering supplies and taking inventory. In large school systems a laboratory assistant has this special responsibility. Any one plan we describe cannot be feasible for all schools, large and small; teachers will select the possibilities which best meet their own needs. Specifically, what goes on in a laboratory or supply center in a school?

Filling daily orders. Students may prepare orders in advance for teachers' classes. However, this presumes that teachers in the science department have organized themselves and have developed a routine for making out orders for class teaching materials that they will need the next day. This plan necessitates submitting orders a day in advance to a laboratory or classroom center where the squad can have access to materials and fill the orders.

When teachers pool their own resources, this kind of procedure can be put into action. Under the guidance of a teacher (or a laboratory assistant), students can deliver this class order to the teacher's room when it is needed. When duplicate equipment is available, the teacher might get his materials in the morning and hold them for the day. Large pieces of equipment, such as microscopes, a manikin, dissection pans and kits, or a microprojector, may be delivered to the teacher at the beginning of the period. Then the material is picked up again toward the end of that same period, and returned to the laboratory or supply center.

How do teachers send in their daily

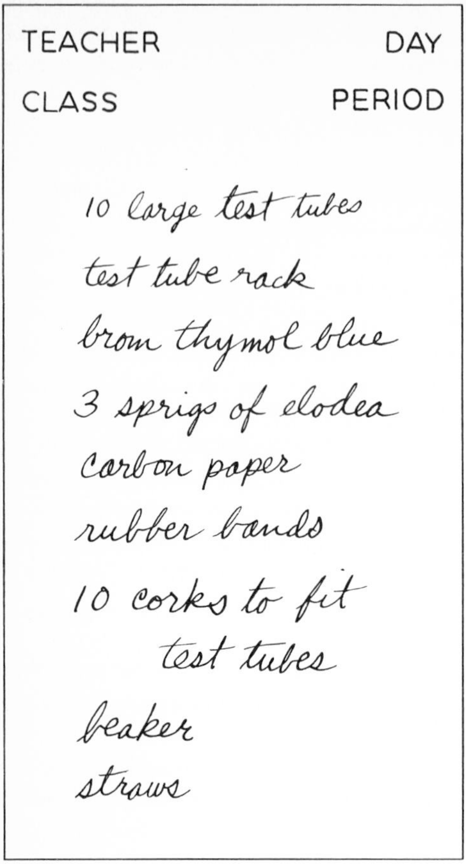

TEACHER
DAY
CLASS
PERIOD
10 large test tubes
test tube rack
brom thymol blue
3 sprigs of elodea
carbon paper
rubber bands
10 corks to fit
test tubes
beaker
straws

Fig. 22-12 Replica of a teacher's order for materials.

PERIODS IN DAY
DAYS
1
2
3
4
5
6
7
8
Mon.
Tues.
Wed.
Thurs.
Cumulative file
Fri.

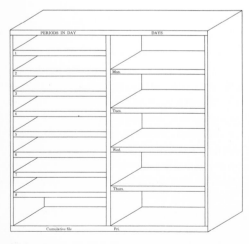

Fig. 22-13 Student-made wooden cabinet with shelves for teachers' daily order slips.

orders for supplies to the supply center in the department? You and your colleagues may want to initiate a standard system in which each teacher submits his order on uniform sized paper, one day in advance. You may want to use the pattern shown in Figs. 22-12 and 22-13. Teachers can check their orders against those of others; or at the end of the day one squad of students examines the orders. When two teachers order the same materials for the next day, they are informed of this and they both agree to share the materials, or one accepts a substitute, or possibly changes his lesson for the next day. The advantage is that the teacher knows beforehand whether he will get the materials he needs so that he has time to arrange another lesson.

That afternoon (or the next morning), students locate the materials that teachers want for the next day, and stack small items on a tray, such as a lunchroom tray. Or they place large pieces or heavy equipment on a cart which can be wheeled through the halls to deliver to the teachers at the start of the day or the lesson for which the materials are needed. (Bottles of strong acids and bases should be carried in wooden boxes as a safety precaution. Glassware, such as Petri dishes, should be stacked in boxes.)

For safety, avoid having the squad make deliveries at the same time that the student body is moving through the halls to their classes. For the same reason, when teachers are not going to keep their materials for the entire day, the pick-up of materials should be timed a few minutes before the end of the class period. When this cannot be accomplished, as occasionally happens, the teachers should assume the responsibility for getting the materials back to the common laboratory supply center. Otherwise the equipment, or clean glassware, and so forth, will not be available for the next teacher who needs it.

When teachers need fresh materials like elodea plants, frogs, protozoa cultures, a pig's uterus for dissection, blood-typing materials, germinating seedlings to show hereditary traits, or a thriving culture of fruit flies, a week's advance notice (in some cases a longer time is needed) must be given to the teacher and the squad who are serving the science teachers. In practice, this works out easily when teachers confer with each other from time to time each month and plan to share perishable materials at the same time. When teachers plan their work in outline at the beginning of the school year, then fresh materials can be purchased, or living materials can be collected and cultured in the laboratory or classroom (see Chapters 15, 18, 19, and 20) and made available when students are ready to study the topic.

Cleaning up. Two or three students in the laboratory have responsibility for dismantling the equipment returned by teachers, and for washing glassware used in class. Then all the materials are returned to labeled shelves, cabinets, or drawers.

Laboratory housekeeping. Plants must be watered, and aquaria and terraria need care. Someone must dust open shelves of models and glassware. Microscopes must be checked and lenses cleaned from time to time. New labels need to be put on cabinets and museum jars, and charts may need mending. Some fish tanks need patching and some broken glassware could be put to new use if the jagged edges were cut off and filed or fire-polished smooth. The wax lining some of the dissection trays is cracked and should be melted slowly over a Bunsen flame.

Possibly one student could add water colors to some of the black and white charts to freshen them and enliven students' interest. Who would prepare cotton-lined display boxes (Riker mounts) for the unassorted fossil specimens on hand? Some student on your squad, perhaps.

Safety in the laboratory. Every month over the school year, student squads in the lab should undertake a fire drill of their own design. Can the students on the squad use the fire extinguishers? Do they know when to use the sand in the sand buckets in the lab? Do they know how to use the fire blanket? All of these materials should be on hand. Also check the freshness of the supplies in the first-aid kit.

In the laboratory, students should not use a flame unless the teacher is present. Regulations should be designed concerning the storage of acids, bases, other dangerous chemicals such as chloroform or iodine, and so forth (safety procedures, p. 447).

Squads for special services

Students with special interests and skills may receive training of many kinds which cannot be learned in "class time." Either squads or special club activities may be developed in the following areas. In many cases, there are opportunities for enrichment here and also situations for students to discover where their interests and abilities lie.

Making models, charts, and slides. Many teachers initiate a routine for listing materials or equipment they would like to have for class use. Often they list their ideas on library cards at the moment they think of them. These cards are filed in a small metal file box. At a given time each teacher submits these cards to one person in the department who has assumed this responsibility. These cards serve as a guide at the time for ordering supplies. But the main use of these teachers' ideas is to provide the stimulus for students who like doing things with their hands and brain. These students may build a piece of equipment such as an incubator or a device to show a tropism, or make a series of models to show the cleavage stages of a developing egg. Other students may make charts to show comparative anatomy or variations in some flowers, fish, or other forms not easily obtainable for class use as firsthand experiences. (See section on model-making, p. 413; chart-making, p. 417.)

Students may supplement the supply of prepared slides in the department. For example, a club or squad may be trained to prepare blood smears (p. 318), whole mounts of small forms (p. 316), stained slides of protozoa (p. 322), and many other kinds of slides.

Curators of living things. When space is available, a museum of living things, plants and animals, can be maintained over the school year so that teachers may bring their classes to this area for many lessons in biology.

Where space is at a premium, there is still opportunity for maintaining living things. A section of a classroom or a laboratory may be given over to three or four aquaria and at least one terrarium, and several shelves may be used to store cultures of protozoa and fruit flies. In another room (to avoid contamination of cultures of protozoa), different kinds of mold cultures may be grown. Perhaps there is also room for a cutting box—a box of sand or light soil—in which cuttings of plants and other forms of vegetative propagation may be grown.

Students may be trained to culture protozoa, subculture them every month or so (directions in Chapter 18), raise fruit flies (directions on p. 199), prepare mold cultures, grow fern prothallia (p. 395), and so forth. Guppies and other small tropical fish can be kept in one tank with snails and water plants. In this way, life cycles of fish, and snail eggs, can be studied in class. Fresh materials for study of plant cells are available at any time. In other aquaria students may maintain *Daphnia, Tubifex,* larvae of some insects, tadpoles, or other fresh-water forms they may obtain initially on field trips or from an aquarium shop. (Maintaining invertebrates, Chapter 18; vertebrates, Chapter 19; plants, Chapter 20.)

In each classroom there should be at least one aquarium and one terrarium. Battery jars of different sizes may be used also to accommodate living things that students bring to class. Small cages may be made by some students of screening and wood frames; observation ant jars may be prepared (p. 358). Directions have been given for collecting living things, keeping them in class, and also for preserving biological materials (see Chapter 15). If several classrooms house different living things, then space has been "stretched" and the science department has living culture centers in each classroom.

Soil-testing squads. Many schools have established excellent relations with the community by serving as a center for testing the kinds of soil people send in to the science department or science teacher. There are many soil-testing kits on the market (see supply house catalogs) and students may be trained to give suggestions for improving soil. This is a useful conservation service. It may be possible to get help from the agricultural county agent in the community.

Landscaping the school grounds. A squad, a small core of interested students, may be trained to plan a nature trail around school (see p. 264), build bird-houses to attract beneficial birds, and plant trees, shrubs, and flower beds which would be useful to the teachers of biology. In this way, classes might be held on the school grounds for studies in reproduction, heredity, behavior, variations and evolution, interrelationships, and conservation. Students may label trees to help other students learn to identify some of the common trees and shrubs.

Book-room squad. A trained core of students can distribute books to teachers' classes at the beginning of the school year, or supplementary reference texts can be supplied to teachers whenever they are needed by a class. An up-to-the-minute inventory can be maintained if a tally sheet is posted on a bulletin board in the book room indicating books on shelves and books in use.

In fact, these students may take responsibility for an important enterprise in the department. There are many excellent paper-bound books now available. Students could begin to build a library of good science books. These paper-backs might be sold (under a teacher's supervision) by a book-room squad before or after school one day a week as a special service.

Teachers can find many ways to bring these readings into daily class experiences. Only a few books are listed here as a sampling for a student's library. (A more comprehensive list of paperbacks is available in *An Inexpensive Science Library*, AAAS, 1515 Massachusetts Ave., N. W., Washington 5, D. C., 1957, $0.10.)

Anchor Books, Doubleday and Co., Inc., 575 Madison Ave., N. Y. 22.
The Human Use of Human Beings, Wiener.
Man on His Nature, Sherrington.
New American Library of World Literature, Inc., 501 Madison Ave., N. Y. 22.

The Sea Around Us, Carson.
The Life of the Spider, Crompton.
The Life of the Bee, Maeterlinck.
Heredity, Race, and Society, Dunn and Dobzhansky.
On Understanding Science, Conant.
The Limitations of Science, Sullivan.
Science and the Modern World, Whitehead.
The Meaning of Evolution, Simpson.
How to Know the Wild Flowers, Stefferud.
How to Know the Birds, Peterson.
Penguin Books, 3300 Clipper Mill Rd., Baltimore 11.
Man and the Vertebrates, 2 vols., Romer.
Beyond the Microscope, Smith.
A Dictionary of Biology, Johnson and Abercrombie.
Viruses and Man, Burnet.
Genetics, Kalmus.
Microbes and Us, Nichols.
Human Physiology, Walker.
Pocket Books, Inc., 630 Fifth Ave., N. Y. 20.
Guide to the Wild Flowers, Gottscho.
Guide to the Trees, Platt.
Microbe Hunters, De Kruif.
Science Book of the Human Body, Sproul.

Research groups. Some of these special services squads regard themselves as clubs and develop a pride in membership. They hold meetings and discuss problems of importance to their operation.

Students with a common interest may approach a teacher with the request that he sponsor their club, for they know he shares their interest. In this way a microscopy club is formed under a teacher's supervision, or a tropical fish club, or a walking club which goes on field trips on Saturdays, or to a week-end school camp.

Each teacher may sponsor at least one "talented" student and give him scope to work on a project. Gradually in such individual work deep interest and enthusiasm is born and spreads so that soon a large group of students select themselves for a consuming program of work. These students working on an original piece of work[2] gain skills in laboratory work, read more, learn what the methods of science are by using them. Here too, gifted students can often discover whether they have the aptitudes, abilities, and other personality factors needed for a career in science.

These students may participate in science fairs, science talent search examinations for scholarships, and seminars, and also be guest speakers in classrooms, in school assembly programs, and at meetings of the PTA.

Through these experiences students learn more, and do more; they also learn that responsibility of leadership involves the ability to share what they know with a larger audience.

Science readings squad. This is a squad which can help to raise the interests of the entire student body if the members have a high level of initiative.

At the lowest level of operation, students might be assigned the task of writing a form letter to those industrial concerns (see listing, p. 475) known to supply free or inexpensive teaching aids —such as vitamin booklets, charts of vitamin deficiencies, booklets which describe how to make something, and so forth. At a higher level, students can handle magazine subscriptions (*National Geographic, Life, Scientific American, Science Newsletter*), and the publications of nearby museums, and state and government publications.

These students might have a bulletin board or hall case assigned to them. They could post articles, pictures, copies of new paper-backs; suggest sources for information on specific topics in biology, such as heredity, health, foods and nu-

trition, safety and accident prevention, and identification of plants and animals in season (birds, insects, shells, flowering plants). It may be possible for this squad of specialists to work with the librarians in preparing exhibits of books in science.

In many schools students have built attractive wall racks along which magazines may be inserted. This arrangement saves desk or table space in a classroom or laboratory.

Mimeographing squad. Some students like to put things into print. When a small squad of reliable students is trained to use a mimeograph or a rexograph machine they release teacher-time for more creative work.

With a system for duplicating the written page, teachers may find it profitable to reproduce writings from original papers (as described on pp. 25, 220). They may devise pencil-and-paper tests which have variety and test reading ability, interpretation of data, synthesis, and application, all the activities that are necessary for an intelligent citizenry in a world of science.

Publishing squad. In fact, classes in science might plan creative work. They might prepare a newsletter in biology, or prepare a small magazine within the department. Students with special interests, those doing independent research, or those who enjoy writing for others might organize such a venture. The help of the mimeographing squad must be solicited and some typists must be put to work. This is a stimulating venture over the year. In fact, several small high schools might merge their efforts and widen their influence and "sales."

Projectionist squads. In many schools a teacher is assigned to "service" the school in the area of audio-visual aids. This means the teacher is responsible for having projectors, tape recorders, and

[2] P. F. Brandwein, *The Gifted Student as Future Scientist*, Harcourt, Brace, New York, 1954.

microphones in good operating condition at all times. He must order films, plan a schedule of showings over the entire year, and train a squad of projectionists to accompany the equipment and film.

Often one room is set apart, equipped with heavy drapes, screens, storage closets for storing films, filmstrips, and slides, projectors for silent and sound films, filmstrips, and slides, and possibly a microprojector (Fig. 17-3) or other type of enlarger of the microscopic field of vision. There may also be an opaque projector on hand to throw pictures from the printed page onto the screen. Equipment for splicing film and rewinding film is also needed. Students must learn how to care for this expensive equipment and store it against drying out (storage facilities, p. 428).

It may be possible to assign one or two students to look through catalogs of free and inexpensive films (see pp. 463, 475), record these on library cards, and build a filing system of films in biology and other areas. Evaluation sheets might be used after showings so that teachers can indicate whether the film should be reordered.

Perpetuation of squads

We have discussed how students' skills can be put to use for a common purpose. How can squads already well-trained be perpetuated? Although it is time-consuming for teachers to start training such squads of students who can give special services, the rewards are high in satisfaction. Responsible students handle equipment carefully and efficiently. When young students are trained they can serve for several years. As they approach graduation, they should train younger students over at least a three-month period to take over these tasks. In this way, a teacher needs to supervise the students, but the work is made routine. This is a saving of time for the teacher, and often brings to students activities which they might not otherwise receive because of the extra time involved if teachers had to do it alone. Youngsters gain a skill and grow in self-confidence as they serve others in useful group work.

High grades in science should not be the decisive criterion set for selecting students for these squads—each student brings his talent. Teachers agree that good will, fair play and cooperation in sharing the load—many of the appreciations and attitudes we aim for in working with young people—often are more readily *caught* in this kind of group work than *taught* by teachers in classrooms.

Student squads in the classroom

Students readily accept a share in improving the atmosphere of the classroom. In small squads, students may turn an ordinary classroom into an attractive, distinctive place conducive to learning. These rooms can look like biology classrooms, places where interesting work is going on—different from the other periods in the day (Fig. 22-14).

Students may bring in cuttings or whole plants. These can be planted in window boxes and maintained by a few students. Another student may care for the fish tank. From nearby, students may bring in enough materials to set up plant and animal habitat studies—desert, woodland, or marsh (directions, p. 394; see Fig. 20-16).

Several students as a squad or committee may gather pictures and articles on topics discussed in class. In this way, bulletin boards in class and in hallways may be kept current and a source of stimulating discussion.

Students may exhibit their hobbies. Sometimes a student takes fine pictures,

Fig. 22-14 An attractive classroom-laboratory where students work on individual or small group projects. (Photo: Phil Palmer from Monkmeyer.)

or has a splendid collection of fossils, shells, or insects. These can be displayed in hall cases with appropriate legends.

A display of glassware with labels draws many students. This might grow into an exhibit of "tools" of biology and how they are used. Simple ideas are dramatic; frequent changes are imperative.

Some teachers have arranged successful weekly exhibits through the spring and fall on flowering plants and mosses and ferns. Budding branches from trees and shrubs near the school can be placed in containers of uniform size. On small library cards, indicate for each plant the name, where it may be found, and an interesting fact.

Some students have also planned contests in which a given number of plants, or birds, or insects in the neighborhood must be identified correctly. Prizes may be small books, or field guides.

We know, too, of some dramatic dis-plays of shells, flowers, leaves, and fruit shapes which focused attention on variations among living things. Legends asked questions about the facts of heredity and variations and their role in effecting changes among living things.

Tutoring squads. In this category of squads we are not considering committee work which is part of classwork, but the long-range routines which should be established early in the year. Aside from those student groups which maintain growing, living things as already described, there is a worthy service in tutoring other students. There will be a student with a block of some sort, or a blank area in past experience, or a student who takes a little longer to learn a point, or students who have been absent for long periods due to accidents or illness, and who thereby fall behind in their work. Many teachers arrange to have other students, often bright students who can communicate ideas, tutor the students who need remedial help or temporary "briefing" on new work.

Laboratory aides. What kind of class management is efficient and effective for distributing slides, medicine droppers, cultures for examination and microscopes? How can dissection pans, toweling, kits, magnifying lenses, and specimens for study be distributed without confusion?

This is how some teachers organize activities for as many as thirty-five students in a group. Six students are given the job of acting as laboratory aides in class. These students distribute slides and coverslips, place lens paper, culture bottles of material to be examined, and medicine droppers in six different "spots" in the room so that the class can divide itself and not crowd around one point of distribution. Microscopes are wheeled into class on a cart; when these are numbered it is possible to assign a specific microscope to each student or group of students. In this way the group of students shares responsibility for specific instruments.

Toward the end of the period, possibly 6 minutes before the end, students return microscopes to the cart, and the laboratory aides collect the materials which they distributed earlier in the period. Then the laboratory squad which brings back materials to the laboratory picks up the materials (see laboratory squads, p. 439).

Safety in the laboratory

Basically, safety precautions for the classroom and laboratory involve good planning and common sense in the use of chemicals and equipment. Certain safety steps should be standard operating procedure for all the members of a science department. Students who work on squads should also be trained in their responsibility in establishing good safety practices.

A pamphlet of concise, yet comprehensive, general instructions concerning the responsibilities of the head of a science department, science teachers, and students in maintaining safety is distributed by the New York City Board of Education. We reprint here some of the safety provisions relevant for teachers of biology from the pamphlet *For Greater Safety in Science Teaching.*[3]

Regulations for Science Chairmen:

File with the principal each term a signed statement that they [the science teachers] have read the rules and that the provisions of this

[3] New York City Board of Education, 110 Livingston Street, Brooklyn 1, N. Y.

report have been complied with. A receipt from each teacher should be kept on file.

Notify the principal in writing each term and immediately in the case of emergencies of any hazards in either main building or annexes, such as:

   (a) Defective gas fixtures, electrical outlets, and connections.
   (b) Seats so defective that they may cause injury.
   (c) Inadequate storage cabinets.
   (d) Lack of fire blankets, extinguishers, fire pails, and sand.

See that a first aid cabinet is ordered and placed in each science laboratory and preparation room and elsewhere as needed, and that ample reserve stocks of tannic acid salve for possible burns, antidotes for poisons and first aid material are provided. At least two copies of the Red Cross booklet on First Aid should be kept with each first aid cabinet.

Inspect first aid cabinets and fire extinguishers at least once a term.

Make certain that combustible and dangerous materials such as poisons are kept securely locked in a metal cabinet. Acids should be stored in an albarene closet, never in ordinary closets or wooden cabinets. Do not store chemicals which react with each other in close proximity such as glycerin and nitric acid, potassium chlorate and organic compounds, and cyanides and acids, etc. No pupils should have access to such lockers and storerooms or closets in stockrooms.

See that the cabinet for the storing of sodium, potassium, calcium, and calcium carbide has printed on it boldly in white, the warning "In case of fire, do not use water."

See that pupils do not handle materials in cabinets reserved for dangerous substances.

Inspect chemical cabinets and keep on hand the dates of such inspection.

Keep tools and sharp-edged instruments under supervision and exercise the greatest care when they are used by pupils.

In making electrical connection for the use of stereopticons, film projectors and the like, use heavy rubber covered wall plugs (to avoid cracking if dropped) and good quality cable (double cords within heavy insulation) which will not kink or easily break. This will avoid short circuits and the danger of both electric shock and fire.

Be responsible for acquainting all squad members with the safety rules and regulations at the beginning of their service.

Secure parent's consent in each case for the work of squad members.

See to it that a metal or earthenware waste jar is provided in every classroom where science experiments are performed. Such waste jar and *not* the wastepaper basket should be used for broken glassware, chemical residues, etc.

Discard unlabeled, contaminated, and undesirable reagents.

See that any demonstrations, experiments, or projects dealing with atomic energy or radioactivity are performed in accordance with safety practices in that field.

The same pamphlet lists important general directions for all science teachers:

I. *Pupils*
1. Pupils are to be under the direct supervision of a teacher at all times and in all places, as required by the By-Laws of the Board of Education.
2. Pupils are not to carry laboratory equipment or apparatus through the halls during the intervals when classes are passing.
3. Pupils are not to transport dangerous chemicals at any time.
4. Pupils are not to handle materials on the demonstration table except under the direction of the teacher.
5. Pupils are not to taste chemicals or

other materials.
6. Before permitting pupils to work with sharp tools, the teacher must be assured that pupils are fully competent to use the tools.
7. At the beginning of each term, pupils should be instructed in general safety precautions.
8. Pupils should be specifically instructed regarding the dangers and the precautions required, at the beginning of each laboratory period where there is a special hazard.
9. Pupils should be cautioned about hazardous activities involving the use of chemicals outside the school—e.g. mixing chemicals to "See what happens," setting fire to gasoline cans, breaking open fluorescent tubes.

II. *Teachers*
1. Teachers must
   (a) Report to the principal any injury or accident immediately.
   (b) Arrange for the completion and filing of the proper forms to be signed by
      (a) the injured party
      (b) witnesses
      (c) teacher concerned, or laboratory assistant
2. Teachers must be fully acquainted with first aid treatments.
3. Teachers should notify the chairman of the department of the existence or development of any hazard that comes to their attention.
4. Teachers are to perform classroom experiments only if they themselves have previously tried them out or have been properly instructed by the chairman or an experienced teacher.
5. When using volatile liquids which are inflammable, such as alcohol, in a demonstration experiment, care must be taken that any flame in the room is at an absolutely safe distance from the volatile liquid.
6. Demonstrations involving explosive mixtures must be so arranged as to shield both pupils and teachers from the results of the explosion. Even when there is no likelihood of an explosion, pupils should be asked to evacuate seats directly in front of the demonstration table whenever there is any possibility of injury to them by the spattering of a chemical, an

overturned burner, inhalation of fumes, etc.

7. Large storage bottles of dangerous chemicals such as acids and alkalies, if on shelves, are to be no more than two feet above the floor. If possible, they should be kept on the floor.

8. Never add water to concentrated sulphuric acid. If it is necessary to prepare diluted acid, the concentrated acid should always be added in small quantities to the water, stirring all the while.

9. Handle all corrosive substances with the greatest care. Special precautions should be taken with concentrated sulphuric acid, nitric acid, glacial acetic acid, and concentrated solutions of caustic alkalies and other corrosive chemicals as phenol, etc.

10. White phosphorus must be kept under water in a double container, one part of which is metal. This form of phosphorus must be cut only under water. If cut in the open air, the friction may be sufficient to ignite the material with very serious results. Use red phosphorus in place of white phosphorus whenever possible.

11. Residues of phosphorus should be completely burned in the hood before depositing in the waste jar.

12. Combustible materials of all types are to be kept in a metal cabinet or albarene closet provided with proper means for closing and locking.

13. Metallic sodium, potassium, and calcium and calcium carbide should not be stored above water solutions or vessels containing water. Metallic sodium and potassium, after the original container has been opened, must thereafter be kept under kerosene. These substances are corrosive and must not come in contact with the skin.

14. Do not demonstrate devices or equipment brought in by pupils before pretesting.

15. When a motion picture machine or other projection apparatus is sent into non-science classrooms a carbon tetrachloride extinguisher should accompany the apparatus.

For the biology teacher in particular, there are some special provisions:

1. *Handling Laboratory Animals*
   Rats, mice, guinea pigs and other laboratory animals should be handled gently by students so as not to unduly excite the animal into biting. Gloves made of thick rubber should be available and used whenever necessary, that is, when there is danger of biting (by excited animals, injured animals, new additions to cage, pregnant or feeding female, etc.). Students and visitors to the laboratory should be cautioned not to insert finger in wire mesh of cage. Appropriate signs should be displayed about cage such as "Keep Hands Off."
   Only specially trained members of the laboratory squad should be permitted to handle laboratory animals. Poisonous snakes should not be kept in the laboratory.

2. *Use of Formaldehyde*
   Specimens preserved in formaldehyde should be thoroughly washed in running water for 24 hours before being handled by students. In taking specimens out of formaldehyde, students should either wear rubber gloves or else use tongs or forceps—depending on the size of the specimen. Adequate ventilation should be provided in any room where formaldehyde is used. ["Fume inhibitors" are available.]

3. *Use of Carbon Tetrachloride*
   Adequate ventilation should be provided in any room where carbon tetrachloride is used.

4. *Precautions for Field Trips*
   (a) Pupils should be instructed about identification of poison ivy, poison sumac, copperhead snakes, etc.
   (b) First aid kits should be taken along on all field trips.
   (c) Students should be instructed as to the proper clothing to take along on a field trip to avoid illnesses due to undue exposure, etc.

5. *Bread Mold and Pollen from Flowers*
   In handling flowers and bread mold, care should be taken that pollen or spores are not excessively distributed through the classroom. Some students may be allergic to pollen or spores.

Common accidents

The common accidents in class or laboratory fall into three categories:
1. cuts from broken glassware
2. burns from hot glass
3. chemical burns

Each of these classes of accidents can be reduced in number by increasing caution on the part of students. The first two categories of accidents are treated by using the standard first-aid methods suggested in the latest *American Red Cross First Aid Textbook*.

In the case of chemical burns, the materials used for first-aid treatments should also be in the first-aid cabinet.

Acid burns. These should be washed immediately with large quantities of water to remove the acid. Then neutralize any remaining acid by covering the burn with a saturated solution of sodium bicarbonate.

Alkaline burns. These should also be flushed immediately with large quantities of water. Then remove any alkali with a saturated solution of boric acid.

First-aid kits. First-aid kits and cabinets should contain the materials listed by the Red Cross textbook.

It is also convenient to prepare several tongue depressors covered with sterile gauze in a plastic bag or envelope. This may be useful in an emergency when there is an epileptic in class. It can be inserted between the teeth to prevent him from biting his tongue.

Ampules of ammonia are also useful in reviving a child who has fainted.

Fireproofing fabrics. There may be occasion to fireproof materials in class or laboratory. Bennett's compendium[4] suggests these two methods. Small samples may be tested after they have soaked in the solution; then you may want to use it on a larger scale.

SOLUTION FOR FIREPROOFING HEAVY CANVAS MATERIALS. Impregnate the fabric with the following solution, squeeze out the excess, and allow the fabric to dry. (You may reduce the quantities given here to suit your needs.)

$(NH_4)_3PO_4$	1 lb
NH_4Cl	2 lb
water	½ gal

SOLUTION FOR FIREPROOFING LIGHT-WEIGHT FABRICS. Impregnate the fabrics with the following solution, squeeze out the excess, and hang up to dry. Frequent washing of the fabric will dissolve out the fireproofing salts so that they will need to be treated again with the same solution.

borax	10 oz
boric acid	8 oz
water	1 gal

PEOPLE, PLACES, AND THINGS

Many communities are concerned with science facilities, either plans for building a new wing or a school, or remodeling ordinary classrooms into science rooms. Where can you get help? Visit other schools and colleges, write to schools which have specialized facilities; consult professional education journals to find manufacturers of equipment and send for their catalogs. Many articles may be found in *Educational Index* which present research findings by consultants such as "The Coordinated Classroom" by D. Harmon, distributed by American Seating Company (Grand Rapids 2, Michigan), 1949.

BOOKS AND PAMPHLETS

For suggestions for planning and developing facilities for effective instruction, you will want to read carefully these references:

Richardson, J., ed., *School Facilities for Science Instruction*, 1954, National Science Teachers Association, 1201 Sixteenth St. N. W., Washington 6, D. C.

Johnson, P., *Science Facilities for Secondary Schools*, No. 17; Supt. Documents, U.S. Govt. Printing Office, Washington 25, D. C., 1952.

Many pamphlets are available on safety in the laboratory and first aid in general. You may want to send for several of these:

Manual of Laboratory Safety (also a chart on safety), Fisher Scientific, 633 Greenwich St., New York 14; 8505 Devonshire Rd., Montreal 9; 1548 N. Lamon Ave., Chicago 51.

First Aid Manual, American Medical Association, 535 N. Dearborn St., Chicago 10, 1952, $0.10.

A First Aid Guide, Accident Prevention Dept., Associated Casualty and Surety Co., 60 John St., New York 38, 1954.

[4] H. Bennett, ed., *Chemical Formulary*, Chemical Publishing Co., New York, 1951.

Section Four **APPENDIX:**

TEACHERS' REFERENCES

Bibliography:

books for a science library

Some of these books are recommended for the teacher's library; many others are suggested as a starting point in building a school library of books in science for the use of both students and teachers. In general, these are technical references, not popularized accounts of science. There are so many books, fine ones, which have recently appeared as popularized accounts that our listing would be without end if we attempted to categorize them here.

We have seen many of these books in school libraries—both high school and college—and in this light they are offered as suggestions in building a professional library of books in science.

Biology (general)

Blair, H., *Biological Effects of External Radiation,* McGraw-Hill, New York, 1954.

Bonner, J. T., *Cells and Societies,* Princeton U., Princeton, N. J., 1955.

Cameron, T. W., *Parasites and Parasitism,* Methuen (Wiley), New York, 1956.

Cloudsley-Thompson, J. L., ed., *Biology of the Deserts,* Institute of Biology, London, 1954.

Comar, C. L., *Radioisotopes in Biology and Agriculture,* McGraw-Hill, New York, 1955.

Du Shane, G., and D. Regnery, *Experiments in General Biology,* Freeman, San Francisco, 1950.

Feldman, W. M., *Biomathematics: Principles of Mathematics for Students of Biological Science,* Hafner, London, 1954.

Gardiner, M., *Principles of General Biology,* Macmillan, New York, 1952.

Hall, T., *A Sourcebook in Animal Biology,* McGraw-Hill, New York, 1951.

——— and F. Moog, *Life Science,* Wiley, New York, 1955.

Henderson, I., and W. Henderson (6th ed. by J. Kenneth), *A Dictionary of Scientific Terms,* Van Nostrand, New York, 1957.

Hollaender, A., ed., *Radiation Biology,* McGraw-Hill, New York, 3 vols., 1954–56.

Jaeger, E. C., *A Sourcebook of Biological Names and Terms,* 3d ed., Thomas, Springfield, Ill., 1955.

Kluyver, A. J., and C. B. Van Niel, *The Microbe's Contribution to Biology,* Harvard U., Cambridge, Mass., 1956.

Lea, D. E., *Actions of Radiations on Living Cells,* 2d ed., Cambridge U., New York, 1955.

Libby, W., *Radiocarbon Dating,* 2d ed., U. of Chicago, Chicago, 1955.

Marsland, D., *Principles of Modern Biology,* rev. ed., Holt, New York, 1957.

Mavor, J., *General Biology,* 4th ed., Macmillan, New York, 1952.

Milne, L., and M. Milne, *The Biotic World and Man,* Prentice-Hall, Englewood Cliffs, N. J., 1953.

Muller, H., C. Little, and L. Snyder, *Genetics, Medicine and Man,* Cornell U., Ithaca, N. Y., 1947.

Rutter, F., *Fundamentals of Limnology,* U. of Toronto, Toronto, 1953.

Schenberg, S., and J. Harley, *Laboratory Experiments with Radioisotopes for High School Science Teachers,* Supt. Documents, U.S. Govt. Printing Office, Washington, D. C., rev. ed., 1957.

Simpson, G. G., C. Pittendrigh, and L. Tiffany, *Life: An Introduction to Biology,* Harcourt, Brace, New York, 1957.

Spector, W. S., ed., *Handbook of Biological Data,* Saunders, Philadelphia, 1956.

Villee, C., *Biology,* 3d ed., Saunders, Philadelphia, 1957.

Weisz, P., *Biology,* McGraw-Hill, New York, 1954.

Botany

Alexopoulos, C., *Introductory Mycology,* Wiley, New York, 1952.

Erdtman, G., *Pollen Morphology and Plant Taxonomy: Angiosperms,* Ronald, New York, 1957.

Fritsch, F. E., and E. Salisbury, *Plant Form and Function,* Bell and Sons, London, 1953.

Fuller, H., and O. Tippo, *College Botany,* rev. ed., Holt, New York, 1954.

Garrett, S. D., *Biology of Root-infecting Fungi*, Cambridge U., New York, 1956.

Gibbs, R., *Botany: An Evolutionary Approach*, Blakiston (McGraw-Hill), New York, 1950.

Gray, A., *Manual of Botany*, ed. M. L. Fernald, 8th ed., American Book, New York, 1950.

Haupt, A. W., *An Introduction to Botany*, 3d ed., McGraw-Hill, New York, 1956.

Hill, J., L. Overholts, and H. Popp, *Botany*, McGraw-Hill, New York, 1950.

Hylander, C., *The World of Plant Life*, Macmillan, New York, 1956.

Northen, H., *Introductory Plant Science*, Ronald, New York, 1953.

Robbins, W., and T. Weier, *Botany*, Wiley, New York, 1950.

Sinnott, E., and K. Wilson, *Botany: Principles and Problems*, McGraw-Hill, New York, 1955.

Smith, G. M., et al., *A Textbook of General Botany*, 5th ed., Macmillan, New York, 1953.

Stanford, E. E., *Man and the Living World*, 2d ed., Macmillan, New York, 1951.

Wilson, C., and W. Loomis, *Botany*, Dryden, New York, 1957.

Zoology

Buchsbaum, R., *Animals Without Backbones*, U. of Chicago, Chicago, 1948.

Guthrie, M., and J. Anderson, *General Zoology*, Wiley, New York, 1957.

Hegner, R., *Parade of the Animal Kingdom*, Macmillan, New York, 1955.

——— and K. Stiles, *College Zoology*, 6th ed., Macmillan, New York, 1951.

Hunter, G., and F. Hunter, *College Zoology*, Saunders, Philadelphia, 1949.

Hyman, L., *Comparative Vertebrate Anatomy*, 2d ed., U. of Chicago, Chicago, 1942.

Romer, A., *The Vertebrate Body*, 2d ed., Saunders, Philadelphia, 1955.

Rugh, R., *The Frog—Its Reproduction and Development*, Blakiston (McGraw-Hill), New York, 1951.

Storer, T., and R. Usinger, *Elements of Zoology*, McGraw-Hill, New York, 1955.

Cells and microscope technique

Bensley, R. R., and S. H. Bensley, *Handbook of Histological and Cytological Technique*, U. of Chicago, Chicago, 1938.

Caspersson, T., *Cell Growth and Cell Function*, Norton, New York, 1950.

Conn, H. J., *Biological Stains*, 5th ed., Biotech. Publications, Geneva, N. Y., 1946.

Cowdry, E., *Laboratory Technique in Biology and Medicine*, 3d ed., Williams and Wilkins, Baltimore, 1952.

De Robertis, E., W. Nowinski, and F. Saez, *General Cytology*, 2d ed., Saunders, Philadelphia, 1954.

Gage, S. H., *The Microscope*, 17th ed., Comstock, Ithaca, N. Y., 1941.

Gray, P., *The Microtomist's Formulary and Guide*, Blakiston (McGraw-Hill), New York, 1954.

Guyer, M., *Animal Micrology*, 5th ed., U. of Chicago, Chicago, 1953.

Hall, R. P., *Protozoology*, Prentice-Hall, Englewood Cliffs, N. J., 1953

Heilbrunn, L. V., *The Dynamics of Living Protoplasm*, Academic, New York, 1956.

Johansen, D., *Plant Microtechnique*, McGraw-Hill, New York, 1940.

Jones, R. McClung, ed., *McClung's Handbook of Microscopical Technique*, 3d ed., Hoeber (Harper), New York, 1950.

Kudo, R., *Protozoology*, 4th ed., Thomas, Springfield, Ill., 1954.

Lee, A. B., *Microtomist's Vade-Mecum*, 11th ed., J. Gatenby and H. Beams, eds., Blakiston (McGraw-Hill), New York, 1950.

Maximow, A., and W. Bloom, *A Textbook of Histology*, 7th ed., Saunders, Philadelphia, 1957.

Sass, J., *Botanical Microtechnique*, 2d ed., Iowa State College, Ames, 1956.

White, P., *The Cultivation of Plant and Animal Cells*, Ronald, New York, 1954.

Wichterman, R., *The Biology of Paramecium*, Blakiston (McGraw-Hill), New York, 1952.

Physiology

Aronoff, S., *Techniques of Radiobiochemistry*, Iowa State College, Ames, 1956.

Asimov, I., *The Chemicals of Life*, Abelard-Schuman, New York, 1954.

Audus, L., *Plant Growth Substances*, Interscience, New York, 1953.

Avery, G., and E. Johnson, *Hormones and Horticulture*, McGraw-Hill, New York, 1947.

Best, C., and N. Taylor, *The Living Body: Text in Human Physiology*, 3d ed., Holt, New York, 1952.

Bonner, J. F., *Plant Biochemistry*, Academic, New York, 1950.

———, and A. W. Galston, *Principles of Plant Physiology*, Freeman, San Francisco, 1952.

Borek, E., *Man, the Chemical Machine*, Columbia U., New York, 1952.

Carlson, A., and V. Johnson, *The Machinery of the Body*, 4th ed., U. of Chicago, Chicago, 1953.

Curtis, O., and D. Clark, *An Introduction to Plant Physiology*, McGraw-Hill, New York, 1950.

Davson, H., *Textbook of General Physiology*, Blakiston (McGraw-Hill), New York, 1951.

Dunn, S., *Elementary Plant Physiology*, Addison-Wesley, Reading, Mass., 1949.

Dutcher, R., C. Jensen, and P. Althouse, *Intro-*

duction to *Agricultural Biochemistry,* Wiley, New York, 1951.

Fruton, J., and S. Simmonds, *General Biochemistry,* Wiley, New York, 1953.

Garrett, H., *Great Experiments in Psychology,* Appleton-Century-Crofts, New York, 1951.

Gerard, R., *The Body Functions,* Wiley, New York, 1941.

———, ed., *Food for Life,* U. of Chicago, Chicago, 1952.

Gortner, R., and W. Gortner, *Outlines of Biochemistry,* 3d ed., Wiley, New York, 1949.

Graff, S., ed., *Essays in Biochemistry,* Wiley, New York, 1956.

Gray, J., *How Animals Move,* Cambridge U., New York, 1953.

Harrow, B., *Casimir Funk: Pioneer in Vitamins and Hormones,* Dodd, Mead, New York, 1955.

———, and A. Mazur, *Textbook of Biochemistry,* 6th ed., Saunders, Philadelphia, 1954.

Hawk, P., B. Oser, and W. Summerson, *Practical Physiological Chemistry,* 13th ed., Blakiston (McGraw-Hill), New York, 1954.

Hutner, S., and A. Lwoff, eds., *Biochemistry and Physiology of the Protozoa,* 2 vols., Academic, New York; vol. 1, 1951; vol. 2, 1955.

Kabat, E., *Blood Group Substances: Their Chemistry and Immunochemistry,* Academic, New York, 1956.

Machlis, L., and J. Torrey, *Plants in Action: A Laboratory Manual of Plant Physiology,* Freeman, San Francisco, 1956.

Meyer, B., and D. Anderson, *Plant Physiology,* 2d ed., Van Nostrand, Princeton, N. J., 1952.

Miller, E., *Within the Living Plant,* Blakiston (McGraw-Hill), New York, 1953.

Mitchell, P. H., *A Textbook of General Physiology,* 5th ed., McGraw-Hill, New York, 1956.

Mitchell, J. W., and P. Marth, *Growth Regulators for Garden, Field, and Orchard,* U. of Chicago, Chicago, 1947.

Mrak, E., and G. Stewart, eds., *Advances in Food Research,* vol. 6, Academic, New York, 1955.

Munn, N., *The Evolution and Growth of Human Behavior,* Houghton Mifflin, Boston, 1955.

Prosser, C., F. Brown, et al., *Comparative Animal Physiology,* Saunders, Philadelphia, 1950.

Ramsey, J., *Physiological Approach to the Lower Animals,* Cambridge U., New York, 1952.

Roeder, K. D., ed., *Insect Physiology,* Wiley, New York, 1953.

Schwimmer, M., and D. Schwimmer, *The Role of Algae and Plankton in Medicine,* Grune and Stratton, New York, 1955.

Selye, H., *The Stress of Life,* McGraw-Hill, New York, 1956.

Sproul, E., *The Science Book of the Human Body,* Watts, New York, 1955 (also Pocket Books).

Stiles, W., *An Introduction to the Principles of Plant Physiology,* 2d ed., Methuen (Wiley), New York, 1950.

Thimann, K., *The Action of Hormones in Plants and*

Invertebrates, Academic, New York, 1952.

———, *The Life of Bacteria: Their Growth, Metabolism, and Relationships,* Macmillan, New York, 1955.

Todd, J., A. Sanford, and B. Wells, *Clinical Diagnosis by Laboratory Methods,* 12th ed., Saunders, Philadelphia, 1953.

Turner, C. D., *General Endocrinology,* 2d ed., Saunders, Philadelphia, 1955.

Went, F., *The Experimental Control of Plant Growth,* Ronald, New York, 1957.

West, E., and W. Todd, *Textbook of Biochemistry,* 2d ed., Macmillan, New York, 1955.

White, A., et al., *Principles of Biochemistry,* McGraw-Hill, New York, 1954.

Health, nutrition, and disease prevention

Baxter, D. V., *Pathology in Forest Practice,* 2d ed., Wiley, New York, 1952.

Birkeland, J., *Microbiology and Man,* 2d ed., Appleton-Century-Crofts, New York, 1949.

Bodansky, M., and O. Bodansky, *Biochemistry of Disease,* 2d ed., Macmillan, New York 1952.

Bowes, A., and C. Church, *Food Values of Portions Commonly Used,* 8th ed., Anna dePlanter Bowes, N. E. corner 7th and Delancey Sts., Philadelphia 6, 1956.

Bracken, A., *The Chemistry of Microorganisms,* Pitman, New York, 1955.

Buchanan, R., and E. Buchanan, *Bacteriology,* 5th ed., Macmillan, New York, 1951.

Burnet, M., *Natural History of Infectious Disease,* Cambridge U., New York, 1953.

Christensen, C. M., *The Molds and Man: An Introduction to the Fungi,* U. of Minnesota, Minneapolis, 1951.

Clifton, C., *Introduction to the Bacteria,* McGraw-Hill, New York, 1950.

Cooley, D., *The Science Book of Wonder Drugs,* Watts, New York, 1954 (also Pocket Books).

Cushing, J., and D. Campbell, *Principles of Immunology,* McGraw-Hill, New York, 1957.

De Kruif, P., *Microbe Hunters,* Harcourt, Brace, New York, 1932 (also Pocket Books).

Diehl, H., *Elements of Healthful Living,* McGraw-Hill, New York, 1955.

Difco Manual of Dehydrated Culture Media and Reagents, 9th ed., Difco Laboratories, Detroit, 1953.

Dubos, R., *Louis Pasteur: Free Lance of Science,* Little, Brown, Boston, 1950.

———, and J. Dubos, *The White Plague: Tuberculosis, Man and Society,* Little, Brown, Boston, 1952.

Frobisher, M., *Fundamentals of Microbiology,* 6th ed., Saunders, Philadelphia, 1957.

Gilbert, F., *Mineral Nutrition of Plants and Animals,* U. of Oklahoma, Norman, 1953.

Kelly, F. C., and K. E. Hite, *Microbiology,* 2d ed., Appleton-Century-Crofts, New York, 1955.

Oginsky, E., and W. Umbreit, *An Introduction to Bacterial Physiology,* Freeman, San Francisco, 1954.

Peltier, G., C. Georgi, and L. Lindgren, *Laboratory Manual for General Bacteriology,* 4th ed., Wiley, New York, 1952.

Salle, A., *Fundamental Principles of Bacteriology,* 4th ed., McGraw-Hill, New York, 1954.

Sarles, W. B., et al., *Microbiology: General and Applied,* 2d ed., Harper, New York, 1956.

Silverman, M., *Magic in a Bottle,* 2d ed., Macmillan, New York, 1951.

Spector, W. S., ed., *Toxicology: Antibiotics,* Saunders, 1957.

U.S. Dept. Agriculture, *Animal Diseases,* Yearbook of Agriculture, U.S. Govt. Printing Office, Washington, D. C., 1956.

———, *Plant Diseases,* Yearbook of Agriculture, U.S. Govt. Printing Office, Washington, D. C., 1953.

Walker, J., *Diseases of Vegetable Crops,* McGraw-Hill, New York, 1952.

Werkman, C., and P. W. Wilson, eds., *Bacterial Physiology,* Academic, New York, 1951.

Zinsser, H., *Rats, Lice and History,* Little, Brown, Boston, 1935.

Heredity and embryology

Adamstone, F., and W. Shumway, *A Laboratory Manual of Vertebrate Embryology,* 3d ed., Wiley, New York, 1954.

Arey, L., *Developmental Anatomy,* 6th ed., Saunders, Philadelphia, 1954.

Asdell, S. A., *Patterns of Mammalian Reproduction,* Comstock, Ithaca, N. Y., 1946.

Auerbach, C., *Genetics in the Atomic Age,* Essential Bks., Fairlawn, N. J., 1956.

Barth, L., *Embryology,* rev. ed., Dryden, New York, 1953.

Beale, G. H., *Genetics of Paramecium Aurelia,* Cambridge U., New York, 1954.

Boyd, W., *Genetics and the Races of Man,* Little, Brown, Boston, 1950.

Brachet, J., *Chemical Embryology,* 2d ed., Interscience, New York, 1950.

Burns, M., *The Genetics of the Dog,* Commonwealth Agricultural Bureau, Slough Bucks, Edinburgh, 1952 (also All-Pets Books, Inc., Fond du Lac, Wisc., n.d.).

Catcheside, D., *The Genetics of Microorganisms,* Pitman, New York, 1951.

Child, C. M., *Patterns and Problems of Development,* U. of Chicago, Chicago, 1941.

Cole, F., *Early Theories of Sexual Generation,* (Clarendon) Oxford U., New York, 1930.

Colin, E., *Elements of Genetics,* 2d ed., Blakiston (McGraw-Hill), New York, 1946.

Crane, M., and W. Lawrence, *The Genetics of Garden Plants,* 4th ed., St. Martin's (Macmillan), New York, 1952.

Darlington, C. D., and E. Ammal, *Chromosome Atlas of Cultivated Plants,* Macmillan, New York, 1945.

———, and K. Mather, *The Elements of Genetics,* 2d ed., Macmillan, New York, 1952.

Demerec, M., ed., *Biology of Drosophila,* Wiley, New York, 1950.

Dunn, L., ed., *Genetics in the Twentieth Century,* Macmillan, New York, 1951.

———, and T. Dobzhansky, *Heredity, Race and Society,* Mentor (New American Library), New York, 1946.

Gates, R. R., *Human Ancestry,* Harvard U., Cambridge, Mass., 1948.

Goldschmidt, R., *Theoretical Genetics,* U. of California, Berkeley, 1955.

———, *Understanding Heredity,* Wiley, New York, 1952.

Goldstein, P., *Genetics Is Easy,* Lantern, New York, 1955.

Hamburger, V., *A Manual of Experimental Embryology,* U. of Chicago, Chicago, 1942.

Hayes, H., F. Immer, and D. Smith, *Methods of Plant Breeding,* 2d ed., McGraw-Hill, New York, 1955.

Hutt, F. B., *Genetics of the Fowl,* McGraw-Hill, New York, 1949.

Li, Ching Chun, *Population Genetics,* U. of Chicago, Chicago, 1955.

Neel, J., and W. Schull, *Human Heredity,* U. of Chicago, Chicago, 1954.

Nelson, O. E., *Comparative Embryology of the Vertebrates,* Blakiston (McGraw-Hill), New York, 1953.

Newman, H., F. Freeman, and K. Holzinger, *Twins: A Study of Heredity and Environment,* U. of Chicago, Chicago, 1937.

Patten, B., *The Early Embryo of the Chick,* 4th ed., Blakiston (McGraw-Hill), New York, 1951.

———, *Human Embryology,* 2d ed., Blakiston (McGraw-Hill), New York, 1953.

Rugh, R., *Experimental Embryology: A Manual of Techniques and Procedures,* Burgess, Minneapolis, 1948.

———, *A Laboratory Manual of Vertebrate Embryology,* Burgess, Minneapolis, 1956.

Shumway, W., and F. Adamstone, *Introduction to Vertebrate Embryology,* 5th ed., Wiley, New York, 1954.

Sinnott, E., L. Dunn, and T. Dobzhansky, *Principles of Genetics,* 4th ed., McGraw-Hill, New York, 1950.

Snyder, L., and P. David, *The Principles of Heredity,* 5th ed., Heath, Boston, 1957.

Spemann, H., *Embryonic Development and Induction,* Yale U., New Haven, Conn., 1938.

Srb, A., and R. Owen, *General Genetics,* Freeman, San Francisco, 1952.

Stern, C., *Principles of Human Genetics,* Freeman, San Francisco, 1949.

Waddington, C., *Principles of Embryology,* Macmillan, New York, 1956.

Wagner, R. P., and H. K. Mitchell, *Genetics and Metabolism,* Wiley, New York, 1955.

Wardlaw, C. W., *Embryogenesis in Plants,* Methuen (Wiley), New York, 1955.

Winchester, A., *Genetics,* Houghton Mifflin, Boston, 1951.

Winge, O., *Inheritance in Dogs,* Comstock, Ithaca, N. Y., 1950.

Witschi, E., *Development of Vertebrates,* Saunders, Philadelphia, 1956.

Evolution

Andrews, H., *Ancient Plants,* Comstock, Ithaca, N. Y., 1947.

Arnold, C., *An Introduction to Paleobotany,* McGraw-Hill, New York, 1947.

Beadnell, C., *A Picture Book of Evolution,* 4th ed., Watts, New York, 1948.

Bernal, J. D., *The Physical Basis of Life,* Routledge, London, 1951.

Berrill, N. J., *The Origin of the Vertebrates,* (Clarendon) Oxford U., New York, 1955.

Beutner, R., *Life's Beginning on the Earth,* Williams and Wilkins, Baltimore, 1938.

Blum, H., *Time's Arrow and Evolution,* 2d ed., Princeton U., Princeton, N. J., 1955.

Burton, M., *Living Fossils,* Vanguard, New York, 1954.

Ceram, C., *Gods, Graves and Scholars: The Story of Archeology,* Knopf, New York, 1951.

Colbert, E., *Evolution of the Vertebrates,* Wiley, New York, 1955.

Dodson, E., *A Textbook of Evolution,* Saunders, Philadelphia, 1952.

Florkin, M., *Biochemical Evolution,* Academic, New York, 1949.

Gregory, W. K., *Evolution Emerging: A survey of changing patterns from primeval life to man,* vols. 1 and 2, Macmillan, New York, 1951.

Huxley, J., *Evolution in Action,* Harper, New York, 1953.

Jepsen, G., E. Mayr, and G. Simpson, *Genetics, Paleontology and Evolution,* Princeton U., Princeton, N. J., 1949.

Kuhn, H., *On the Track of Prehistoric Man,* Random House, New York, 1955.

Lack, D., *The Natural Regulation of Animal Numbers* (Clarendon), Oxford U., New York, 1954.

Lull, R. S., *Organic Evolution,* Macmillan, New York, 1947.

MacGowan, K., *Early Man in the New World,* Macmillan, New York, 1950.

Moody, P., *Introduction to Evolution,* Harper, New York, 1953.

Moore, R., *Man, Time and Fossils,* Knopf, New York, 1953.

Oparin, A., *The Origin of Life,* Macmillan, New York, 1938 (also Dover).

Raymond, P., *Prehistoric Life,* Harvard U., Cambridge, Mass., 1950.

Richards, H., *Record of the Rocks,* Ronald, New York, 1953.

Romer, A., *Man and the Vertebrates,* U. of Chicago, Chicago, 1941.

Scheele, W., *Prehistoric Animals,* World Pub., Cleveland, 1954.

Simpson, G. G., *Life of the Past,* Yale U., New Haven, Conn., 1953.

———, *The Meaning of Evolution,* Yale U., New Haven, Conn., 1949; also Mentor (New American Library), New York, 1952.

———, *The Major Features of Evolution,* Columbia U., New York, 1953.

Smart, W., *The Origin of the Earth,* Cambridge U., New York, 1953.

Conservation and ecology

Allen, S., *Conserving Natural Resources,* McGraw-Hill, New York, 1955.

Andrewartha, H., and L. Birch, *The Distribution and Abundance of Animals,* U. of Chicago, Chicago, 1954.

Bear, F. E., ed., *Chemistry of the Soil,* Reinhold, New York, 1955.

Bennett, H. H., *Elements of Soil Conservation,* 2d ed., McGraw-Hill, New York, 1955.

Black, J. D., *Biological Conservation,* McGraw-Hill, New York, 1954.

Carhart, A., *Water—or Your Life,* Lippincott, Philadelphia, 1951.

Carson, R., *The Sea Around Us,* Oxford U., New York, 1951 (also Mentor).

Dale, T., and V. G. Carter, *Topsoil and Civilization,* U. of Oklahoma, Norman, 1955.

Forbes, R., and A. Meyer, *Forestry Handbook,* Ronald, New York, 1955.

Gabrielson, I., *Wildlife Conservation,* Macmillan, New York, 1952.

Gustafson, A., et al., *Conservation in the United States,* 2d ed., Comstock, Ithaca, N. Y., 1944.

Hambidge, G., ed., *Hunger Signs in Crops,* Amer. Soc. Agronomy and Natl. Fertilizer Assoc., Washington, D. C., 1941.

Kellogg, C., *The Soils That Support Us,* Macmillan, New York, 1951.

King, T., *Water: Miracle of Nature,* Macmillan, New York, 1953.

Metcalf, C., W. Flint, and R. L. Metcalf, *Destructive and Useful Insects,* 3d ed., McGraw-Hill, New York, 1951.

Oosting, H., *The Study of Plant Communities,* 2d ed., Freeman, San Francisco, 1956.

Roth, B., *Soil and Water Conservation,* Boy Scouts of America, New Brunswick, N. J., 1953.

Smith, G. H., *Conservation of Natural Resources,* Wiley, New York, 1950.

U.S. Dept. Agriculture, Yearbook 1957, *Soil,* U.S. Govt. Printing Office, Washington D. C.

Watts, M. T., *Reading the Landscape: An Adventure in Ecology,* Macmillan, New York, 1957.

Weaver, R., project leader, *Handbook for Teaching of Conservation and Resource-Use,* Natl. Assoc. Biology Teachers, Ann Arbor, Mich., 1955.

Woodbury, A., *Principles of General Ecology,* Blakiston (McGraw-Hill), New York, 1954.

Science in general

Ackerknecht, E., *A Short History of Medicine,* Ronald, New York, 1955.

Barnett, L., ed., *The World We Live In,* Simon and Schuster, New York, 1955.

Beck, W., *Modern Science and the Nature of Life,* Harcourt, Brace, New York, 1957.

Bronowski, J., *The Common Sense of Science,* Harvard U., Cambridge, Mass., 1953.

Butterfield, H., *The Origins of Modern Science, 1300–1800,* Macmillan, New York, 1951.

Cohen, I. B., and F. Watson, eds., *General Education in Science,* Harvard U., Cambridge, Mass., 1952.

Conant, J. B., ed., *Case Studies in the History of Science,* 4 vols., Harvard U., Cambridge, Mass., 1950–1953.

———, *On Understanding Science,* Yale U., New Haven, Conn., 1947; Mentor, New York, 1952.

Cooper, H., ed., *Scientific Instruments,* Chemical Pub., New York, vol. 1, 1946; vol. 2, 1949.

Dawes, B., *A Hundred Years of Biology,* Macmillan, New York, n.d.

Eddington, A., *The Nature of the Physical World,* Cambridge U., New York, 1932.

Farber, E., *The Evolution of Chemistry,* Ronald, New York, 1952.

Fox, R., *Milestones of Medicine,* Random House, New York, 1950.

Frank, P., *Modern Science and Its Philosophy,* Harvard U., Cambridge, Mass., 1949; (also Braziller, New York, 1955).

Gabriel, M., and S. Fogel, eds., *Great Experiments in Biology,* Prentice-Hall, Englewood Cliffs, N. J., 1955.

Glasstone, S., *Sourcebook on Atomic Energy,* Van Nostrand, Princeton, N. J., 1950.

Goldstein, P., *How to Do an Experiment,* Harcourt, Brace, New York, 1957.

Heath, A. E., ed., *Scientific Thought in the Twentieth Century,* Watts, New York, 1951.

Hecht, S., *Explaining the Atom,* rev. ed., Viking, New York, 1954.

Heyerdahl, T., *Kon-Tiki: Across the Pacific by Raft,* Rand McNally, Skokie, Ill., 1950 (also Pocket Books).

Jaffe, B., *Men of Science in America,* Simon and Schuster, New York, 1944.

Johnson, M., and M. Abercrombie, *A Dictionary of Biology,* Penguin, Baltimore, 1954.

Kaempffert, W., *Explorations in Science,* Viking, New York, 1953.

Leicester, H. M., *The Historical Background of Chemistry,* Wiley, New York, 1956.

Moulton, F., and J. Schifferes, eds., *The Autobiography of Science,* Doubleday, Garden City, N. Y., 1950.

Nordenskiöld, E., *The History of Biology,* Tudor, New York, 1935.

Northrop, F. S., *The Logic of the Sciences and the Humanities,* Macmillan, New York, 1947.

Schuck, H., et al., *Nobel: The Man and His Prizes,* U. of Oklahoma, Norman, 1951.

Shapley, H., ed., *Climatic Change: Evidence, Causes, and Effects,* Harvard U., Cambridge, Mass., 1954.

———, S. Rapport, and H. Wright, *A Treasury of Science,* 3d ed., Harper, New York, 1954.

Singer, C., *A History of Biology,* Abelard-Schuman, New York, 1950.

Spencer, S., *Wonders of Modern Medicine,* McGraw-Hill, New York, 1953.

Walker, K., *The Story of Medicine,* Oxford U., New York, 1955.

Watkeys, C. W., ed., *An Orientation in Science,* McGraw-Hill, New York, 1938.

Wilson, E. B., Jr., *An Introduction to Scientific Research,* McGraw-Hill, New York, 1952.

Natural history and identification of plants and animals

General

Allee W. C., et al., *Principles of Animal Ecology,* Saunders, Philadelphia, 1949.

Audubon Nature Bulletins, National Audubon Society, New York.

Beebe, W., *Half Mile Down,* rev. ed., Duell, Sloan & Pearce, New York, 1951.

Buchsbaum, R., *Life in the Sea,* U. of Oregon, Eugene, 1955.

Bullough, W. S., *Practical Invertebrate Anatomy,* St. Martin's (Macmillan), New York, 1954.

Burton, M., *The Story of Animal Life,* vols. 1 and 2, Bentley, Cambridge, Mass., 1949.

Cameron, T. W., *Parasites and Parasitism,* Methuen (Wiley), New York, 1956.

Cushman, J., *Foraminifera: Their Classification and Economic Use,* 4th ed., Harvard U., Cambridge, Mass., 1948.

Davis, C., *The Marine and Fresh Water Plankton,* Michigan State U., East Lansing, 1955.

De Latil, P., *The Underwater Naturalist,* Houghton Mifflin, Boston, 1955.

Dowdeswell, W., *Animal Ecology,* Methuen (Wiley), New York, 1952.

Dulles, M., *Greenhouse Gardening Around the Year,* Macmillan, New York, 1956.

Fairchild, D., *The World Was My Garden*, Scribner, New York, 1938.

Günther, K., and K. Deckert, *Creatures of the Deep Sea*, Scribner, New York, 1956.

Hall, R. P., *Protozoology*, Prentice-Hall, Englewood Cliffs, N. J., 1953.

Hausman, L., *Beginner's Guide to Fresh Water Life*, Putnam, New York, 1950.

———, *Beginner's Guide to Sea Shore Life*, Putnam, New York, 1949.

Hillcourt, W., *Field Book of Nature Activities*, Putnam, New York, 1950.

Huxley, J., and W. Suschitzky, *Kingdom of the Beasts*, Vanguard, New York, 1956.

Jaques, H. E., *Plant Families: How to know them*, Brown, Dubuque, Iowa, 1948.

Jordan, E. L., *Hammond's Illustrated Nature Guide*, Hammond, New York, 1955.

Kudo, R., *Protozoology*, 4th ed., Thomas, Springfield, Ill., 1954.

Little, V., *General and Applied Entomology*, Harper, New York, 1957.

MacGinitie, G., and N. MacGinitie, *Natural History of Marine Animals*, McGraw-Hill, New York, 1949.

Martin, A., H. Zim, and A. Nelson, *American Wildlife and Plants*, McGraw-Hill, New York, 1951.

Merck and Co., *Veterinary Manual*, Rahway, N. J., 1955.

Miner, R. W., *Fieldbook of Seashore Life*, Putnam, New York, 1950.

Morgan, A., *Fieldbook of Animals in Winter*, Putnam, New York, 1939.

———, *Fieldbook of Ponds and Streams*, Putnam, New York, 1930.

Muenscher, W., *Aquatic Plants in the United States*, Comstock, Ithaca, N. Y., 1944.

———, *Keys to Woody Plants*, 6th ed., Comstock, Ithaca, N. Y., 1946.

Murie, O. J., *Field Guide to Animal Tracks*, Houghton Mifflin, Boston, 1954.

Needham, J., and P. Needham, *A Guide to the Study of Fresh Water Biology*, 4th ed., Comstock, Ithaca, N. Y., 1953.

———, et al., *Culture Methods for Invertebrate Animals*, Comstock, Ithaca, N. Y., 1937.

Palmer, E. L., *Fieldbook of Natural History*, McGraw-Hill, New York, 1949.

Pennak, R., *Freshwater Invertebrates of the United States*, Ronald, New York, 1953.

Pratt, H. S., *A Manual of the Common Invertebrate Animals* (exclusive of insects), Blakiston (McGraw-Hill), New York, 1935.

Ray, C., and E. Ciampi, *The Underwater Guide to Marine Life*, Barnes, New York, 1956.

Smith, R., et al., *Intertidal Invertebrates of the Central California Coast*, U. of California, Berkeley, 1954.

Stephensen, E., and C. Stewart, *Animal Camouflage*, 2d ed., Pitman, New York, 1955.

Sumner, L., and J. Dixon, *Birds and Mammals of the Sierra Nevada*, U. of California, Berkeley, 1953.

Teale, E. W., *North with the Spring*, Dodd, Mead, New York, 1951.

Welch, P., *Limnology*, 2d ed., McGraw-Hill, New York, 1952.

Yapp, W. B., ed., *Borradaile's Manual of Elementary Zoology*, 12th ed., Oxford U., New York, 1955.

Zim, H., and L. Ingle, *Sea Shores*, Simon and Schuster, New York, 1955.

Algae

Forest, H. S., *Handbook of Algae: Special Reference to Tennessee and Southeast*, U. of Tennessee, Knoxville, 1954.

Prescott, G., *Algae of the Western Great Lakes Area*, Cranbrook Institute of Science, Cranbrook, Mich., 1951.

Taylor, W. R., *Marine Algae of North Eastern Coast*, U. of Michigan, Ann Arbor, 1937.

Tiffany, L., and M. Britton, *The Algae of Illinois*, U. of Chicago, Chicago, 1952.

Mushrooms

Christensen, C., *Common Edible Mushrooms*, U. of Minnesota, Minneapolis, 1943.

Eifert, V., *Exploring for Mushrooms*, Illinois State Museum, Springfield, 1952.

Fitzpatrick, H., and W. Ray, *Some Common Edible and Poisonous Mushrooms*, Cornell Extension Bull. 386, Ithaca, N. Y., 1955.

Thomas, W., *Fieldbook of Common Mushrooms*, rev. ed., Putnam, New York, 1948.

Mosses

Bodenberg, E. T., *Mosses*, Burgess, Minneapolis, 1954.

Conard, H., *How to Know the Mosses*, Wm. Brown, Dubuque, Iowa, 1944.

Ferns

Cobb, B., *A Field Guide to the Ferns and Their Related Families*, Houghton Mifflin, Boston 1956.

Durand, H., *Fieldbook of Common Ferns*, Putnam, New York, 1949.

Shaver, J., *Ferns of Tennessee*, G. Peabody College for Teachers, Nashville, Tenn., 1954.

Wild flowers

Gottscho, S., *The Pocket Guide to the Wild Flowers*, Pocket Books, New York, 1951.

Greene, W., and H. Blomquist, *Flowers of the South*, U. of North Carolina, Chapel Hill, 1953.

Housman, L., *Beginner's Guide to Wild Flowers*, Putnam, New York, 1948.

Hylander, C., *Wild Flower Book*, Macmillan, New York, 1954.

Moldenke, H., *American Wild Flowers*, Van Nostrand, Princeton, N. J., 1949.

Stefferud, A., *How to Know the Wild Flowers,* Holt, New York, 1950; also Mentor.

Taylor, N., ed., *Mathews' Field Book of American Wild Flowers,* 4th ed., Putnam, New York, 1955.

Walcott, M., *Wild Flowers of America,* Crown, New York, 1953.

Wherry, E., *Wild Flower Guide,* Doubleday, Garden City, N. Y., 1948.

Trees and shrubs

Cope, J., and F. Winch, *Know Your Trees,* Cornell 4-H Club Bull. 85, Cornell U., Ithaca, N. Y., 1955.

Graves, A., *Illustrated Guide to Trees and Shrubs,* Harper, New York, 1956.

Hottes, A., *The Book of Shrubs,* 6th ed., De La Mare (Dodd, Mead), New York, 1952.

———, *The Book of Trees,* 3d ed., De La Mare (Dodd, Mead), New York, 1952.

Longyear, B., *Trees and Shrubs of the Rocky Mountain Region,* Putnam, New York, 1927.

Muenscher, W., *Keys to Woody Plants,* 6th ed., Comstock, Ithaca, N. Y., n.d.

Petrides, G., *A Field Guide to the Trees,* Houghton Mifflin, Boston, 1951.

Platt, R., *American Trees,* Dodd, Mead, New York, 1952.

Shells

Abbott, R. T., *American Sea Shells,* Van Nostrand, Princeton, N. J., 1954.

Dudley, R., *My Hobby is Collecting Sea Shells and Coral,* Hart Book Co., New York, 1955.

Morris, P. A., *A Field Guide to the Shells of Atlantic and Gulf Coasts,* Houghton Mifflin, Boston, 1951.

———, *A Field Guide to the Shells of the Pacific Coast and Hawaii,* Houghton Mifflin, Boston, 1952.

Verrill, A. H., *Shell Collector's Handbook,* Putnam, New York, 1950.

Insects and spiders

Crompton, J., *The Life of the Spider,* Mentor (New American Library), New York, 1954.

Ford, E. B., *Moths,* Macmillan, New York, 1955.

Gaul, A., *The Wonderful World of Insects,* Rinehart, New York, 1953.

Gertsch, W. J., *American Spiders,* Van Nostrand, Princeton, N. J., 1949.

Hussey, L., and C. Pessino, *Collecting Cocoons,* Crowell, New York, 1953.

Imms, A. D., *Insect Natural History,* Blakiston (McGraw-Hill), New York, 1951.

Klots, A., *Field Guide to the Butterflies,* Houghton Mifflin, Boston, 1951.

Needham, J., and M. Westfall, *A Manual of Dragonflies of North America,* U. of California, Berkeley, 1954.

Ross, H., *A Textbook of Entomology,* Wiley, New York, 1948.

Swain, R., *The Insect Guide,* Doubleday, New York, 1948.

Urquhart, F., *Introducing the Insect,* Holt, New York, 1949.

U.S. Dept. of Agriculture, *Insects,* 1952 Yearbook, U.S. Govt. Printing Office, Washington, D. C.

Von Frisch, K., *The Dancing Bees,* Harcourt, Brace, New York, 1955.

Zim, H., and C. Cottam, *Insects,* Simon and Schuster, New York, 1951.

RECORDINGS

The Songs of Insects, 12″, 33⅓ rpm, Cornell U. Records, Ithaca, N. Y.

Fish

Axelrod, H., and L. Schultz, *Handbook of Tropical Aquarium Fish,* McGraw-Hill, New York, 1955.

———, and W. Vorderwinkler, *Salt Water Aquarium Fish,* Sterling, New York, 1956.

Breder, C., *Marine Fish of the Atlantic Coast,* Putnam, New York, 1929.

Curtis, B., *The Life Story of the Fish,* Harcourt, Brace, New York, 1949.

LaMonte, F., *North American Game Fishes,* Doubleday, New York, 1945.

Norman, J., *A History of Fishes,* Wyn, New York, 1948.

Amphibians and reptiles

Bishop, S., *Handbook of Salamanders,* Comstock, Ithaca, N. Y., 1952.

Carr, A., *Handbook of Turtles,* Comstock, Ithaca, N. Y., 1952.

Ditmars, R., *The Reptiles of North America,* rev. ed., Doubleday, Garden City, N. Y., 1936.

———, *Fieldbook of North American Snakes,* Doubleday, Garden City, N. Y., 1939.

———, *Reptiles of the World,* Macmillan, New York, 1946.

Ley, W., *Salamanders and Other Wonders,* Viking, New York, 1955.

Netting, G., and G. Orton, *A Field Guide to the Amphibia and Reptiles,* Houghton Mifflin, Boston, 1950.

Oliver, J., *Natural History of North American Amphibians and Reptiles,* Van Nostrand, Princeton, N. J., 1955.

Pope, C., *The Reptile World,* Knopf, New York, 1955.

Schmidt, K., and D. Davis, *Fieldbook of Snakes of North America and Canada,* Putnam, New York, 1941.

Smith, H. M., *Handbook of Lizards,* Comstock, Ithaca, N. Y., 1946.

Wright, A. H., and A. Wright, *Handbook of Frogs and Toads of the United States and Canada,* Comstock, Ithaca, N. Y., 1949.

RECORDINGS

Voices of the Night, 12″, 33⅓ rpm, Cornell U. Records, Ithaca, N. Y.

Birds

Barruel, P., *Birds of the World,* Oxford U., New York, 1954.
Eliot, W., *Birds of the Pacific Coast,* Putnam, New York, 1923.
Griscom, L., *Audubon's Birds of America,* Macmillan, New York, 1950.
Headstrom, R., *Birds' Nests: A Field Guide,* Ives Washburn, New York, 1949.
Lemmon, R., *How to Attract the Birds,* Doubleday, Garden City, N. Y., 1947.
Mason, R. C., *Picture Primer: Attracting Birds,* Houghton Mifflin, Boston, 1952.
Peterson, R., *A Field Guide to the Birds,* Houghton Mifflin, Boston, 1947.
———, *How to Know the Birds,* Houghton Mifflin, Boston, 1948; (also Mentor).
———, G. Mountfort, and P. Hollom, *A Field Guide to the Birds of Britain and Europe,* Houghton Mifflin, Boston, 1954.
Pettingill, O., *A Guide to Bird Finding East of the Mississippi,* Oxford U., New York, 1951.
———, *A Guide to Bird Finding West of the Mississippi,* Oxford U., New York, 1953.
Pough, R., *Audubon Guides, All the Birds of Eastern and Central North America,* Doubleday, N. Y., 1953.
———, *Audubon Water Bird Guide,* Doubleday, Garden City, N. Y., 1951.
Saunders, A., *A Guide to Bird Songs,* Doubleday, Garden City, N. Y., 1951.
Wallace, G., *An Introduction to Ornithology,* Macmillan, New York, 1955.

RECORDINGS

Music and Bird Songs, 10″, 33⅓ rpm, Cornell U. Records, Ithaca, N. Y.
Florida Bird Songs, 10″, 78 rpm, Cornell U. Records, Ithaca, N. Y.
Bird Songs of Dooryard, Field and Forest, 3 vols., 33⅓ rpm; Ficker Records, 27 Arcadia Rd., Old Greenwich, Conn.

Mammals

Bourlière, F., *Mammals of the World,* Knopf, New York, 1955.
———, *The Natural History of Mammals,* Knopf, New York, 1954.
Burt, W., and R. Grossenheider, *A Field Guide to the Mammals,* Houghton Mifflin, Boston, 1952.
Cahalane, V. H., *Mammals of North America,* Macmillan, New York, 1947.

Palmer, R., *The Mammal Guide,* Doubleday, Garden City, N. Y., 1954.
Sanderson, I., *How to Know the American Mammals,* Mentor (New American Library), New York, 1955.
———, *Living Mammals of the World,* Hanover House (Doubleday), Garden City, N. Y., 1955.
Zim, H., and D. Hoffmeister, *Mammals,* Simon and Schuster, New York, 1955.

Science education: professional guides

Blough, G., and M. Campbell, *Making and Using Classroom Science Materials in the Elementary School,* Dryden, New York, 1954.
———, and A. Huggett, *Elementary School Science and How to Teach It,* Dryden, New York, 1951.
Brandwein, P., *The Gifted Student as Future Scientist,* Harcourt, Brace, New York, 1954.
Burnett, R. W., *Teaching Science in the Elementary School,* Rinehart, New York, 1953.
———, *Teaching Science in the Secondary School,* Rinehart, New York, 1957.
Craig, G. S., *Science for the Elementary School Teacher,* Ginn, Boston, 1940.
Croxton, W., *Science in the Elementary School Including an Activity Program,* McGraw-Hill, New York, 1939.
Elder, A., *Demonstrations and Experiments in General Chemistry,* Harper, New York, 1937.
Freeman, K., et al., *Helping Children Understand Science,* Winston, Philadelphia, 1954.
Heiss, E., E. Obourn, and C. Hoffman, *Modern Science Teaching,* Macmillan, New York, 1950.
Hoff, A., *Secondary School of Science Teaching,* McGraw-Hill, New York, 1947.
Jersild, A. T., and R. J. Tasch, *Children's Interests and What They Suggest for Education,* Bur. Publications, Teachers College, Columbia U., New York, 1951.
Johnson, P., *Science Facilities for Secondary Schools,* Office of Education, U.S. Govt. Printing Office, Washington, D. C., 1952.
Lynde, C., *Science Experiences with Ten-Cents Store Equipment,* 2d ed., Van Nostrand, Princeton, N. J., 1950.
Miller, D., and G. Blaydes, *Methods and Materials for Teaching Biological Sciences,* McGraw-Hill, New York, 1938.
National Education Association, *Science for Today's Children,* 32nd Yearbook Bull. Dept. Elementary School Principals, Washington, D. C., 1953.
———, *Science in Secondary Schools Today,* Bull. Nat. Assoc. Secondary School Principals, Washington, D. C., January, 1953.
National Society for Study of Education, 46th Yearbook, *Science Education in American Schools,* Washington, D. C., 1947.

Richardson, J., ed., *School Facilities for Science Instruction,* Nat. Sci. Teachers Assoc., Washington, D. C., 1954.

———, *Science Teaching in Secondary Schools,* Prentice-Hall, Englewood Cliffs, N. J., 1957.

———, and G. Cahoon, *Methods and Materials for Teaching General and Physical Science,* McGraw-Hill, New York, 1951.

Science Clubs of America, *Sponsors' Handbook: Thousands of Science Projects,* Science Service, 1719 N St. N. W., Washington 6, D. C.

Sutton, R., *Demonstration Experiments in Physics,* McGraw-Hill, New York, 1938.

Swezey, K., *Chemistry Magic,* McGraw-Hill, New York, 1956.

Yates, R. F., *Science with Simple Things,* Appleton-Century-Crofts, New York, 1942.

Weisbruch, F., *Lecture Demonstration Experiments for High School Chemistry,* Educational Pub., St. Louis, 1951.

Wells, H., *Secondary Science Education,* McGraw-Hill, New York, 1952.

Suggested journals and magazines

American Biology Teacher, National Association of Biology Teachers, Bryan, Ohio.

American Scientist, Sigma Xi, 54 Hillhouse Ave., New Haven 11, Conn.

Canadian Nature, Audubon Society of Canada, 181 Jarvis St., Toronto 2, Ontario.

Cornell Rural School Leaflets, N. Y. State College of Agriculture, Cornell U., Ithaca, N. Y.

Look and Listen, Britain's Audio-Visual Aids Journal, 62 Doughty St., London, W.C.1.

National Geographic, National Geographic Society, 16 and M Sts. N.W., Washington 6, D. C.

Natural History, American Museum of Natural History, Central Park W. and 79 St., New York.

Nature, Macmillan Co., St. Martin's St., London, W.C.2.

Review of Educational Research, Amer. Educ. Research Assoc., 1201 16 St. N.W., Washington, D.C.

Science, A.A.A.S., 1515 Massachusetts Ave. N.W., Washington 5, D. C.

Science Education, Nat. Assoc. for Research in Sci. Teaching; Clarence Pruitt, ed., U. of Tampa, Florida.

Science News Letter, Sci. Service, 1719 N St. N.W., Washington 6, D. C.

Scientific American, Sci. American, Inc., 415 Madison Ave., New York 17.

The Science Teacher, Nat. Sci. Teachers Assoc., 1201 16 St. N.W., Washington 6, D. C.

World Science Review, 11 Eaton Place, London, S.W.1.

Films and filmstrips

We hope that teachers will find this listing useful as a guide to films and filmstrips, recordings, and slides. Listings of films and filmstrips always seem to be incomplete or out of date; new films and filmstrips are produced regularly, and price quotations vary. This listing is subject to the same troubles; we recommend that teachers consult the reference aids listed below, and obtain catalogs from some of the distributors, also listed below.

The prices indicated here for *films* are *rental* fees; for *filmstrips, purchase* prices. (Filmstrips are not distributed on a rental basis.) Consult our Directory of Distributors for addresses; write to these distributors for catalogs, with purchase prices, when you want to purchase rather than rent films.

Where films are listed as "free" there is no rental fee; the school pays postal charges only. Many such films are available from industry and from state and government agencies (conservation, agriculture, forestry and wildlife, etc.). In many cases, these films are distributed through film libraries in your city.

In the Directory we have listed one address for each company; some of the larger ones maintain branch offices or are affiliated with film libraries. In ordering materials for your school try to locate a nearby film library or branch office, which may be much nearer to you than the address we give, and will thereby speed your orders.

Films, especially free films in popular demand, need to be ordered weeks, even months, in advance. When possible, plan large units of work for the school year early in September, and mark off several alternate days for each area of work for showing films. Then order early and submit alternate choices of days whenever feasible. In this way films reach the school a day or two before classes so that they augment the day's lesson, rather than detract from them because they do not fit into the sequence of work.

Films should be previewed for relevance to the day's work, suitability for the age level of students, and appropriateness in your community. Many teachers develop a file of their own approved films in this way, using library cards indicating the source of the film, color or black-and-white, sound or silent, rental or free, and a brief summary of the film or filmstrip (or attach the guide).

There are many techniques in showing films. A film or filmstrip need not be shown in its entirety; start the film at the place you want to use in your lesson to illustrate a point which cannot be demonstrated firsthand. A silent film may be stopped at times, so that a teacher may ask questions, direct students' observations, reverse and repeat a section for closer study and interpretation, or give students the time to ask questions while the film is still on hand. At the end of the film, students may be asked to summarize the main ideas, develop in words the concepts which were progressively developed in the film. See also the accompanying volume, *Teaching High School Science: A Book of Methods*, Section V.

Suggestions for facilities for storing films and filmstrips are described in Chapter 22.

Reference aids

Consult these reference aids for keeping informed about new films; add new titles to your file. You will notice that many of the films listed in these sources are free or inexpensive. Refer to the Directory of commercial film distributors (below) for purchase and rental of films and filmstrips; also check the film libraries of colleges, state education departments, and health agencies in your own area for free films and filmstrips.

3434 U.S. Government Films, Office of Education, U.S. Govt. Printing Office, Washington 25, D. C., $0.70.
Blue Book of 16-mm. Films, Educational Screen, 64 E. Lake St., Chicago 1, $1.50.

Directory of 2660 Film Libraries (16 mm), Office of Education, U.S. Govt. Printing Office, Washington 25, D. C., $0.35.

Educational Film Guide, H. W. Wilson Co., 950 University Ave., New York 52, $3.00.

Educator's Guide to Free Films, Educator's Progress Service, Randolph, Wisc., $5.00.

Educator's Guide to Free Slidefilms, Educator's Progress Service, Randolph, Wisc., $4.00.

Evaluation of Current Films (monthly), Educational Film Library Association.

Film Library Catalogue, Dept. of Commerce, Albany 1, N. Y.

Filmstrip Guide, H. W. Wilson Co., 950 University Ave., New York 52, $3.00.

Films for Classroom Use, Teaching Film Custodians, Inc., 25 W. 43 St., New York 36.

Filmstrips: A Descriptive Index and User's Guide, Falconer, McGraw-Hill Book Co., New York, $5.00.

Films, Recordings, and Slides, N. Y. State College of Agriculture, Cornell U., Ithaca, N. Y.

General Motors Motion Picture Catalog, General Motors Corp., Detroit 2; or 405 Montgomery St., San Francisco 4.

Lifelong Learning, Dept. Visual Institute, U. of California, Berkeley 4.

Mental Health Motion Pictures, U.S. Dept. Health, Education, and Welfare, Washington, D. C.

Modern Index and Guide to Free Educational Films from Industry, Modern Talking Picture Service, Inc., 45 Rockefeller Plaza, New York 20.

Motion Pictures and Slide Films, General Electric Film Library, P.O. Box 5970A 840 South Canal St., Chicago; or Peachtree Rd., Atlanta; or 4966 Woodland Ave., Cleveland; or 1801 N. Lamar St., Dallas; or 710 2d Ave., Seattle.

Reference Catalog of Medical Films and Filmstrips, Veterans' Administration, Washington, D. C.

Shell Motion Picture Catalogue, Film Library, 50 W. 50 St., New York 20; or 100 Bush St., San Francisco 6.

U.S. Govt. Films for Schools and Industry, United World Films, Inc., 1445 Park Ave., New York 29 (depository agency of U.S. Office Education films, and many government films).

PERIODICALS

Audio-Visual Guide
Educational Screen
Film World and AV World
See and Hear

Directory of distributors

While only the central office is given for most of these film distributors, many of them have branch offices in a number of the larger cities. Before you order films, check the office nearest you.

United States

Abbott Laboratories, Professional Service Dept., North Chicago, Ill.

Allis-Chalmers Manufacturing Co., Films Section, Milwaukee 1, Wisc.

Almanac Films, Inc., 516 5th Ave., New York 18.

American Can Co., 100 Park Ave., New York.

American Cancer Society, 47 Beaver St., New York 4.

American Film Registry, 24 E. 8 St., Chicago 5.

American Guernsey Cattle Club, 70 Main St., Peterborough, N. H.

American Museum of Natural History, 79 St. and Central Park W., New York.

American National Cattlemen's Association, 801 E. 17 St., Denver 18.

American Petroleum Institute, 50 W. 50 St., New York.

American Potash Institute, 1102 16 St. N.W., Washington 6, D. C.

American Society of Bakery Engineers, Visual Ed. Dept., 208 3d Ave. S.E., Minneapolis 14.

American Waterways Operators', Inc. 1319 F St. N.W., Washington 4, D. C.

Associated Bulb Growers of Holland, 29 Broadway, New York.

Associated Films, Inc., 79 E. Adams St., Chicago 3.

Association Films, Inc., 347 Madison Ave., New York 17.

Athena Films, Inc., 165 W. 46 St., New York 19.

Audio Film Center, 101 W. 31 St., New York.

Audio Productions, Inc., 630 9th Ave., New York 19.

Australian News & Information Bureau, 636 5th Ave., New York 20.

Bailey Films, Inc., 6509 De Longpre Ave., Hollywood 28.

Bausch & Lomb Optical Co., Film Distribution Service, 635 St. Paul St., Rochester 2, N. Y.

Beet Sugar Development Foundation, P.O. Box 531, Fort Collins, Colo.

Stanley Bowmar Co., 513 W. 166 St., New York 32.

Brandon Films, Inc., 200 W. 57 St., New York.

Bray Studios, 729 7th Ave., New York 19.

Bureau of Communication Research, 13 E. 37 St., New York 16.

J. I. Case & Co., Racine, Wisc.

Colonial Films, 71 Walton St. N.W., Atlanta 6.

Connecticut Light and Power Co., Hartford.

Coronet Films, Coronet Bldg., Chicago 1 (write to film library nearest you).

William Cox Enterprises, 2900 S. Sawtelle Blvd., Los Angeles, 24.

Curriculum Films, distributed by Educational Projections, Inc., 10 E. 40 St., New York 16.

Davey Tree Expert Co., Kent, Ohio.

De Kalb Agricultural Association, Educational Division, De Kalb, Ill.

Denoyer-Geppert Co., 5235 N. Ravenswood Ave., Chicago 40.

Dow Chemical Co., Advertising Dept., Midland, Mich.

Edited Pictures System, Inc., 165 W. 46 St., New York 19.

Encyclopaedia Britannica Films, Inc. (EBF), 1150 Wilmette Ave., Wilmette, Ill.

Ethyl Corp., Chrysler Bldg., New York 17.

Farm Film Foundation, 1731 Eye St. N.W., Washington 6, D. C.

Ferry-Morse Seed Co., Advertising Dept., 328 Monroe St., Detroit 31.

Film Strip of the Month Club, Inc. (Popular Science), 353 4th Ave., New York 10.

Films of the Nations Distributors, Inc., 62 W. 45 St., New York 36.

Fish and Wildlife Service, U.S. Dept. Interior, P.O. Box 128, College Park, Md.

Gateway Productions, Inc., 40 Fremont St., San Francisco 5.

General Electric Corp., Advertising Division, 1 River Rd., Schenectady 5, N. Y. (or nearest G.E. film library).

General Motors, Dept. Public Relations, 3044 W. Grand Blvd., Detroit 2.

Golden Key Productions, Inc., Film Distributors, 1921 Hillhurst Ave., Hollywood 27.

Harcourt, Brace and Company, 750 Third Ave., New York 17.

Hawaii Press Bureau, 1040 National Press Bldg., Washington 4, D. C.

Heidenkamp Nature Pictures, 538 Glen Arden Dr., Pittsburgh 8.

Hy-Line Poultry Farms, 1206 Mulberry St., Des Moines 9, Iowa.

Ideal Pictures Corp., 58 E. South Water St., Chicago 1.

Indiana U. Films, Audio-Visual Center, Bloomington, Ind. (or Educational Film Library Assoc., New York).

Institute of Visual Training, 40 E. 49 St., New York 17.

Institutional Cinema Service, Inc., 165 W. 46 St., New York 19.

Instructional Films, Inc., 1150 Wilmette Ave., Wilmette, Ill.

International Film Bureau, Inc., 57 E. Jackson Blvd., Chicago.

International Film Foundation, Inc., 345 E. 46 St., New York 17.

International Paper Co., 220 E. 42 St., New York.

Iowa State University, Bur. Visual Instruction, Iowa City.

Jam Handy Organization, 2821 E. Grand Blvd., Detroit 11 (look for regional office in your city or state).

Kansas State College, Dept. Poultry Husbandry, Manhattan, Kan.

Knowledge Builders, 625 Madison Ave., New York 22.

Lederle Laboratories, Div. American Cyanamid Co., 30 Rockefeller Plaza, New York 20.

Library Films, Inc., 25 W. 45 St., New York 19.

Life Filmstrips, Time & Life Bldg., 9 Rockefeller Plaza, New York 20.

Mallinckrodt Chemical Works, Advertising Dept., 3600 N. 2d St., St. Louis 7.

March of Time, 369 Lexington Ave., New York 17.

McGraw-Hill Publishing Co., Films Div., 330 W. 42 St., New York (also distributes Popular Science filmstrips).

Metropolitan Life Insurance Co., 1 Madison Ave., New York 10.

Milk Industry Foundation, Chrysler Bldg., New York 17.

Minneapolis-Moline Co., Box 1050, Minneapolis 1, Minn.

Modern Talking Picture Service, Inc., 45 Rockefeller Plaza, New York 20.

Monsanto Chemical Co., St. Louis 4.

National Audubon Society, 1130 5th Ave., New York.

National Cancer Institute, Bethesda 14, Md.

National Fertilizer Association, 616 Investment Bldg., Washington 5, D. C.

National Film Board of Canada, Suite 2307, RKO Bldg., 6th Ave., New York 20.

National Garden Bureau, 407 S. Dearborn St., Chicago 5.

National Plant Food Institute, 1700 K St. N.W., Washington 6, D. C.

National Tuberculosis Association, 1790 Broadway, New York 19.

New Holland Machine Co., Film Dept., New Holland, Pa.

New York Botanical Garden, Bronx Park, N. Y.

New York State College of Agriculture, Film Library, Cornell U., Ithaca, N. Y.

New York State Dept. Commerce, Film Library, Albany.

New York State Society for Medical Research, 2 E. 63 St., New York 21.

New York *Times,* Education Office, 229 W. 43 St., New York 36.

New York University Film Library, 26 Washington Place, New York 3.

North Carolina State College, Dept. Visual Aids, Raleigh, N. C.

Ohio State University, Dept. Photography, Columbus 10, Ohio.

Samuel Orleans & Associates, Inc., 211 W. Cumberland Ave., Knoxville 15, Tenn.

Photolab, Inc., 3825 Georgia Ave., N.W., Washington 11, D. C.

Popular Science Publishing Co., Inc., Audiovisual Div., Filmstrip-of-the-Month Club, 353 4th Ave., New York 10.

Shell Oil Co., 50 W. 50 St., New York 20; or 624 S. Michigan Ave., Chicago 5.

Sinclair Refining Co., 155 N. Wacker Drive, Chicago 6; or 600 5th Ave., New York.

Skibo Productions, Inc., 165 W. 46 St., New York.

Society of American Bacteriologists, Committee on Visual Aids, School of Medicine, U. of Pennsylvania, Philadelphia 4.

Society for Visual Education, Inc., 1345 W. Diversey Pkwy., Chicago 14.

Socony-Mobil Oil Co., 26 Broadway, New York 4.

Soil Conservation Service, Washington, D. C. (write to state soil conservation office).

E. R. Squibb & Sons, 745 5th Ave., New York.

Sterling-Movies, U.S.A., Inc., 205 E. 43 St., New York 17.

Swift & Co., Public Relations Dept., Union Stock Yards, Chicago 9.

Teaching Films Custodians, Inc., 25 W. 43 St., New York 18, for long-term loans; for short loans, contact your regional film library.

Tennessee Valley Authority, Div. of Agricultural Relations, Knoxville, Tenn.

Texas Co., 205 E. 42 St., New York 17.

Union Pacific Railroad, Agricultural Dept., 1416 Dodge St., Omaha 2.

U.S. Atomic Energy Commission, 1901 Constitution Ave., Washington, D. C.

U.S. Department of Agriculture, Washington 25, D. C.; consult regional film library.

U.S. Forest Service, U.S. Dept. Agriculture, Washington 25, D. C.

U.S. Public Health Service, Communicable Disease Center, Atlanta, Ga.

United World Films, Inc. (UWF), 1445 Park Ave., New York 29.

University of California, University Extension, Visual Dept., 2272 Union St., Berkeley.

Venard Organization, 702 S. Adams St., Peoria 2, Ill.

Visual Education Consultants, 2066 Helena St., Madison 4, Wisc.

Ward's Natural Science Establishment, 3000 E. Ridge Road, Rochester 7, N. Y.

West Coast Lumbermen's Association, 1410 S.W. Morrison St., Portland 5, Ore.

Western Pine Association, 510 Yeon Bldg., Portland, Ore.

Westinghouse Electric Corp., School Service, 306 4th Ave., P.O. Box. 1017, Pittsburgh 30.

Wilner Films & Slides, P.O. Box 231, Cathedral Station, New York 25.

Wisconsin Alumni Research Foundation, P.O. Box 2059, Madison, Wisc.

Wistar Institute, 36 St. and Woodland Ave., Philadelphia.

Wool Bureau, Inc., 16 W. 46 St., New York 19.

Young America Films, Inc., 18 E. 41 St., New York 17.

Zurich-American Insurance Co., 135 La Salle St., Chicago 3.

United Kingdom

Science and Film, % Scientific Film Association, 164 Shaftesbury Ave., London, W.C.2.

Canada

Audio-Visual Supply Co., Toronto General Trusts Building, Winnipeg, Manitoba.

Canadian Film Institute, 142 Sparks St., Ottawa (evaluation of science films, $5.00).

General Films Limited, Head Office, 1534 13th Ave., Regina, Saskatchewan (look for regional office in your city).

Radio-Cinema, 5011 Verdun Ave., Montreal, Quebec.

Selected listing of films and filmstrips

The films listed here are sound and black-and-white unless otherwise indicated. All films have been selected for viewing within a class period of 40 to 45 minutes. As previously stated, prices are for rental unless otherwise noted; they are subject to change. For complete names, departments, and addresses of the distributors listed see the preceding Directory. The following abbreviations are used throughout.

f = film
fs = filmstrip
si = silent
c = color
rls = reels
ser = series

General

Atom and Biological Science (f), EBF; free, U.S. Atomic Energy Commission Field Offices.

Atom and Medicine (f), EBF, $2.50.

Atom and You (f), Paramount News; free, U.S. Atomic Energy Commission Field Offices.

Atomic Radiation; Atomic Energy (2 f), EBF, $2.50 ea.

Bikini—Radiological Laboratory (f), U.S. Atomic Energy Commission Field Offices, free.

Great Names in Biology (stories of 6 scientists) (ser 6 fs, c), EBF, $6.00 ea.

Magic of the Atom Series: The Atom and the Doctor; Atomic Greenhouse; Eternal Cycle; Tagging the Atom; The Atomic Zoo; The Riddle of Photosynthesis; Atomic Age Farmer (7f), Handel Film Corp.; free, U.S. Atomic Energy Commission Field Offices.

New Frontiers of Medicine (f), March of Time, $3.00.

New Frontiers of Science (f), N. Y. *Times*, $2.00.

Radioactivity Laboratory Demonstration (f, c), U.S. Army, free.

Scientific Method (f), EBF, $2.00.

Cells and Protozoa

Cell, the Structural Unit of Life (f), Coronet; available through film libraries, $2.00.

Cell Division and Growth (f), Abbott, free.

Cells and Their Functions (f), Athena, $4.50.

The Compound Microscope (fs), Visual Educ. Consultants, $3.00.

The Compound Microscope (f, c), Bausch & Lomb, free.

Eyes of Science (f, si), Bausch & Lomb, free.

The Microscope and Its Use (f), Young America, $2.00.

Mitosis and Meiosis (f, c), Indiana U., inquire rental.

Protoplasm—the Beginning of Life (f), Bray, $3.00.

Seifritz on Protoplasm (f), N.Y.U. Film Library, $6.00.

Thinnest Slice (f), U. of Calif., $2.50.

Plants and their functions

Atoms and Agriculture (f), EBF; free, U.S. Atomic Energy Field Offices.

Budding Yeasts (f, si), Soc. Amer. Bacteriologists, $0.50.

Ferns (f), Almanac, $2.00.

Food from the Sun (fs), Sugar Information, free.

Fungus Plants (f), EBF, $2.50.

Gift of Green (photosynthesis) (f, c), N. Y. Botanical Garden, $2.00.

Green Plants (fs, c), Harcourt Brace, $5.50.

Growth of Bacteria, Yeasts, and Molds (f, si), Soc. Amer. Bacteriologists, $2.00.

How Plants Grow and Reproduce (fs, c), Soc. Visual Educ., $5.00.

Hunger Signs in Crops (fs), De Kalb Agricultural Assoc., free.

Insect Catchers of the Bog Jungle (f, c), U. of Calif., $4.00.

Kinds of Plants (all phyla) (fs, c), Soc. Visual Educ., $5.50.

Leaves (f), EBF, $2.50.

Life Cycle of a Plant (f), UWF, $2.00.

Life of a Plant (f, c), EBF, $4.00.

Life of Plants (f), UWF, $1.50.

Life Story of a Fern (f), UWF, $2.00.

Making the Most of a Miracle (miners for plants; N. J. Experimental Station) (f, c), free, Film Library, N. Y. State College Agriculture, Cornell U., Ithaca, N. Y.

Microscopic Plant Life in the Bake Shop (f, si), Amer. Soc. Bakery Engineers, free.

Nature Activities for Camp, Club and Classroom (f, si, c), Nat. Audubon Soc., $1.00.

Parasitic Plants (f), EBF, $2.50.

Photosynthesis (f), UWF, $4.00.

Pin Mold (f), Internat. Film Bur.; free, state conservation dept.

Plant Growth (f), EBF, $1.50.

Plant Traps (f, c), EBF, $4.00.

Power of Plants (f), Almanac, $2.00.

Roots of Plants (f), EBF, $2.50.

Seeds and How They Grow (bean, corn) (f, c), Wm. Cox, inquire rental.

Soil Testing for Lime Requirements (f, c), Film Library, N. Y. State College Agriculture, Cornell U., Ithaca, N. Y.

Spermatophytes and General Biology (fs), Bowmar, $2.50.

Story of Yeast (f), Amer. Soc. Bakery Engineers, free.

Thallophytes, Small Bryophytes and Pteridophytes (fs), Bowmar, $2.50.

The Big Test (f), Nat. Fertilizer Assoc., free.

Time Lapse Studies of Growing Trees (f, c), State U. of N. Y., $3.00.

Animals and their functions

Invertebrates (excluding insects)

Animal Life (f), EBF, $1.50.

Animal Parade (sea anemone to man) (fs), Bowmar, $2.00.

Annelida (3 f, si, c), Iowa State U., $3.00 ea.

Arachnids (f), UWF, $3.00.

Beach and Sea Animals (f), EBF, $2.50.

Biology of Spiders, Reproduction, The Black Widow (fs), Bowmar, $3.00.

Blood Circulation in Marine Animals (f, si), Iowa State U., $3.00.

Coelenterata (2 f, si, c), Iowa State U., $3.00 ea.

Earthworm (f), Almanac, $2.00.

Echinodermata (2 f, si, c), Iowa State U., $3.00 ea.

Eyes Under Water (f), Almanac, $2.00.

Life in Ponds, Lakes and Streams (fs, c), Jam Handy, $6.75.

Marine Invertebrates of the Maine Coast (set 34 Kodachromes, 2″ × 2″) Ward's, $25.50.

Mollusca (2 f, si, c), Iowa State U., $3.00 ea.

Parade of Invertebrates (4 f, si, c), Iowa State U., $3.00 ea.
Pond Life (f), EBF, $2.00.
Ponds (f), Almanac, $2.00.
Protective Coloration in Nature (set 10 Kodachromes, 2″ × 2″), Bowmar, $5.00.
Salt Water Wonderland (f, c), Almanac, $3.00.
The Sea (f), Teaching Film Custodians, $1.50.
Sea Zoo (f), Almanac, $2.00.
Seashore Life (f, c), EBF, $2.50.
Spiders (f, c), EBF, $4.00.
Tiny Water Animals (f), EBF, $2.50.

Insects

Adaptive Coloration of Insects (set 30 Kodachromes, 2″ × 2″) Ward's, $22.50.
Ant City (f), Almanac, $2.00.
Ants (f), EBF, $2.50.
Arthropoda (f, si, c), Rutgers U., $2.50.
Arthropoda (2 f, si, c), Iowa State U., $3.00 ea.
Arthropoda (fs), Bowmar, $2.50.
Battling the Borer (f, c), Allis-Chalmers, free.
Bee City (f), Almanac, $2.00.
Biology of Insects (active camouflage) (fs), Bowmar, $3.00.
City of Wax (f), Skibo, $1.50.
Corn Borer, Gangster of the Corn Fields (fs), De Kalb Agricultural Assoc., free.
Dances of the Bees (Von Frisch's work) (f, si), Wilner, $5.50.
House Fly (f), EBF, $2.50.
Insects (f, c), EBF, $4.00.
Insects and How They Live (set 10 Kodachromes, 2″ × 2″), Bowmar, $5.00.
Life Cycle of the Mosquito (f), Almanac, $2.00.
Life History of the Monarch Butterfly (set 10 Kodachromes, 2″ × 2″), Bowmar, $5.00.
Moth and Butterfly (f), Amer. Film Registry, $1.50.
Pond Insects (f), EBF, $2.50.
Story of the Bees (f), UWF, $6.00.
Vegetable Insects (f), Internat. Film Bur.; free, state conservation dept.
Your Enemy-Grasshopper (f, c), U.S. Dept. Agriculture; free, state universities, film libraries.

Vertebrates

Audubon's Birds of America (set 6 fs, c), EBF, $6.00 ea.
Birds Are Interesting (f, c), EBF, $4.00.
Birds of the Dooryard (f, c), Coronet, film libraries, $2.50.
Camera Thrills of Wildest Africa (f), Almanac, $1.50.
Chordata: Man and Other Primates (fs), Bowmar, $2.50.
Dwellers of Swamps and Pond; Salamanders and Their Young (2 f, si, c), Iowa State U., $3.00 ea.
Fifty Common Birds of House and Garden (Dr. Allen, Cornell) (set Kodachromes, 2″ × 2″), Ward's, $42.50.

Frogs and Toads (set 26 Kodachromes, 2″ × 2″), Ward's, $15.00.
Frog and You (fs), Visual Educ. Consultants, $3.00.
The Fur Seal (Pribilof Islands) (f), Almanac, $2.00.
Lizards, Snakes and Tortoises (f), Bailey, $2.50.
Reptiles (f, c), EBF, $5.00.
Slithering Snakes and Hard-shelled Turtles (fs), Bowmar, $2.75.
Snakes Are Interesting (f, c), Associated Film Artists, $3.00.
Song Birds as Neighbors (f, si), Bray, $1.50.

Note: Many color slides in the field of nature study are available from biological supply houses as well as from film libraries. Consult the catalogs of supply houses (Directory, p. 479).

Functions of the human body

Nutrition and digestion

Alimentary Tract (f), EBF, $2.50.
Citrus in Nutrition (f, c), U. of Calif., $1.00.
Digestion of Foods (f), EBF, $2.50.
Digestion (Chemical) (f), UWF, $3.00.
Digestion (Mechanical) (f), UWF, $3.00.
Food (f), Young America, $2.00.
Foods and Nutrition (f), EBF, $2.50.
Handling of Laboratory Animals (f), New York State Soc. Medical Research, free.
Hidden Hunger (f), Swift, free.
Human Digestion (f), Athena, $3.00.
Magic Alphabet (f), (Eijkman) Teaching Film Custodians, local film library.
Menacing Shadows (f), Westinghouse, free.
Modest Miracle (f), Amer. Soc. Bakery Engineers, free.
Obesity (f), EBF, $2.00.
Proof of the Pudding (f), Metroplitan Life, free.
Rice and Health (story of Bataan experiment) (f, c), U. of Calif., $2.00.
Story of Human Energy (f), Modern Talking Pic., free.
Strange Hunger (f), Amer. Soc. Bakery Engineers, free.
Three Squares (f, c), U.S. Dept. Agriculture; free, film libraries.
Understanding Vitamins (f, c), EBF, $4.75.
A Way in the Wilderness (Goldberger's experiments) (f), Teaching Film Custodians, local film library.
Yesterday, Today, and Tomorrow (food preservation) (f), Modern Talking Pic., free.

Circulation and related life functions

Alcohol and the Human Body (f), EBF, $3.50.
Anatomical Models (f), Denoyer-Geppert, free.
Blood (f, si), EBF, $2.00.
Brothers in Blood (f), Teaching Film Custodians, local film library.

Circulation (f), UWF, $3.00.
Circulation (f), Amer. Heart Assoc.; free, local or state chapter.
Circulatory Control (f, si), EBF, $2.00.
Circulatory System (f, 2 rls, si), Bray, $3.50.
Control of Body Temperature (f), EBF, $2.50.
Doctor Examines Your Heart (f), Bray, $3.50.
Elimination (f), UWF, $2.50.
Heart (f), Almanac, $2.00.
Heart—How It Works (f), McGraw-Hill, $3.00.
Heart and Circulation (fs), EBF, $2.50.
How the Organs of the Body Function (f, 3 rls), Bray, $7.50.
How the Respiratory System Functions (f), Bray, $3.00.
Human Body (set 16 fs), EBF, $3.00. ea.
Human Skin (f), Bray, $3.00.
Mechanisms of Breathing (f), EBF, $2.50.
Nine Basic Functional Systems of the Human Body (f), Bray, $3.00.
Prescription for Life (f), Amer. Red Cross; free, county chapter.
Respiration (f), UWF, $3.00.
Urinary System (f, si), Bray, $2.00.
Work of the Blood (fs), Popular Sci. (McGraw-Hill), $6.00.
Work of the Kidneys (f), EBF, $2.50.
Your Life Stream (fs, c), Harcourt, Brace, $5.50.

Behavior

Act Your Age (f), Coronet, film libraries, $2.50.
Action and Reaction (instincts; trial and error) (f), Almanac, $2.00.
Alcohol and Narcotics (4 fs, c), Young America, $6.00 ea.
Animal Cunning (f), Ideal, $3.00.
Battle of the Centuries (termite behavior) (f), Teaching Film Custodians, local film library.
Behavior in Animals and Plants (f, c), Coronet, inquire film library.
Behavior of Animals and Plants (5 fs, c), Curriculum Films, $3.95 ea.
Can Animals Think? (f), Almanac, $2.00.
Conditioned Reflexes (Pavlov's theories) (f, si), Brandon, $5.00.
Control Your Emotions (f), Coronet, film libraries, $2.50.
Developing Your Personality (6 fs, c), EBF, $6.00 ea.
Development of the Nervous System in Vertebrates and Invertebrates (f, si), Brandon, $4.00.
Do Better on Your Examinations (f), Coronet, film libraries, $2.00.
Drug Addiction (f, 2 rls), EBF, $4.50.
Embryology of Human Behavior (f), EBF, $2.50.
Endocrine Glands (f), EBF, $2.50.
Experiment (f), General Motors, free.
Fears of Children (f), Internat. Film Foundation, $4.00.
Growth of Motor Behavior (Gesell's work) (f, si);

Behavior Patterns at One Year (f); EBF, $2.50 ea.
How Animals Defend Themselves (f), Ideal, $3.00.
How the Ear Functions; How the Eye Functions (2 f), Knowledge Builders, $2.00 ea.
How to Concentrate (f), Coronet, film libraries, $2.00.
Human Brain (f), EBF, $2.50.
Life with Baby (Gesell's work) (f, 2 rls), Audio Film Center, $3.00.
Magic Pathways (f, c), Sterling-Movies, free.
Mental Health (f), EBF, $2.50.
Motivation and Reward in Learning (f), Penn State College, $2.50.
Movements of Some Common Plants (f, si), Iowa State U., $2.00.
Nervous System (fs), Popular Sci. (McGraw-Hill), $6.00.
Nervous System (f), EBF, $2.50.
Nervous System; Glandular System (2 fs), Soc. Visual Educ., $3.50 ea.
Preface to Life (f), UWF, $2.50.
Problem Solving in Infants (f, si), Internat. Film Bur., $4.00.
Problem Solving in Monkeys; Testing Animal Intelligence (2 f, si), Internat. Film Bur., $2.50 ea.
Of Pups and Puzzles (f), Teaching Film Custodians, local film library.
Reactions in Plants and Animals (f), EBF, $2.50.
Science of Seeing (fs), General Electric, free.
Self-conscious Guy (f), Coronet, film libraries, $2.00.
Sensitivity of Plants (f), Almanac, $2.00.
Shy Guy (f), Coronet, film libraries, $2.00.
Shyness (f), McGraw-Hill, $3.00.
Terrible Twos and Trusting Threes (child behavior) (f), McGraw-Hill, $3.50.
Training of the Young (f), Almanac, $2.00.
Willie and the Mouse (experiments in learning) (f), Teaching Film Custodians, local film library.
You and Your Attitudes (f), Association Films, $2.50.

Health; disease prevention

Advent of Anesthesia (f), Mallinckrodt, free.
Allergies (f, c), EBF, $4.00.
And the Earth Shall Give Back Life (antibiotics) (f), Squibb, free.
Antibiotics (f, c), EBF, $5.00.
Antibiotics (fs), Photolab, $1.25.
Bacteria: Friend or Foe (f, c), EBF, $4.00.
Behind the Shadows; Another to Conquer; Let My People Live; The Inside Story (4 f), Nat. Tuberculosis Assoc.; free, state tuberculosis associations.
Biology of Domestic Flies (f), U.S. Public Health, free.
Body Defenses Against Disease (f), EBF, $2.50.
Body Fights Bacteria (f), McGraw-Hill, $3.00.
Cancer (f, c) EBF, $4.00.

Cancer, the Problem of Early Diagnosis (f, c), Audio Productions, free.

Captain of the Men of Death (tuberculosis) (f), Zurich-American Insurance Co.; free, local agencies.

Challenge: Science Against Cancer (f), Nat. Cancer Inst., free.

Chills and Fever, Why? (malaria) (fs), U.S. Public Health, free.

Clean Waters (f, c), General Electric, free.

Close Shaves; Having a Wonderful Time (accident prevention) (2 f), Zurich-American Insurance Co.; free, local agencies.

Community Health and You (f), McGraw-Hill, $3.00.

Conquest of Pain (Morton) (f, 2 rls), Teaching Film Custodians, local film library.

The Danger Point (colds and respiratory diseases) (f, c), Association Films, free.

Death of a Cell (ingestion by phagocyte) (f), Squibb, free.

Drug Addiction (f), EBF, $4.50.

The Fight Against Rabies (fs), U.S. Public Health, free.

From One Cell (f, c), Amer. Cancer Soc., free.

Great Heart (Father Damien and lepers) (f), Teaching Film Custodians, local film libraries.

Heart Disease (f), EBF, $2.50.

How to Prevent Disease (vaccination, Schick test) (f ser, si), Bray, $1.50. ea.

Immunization (f), EBF, $2.50.

Jenner and the Story of Smallpox (fs), Metropolitan Life, free.

Jimmy Beats Rheumatic Fever (fs), Metropolitan Life, free.

Keep Foods Safe to Eat (fs), Popular Sci. (McGraw-Hill), $6.00.

Kerchoo and You (fs), Visual Educ. Consultants, $3.00.

Koch; Reed; Pasteur (3 fs), Metropolitan Life, free.

Magic Bullets (Ehrlich and syphilis) (f), U.S. Public Health; free, local health dept.

Making Water Safe to Drink (fs, c), Popular Sci., $6.00.

Man Against Microbe (f, c), Metropolitan Life, free.

Man's Greatest Friend (Pasteur and dogs) (f), Teaching Film Custodians, local film libraries.

Management of Obesity (Jolliffe) (f), Squibb, free.

Modern Nutrition (doctors discuss deficiency symptoms) (f, c), Squibb, free.

Municipal Sewage Treatment Plants (4 fs), U.S. Public Health; free, local health dept.

Nations United for Spring Beauty (plant-bulb disease inspection) (f, c), Films of the Nations Distrib., free.

Outbreak (foot-and-mouth disease) (f, c), U.S. Dept. Agriculture; free, regional film libraries.

Pasteur, the Benefactor (f, 2 rls), Almanac, $3.50.

Prescription for Life (blood donation) (f, c), Squibb; free, local Red Cross chapters.

Rabies Can Be Controlled (f, c), Lederle Labs., free.

Rx—The Story Behind Your Doctor's Prescription (f), Squibb, free.

Science Against Cancer (f), Internat. Film Bur., $2.50.

Sniffles and Sneezes (f), McGraw-Hill, $3.00.

Stem Rust (f), U.S. Dept. Agriculture; free, regional film libraries.

Story of Dr. Jenner (f), Teaching Film Custodians, local film libraries.

Story of Louis Pasteur (Paul Muni) (f), EBF, inquire rental.

Structure and Care of Heart; Heart of Our Nation (2 fs), Zurich-American Insurance Co.; free, local agencies.

That Mothers Might Live (story of Semmelweiss) (f), Teaching Film Custodians, local film library.

They Live Again (Banting) (f), Teaching Film Custodians, local film libraries.

Tobacco and the Human Body (f), EBF, $3.00.

Trudeau and the Crusade Against Tuberculosis (fs), Metropolitan Life, free.

Tuberculosis (f), EBF, $2.50.

Tuberculosis: What It Is and What To Do About It (fs), Nat. Tuberculosis Assoc.; free, local tuberculosis agencies.

The Valiant Heart (rheumatic fever) (f), Squibb; free, Amer. Heart Assoc.

Winning the War Against Rats and Mice with Warfarin (fs), Wisconsin Alumni Research Foundation, free.

Wonder Engine of the Body (heart) (f), Bray, $3.50.

Worms in Your Muscles: Hookworm Disease and Hookworm Infection (fs), U.S. Public Health, free.

Yellow Jack (Walter Reed) (f), Teaching Film Custodians, local film libraries.

Your Health Department in Action (f), Orleans, $4.00.

Reproduction

Alaska's Silver Millions (salmon run) (f), American Can, free.

Asexual Reproduction (f), Indiana U., $2.00.

Beetles (f), EBF, $2.50.

Biography of a Male Fish (stickleback) (f), Internat. Film Bur., $2.00.

Blossom Forth the Fruit (f, c), Cornell Extension Service, $1.00.

Born to Die (plants) (f), Skibo, $1.50.

Butterflies (f), EBF, $2.50.

Cell Division: Basis of Growth in All Living Things (f), U. of Calif., $2.50.

Cicada (f), U.S. Dept. Agriculture, free.

Development of the Chick (f), Almanac, $2.00.
Development of the Frog (f), UWF, $3.50.
Early Development of the Rabbit Egg (f, si), Wistar Inst., $1.50.
Early Divisions, 2 to 8 Cells of Living Monkey Egg (f, si), Wistar Inst., $1.50.
European Corn Borer (f, c), U.S. Dept. Agriculture, free.
Ferns (alternation of generation) (f), Almanac, $2.00.
Fertilization (f, si), EBF, inquire rental.
Flowers at Work (f, c), EBF, $2.50.
Forming an Egg (f, si), Kansas State College, $3.00.
From Flower to Fruit (f, si), EBF, inquire rental.
Green Vagabonds (seed dispersal) (f), Almanac, $2.00.
Growing a Flower Garden from Seeds; Where New Flowers Are Bred (2 f, c), Nat. Garden Bur., free.
Growth of Bacteria, Yeasts, Molds (f, si), $2.00; *Budding Yeasts* (f, si), $0.50; Soc. Amer. Bacteriologists.
Honey Bee (f), EBF, $2.50.
Human Development (f, si), Bray, $3.00.
Human Growth (f, c), U. of Oregon, $8.00.
Human Reproduction (f), McGraw-Hill, $3.00.
In the Beginning (rabbit egg) (f), UWF, $1.50.
Life Cycle of a Frog (f), UWF, $3.00.
Life Cycle of a Trout (f), UWF, $3.00.
Life Story of a Fern (f), UWF, $3.00.
Metamorphosis (fs, c), *Life*, $6.00.
Miracle of Life (cell division, fertilization) (f), Almanac, $2.00.
Mitosis and Meiosis (f, c), Indiana U., inquire rental.
Monarch Butterfly Story (f, c), EBF, $4.00.
Mosquito (f), EBF, $2.50.
The Newt (f), free, state conservation dept.
The Onion (f), free, state conservation dept.
Ovulation, Fertilization, Early Development of the Mammalian Egg (f, si), U.S. Dept. Agriculture, $1.50.
The Rabbit's Development (f), free, state conservation dept.
Reproduction Among Mammals (pig) (fs), EBF, $3.00.; also (f), $2.50.
Reproduction in Animals (f, c), Coronet, inquire film library.
Reproduction in the Lower Forms of Life (f, si), Bray, $1.50.
Reproduction in Higher Forms (f, si), Bray, $1.50.
Sanctuary of the Seals (f), Teaching Film Custodians, local film libraries.
Seed Dispersal (f), EBF, $2.50.
Seeds and How They Grow (f, c), Wm. Cox, inquire rental.
Sexual Reproduction in Plants (fs), De Kalb Agricultural Assoc., free rental.

Springtime in Holland (bulbs) (f, c) Associated Bulb Growers of Holland, free.
Sunfish (f), EBF, $2.50.

Improving heredity

Acres of Chix (f, c), De Kalb Agricultural Assoc., free.
Acres of Gold (hybrid corn) (f, c), De Kalb Agricultural Assoc., free.
Animal Breeding (f), EBF, $3.00.
Background for Beauty (f, c), Ferry-Morse, free.
Bees for Hire (f, c), Texas Co., free.
Better Breed (f), UWF, inquire rental.
Better Gardens for Better Living (f, c), Ferry-Morse, free.
Better Seed (breeding potatoes) (f, c), Farm Film Foundation, free.
Better Seed for Better Grasslands (f, c), U.S. Dept. Agriculture, free.
Breeding Better Food Crops (f, c), Nat. Garden Bur., free.
Breeding Champion Sugar Canes for Hawaii (f, c), Hawaii Press Bur., free.
Corn (f, c), U.S. Dept. Agriculture, $1.50.
Corn Colors and Corn Mixtures; Hidden Values in Hybrid Corn (2 fs, c), De Kalb Agricultural Assoc., free.
Cow Business (f, c), Amer. Nat. Cattlemen's Assoc., free.
Culling Sheep (f, c), Union Pacific Railroad, free.
From Good Earth to Good Tables (pollination) (f, c), Modern Talking Pic., free.
Gardening with Seed (f, c), Nat. Garden Bur., free.
Genetics (fs, c), De Kalb Agricultural Assoc., free.
Golden Heritage (cattle breeding) (f, c), Amer. Guernsey Cattle Club, free.
Green Giant's Magic (peas and corn) (f, c), Modern Talking Pic., free.
Heredity (fs), Popular Sci. (McGraw-Hill), $3.00.
Heredity (f), EBF, $2.50.
Heredity and Environment (f), Coronet, film libraries, $2.00.
Heredity and Prenatal Development (f), McGraw-Hill, $4.00.
Horse Raising (f, c), Ideal, inquire rental.
Hybrid Corn (f, c), Allis-Chalmers, free.
Improving Chickens by Crossing Inbreds (f, c), Hy-Line, free.
Judging Dairy Cattle (fs), Amer. Guernsey Cattle Club, free.
Man Made Miracles (f, c), Amer. Guernsey Cattle Club, free.
More Corn per Acre (f, c), N. C. State College, inquire rental.
New Chicken (fs, c), De Kalb Agricultural Assoc., free.

Operation of a Forest Nursery (f), U.S. Forest Service, free.
Pioneer Stud (merino sheep) (f), Wool Bur., free.
Plant Growth and Mutation (f), U. of Calif., $2.00.
Producing Quality Milk (f), Milk Industry Foundation, free.
Story of Dr. Carver (f), Teaching Film Custodians, $2.00.
Twins Are Individuals (f, si), EBF, $2.50.
Where New Flowers Are Bred (f, c), Nat. Garden Bur., free.

Evolution

Boundary Lines (f, c), N.Y.U., $3.50.
Camouflage in Nature Through Form and Color Matching (f, c), Coronet, film libraries, $4.00.
Digging Up the Dinosaurs; History of the Horse; The Story of Ancient Man (3 sets Kodachromes, 2″ × 2″), Amer. Museum of Natural History, inquire rental or purchase.
Dinosaurs (fs), Bowmar, $3.00.
Evolution (f, 3 rls), Almanac, $4.50.
Fingers and Thumbs (development of man's hand) (f, 2 rls), Almanac, $3.00.
The Fossil Story (f, c), Shell, free.
History of the Horse in North America (f, c), U. of Calif., $3.00.
How Nature Protects Animals (f), EBF, $2.50.
In the Beginning (story of Grand Canyon) (f, c), Modern Talking Pic., free.
Lascaux, Cradle of Man's Art (f, c, 2 rls), N.Y.U. Film Library, $7.00.
Life in a Garden (f, c), McGraw-Hill, $5.00.
Living Desert (6 fs, c), EBF, $6.00 ea.
Lost World (dinosaurs, based on story by A. Conan Doyle (f), Instructional, inquire rental.
Man, One Family (f), Brandon, $2.50.
Marine Communities (f, si, c), Iowa State U., $3.00.
Men of the Old Stone Age; Men of the New Stone Age (2 fs), Soc. Visual Educ., $3.50 ea.
Prehistoric Life (6 fs, c), EBF, $6.00 ea.
Prehistoric Times: the World Before Man (f, c), Coronet, film libraries, $3.00.
The Strands Grow (balance) (f, c), EBF, $5.50.
This Vital Earth (interrelationships) (f, c), EBF, $4.00; free, Soil Conservation Service.
The World We Live In (ser fs, c), Life, $6.00 ea.

Conservation

500,000 to 1 (insects, destructive and helpful) (f, c), Sinclair, free.
American Frontier (f), Amer. Petroleum Inst., free.
Animal Environments (8 fs, c), Curriculum Films, $3.95 ea.
Animal Life and the Soil (fs), EBF, $3.00.
Arteries of Life (f, c), EBF, $4.00.
Balanced Aquarium (f, c), EBF, $4.00.

Battle of the Beetles (f, c), U.S. Forest Service, free.
Battle of the Budworm (f, c), International Paper, free.
Battling the Borer (f, c), Allis-Chalmers, free.
Beneath Our Feet (f), Teaching Film Custodians, local film libraries.
Bird Nesting Time (balance, destroying insects) (f, c), Minneapolis-Moline, free.
Birth of the Soil (f, c), EBF, $4.00.
Blades of Green (f, c), Union Pacific Railroad, free.
Bounty of the Forest (f, c), Western Pine Assoc., free.
Building a Pond (f, si), Case, free.
Carbon-Oxygen Cycle (f, si), EBF, inquire rental.
Chaparral (f, c), U. of Calif., $6.00.
Chemical Weed Control (f, c), Dow Chemical, free.
Conservation in Action (f, c), U.S. Fish and Wildlife Service, free.
Conservation Is Everybody's Business (ser 4 fs), Popular Sci., $6.50 set.
Conservation of Natural Resources (f), EBF, $2.50.
Conservation Road—the Story of Our Natural Resources (f), Instructional, inquire rental.
Conservation Today (fs), Colonial, $6.00.
Conserving Our Resources (8 fs), Curriculum Films, inquire purchase.
County Agricultural Agent (f, c), Venard, free.
Enough and for All (f, c), Venard, free.
Erosion (man-made) (f), Soil Conservation Service, free.
Everyman's Empire (f, c), U.S. Dept. Agriculture, free, local film libraries.
Feed the Soil and It Will Feed You (f, c), Beet Sugar Development, free.
First Job: Conservation (f, c), Davy Tree Expert Co., free.
Forest Conservation (f, c), EBF, $4.00.
From the Ground Up (f, c), Soil Conservation Service, free.
From the Ridge to the River (f, c), U.S. Dept. Agriculture, free.
Grass: the Big Story (f, c), U.S. Dept. Agriculture, free.
Grassland Report (f, c), New Holland Machine, free.
Gypsy Moth (f, c), U.S. Dept. Agriculture, free.
Heritage We Guard (f), U.S. Dept. Agriculture, free.
How Soil Is Formed (fs), EBF, $3.00.
Hunger Signs; Life of the Soil (2 f, c), Nat. Fertilizer Assoc., free.
In Partnership with Nature (f, c), Modern Talking Pic., free.
Jungle Giants (f), Teaching Film Custodians, local film libraries.
Killers (f), Teaching Film Custodians, local film libraries.
Killing Weeds with 2, 4 D (f, c), U.S. Dept. Agriculture, free.

Land and Life (f, c), TVA, free.
Life of the Soil (f), Soil Conservation Service, free.
Living Forest (f, c), EBF, inquire rental.
Living Water Series (f, 2 rls), EBF, $4.00.
Look to the Land (f, 2 rls, c), EBF, $7.00.
Lower Souris Refuge (f, si, c), U.S. Fish and Wildlife Service, free.
Making the Most of a Miracle (plant nutrition) (f, c), Farm Film Foundation, free.
Making of the River (f, c), Coronet, film libraries.
Man Against Insects (fs), Popular Sci. (McGraw-Hill), $3.00.
Marvels in Miniature (barrier reef) (f, c), Australian News and Information Bur., $2.50.
Master Element (water) (f, c), American Waterways Operators, free.
Masters of the Soil; This Is Our Land (2 f), Ethyl Corp., free.
Minerals and the Soil (fs), EBF, $3.00.
More Food from Fewer Acres (irrigation) (f, c), Case, free.
Muddy Waters (f), Soil Conservation Service, free.
Natural Resources—Key to America's Strength (fs), N. Y. Times, $3.00.
Nature's Half Acre (f, c), Association Films, $10.00.
New Paul Bunyan (f, c), Modern Talking Pic., free.
Nitrogen Cycle (f), UWF, $3.00.
Nutrient-deficiency Symptoms in Plants (slides, c), Nat. Plant Food Inst., $0.25 ea.
Our Soil Resources (f), EBF, $2.50.
Pipeline to the Clouds (f, c), General Electric, free.
Planning to Prosper (f, c), Allis-Chalmers, free.
Plant Life and the Soil (fs), EBF, $3.00.
Plant Speaks Through Leaf Analysis; Plant Speaks Through Deficiency Symptoms; New Soils for Old; Plant Speaks, Soil Tests Tell Us Why (4 f, c), Amer. Potash, free.
Rain on the Plains (f), U.S. Dept. Agriculture, free.

Raindrops and Soil Erosion (f, c), Soil Conservation Service, free.
River (f), UWF, inquire rental.
Rivers and the Soil (f, c), Minneapolis-Moline, free.
River Run; Then It Happened; Terracing in the Northeast (3 f, c), U.S. Dept. Agriculture, free.
Save the Soil (f), U.S. Dept. Agriculture, free.
Seeds of Destruction (f, c), EBF, $4.00.
Soil Conservation (8 fs), EBF, $3.00 ea.
Soil and Life (terracing) (f, c), Case, free.
Soybeans—Feature Story (f, c), Modern Talking Pic., free.
Story of Fertilizers (fs), Visual Educ. Consultants, $3.00.
Story of West Coast Lumber (fs), West Coast Lumbermen's Assoc., free.
A Strand Breaks (web-of-life series) (f, c), EBF, $5.50.
To Conserve Our Heritage (f, c), Minneapolis-Moline, free.
Topsoil (f), Soil Conservation Service, free.
Tree Bank (f, c), U.S. Forest Service, free.
Trees for Tomorrow (f), free, N. Y. State College Agriculture.
Upstream Where Floods Begin (f), Soil Conservation Service, free.
Water (f), U.S. Dept. Agriculture, free.
Water: Friend or Enemy (f, c), Association Films, $2.00.
Weather or Not (f), Nat. Fertilizer Assoc., free.
Wonders of the Sea (f), Teaching Film Custodians, local film library.
World at Your Feet (f, c), Internat. Film Bur.; free, state conservation dept.
World That Nature Forgot (f, c), Monsanto, free.
Your Enemy—Grasshopper (f, c), U.S. Dept. Agriculture, free.
Your Valley, Your Future (f, c), Connecticut Light and Power, free.
Yours Is the Land (f, 2 rls, c), EBF, $7.00.

Field work in biology

We think of field stations and nature camps as a kind of bibliography for the professional growth of teachers. Many universities offer courses at camps and field stations. Many well-known biological research stations attract research biologists and teachers of biology. Some are open the year round, others for a 6- to 8-week summer session, for research work only. We offer this list only by way of suggestion. Further information can be obtained from the director of the field station or camp.

Gulf Coast Research Laboratory
Ocean Springs, Miss.
Year round and summer session:
Marine geology, zoology.

Institute of Marine Biology
U. of Oregon, Eugene, Ore.
Summer session:
Marine biology, algology, invertebrate zoology.

Marine Biological Laboratory
Woods Hole, Mass.
Summer sessions:
Research and courses in embryology, physiology, marine botany, invertebrate zoology, marine ecology.

Marine Laboratory
1 Rickenbacker Causeway, Miami 54, Fla.
Year round and summer session:
Marine biology, geology, ichthyology, oceanography.

Mount Desert Island Biological Laboratory
Salisbury Cove, Maine
Summer work:
Research, no courses.

Purdue U. Conservation Education Camp
Lafayette, Ind.
Summer session:
Conservation education.

Science Lodge, Institute of Arctic and Alpine Research
U. of Colorado, Boulder, Colo.
Year round:
No classes, accommodations and cooperation on field research.

Scripps Institution of Oceanography
U. of California (at La Jolla)
Year round:
No classes, research and graduate study in marine geophysics, physical oceanography, submarine geology, marine biology, marine chemistry, geochemistry.

Trout Lake Biological Laboratory
U. of Wisconsin, Madison, Wisc.
Summer session:
Research station; no courses (courses in hydrobiology at University campus).

U. of Michigan Biological Station
Ann Arbor, Mich.
Summer session:
Marine biology, botany, fresh-water biology, botany, zoology.

U. of New Hampshire
Durham, N. H.
Summer session:
Marine invertebrate zoology.

Virginia Fisheries Laboratory
Gloucester Point, Va.
Year round:
Marine biology, fisheries science.

Walla Walla College Biological Station
Anacortes, Wash.
Summer session:
Marine invertebrates, marine botany, ichthyology, ornithology, oceanography, fisheries biology, parasitology, invertebrate physiology, entomology.

West Coast Nature School
San Jose State College, San Jose 14, Calif.
Summer session:
Field biology.

Use of free and inexpensive materials

Most of the companies and institutions listed here distribute useful free material on request; some charge a small sum, well under a dollar. We cannot, of course, list all the distributors of free and inexpensive materials, for we do not know them all. We have not attempted to list the specific materials available, since these change fairly often whereas the companies offering these materials do not usually change their public relations policies.

We recommend that the teacher send for a list of booklets, charts, films, or filmstrips available from the companies, and then select the materials useful for classwork. These can be filed in manila envelopes or file folders, properly labeled, ready for teacher or student use. We hope that individual students in class will not send for materials, for this creates a strain on any company's policy of good will.

There is much abuse as well as use of free teaching aids. When you have found a successful way to use some aid in the classroom, why not submit the method to a teachers' publication so that other teachers may gain from your experience?

Directory of distributors

Alcoholics Anonymous, P.O. Box 459, Grand Central Annex, New York 17.

American Aberdeen Angus Breeders' Association, 9 Dexter Park, Chicago 9.

American Can Co., 100 Park Ave., New York 17.

American Cancer Society, 47 Beaver St., New York 14; or 1416 6th Ave., San Diego 1.

American Dental Association, Order Dept., 222 E. Superior St., Chicago 11.

American Diabetes Association, Inc., 1 E. 45 St., New York.

American Educational Publishers, 400 S. Front St., Columbus 15, Ohio.

American Forest Products, Inc., 1816 N St. N.W., Washington 6, D. C.

American Gas Association Educational Service, 420 Lexington Ave., New York 17.

American Guernsey Cattle Club, Peterborough, N. H.

American Hampshire Sheep Association, 72 Woodland Ave., Detroit 2.

American Heart Association, Inc., 44 E. 23 St., New York 10.

American Hereford Association, 300 W. 11 St., Kansas City, Mo.

American Institute of Baking, Consumer Service Dept., 400 E. Ontario St., Chicago 11.

American Museum of Natural History, 79 St. and Central Park W., New York.

American National Red Cross, Washington 13, D. C.

American Nature Association, 1214 16 St. N.W., Washington 6, D. C.

American Optical Co., Instrument Division, Buffalo 15, N. Y.

American Potash Institute, 1102 16 St. N.W., Washington 6, D.C.

American Society of Bakery Engineers, 121 W. Wacker Dr., Chicago 1.

Armour & Co., Education Dept., Union Stockyards, Chicago 9.

Bausch & Lomb Optical Co., 635 St. Paul St., Rochester 2, N. Y.

Better Light, Better Sight Bureau, 420 Lexington Ave., New York 17.

Better Vision Institute, Inc., 630 5th Ave., New York 20.

Borden Company, Educational Service, 350 Madison Ave., New York 17.

Bristol-Myers Co., 630 5th Ave., New York 20.

Bureau of Land Management, U.S. Dept. Interior, Washington 25, D. C.

California Dairy Industry Advisory Board, 907 12 St., Sacramento 14.

California Dept. Mental Hygiene, Sacramento 14.

California Fruit Growers Exchange, P.O. Box 5030, Metropolitan Station, Los Angeles 54.

California Redwood Association, 576 Sacramento St., San Francisco 11.

California State Dept. Natural Resources, Conservation Education, State Office Bldg., Sacramento 14.

Cambosco Scientific Co., 37 Antwerp St., Brighton 35, Mass.

Carnegie Institution of Washington, Cold Spring Harbor, L. I., N. Y.

Carolina Biological Supply Co., Elon College, N. C.

J. I. Case & Co. (conservation pamphlets and filmstrips), 700 State St., Racine, Wisc.

Cereal Institute, Inc., Educational Service, 135 S. La Salle St., Chicago 3.

Chicago Natural History Museum, Educational Dept., Roosevelt Rd., Chicago 5.

Church & Dwight, Inc. (pictures of birds), 70 Pine St., New York.

Cinchona Products Institute, Inc., 10 Rockefeller Plaza, New York 20.

Conservation Foundation, 30 E. 40 St., New York 16.

Continental Baking Co., Inc., 630 5th Ave., New York 20.

Corn Industries Research Foundation, 3 E. 45 St., New York 17.

Corning Glass Works, Public Relations Dept., 718 5th Ave., New York 19.

Cream of Wheat Corp., 730 Stenson Blvd., Minneapolis 13, Minn.

Crown Zellerbach Corp., Rincon Annex, Box 3475, San Francisco.

Denoyer-Geppert Co., 5235 N. Ravenswood Ave., Chicago 40.

Diamond Crystal Salt Co., St. Clair, Mich.

Dow Chemical Co., Midland, Mich.

E. I. du Pont de Nemours Co., Inc., Public Relations Dept., 1007 Market St., Wilmington 98, Del.

Educators' Mutual Insurance Co., Lancaster, Pa.

Evaporated Milk Association, 228 N. La Salle St., Chicago 1.

Farmers' & Manufacturers Beet Sugar Association, Education Dept., Saginaw, Mich.

Fels & Co., 73 St. and Woodland Ave., Philadelphia 42.

Fisher Scientific Co., 717 Forbes St., Pittsburgh 19.

General Biological Supply House, 8200 S. Hoyne Ave., Chicago 20.

General Foods Corp., 250 Park Ave., New York 17.

General Mills, Inc. 400 2d Ave., S., Minneapolis 1, Minn.

John Hancock Mutual Life Insurance Co., 200 Berkeley St., Boston 17.

Hershey Chocolate Corp., Hershey, Pa.

Health Information Foundation, 420 Lexington Ave., New York 17.

Health Publications Institute, Inc., Raleigh, N. C.

H. J. Heinz Co., Public Relations Dept., 1062 Progress Street, Pittsburgh 12.

Hoffman-La Roche, Inc., Vitamin Division, Nutley, N. J.

Holstein-Friesian Association of America, 1 S. Main St., Brattleboro, Vt.

Illinois State Department of Health, Springfield.

Illinois State Natural History Survey, Natural Resources Bldg., Urbana.

Illuminating Engineering Society, 1860 Broadway, New York 23.

Indiana Dept. Conservation, Division Parks, Lands, and Waters, Indianapolis 9.

Innes Publishing Co. (aquarium literature), 12 St. at Cherry, Philadelphia 7.

International Harvester Company, 180 N. Michigan Ave., Chicago 1.

International Paper Co., Southern Kraft Division, Mobile 9, Ala.

Johnson & Johnson Co., Education Dept., New Brunswick, N. J.

Kellogg Company, Home Economics Services, Battle Creek, Mich.

Knox Gelatin Co., 655 Chestnut St., Johnstown, N. Y.

Kraft Food Co., 500 N. Peshtigo Court, Chicago 90.

Laboratory of Applied Psychology, Box 2162, Yale Station, New Haven, Conn.

La Motte Chemical Products Co., Towson 4, Baltimore, Md.

Lederle Laboratories, Division American Cyanamid Co., 30 Rockefeller Plaza, New York 20.

Leitz Optical Co., 468 4th Ave., New York 16.

Louisiana Department Wildlife and Fisheries, Visual Education Dept., 126 Civil Courts Bldg., New Orleans 16.

Maryland Society for Medical Research, 522 W. Lombard St., Baltimore 1.

Mentor Books (New American Library of World Literature), 501 Madison Ave., New York 22.

Merck & Co., Inc., Rahway, N. J.

C. Merrill Book Co., Columbus 15, Ohio.

Metropolitan Life Insurance Co., School Service Dept., 1 Madison Ave., New York 16; or 600 Stockton St., San Francisco 20.

Minneapolis-Moline Co. (conservation materials), Minneapolis 1, Minn.

National Academy of Sciences, 2101 Constitution Ave., Washington 25, D. C.

National Association of Manufacturers, 2 E. 48 St., New York 20.

National Association for Mental Health, Inc., 10 Columbus Circle, New York.

National Audubon Society, 1130 5th Ave., New York 28.

National Cancer Association, 1739 H St. N.W., Washington 6, D. C.

National Cancer Institute, 9000 Wisconsin Ave., Bethesda, Md.

National Chinchilla Breeders Association, Inc., P.O. Box 1806, Salt Lake City 10.

National Confectioners' Association, 221 N. La Salle St., Chicago 1.

National Cotton Council of America, P.O. Box 18, Memphis 1, Tenn.

National Dairy Council, 111 N. Canal St., Chicago 6.

National Epilepsy League, Inc., 130 N. Wells St., Chicago 6.

National Fertilizer Association, 616 Continental Bldg., Washington 5, D. C.

National Foundation for Infantile Paralysis, Inc., 301 E. 42 St., New York.

National Institute of Mental Health, Public Health Service, 9000 Wisconsin Ave., Bethesda, Md.

National Live Stock & Meat Board, 407 S. Dearborn St., Chicago 5.

National Safety Council, 425 N. Michigan Ave., Chicago 11.

National Society for the Prevention of Blindness, 1790 Broadway, New York 19.

National Tuberculosis Association, 1790 Broadway, New York 19.

National Vitamin Foundation, Inc., 15 E. 58 St., New York.

National Wildlife Federation, Education Dept., 232 Carroll St. N.W., Washington 10, D. C.

New Hampshire Dept. Health, Office Health Education, 66 South St., Concord.

New York City Dept. Health, 125 Worth St., New York 13.

New York City Cancer Committee, 7 E. 52 St., New York 21.

New York Heart Association, Inc., 485 5th Ave., New York.

New York State College of Agriculture, Cornell University, Ithaca, N. Y.

New York State Dept. Health, Office Health Education, 18 Dove St., Albany 6.

New York Zoological Society, Bronx Park, New York 60.

Nutrition Foundation, Inc., 99 Park Ave., New York 16.

Pet Milk Co., 64 Pine St., San Francisco.

C. Pfizer Co., Inc., 11 Bartlett St., Brooklyn 6, N. Y.

Quaker Oats Co., Advertising Dept., 141 W. Jackson Blvd., Chicago 4.

Ralston-Purina Co., Nutrition Service, St. Louis 2.

A. I. Root Co. (booklets on bees), Medina, Ohio.

Row, Peterson & Co., Evanston, Ill.

Science Clubs of America, Science Service, 1719 N St. N.W., Washington 6, D. C.

Science Research Associates, 57 W. Grand Ave., Chicago 10.

Society for Visual Education, Inc., 1345 W. Diversey Pkwy., Chicago 14.

Soil Conservation Service, U.S. Dept. Agriculture, 209 S.W. 5th Ave., Portland 4, Ore.; or Washington 25, D. C.

Southern Pine Association, National Bank Commerce Bldg., P.O. Box 1170, New Orleans 4.

Standard Brands, Inc., 625 Madison Ave., New York 22.

Standard Oil Company of New Jersey, Education Dept., 30 Rockefeller Plaza, New York 20.

Sugar Information, Inc., 52 Wall St., New York 5.

Swift & Co., Agricultural Research Dept., Union Stockyards, Chicago 9.

Tennessee Valley Authority, Health and Safety Dept., Chattanooga 1, Tenn.

United Fruit Co., Education Dept., Pier 3, North River, New York 6.

U.S. Atomic Energy Commission, Washington 25, D. C.; or 70 Columbus Ave., New York.

U.S. Beet Sugar Association, Tower Bldg., Washington 5, D. C.

U.S. Dept. Agriculture, Agricultural Research Service, Washington 25, D. C.

U.S. Dept. Agriculture, Experimental Fur Station, Petersburg, Alaska.

U.S. Dept. Health, Education, & Welfare, Education Division, Washington 25, D. C.

U.S. Fish & Wildlife Service, Dept. Interior, Washington 25, D. C.

U.S. Forest Service, San Francisco 11; Milwaukee 3; Missoula, Mont.; Portland 8, Ore.

U.S. Government Printing Office, Washington 25, D. C.

U.S. Public Health Service, Communicable Disease Center, Atlanta, Ga.

University of Illinois, Dept. Horticulture, College Agriculture, Urbana.

Upjohn Co. (vitamin book) Kalamazoo, Mich.

Ward's Natural Science Establishment, 3000 Ridge Road E., Rochester 9, N. Y.

Welch Manufacturing Co., 1515 N. Sedgwick St., Chicago 10.

Western Pine Association, Dept. Public Relations, 510 Yeon Bldg., Portland 4, Ore.

Westinghouse Electric Corp., School Service, Box 1017, 306 4th Ave., Pittsburgh 30.

Weyerhaeuser Timber Co., First National Bank Bldg., St. Paul 1, Minn.

Wheat Flour Institute, 309 W. Jackson Blvd., Chicago 6.

Whitman Publishing Co., 1220 Mound Ave., Racine, Wisc.

Reference aids

There are many compilations of free and inexpensive materials which have been published to meet the constant search of teachers for classroom aids. For those teachers who will want to go beyond the directory we have accumulated, we have added a short bibliography of some publications we have encountered. (Prices are given when they are known.) Be sure to check the distributors of free films and filmstrips (p. 464).

Sources of Free and Inexpensive Educational Materials, Field Enterprises, Inc., Education Division, Merchandise Mart Plaza, Chicago 54, 1955, $5.00.

Free and Inexpensive Learning Materials, George Peabody College for Teachers, Division of Surveys and Field Services, Nashville 5, Tenn., 1956, $1.00.

Elementary Teachers Guide to Free Curriculum Materials, Educators' Progress Service, Randolph, Wisc., 1956, $5.50.

Sources of Teaching Materials, C. Williams, Bur. Educational Research, Ohio State U., 1955.

Sources of Free and Inexpensive Pictures for the Classroom, B. Miller, Box 369, Riverside, Calif., 1956, $0.50.

Free and Inexpensive Teaching Aids for High Schools, C. Holland, Nat. Assoc. Secondary School Principals, N.E.A., 1201 16 Street N.W., Washington 6, D. C., 1949, $1.00.

Sources of Free and Inexpensive Materials in Health Education, Teachers College, Temple U., Curriculum Laboratory, 1954, $0.25.

"Free and Inexpensive Teaching Materials For Science Education," M. Beuschlein and J.

Sanders, *Chicago Schools Journal,* vol. 34, Nos. 5, 6, 1953. (available as reprint)

Conservation Teaching Aids, Michigan Dept. Conservation, Education Division, 1951.

Catalog of Man and Nature Publications, Amer. Museum Natural History, New York 24.

Health Materials and Resources for Oregon Teachers, State Dept. Education, Salem, Ore., 1955.

1001 Valuable Things Free, 2d ed., M. Weisinger, Bantam Books, New York, 1957.

A Wonderful World for Children (free and inexpensive materials), P. Cardozo, Bantam Books, New York, 1956.

General Motors Aids to Educators, General Motors Corp., 1956.

Catalog of Free Educational Material on the Banana and Related Subjects, United Fruit Company, Educational Service Dept., Pier 3, North River, New York 6.

Choosing Free Materials for Use in the Schools, Amer. Assoc. of School Administrators, N.E.A., 1201 16 Street N.W., Washington 6, D. C. 1955, $0.50

Using Free Materials in the Classroom, Association Supervision and Curriculum Development, N.E.A., 1201 16 St. N.W., Washington 6, D. C., 1953, $0.75.

Sponsor Handbook; Thousands of Science Projects, Science Service, 1719 N St. N.W., Washington 6, D. C., 1957, $0.25 ea.

Teaching Aids, Westinghouse Electrical Corp., School Service, 306 4th Ave., Pittsburgh 30.

Hobby Publications, Superintendent of Documents, U.S. Govt. Printing Office, Washington 25, D. C.

Directory of supply houses

United States

Ainsworth & Sons, Inc., 2151 Lawrence St., Denver 5.

Allied Chemical & Dye Corp., 40 Rector St., New York 6.

Aloe Scientific, Division of A. S. Aloe Co., 5655 Kingsbury St., St. Louis 12.

American Hospital Supply Corp., 40-05 168 St., Flushing, N. Y.; or 2020 Ridge Ave., Evanston, Ill.

American Optical Co., Buffalo 15, N. Y.

American Type Culture Collection (bacteria), 2029 M St. N.W., Washington 6, D. C.

Bausch & Lomb Optical Co., 635 St. Paul St., Rochester, N. Y.

Biddle & Company, 1316 Arch St., Philadelphia 7.

Biological Research Products Co., 243 W. Root St., Chicago.

California Biological Service, 1612 W. Glenoaks Blvd., Glendale.

California Botanical Materials Co., 861 E. Columbia Ave., Pomona.

Cambosco Scientific Co., 37 Antwerp St., Brighton 35, Mass.

Carolina Biological Supply Co., Elon College, N. C.

Central Scientific Co., 1700 N. Irving Park Rd., Chicago 13.

Certified Blood Donor Service, 146-16 Hillside Ave., Jamaica 35, N. Y.

Chicago Apparatus Co., 1735 N. Ashland Ave., Chicago 22.

Clay-Adams Co., 141 E. 25 St., New York 10.

Corning Glass Works, Corning, N. Y.

Denoyer-Geppert Co., 5235 N. Ravenswood Ave., Chicago 40.

Difco Laboratories, Inc., Detroit 1.

Dow Chemical Co., Midland, Mich.

Eastman Kodak Co., 343 State St., Rochester 4, N. Y.

Eimer and Amend, Greenwich & Morton Sts., New York 14.

Erb & Gray Co., 854 S. Figueroa St., Los Angeles 14.

Fisher Scientific Supply Co., 139 Fisher Bldg., Pittsburgh 19.

General Biochemicals, Inc., 677 Laboratory Park, Chagrin Falls, Ohio.

General Biological Supply House, Inc. (Turtox), 8200 S. Hoyne Ave., Chicago 20.

Gradwohl Laboratories, 3514 Lucas Ave., St. Louis 3.

Graf-Apsco Co., 5868 N. Broadway, Chicago 40.

Harshaw Scientific Division, Harshaw Chemical Co., 1945 E. 97 St., Cleveland 6.

Kelly-Koett Manufacturing Co., 24 E. 6th St., Covington, Ky.

Kimble Glass, P.O. Box 1035, Toledo 1, Ohio.

Knickerbocker Blood Donor Service, 300 W. 43 St., New York.

Charles Lane Corp. (cabinets), 105 Chambers St., New York 7.

Lederle Laboratories, Div. American Cyanamid Co., Midtown Rd., Pearl River, N. Y.

Leitz, Inc., 468 4th Ave., New York 16.

Los Angeles Biological Laboratories, 2977 W. 14 St., Los Angeles 6.

Marine Biological Laboratory, Woods Hole, Mass.

Merck & Co., Rahway, N. J.

Monsanto Chemical Co., 1700 S. 2d St., St. Louis 4.

Nalge Co., Inc. (plastic ware), Rochester 2, New York.

New York Scientific Supply Co., 28 W. 30 St., New York.

Nutritional Biochemicals Corp., 21010 Miles Ave., Cleveland 2.

Nystrom & Co., 3333 N. Elston Ave., Chicago 18.

Oregon Biological Supply Co., 1806 S.E. Holgate Blvd., Portland.

Pacific Laboratory Apparatus Co., 3555 Whittier Blvd., Los Angeles 23.

Polaroid Corp., Cambridge 39, Mass.

Product Design Co. (conservation kits), 2796 Middlefield Rd., Redwood City, Calif.

Charles Pfizer & Co., 11 Bartlett St., Brooklyn, N. Y.

Research Specialties Co., 2005 Hopkins St., Berkeley 7, Calif.

Sheldon Equipment Co., 149 Thomas St., Muskegon, Mich.

Sprague-Dawley, Inc. (laboratory rats), P.O. Box 2071, Madison 5, Wisc.

Standard Scientific Corp., 34 W. 4th St., New York.

Testa Manufacturing Co., 418 S. Pecan St., Los Angeles 33.

United Scientific Co., 204 Milk St., Boston 9.

Ward's Natural Science Establishment, 3000 Ridge Rd. E., Rochester 9, N. Y.

Welch Manufacturing Co., 1515 N. Sedgwick St., Chicago 10.

Western Laboratories, 826 Q. St., Lincoln, Neb.

Windsor Biology Gardens, Moore's Creek Rd., Bloomington, Ind.

United Kingdom

United Scientific Instruments, Ltd., 62 Sherland Rd., Maida Vale, London W.9.

Laboratory Glassware Manufacturers, 200 Ravenscroft Rd., Beckenham, Kent.

C. Hearson and Co., Ltd., 68 Willow Walk, Bermondsey, London S.E. 1.

Scientific Instrument Manufacturers' Association of Great Britain, Ltd., 17 Princess Gate, London, S.W. 7.

National Collection of Type Cultures (bacteria), Chelsea Gardens, London S.W.

Canada

Beaconing Optical and Precision Materials Company, Ltd., 455 Craig W., Montreal.

Canadian Laboratory Supplies, Ltd., 403 St. Paul W., Montreal.

Fine Chemicals of Canada, Ltd., Toronto.

General Optical Co., Ltd., Montreal.

Richards Glass Co., Ltd., Toronto.

Reference tables

Systems of measure

Metric system

1 meter = 100 centimeters (cm) = 1000 millimeters (mm)
1 micron (μ) = 1/1000 millimeter
1 liter = 1000 milliliters (ml) = 1000 cubic centimeters (cc)
1 gram (gm) = 1/1000 kilogram (kg) = 1000 milligrams (mg)

Apothecaries' weight

1 pound = 12 ounces = 96 drams
1 dram = 3 scruples = 60 grains

Avoirdupois weight

1 pound = 16 ounces = 256 drams
1 dram = 27 11/32 grains = 1/16 ounce

Dry measure

1 quart = 2 pints = 1/8 peck = 1/32 bushel

Liquid measure

1 pint = 4 gills = 16 fluid ounces
1 quart = 2 pints = 1/4 gallon

Kitchen measure

1 common tumbler = 1/2 pint
60 drops = 1 teaspoon
3 teaspoons = 1 tablespoon
16 tablespoons = 1 cup
2 cups = 1 pint

Conversion factors

Weight

1 gram = 0.03527 ounce
1 kilogram = 2.205 pounds

1 ounce = 28.35 grams
1 pound = 0.4536 kilogram

Length

1 centimeter = 0.3937 inch
1 meter = 3.281 feet

1 inch = 2.54 centimeters
1 foot = 0.3048 meter

Volume

1 gallon = 3.785 liters = 231 cubic inches
1 cubic centimeter = 0.0610 cubic inch
1 teaspoon = 4 cubic centimeters
1 tablespoon $\cong$ 15 cubic centimeters $\cong$ 1/2 fluid ounce

International atomic weights

	Symbol	Atomic No.	Atomic Weight		Symbol	Atomic No.	Atomic Weight
Actinium	Ac	89	227*	Neodymium	Nd	60	144.27
Aluminum	Al	13	26.97	Neon	Ne	10	20.183
Americium	Am	95	241*	Neptunium	Np	93	237*
Antimony	Sb	51	121.76	Nickel	Ni	28	58.69
Argon	A	18	39.944	Niobium	Nb	41	92.91
Arsenic	As	33	74.91	Nitrogen	N	7	14.008
Astatine	At	85	211*	Osmium	Os	76	190.2
Barium	Ba	56	137.36	Oxygen	O	8	16.0000
Berkelium	Bk	97	243*	Palladium	Pd	46	106.7
Beryllium	Be	4	9.02	Phosphorus	P	15	30.98
Bismuth	Bi	83	209.00	Platinum	Pt	78	195.23
Boron	B	5	10.82	Plutonium	Pu	94	239*
Bromine	Br	35	79.916	Polonium	Po	84	210*
Cadmium	Cd	48	112.41	Potassium	K	19	39.096
Calcium	Ca	20	40.08	Praseodymium	Pr	59	140.92
Californium	Cf	98	244*	Promethium	Pm	61	147*
Carbon	C	6	12.010	Protactinium	Pa	91	231
Cerium	Ce	58	140.13	Radium	Ra	88	226.05
Cesium	Cs	55	132.91	Radon	Rn	86	222
Chlorine	Cl	17	35.457	Rhenium	Re	75	186.31
Chromium	Cr	24	52.01	Rhodium	Rh	45	102.91
Cobalt	Co	27	58.94	Rubidium	Rb	37	85.48
Copper	Cu	29	63.54	Ruthenium	Ru	44	101.7
Curium	Cm	96	242*	Samarium	Sm	62	150.43
Dysprosium	Dy	66	162.46	Scandium	Sc	21	45.10
Erbium	Er	68	167.2	Selenium	Se	34	78.96
Europium	Eu	63	152.0	Silicon	Si	14	28.06
Fluorine	F	9	19.00	Silver	Ag	47	107.880
Francium	Fr	87	223*	Sodium	Na	11	22.997
Gadolinium	Gd	64	156.9	Strontium	Sr	38	87.63
Gallium	Ga	31	69.72	Sulfur	S	16	32.066
Germanium	Ge	32	72.60	Tantalum	Ta	73	180.88
Gold	Au	79	197.2	Technetium	Tc	43	99*
Hafnium	Hf	72	178.6	Tellurium	Te	52	127.61
Helium	He	2	4.003	Terbium	Tb	65	159.2
Holmium	Ho	67	164.94	Thallium	Tl	81	204.39
Hydrogen	H	1	1.0080	Thorium	Th	90	232.12
Indium	In	49	114.76	Thulium	Tm	69	169.4
Iodine	I	53	126.92	Tin	Sn	50	118.70
Iridium	Ir	77	193.1	Titanium	Ti	22	47.90
Iron	Fe	26	55.85	Uranium	U	92	238.07
Krypton	Kr	36	83.7	Vanadium	V	23	50.95
Lanthanum	La	57	138.92	Wolfram	W	74	183.92
Lead	Pb	82	207.21	Xenon	Xe	54	131.3
Lithium	Li	3	6.940	Ytterbium	Yb	70	173.04
Lutecium	Lu	71	174.99	Yttrium	Y	39	88.92
Magnesium	Mg	12	24.32	Zinc	Zn	30	65.38
Manganese	Mn	25	54.93	Zirconium	Zr	40	91.22
Mercury	Hg	80	200.61				
Molybdenum	Mo	42	95.95				

NOTE: Any table of this sort rapidly becomes dated; as of late 1957 there were 102 elements (including einsteinium, fermium, mendelium, etc., not shown).

*Not yet confirmed by chemical analysis.

Temperature conversion

It is simple to convert Fahrenheit into centigrade temperatures (and vice versa) without memorizing any formulas. All that need be remembered is that $0°C = 32°F$ (the freezing point of water) and that each Fahrenheit degree is only 5/9 as large as a centigrade degree. Thus if you knew the temperature in Fahrenheit degrees, you would subtract 32 and take 5/9 of the result to find the temperature in centigrade degrees. And if you knew the centigrade temperature, you would multiply it by 9/5 and add 32 to the result to find the Fahrenheit temperature.

The illustration on this page is useful in understanding the relationship between these two temperature scales; or it can be used for the conversion itself: simply read directly across from one thermometer scale to the other.

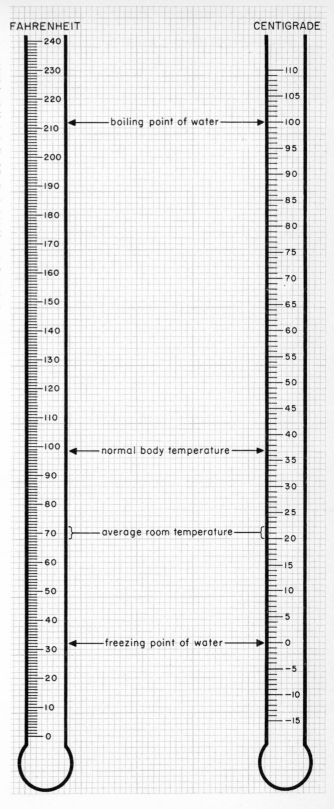

Index

Numbers in italics indicate pages bearing illustrations.
No separate listing is shown for related text on same page.

of crocus, *157*
Corn kernels, carbon dioxide produced by, 97, 98
dissection of, 178
effect of oxygen shortage on, 103, 104
germination of, 398
glucose stored by, 14
heat produced by, 104
heredity in, 195
oxygen needed in germination of, 102
similarity in first leaves of seedlings, 213
survival count of seedlings, 213
Corn borer, European, 234
Corn smut, 228
Cornmeal medium, for culture of *Drosophila*, 200
Cornmeal-molasses-rolled oats medium, for culture of *Drosophila*, 200
Coronary arteries, 71
Corpuscles. *See* Blood cells
Cost, of apparatus and equipment, 432–38
Costello's method, of fern culture, 396–97
Cotyledon secunda, 156
Cotyledons, 107
Coulter, J. M., 148
Cover crops, 238, 240, 265
Cow, kidney of, 91
lungs of, 90
Crab, collecting, 248
hermit, *233*
preserving, 260–61
Crassula, 20
Crayfish, anatomy of, 272, *273*
circulatory system of, 272, *273*
collecting, 248, 257
digestive system of, 272, *273*
dissection of, 272
drying, 261
excretory system of, *273*
nervous system of, 272
preserving, 257
reproductive system of, 272, *273*
sperms of, 272
Cream of Wheat medium, for culture of *Drosophila*, 200
Crenation, of blood cells, 76
Cresol, for sterilizing culture media, 383
Cresol red, range of, 407
Crocus, 157, 176
Crops, cover, 238, 240, 265
rotation of, 232–33, 236
on school grounds, 265
Crossing, of *Drosophila*, 198, 201–03, 204–05

Croton, 159–60
Crowfoot, 215
Crustaceans, collecting, 248, 351
culturing, 351*ff.*
mounting in glycerin jelly, 317
preserving, 260
Cryptocercus, 311
Cryptocoryne, 363
Crystal violet, 320
Crystal violet, ammonium oxalate solution, 321
Culture center, 427–28
maintaining, 334
Cultures, bacteria-free, 340–41
indicators for testing media of, 385
inoculating media for, *384*
sterilizing media for, 382–83
stock, for *Drosophila*, 199–200
Culturing, of algae, 375–78
of ants, 358
of *Artemia*, 354
of bacteria, 380–85
of butterflies, 357
of ciliates, 338–41
of crustaceans, 351*ff.*
of *Cyclops*, 353
of *Cypris*, 353
of *Daphnia*, 351, 352
of earthworms, 348
of *Enchytraeus*, 348–49
of *Eubranchipus*, 353
of ferns, 394–97
of flagellates, 341–42
of fruit flies, 199, 200
of *Gammarus*, 353–54
of *Hydra*, 345–46
of insectivorous plants, 233
of insects, 357–59
of lichens, 391
of marine invertebrates, 355
of molds, 388–91
of mosses, 392–94
of moths, 357
of planarians, 346–47
of praying mantis, 357
of protozoa, 264, 334–42
of rhizopods, 334–38
of rotifers, 347
of seed plants, 397–401
of slime molds, 386–87
of snails, 350–51
of sponges, 344–45
of *Spirogyra*, 376, 378
of *Tenebrio* beetles, 357–58
of termites, 358–59
of *Tribolium confusum*, 357
of *Tubifex*, 349, 350
of vinegar eels, 348
of woodlice, 354–55
of worms, aquatic, 349–50
of yeast, 391

Curator, student, 264, 442
Curricular pattern, 1
techniques and procedures within, 4–6
Curtis, G., 114
Cuscuta (dodder), *229*–30, 297, 400
Cut leaf, *293*
Cuttings, definition of, 157–58
dipped in hormone powder, 117
growth of, effect of leaves and buds on, 115–16
in hydroponic solution, 112
leaf, 159
soaked in solution of indolebutyric acid, 116–17
stem, 158–59
Cyclops, 305, *352*, 353
Cyclosis, 312
Cypris, *352*
Cytoplasm, chlorophyll in, 17, 18
streaming of, 312

Dace, red-bellied, 365
Daffodil, 20, 157, 176, 177
Dahlia, 157, 298
Daisy, 177
"Damping off," 396, 399
Damsel fly, collecting, 248
mounting, 261
preserving, 250
spreading wings of, 262
Dandelion, 176, 177, 215, 216
Daphnia, 31, 376, 378
for aquarium, 362, 364
collecting, 248
culturing, *351*, 352
digestion by, 32
eggs of, 165–66
as food, for *Hydra*, 346
for medaka, 365
for salamander, 366, 367
heart beat in, 70–71, 352
ingestion in, 352
under microscope, 305
mounting, 316
and oxygen–carbon dioxide cycle, 87
Darkroom, 429
Darwin, Charles, 212, 235
quoted, 220–21
D.D.T., 234
Dehydration, of specimens, 260, 317, 326–27
Dehydrogenase, 313
Delafield's hematoxylin, 323, 329
DeLong, D., 263, 359 and *n.*
Demerec, M., 199 and *n.*, 317 and *n.*
Demonstration table, 424, 425
Dennstaedtia punctilobula, 394

Dentate leaf, *293*
Dero, culturing, 350
  digestion by, 32
  as food for *Hydra,* 30–31, 346
  heart beat in, 71
  ingestion by, 30
  under microscope, 305
  and oxygen–carbon dioxide cycle, 87
  respiration in, 349
Desmids, 254, 255, *378*
Desmognathus fuscus, 367
De Vries, theory of, 224
Diabetes, 82
Dialyzing tubing, 35, 65 and *n.*
Diaphragm, action of, in breathing, *88*
Diastase, 34, 57, 58
Diatoms, 249, *378,* 379
Dicotyledons, 14, 178, 214, 296, *297,* 298, *299*
Dicranum moss, 366, 392
Dictyuchus, 337, 389
Didinium, 340, *341*
Didymium, 386
Dieffenbachia, 158
Diet, questions on, 41
  recommended daily allowances in, 39
  See also Foods
Difco's Bacto-Neurospora culture agar, 389
Difflugia, 337, 343
Diffusion, 22, 32–35
  osmosis distinguished from, 34*n.,* 52
Diffusion model, 52
Digestion (digestive system), in animals, 58–66
  by amylase, 60, 61, 63–64
  by lipase, 64
  by pepsin, 62–63
  by trypsin, 63
  in clam, 274, *275*
  in cockroach, 278
  in crayfish, 272, *273*
  and diffusion, 32–35
  in *Drosophila* larvae, 32
  in earthworm, 270
  of fats, 64
  in fetal pig, 288
  in fish, 280
  food tube in, 32–35
  in frog, 32, 281
  gastric, 62–65
  in grasshopper, 277
  in insectivorous plants, 66
  in microscopic many-celled organisms, 32
  model of, 411
  in molds, extracellular, 66

in *Paramecium,* 29
in pigeon, 286, *287*
in plants, 56–58
  effect of temperature on, 58
  enzyme activity in, 56–58
  insectivorous, 66
of proteins, in animals, 62–63
  in plants, 58
  in protozoa, 29–30
  in rat, 290, *291*
  in seeds, 56–57
  in snake, 284
of starch, in animals, 58–61
  in plants, 56–58
  in starfish, 276
  in turtle, 285
Dilutions, 403–04
Dinosaurs, 223
Dionaea (Venus fly-trap), *233,* 294, 400
Dip net, 227, *248*
Diphyllobothrium, 230
Disc technique, in chromatography, 16, *17*
Disinfectant, seed, 409
Dissection, of clam, 274
  of cockroach, *278–79*
  of crayfish, *272–73*
  of earthworm, *270–71*
  of fetal pig, *288–89*
  of fish, 168, *280*
  of frog, 32, 90, *281–83*
  of grains of corn, 178
  of grasshopper, *277*
  of heart, of beef, sheep, or hog, 71
  of pig uterus, 176
  of pigeon, *286–87*
  of rat, 174, *290–91*
  of seeds, 178
  of snake, *284*
  of starfish, *276*
  of turtle, *285*
Dissection pans, making, 410
Ditmars, R., 217
Dobson flies, preserving, 250, 261
Dodder, *229–30,* 297, 400
Dogwood, *294*
Dominant traits, 201, 202
Dragonfly, classification of, 252
  collecting, 248, 249
  mounting, 261
  preserving, 250
  spreading wings of, 262
Drosera (sundew), *233,* 400
Drosophila (fruit flies), chromosomes of, 197, 201, 202, 203
  map of, *197*
  culturing, 199–200, 264
  distinguishing male from female, *198*

eggs of, 166
etherization of, 197–98, *199*
as food, for *Drosera,* 400
  for *Hyla crucifer,* 369
  for lizards, 370
  for salamanders, 366, 367
genes of, 196, 201, 202, 206
  on chromosomes, *197*
heredity in, 196–203, *204–05*
  and chromosomes, 197, 201, 202, 203
  and crossing, 198, 201–03, *204–05*
  and mating, 196
  and sex identification, 196, 197, *198*
  and sex linkage, 202–03, *204–05*
  stocks for study of, 196
  and test cross, 201
larvae of, *31*
  digestion in, 32
  metamorphosis of, 166
  mounted in syrup, 316
  mouth parts of, 31
  overcrowding among, 213
  response to light, 125
  stock cultures of, 199–200
  subculturing, 199
Dry heat sterilization, 382
Dry ice, for seeding clouds, 242
Duckweed (*Lemna*), 363, 364, *400,* 401
Ductless glands, 138
Dugesia tigrina, 346
Dung agar, for culturing molds, 388
Dunn, S., 114
DuShane, G., 339 and *n.*
Dyes, aniline, 320
  vital, 77, 309

Earthworm, anatomy of, 270–*71*
  circulation in, 74, 270, *271*
  collecting, 251, 257, 348
  conditioning, 132
  dissection of, 270
  as food for specimens in vivaria, 366, 367, 369, 370, 371
  light avoided by, 125
  maintaining, 348
  maze for conditioning, *132*
  nervous system of, 270, *271*
  parasitic protozoa in, 310
  preserving, 257
  regeneration in, 156
  reproductive system of, 270, *271*
  response to contact, 127
  sperms of, 270

Fertilization (*cont.*)
in snails, 164
as union of sperm and egg, 164
Fertilization membrane, *165*
Fertilizer, 243, 265, 406
Fetus, of pig, 176, 288, *289*
of rat, 174
Feulgen nuclear reagent, 323
Fibrin, 63, 78
Fibrovascular bundles, of jewel-weed, 43, 44
of celery, 44, 313
Ficus elastica. See Rubber plant
Fiddler crab, 248, 260
Field experiment, in supplying nitrates to grass, 235
Field trip, collecting on, 177, 248–55
elementary school, 4, 5, 6
erosion studied on, 10, 238–39
and fruits and seeds on trees, 178
indoor, 263–64
planning, 246, *247*
pond studied on, 226–27
precautions for, 449
procedures for, 7–8
tree census on, 240
variations found on, in plants, 215
in shells, 217
Fieldbook of Ponds and Streams, 227
Fifth-grade activities, 5
Fight to Live, The, 217
Film cement, 409
Film distribution, directory of, 464–73
Film room, 428–29
Filtration, of water, 242
Fir seedlings, 214
Fireproofing fabrics, 450
First aid cabinet, 447, 448, 450
First-grade activities, 4
Fish, anatomy of, *280*
aquarium care of, 361–66
brain of, *280*
chromatophores in, 72, 309
circulatory system of, 280
collecting, 258
digestive system of, 280
diseases of, 366
dissection of, 168, 280
excretory system of, 280
gills of, 90
mitotic stages in egg of (white-fish), *161*
native, for aquarium, *365*–66
nervous system of, 280
ovaries of, 168
preserving, 258, 260
reproductive system of, 280

respiratory system of, 280
roe of, 212
testes of, 168
tropical, for aquarium, 364–*65*
Fissidens, 392
Fission, 153–54
in *Paramecium,* 153
Fixatives, 256–59 *pass.,* 322, 324–26
Flagellates, in beetles, 311
classification of, *343, 344*
in cockroach, 311
collecting, 341
culturing, 341–42
in termites, 232, 251, *311,* 359
Flatworms. *See* Planarians
Flemming's fixative, 325
Flies, classification of, 252
collecting, 248
as food for frog, 369
fruit. *See Drosophila*
mounting, 262, 316
preserving, 250
"Flip book," 208
Florence flask model of air sac, 75
Floscularia, 347
Flour beetle, 11, 357
Flower key, 177
Flowerpot culture, of ferns, 395–96
of mosses, 393–94
Flowers, study of, 176–79, 264
Fogel, S., 26 and *n.*
Food chains, 228–29, 264
of parasites and hosts, 230
in pond, 227
saprophytes in, 231
in stream, 228
Food for Life, 84
Food-getting, 2–3
by amphibians, 31
by annelid worms, 30
by chameleons, *31*
by hydras, 30–31, 346
by insects, 31
by planarians, 30
by protozoa, 29–30
Foods, "basic seven," 40, 41
calories in, 38–39
library research on, 40
and nutrient tests, 36
pH values of, 408
plants as makers of, 13–28
preserving, 9–10
solubility of, 32
vitamin content of, 37–38
See also Diet
Foot, of frog, circulation in, 72–*73*
For Greater Safety in Science Teaching, 447

Ford, N., 335 and *n.*
Formaldehyde, safe uses of, 449
Formalin, as disinfectant, 97, 256*ff.*
as fixative, 330
as hardening agent for plant tissues, 325
as macerating fluid, 316
Forsythia, 158, 176
Fossils, 211, 212
storage of, 438
Fourth-grade activities, 5
Fox, H. Munro, 18
Fragaria (strawberry), stolon of, 156, *157*
Fragmentation, of rock, 238
Freehand sections, 315
Fresh Water Invertebrates of the United States, 227, 263
Frings, H., 339 and *n.*
Fritillaria, cross section of ovary of, *178*
Frogs, anatomy of, *281–83*
anesthetizing, 132, 281
blinking reflex of, 127
blood cells of, 76, *283*
breathing movements of, 127, 281
ciliary motion in, 32, 281, 282, 309
circulation in, 72–74, 281
collecting, 259
decerebrated, *128–29*
diffusion through intestine of, 34, *35*
digestion by, 32, 281
dissection of, 32, 90, *281–83*
eggs of, 169, 212, 282, 367
artificial fertilization of, 171
artificial parthenogenesis in, 171–72
cleavage stages of, *169,* 368
collecting, 259, 367
effect of temperature on development of, 170, 368
preserving, 259
in vivaria, 368
epithelial tissue of, *283*
excretory system of, *282*
feeding reactions of, 127
fertilization in, 169, 170
artificial, 171
as food for snake, 371
gastrocnemius muscle of, 131–32
dissection of, *131*
head of, longitudinal section of, *130*
heart beat of, 69–*70,* 281
ingestion by, 31
lungs of, 74, 90

Lepidoptera (*cont.*)
mounting, 261
preserving, 250
LeRoy, W., 335 and *n*.
Lesson, techniques within, 6–8
extending, 8–10
in use of microscope, 304–05
Lettuce leaves, conduction in, 44
similarity among first, 214
stomates of, 21
Leucocytes. *See* White blood cells
Library, use of, in study of nutrition and health, 40
science, 428
Lichens, 231, *232*, 391
Life magazine, 418, 444
Life span, human, *9*
Light, for aquarium, 364
and chlorophyll development, 206, 215
responses to, of animals, 124–25
of plants, 142–44
role in photosynthesis, 14, 15–16, 114
Lignin test, 408
Ligustrum (privet), 158, 160
Liliaceae, 14
Lily, anther of, *178*
bulb of, 157, *295*
Calla, 156
Lima bean, carbonic acid excreted by roots of, 96, 97
growth of, and root initiation, 115–16
variations in length of, 214
starch grains of, *16*
Limewater, 408
as indicator of carbon dioxide, 85, 95, *96*, 97, 100
Linden, 214
Linkage, 203
sex, in *Drosophila*, 202–03, *204–05*
Lionotus, 341
Lipase, 64
Liriodendron. See Tulip
Litmus, range of, 407
Litmus milk test, 64
Liver fluke, Oriental, 230
Liverworts, 391–92
Lizards, vivaria for, 370
Lobed leaf, *293*
Locke's solution, 408
Locust, 260
Locust tree, 177
Loeffler's methylene blue solution, 330
Ludwigia, 363
Lugol's solution, 409
Lumbricus. See Earthworm

Lunularia, 392
Lung(s), of frog, 74, 90
mammalian, 90
water excreted by, 91
Lung capacity, human, 89
Lupine, measurement of growth of, 109–10
Lycopersicum. See Tomato
Lycopodium, 396, 397
Lymnaea. See Snails
Lymph sac, of frog, 132
Lymphocytes, 76
Lysol, for sterilizing culture media, 383

Maceration of tissues, 312, 315–16
Magnesium, in frog muscle, 37
for plant growth, 113
Magnesium sulfate, in anesthetization, 314
Magnification, with microscope, degree of, 303–04
Maidenhair fern, 395
Maize. *See* Corn
Malarial plasmodium, 155, 230, 344
Maltose, 59
Mammals, anatomy of, 288–91
blood cells of, 76–77
collecting, 259
heart of, *71*
lungs of, 90
maintaining, 371–73
ovaries of, 174, *175*
preserving, 259
skeleton of, preparing, 410
testes of, 174, 176
Manganese, for plant growth, 113
Mannose, 192
Manometer, 420
Mantis. *See* Praying mantis
Manure, green, 242
Maple, flowers of, 176
measuring variations in, 214
seeds of, 398
transpiration in leaves of, 47
Marasmius, 389
Marchantia, 392
Marsilia, 363, 394, 395
Marth, P., 116 and *n*.
Mastigophora, 341
Maturation, in ovaries and testes, 163
Mayer's albumen, 330
Mayer's paracarmine, 323
Maze, for earthworms, 132
for rat, 133
m-cresol purple, range of, 407
Mealworm, 31, 357–58, 369, 400

Meat extract agar, for culturing bacteria, 381
Meat extract broth, for culturing bacteria, 380–81
Medaka, 168, 364, 365
Mediterranean fruit fly, 234
Medulla, human, *137*
Meiosis. *See* Reduction division
Melanoplus. See Grasshopper
Melon seedlings, 214
Mendel, G., reading from, 207
Menthol crystals, 314
Mercury, in experiments with seedlings, 98, 104
Mesogonistius chaetodon, 365
Metamorphosis, of insects, 166–67, *168*, 357, 358
of tadpole, 172–73, 368
Metaphase, *161*
Methyl cellulose, for slowing down protozoa, 314
Methyl green, 322, 328, 329
Methyl orange, 328, 329, 406
range of, 407
Methyl Parasepts, 200 and *n*.
Methyl red, 329, 406
range of, 407
Methyl violet, 329
Methylene blue, 90, 309, 320, 330
Mett tubes, 63
Meyers Hybrid Seed Corn Company, 195
Mice, gestation period of, 373
heredity in, 194
maintaining, 371*ff*.
Microaquarium, *86*, 87, 228, 229
Microphone, 445
Micropipette, 76, 153
Microprojection, 305–*06*
Microscope, binocular, *303*, 304, *416*
examination under, of budding, 154
of chick embryo, 174
of chloroplasts, 17–18, 255
of chromosomes, 317, 318
of circulation in frog, 73
of clam, 274
of conjugation, 164
of *Dero*, 305
of disproof of spontaneous generation, 153
of fertilization in animals, 164*ff*.
of fission of protozoa, 153
of human blood cells, 75, 76
of lichens, 231, *232*
of mildew, *390*
of mitosis, 160, *161*, 162
of oil drops in emulsion, 64
of planarians, 347

Plants (*cont.*)
  monocotyledonous, 14, 178, 213–14, 296, 298
  overcrowding of, 212–13
  oxidation in, 95, 96
  oxygen absorbed by, 101–04
  preservatives for, 326
  related to animals, 226*ff.*
  reproduction in. *See* Reproduction, in plants
  respiration in, 95*ff.*
  responses of. *See* Responses, of plants
  seed, culturing, 397–401
  similarity in related, 213–14
  soil for, 236
  starch made by, 6–7, 14–16
  sugar made by, 14, 15
  for sunlight, 398
  transpiration in, 46–52
    and lifting power, 50, *51, 52*
  variations in, 214–16
  for windows without sun, 398
Plasma, and fibrin clot, 78
Plasmodium, malarial, 155, 230, *343*, 344
  of slime mold, *386*, 387
Plasmolysis, 22, 308
Plaster, "fossils" in, 211
Plaster of Paris, models in, 413, *414–15*
Plastic, animals imbedded in, 212
  models in, 414–16, *417*
Platelets, 76
Plating, of Petri dish, 383–*84*
Platy, *365*
Plethodon, 367
Pleurococcus (Protococcus), 254, 379
Plumatella, 257
p-nitrophenol, range of, 407
Pocket garden, to show geotropism, 146–47
  to show hydrotropism, *144*
Poinsettia, photoperiodism in, 120
Polar body, of starfish, *165*
Polarity, in plants, 149
Pollen grains, 178, 179, *180*, 184, 185
  care in handling of, 449
Pollination, artificial, 178–79, 206, 265
Pollution, of water, 241
Polyneuritis, in pigeon, 37
Polyphemus, 167
Polypodium vulgare, 395
Polystichum acrostichoides, 395
Polytrichum, 392
Pond, study of, 226–27, 265
Porcellio, 354, *355*
Pork tapeworm, 230
Potamogeton, 363

Potassium, for plant growth, 113
  solid, forceps for handling, 19*n*.
Potassium chloride, effect on heart beat of frog, 70
Potassium hydroxide, carbon dioxide absorbed by, 98, 99, 100, 102
  as macerating fluid, 315–16
Potassium iodide, absorption of, 65
Potassium permanganate, as disinfectant, 97
  for fish disease, 366
Potassium pyrogallate solution, 101, 103, 409
Potato, carbon dioxide produced by, 100
  effect of darkness on growth of, 216
  "eyes" in, 157
  and grafting, 160
  osmosis through, 52–*53*
  starch grains of, *16*
  stem of, 297
  sweet, 157, 298
Potato bug, 253, 263
Potato-dextrose agar, for culturing molds, 388
Potato medium, for culturing bacteria, 381
Potentilla, stolon of, 156
Potometer, 49, *51*
Practical Physiological Chemistry, 65, 76
Praying mantis, culturing, 357
  egg mass of, *31*, 166–67, 213, 357
  collecting, 357
  metamorphosis of, 167, 357
  nymphs of, 31, 167, 357
  overcrowding in, 213
  preserving, 260
Pregnancy, Rh factor in, 193
Preserving methods, for animal specimens, 250, 251, 255–61 *pass.*
  for plant specimens, 326
Privet, 158, 160
Probability, law of, 193–94
Problem-solving, by man, 137
Projects (long-term), 9–10
  on beetles, variations among, 263
  on chick embryo, hematology of, 11
    slides of, 174, *175*
  in chlorophyll study, 120–21
  in chromatography, 16
  in digestion research, 65–66
  in dormancy in seeds, 121
  and elementary schools, 4, 5
  on extraction of yeast nucleoproteins, 187–88

in film-making, 235
group, 8
inventory-type, 10
as investigation, 7
on nature trails around school, 264–65
in photoperiodism, 120–21
in photosensitization, 10–11
in photosynthesis, 121
in radioactivity, 44
on rat, learning by, 133
in tissue culture techniques, 119–20
Project room, 428
Projectionist squads, 444–45
Projectors, 444, 445
Projectors, storage of, 429
Promethea, 167
Propane burner, 423, *424*
Prophase, *161*
Proteins, component elements of, 61
  daily requirements of, 39
  digestion of, in animals, 62–63
    in plants, 58
  tests for, 36, 61–62, 188
  tests for components of, 61
Proteoses, 62
Prothallia, of fern, culturing, 395, *396*, 397
Protococcus (Pleurococcus), 254, 379
Protonemata, of mosses, 392–93
Protoplasm, imitating appearance of, 8
Protozoa, chemotropism of, 126
  classification of, 220, 253, 342, *343*, 344
  collecting, 248
  concentration of, for microscopic study, 313–14, 322
  conjugation in, 164
  contractile vacuoles of, 314
  culturing, 264, 334–42
  fission in, 153, 154
  fixation of, 322
  ingestion by, 29–30
  under microscope, 248, 305, 313–14
  as parasites, in earthworms, 310
    in frogs, 228, 230, 283, 310
    in termites, 232, 251
  slowing down, for microscopic study, 314
  spore formation in, 155
  stained slides of, permanent, 322–24
    temporary, 322
  tropisms of, 124, 126
Prune agar, for culturing molds, 388
Pseudomonas hydrophilus, 119

Runoff water, 236, 239, 240
Rye, 213, 238

Sabouraud's medium for fungi, 389
Saccharomyces cerevisiae, 391
Saccharomyces ellipsoideus, 391
Saccorhiza, 312
Sachs' solution, 113
Safety, in laboratory, 441, 447–50
Safranin, 320, 328
Sagittaria, 215, *262, 263*
Salamanders, collecting, 251, 259
  diseases of, 367
  food for, 366, 367
  ingestion by, 31
  iodine fed to tadpole, 172
  preserving, 259
  in vivaria, 366–67
Saline solution, physiological, 409
Saliva, cane sugar changed to glucose by, 15
  experiments with, 10, 58*ff.*
  flow of, in reflex, 134
  starch digested by, 58–59, 60, 61
Salivary chromosome smears, 317
Salix, 158
Salvinia, 363, 364, 394, 395
Sanctuaries, value of, 235
Sand dollar, drying, 260
Sanford, A., 76, 77
Sansevieria, 156, 159
Saprolegnia, 366, 367, 389
Saprophytes, 228
  in food chain, 231
Sarcina lutea, 321
Sarracenia, 400
Sassafras tree, 214
Saxifraga, stolon of, 156
Scallop, 217, *356*
Schaudinn's fixative, 322
School camps, 427
School Facilities for Science Instruction, 425
School grounds, 265, 426–27
  landscaping, 442–43
School nature museum, 427
Science, 26, 93, 118
Science, meaning of, 12
Science News Letter, 444
Scientific American, 26, 93, 444
Scientific Monthly, 26, 93
Scion, and stock, 160
Scorpion, 260
Scratch reflex, in frog, 127, 130–31
Scutellum, of seed, *109*
Sea anemone, *233*
Sea cucumber, *356*
Sea urchin, *356*

drying, 260
  fertilization in, 164
Second-grade activities, 4
Sectioning, of tissues, 328
Sections, freehand, 315
Sedimentary rock, 211, 238
Sedimentation, in jar, *211*
Sedum, 159
  epithelium of, *21*
Seed disinfectant, 109, 409
Seeding, of clouds, 241–42
Seeds, carbon dioxide produced by, 97–99
  coat of, *109*
  comparison of oxidation in, 102–03
  of corn, recessive genes for albinism in, 195
  diastase extracted from, 57
  dicotyledonous, 178, 214
  digestion of starch in, 56–57
  dispersal of, adaptations for, *179*
  dissection of, 178
  dormancy in, 121
  drowned, growth stopped in, 103–04
  embryo of, *109*
  F₁, from cross in pea plants, 195
  of flowering plants, 265
  germination of, 107, 108, 109, 110, 178, 398–99
    percentage of, 215
  growth of, 107–09
    effect of darkness on, 114
    effect of oxygen shortage on, 103–04
    in hydroponic solution, 111–12
    measurement of, 109–10
  heat produced by, 104
  imbibition pressure of, 54
  measuring variations in, 214
  monocotyledonous, 178
  overproduction of, 212–13
  oxygen absorbed by, 101–03
    and oxygen shortage, effect of, 103–04
  of pests, spread of, 234
  of sorghum, and heredity, 196
  sterilization of surfaces of, 109
  variations in, 214, 215
  viability test for, 109
Segregation, law of, in *Drosophila*, 201
  in maize, 195
Seison, 347
Selaginella, 397
Self-demonstration, technique of, 6

Semilunar valves, 71
Sempervivum, effect of humidity on growth of, 215, 216
  stomates of, 21
  transpiration observed in, 47
Sense organs, human, 134–35
Sepal, 177
Serrate leaf, *293*
Serum, anti-*A* and anti-*B*, 79, 80
Seventh-grade activities, 5
Sex linkage, in *Drosophila*, 202–03, *204–05*
Sexual reproduction, in animals, 163, 164–76, 270–91 *pass.*
  in plants, 176–88
Sheep, heart of, 71
  kidney of, 91
  lungs of, 90
Shells, mollusk, drying and mounting, 260–61
  variations within species of, 217
Shields, L., 236 and *n.*
Shipworm, 260
Shive's solution, 113, 115, 393
Shoot apex, *109*
Shrimp, brine, 316, *354*
  larva of, *166*
  fairy, *353*
  Gammarus, 353–54
Shrubs, flowers of, 176
  planted by schools, 264
  variations in color of leaves on, 215
Sigmoid curve, growth shown by, *107*
Silt, 240
Silver nitrate solution, as stain for ciliates, 323
Simpson, G. G., 235
Sixth-grade activities, 5
Skeletons, preparation of, 410
  storage of, 436
  study of, 224
Skin, human, and excretion, 91–92
  receptors in, 134
Skink, 370
Slides, storage of, *430*
  as visual aids, 416–17
Slime molds, *386–87*
Slugs, 251, 370
Small intestine, digestion in, 63, 64, 65
  length of, 66
Smear slide techniques, 317, *318–22*
Smilax, 294, 295
Snails, *350*
  for aquarium, 364
  ciliary motion of epithelial tissue from, 309

collecting, 248, 251, 258
eggs of, 164, 350
embryo, heart beat of, 70, 351
epithelial cells of, 274
as food for turtle, 370
maintaining, 350, 351
preserving, 258
sperms of, 164
Snake, anatomy of, *284*
cages for, 370–71
care of, 264, 370–71
Snake plant, 156
Snapping turtle. *See* Turtle
Sodium chlorate, effect on heart beat of frog, 70
Sodium chloride, tasting, 135
Sodium citrate, as anticoagulant, 76, 77
Sodium hydroxide, nucleoproteins extracted by, 188
solid, forceps for handling, 19*n*.
Sodium oxalate, as anticoagulant, 76, 77, 89
Soil(s), acidity of, 236–37
capillarity of, 236
erosion of, elementary school study of, 4, 5, 6
raindrop, 240
reduced by roots, 236
sheet, 240
and slope of land, 238–40
leaves added to, 238
living organisms in, 235
pH of, 237
profile of, 237–38
and roots, binding force of, 236
and "runoff" water, 236, 239, 240
temperature of, 240–41
testing kits for, 242
texture of, 236
types of, for plants, 236
water held by, 236
Soil acidifier, 409
Soil-testing squads, 442
Solomon's-seal, 156
rhizomes of, *156*
Solubility rules, 404–05
Solution A, 336
Solutions, preparing, 403–10
Sorghum, 196
Soybeans, 102–03
Space, for school work, 423–29
Spallanzani, experiments of, in digestion, 66
disproving spontaneous generation, 151–52
Sparrow, thistle, 234
Sperm, of earthworm, 270
entry of, *165*
of frog, 169, 170, 171, 283

of snail, 164
Sperm suspension, obtained from frogs, 171
Spermatogenesis, *163*
Spermatophytes, 397–401
Sphagnum moss, for vivarium, 366
Spider plant, stolon of, 156
Spiders. *See* Arachnids
Spirillum rubrum, 321
Spirodela, 401
Spirogyra, chloroplasts in, *18*
conjugation in, *185,* 379
culturing, 376, 378
as food for *Difflugia,* 337
pyrenoid activity of, 379
reduction division in, 163
silky threads of, 254
Spirostomum, 126, 314, 340, *341*
Sponge, collecting, 248, 256
maintaining, 344–45
mounting, 260
preserving, 248, 256
Spongilla, 344. *See also* Sponge
Spontaneous generation, disproved in experiments, 151–53
Sporangia, 155
Spore formation, 154–55
in *Penicillium notatum, 155*
Sporophyte generation, 185
Sporozoa, 310
Spreader, for wings of insects, *262*
Spring peeper, 368, 369
Spruce seedlings, 214
Squads, student. *See* Student squads
Squash bug, 262
Squash leaf, *110*
Squash seeds, germinating, 398
Squids, 260
Stain Technology, 318
Staining, of bacteria, 232, 320–21
of blood cells, 75, 76, 77, 319
histological, 328
of pollen grains, 179, 184
of protozoa, 322–24
vital, 309
Stains, preparation of, 328–29
Stalactites, 242
Stalagmites, 242
Stamen, 177, 178
Starch, digestion of, in animals, 58–61
in plants, 56–58
experiments with, 6–7
insolubility of, 34
made by green leaves, 6–7, 14–16
and saliva, 10
tests for, 14, 15–16, 36

Starch grains, *16*
Starch paste, 57, 409
Starfish, *356*
anatomy of, *276*
cleavage stages in eggs of, 160, *165*
culturing, 355
digestive system of, 276
dissection of, 276
fertilization in, 164–65
mounting, 260
reproductive system of, 276
Starling, 234
Stems, anatomy of, 296–97
circulation in, and radioactive tracer, 44–45
cuttings from, 158–59
and grafting, 160
growth of, measurement of, 110
stimulated by hormones, 115
response of, to gravity, 145–46
to light, 142–43
rise of water in, 52
structure of, 54
Stentor, contractile vacuoles of, 314
culturing, 338, 340, 341
as food for *Chaos,* 29, *30,* 337
in mixed culture, *305*
response to contact, 126
Sterilization, of culture media, 382–83
Stickleback, 365
Stimuli, reception of, in man, 134–35
Stock cultures, of *Drosophila,* 199–200
Stolons (runners), 156, *157,* 265, 297
Stomates, 20, 21, 22, 46*ff.,* 292
Storage, of chemicals, 447, 448, 449
facilities for, *428, 429, 430–31*
Strawberry, stolon of, 156, *157*
Streams, study of, 227–28
Strip cropping, 239
Student curator, 264, 442
Student squads, 264, 438, 439
book-room, 443
in classroom, 445–46
laboratory, 439–41, 447
mimeographing, 444
perpetuation of, 445
projectionist, 444–45
publishing, 444
science readings, 444
soil-testing, 442
for special services, 441–45
tutoring, 446–47
Stylonychia, 339, 340

White, P., 119 and *n.*, 120
White blood cells, *76, 319*
  amoeboid movement of, 77
  staining, 319
White's solution, 120
Whitefish, mitosis in egg of, *161*
Willow, 158
Wistaria, 177
Wolffia, 400–01
Wood, models in, 413–14
Wood lot, in elementary school, 5
Wood stain, acidproof, 410
Wood turtle. *See* Turtle
Woodlice, 354–55
Woodroach, 311
Work space, 423–29
Worms, anesthetization of, 260
  antipepsin action of, 63

cleavage stages in eggs of, 160, 162
culturing, 264
gills of, 90
parasitic, 230, 256
regeneration of, 156
See also names of specific worms
Wright, S., 235
Wright's blood stain, 75, 76, 319

Xanthine (xanthophyll), 16, 17
Xanthoproteic test, 36, 61–62

Yearbooks, of U.S. Department of Agriculture, 241
Yeasts, 228, 231
  alcohol produced by, 100, 101

budding in, *154*
collecting, 387–88
culturing, 391
nucleoproteins extracted from, 187–88
role in bread-making, *100*
spore formation in, 155

Zea mays, cross section of stem of, *296*
Zebrina, 21
Zenker's fixative, 322, 326
Zinc, for plant growth, 113
Zoochlorellae, in *Hydra,* 321
Zoomastigina, 344
Zoospore, 184, *185,* 379
Zygnema, 337
Zygospore, *184,* 185